3rd edition

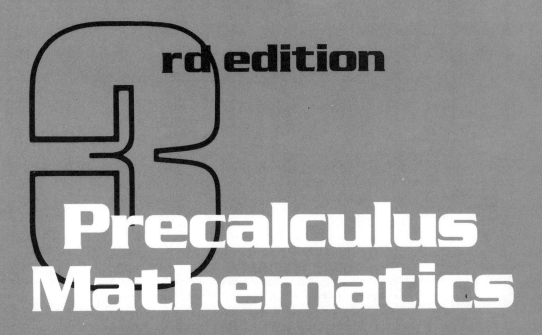

Precalculus Mathematics

Daniel D. Benice

Professor of Mathematics
Montgomery College
Rockville, Maryland

Prentice-Hall, Inc., Englewood Cliffs, New Jersey 07632

Library of Congress Cataloging-in-Publication Data

Benice, Daniel D.
    Precalculus mathematics.

    Includes index.
    1. Algebra.   2. Trigonometry.   I. Title.
QA152.2.B46   1986   512'.1   85-12165
ISBN   0-13-695503-7 (pbk.)

Editorial/production supervision: Zita de Schauensee
Interior design: Maureen Eide and Maria McColligan
Cover design: Bruce Kenselaar
Manufacturing buyer: John Hall

ISBN   0-13-695503-7   01

Prentice-Hall International (UK) Limited, *London*
Prentice-Hall of Australia Pty. Limited, *Sydney*
Prentice-Hall Canada Inc., *Toronto*
Prentice-Hall Hispanoamericana, S.A., *Mexico*
Prentice-Hall of India Private Limited, *New Delhi*
Prentice-Hall of Japan, Inc., *Tokyo*
Prentice-Hall of Southeast Asia Pte. Ltd., *Singapore*
Editora Prentice-Hall do Brasil, Ltda., *Rio de Janeiro*
Whitehall Books Limited, *Wellington, New Zealand*

Contents

7 Trigonometric Functions 262

8 Conics 399

9 Systems of Equations 434

10 Sequences and Series 476

Appendix 509

Answers to Selected Exercises 521

Index 564

Preface

Goals of This Book

The third edition of *Precalculus Mathematics* is a considerably revised version of the second edition. The intention of the text remains unchanged—to offer an easy-to-read style text that includes calculus-oriented examples as well as the standard material on algebra, trigonometry, geometry, and elementary functions.

Many precalculus courses are nearly indistinguishable from ordinary algebra and trigonometry courses. As a result, even successful precalculus students often stumble and fall when they must do some of these problems in calculus without having the proper background: solve a geometric max/min or related rates problem, determine the domain and range of a function, factor negative and fractional exponents, use *e* and ln with authority, divide one polynomial by another, compute a difference quotient, determine algebraically where two curves meet, etc.

This text includes truly calculus-oriented algebra, so that a precalculus course taught from it will go beyond ordinary algebra and trigonometry to include the settings and specific algebra problems students face in calculus courses. Later, both the calculus instructor and students benefit because the appropriate algebra has been taught in the precalculus course.

Organization

Flexibility is built into the text. Although my personal preference is to teach the chapters in the sequence written, you may prefer another sequence. As long as you first cover Chapters 1, 2, and 3 in sequence, Chapters 4 through 9 can be presented in any order you prefer.

The prerequisite you establish as well as the length of your course (one semester, two quarters, two semesters, 3 hours, 5 hours, etc.) will determine which chapters or sections are to be covered thoroughly or briefly or even omitted. For example, most of the material in Chapter 1 should be a review, with the exception of the binomial theorem. Some parts of Chapter 2 are probably familiar to most students. Chapter 4 can be omitted if you are pressed for time, but I would urge you to cover 4.2 (Geometric Applications) since calculus students have difficulty with this kind of material. How much of Chapter 8 (Conics) you decide to cover may depend on how you present conics in your calculus course as well as the length of your precalculus course. More comments and suggestions of this nature can be found in the Instructor's Manual, which also includes a variety of course outlines.

You will find the binomial theorem introduced early. Too, lines and slopes are presented early in the text. Domain and range are explained in a neatly organized fashion using "keys."

Accuracy

I have personally done every exercise in the text. As a check, my colleague Dennis Freeman (who has carefully reviewed the book) has also done every exercise in the text. This should minimize errors in answers and in the exercises themselves, and eliminate any inconsistent forms that can creep into the answer section.

Answers

Asterisks are used to mark all exercises that have answers given at the back of the book. Answers to the other exercises are given in the Instructor's Manual. In addition, you will find nearly 300 graphs in the answer section. This will be a valuable aid to students trying to check their graphs and master the techniques presented in the text.

Applications

This edition includes a variety of applications that should interest students, give them chances to apply the algebra they are learning, and prepare them for applications they will encounter in calculus. The applications sections include: distance and velocity (4.4), functions in economics (4.3), geometric applications (4.2), exponential growth and decay (6.7), and formula manipulation (1.8).

In addition, there are numerous brief applications woven in throughout the book. A partial list includes: modulation of carrier waves, honey bees and polar coordinates, predator-prey interaction, domain determined by application setting, airport ceilometers, magnitude of a resultant force, center-pivot irrigation, Loran navigation system, maximum and minimum values of quadratic functions that represent distance, revenue and profit, and series used to generate tables.

Calculators

The text can be used with or without a hand-held calculator. I believe that care should be taken to stress the understanding of concepts in situations where a calculator can be used to circumvent learning. For example, it would be unfortunate if students leave the course needing a calculator to determine the value of such expressions as e^0, $\ln e$, $e^{\ln 3}$, $\sin \dfrac{\pi}{2}$, $\cos \pi$, and $\cos \dfrac{\pi}{6}$.

Instructor's Manual

An Instructor's Manual is available. It contains answers to those exercises not answered in the text. The manual also contains course outlines and teaching suggestions.

New in This Edition

Here are a few of the changes that have been made:

1. An earlier introduction to right triangles is presented, thus enabling easier manipulations and earlier applications.
2. More is given on inverses and inverse function notation. One-to-one functions are considered.
3. Calculators are accepted. While the excellent tables remain for those who choose to use them, calculators (with guidelines) are encouraged.
4. There are more examples and exercises on "e" and natural logarithms.
5. Extra guidance is provided in the examples dealing with domain and range.
6. The first two sections of the chapter on polynomial and rational functions have been expanded and now include an example of finding the zeros of a quartic polynomial function.
7. There are now more trigonometric graphs and also more polar graphs.
8. The already extensive section on geometric applications has been expanded.
9. The section on mathematical induction has been expanded.
10. Additional examples and exercises have been inserted throughout the book to improve understanding and help students master the concepts.

Reviewers

I am grateful for the assistance of the following reviewers of *Precalculus Mathematics* who have helped me to improve the text.

Third Edition

Dorys J. Barban, Montgomery College
Sherry Blackman, College of Staten Island
Humberto Canate, Hostos Community College
Dennis Freeman, Montgomery College

Barry Glinski, Quinsigamond Community College
John J. Hanevy, S.U.N.Y.at Cobleskill
Jack L. Harmon, Montgomery College
William J. Kohler, Clark University
Madeline Lisbeth, Northern Virginia Community College
Carroll L. Matthews, Montgomery College
Diana Staats, Dutchess Community College
Charles M. Wheeler, Montgomery College

Second Edition

Florence H. Ashby, Montgomery College
Dennis Freeman, Montgomery College
Jack L. Harmon, Montgomery College
B. C. Horne, Virginia Polytechnic Institute and State University
Thomas R. Lupton, University of North Carolina at Wilmington
Maurice L. Monahan, South Dakota State University
E. James Peake, Iowa State University
Arlene K. Sherburne, Montgomery College

First Edition

Donald R. Burleson, Middlesex Community College
R. A. Close, Pan American University
Richard C. Detmer, University of Tennessee at Chattanooga
Edward Doran, Community College of Denver
Samuel Goldberg, Oberlin College
Joseph J. Hansen, Northeastern University
Kenneth Hoffman, Massachusetts Institute of Technology

Dedication

To my brother Ronald J. Benice

DANIEL D. BENICE
Rockville, Maryland

Real and Complex Numbers

1.1 INTRODUCTION TO REAL NUMBERS

This first chapter provides a brief review of some basic algebra—skills, definitions, and concepts you will need later in the book, as well as in calculus. It is assumed, however, that you know the fundamentals of elementary algebra.

Most of this chapter, and most of this text for that matter, deals with *real numbers*. An extension of the real numbers will be introduced at the end of this chapter. What *is* a real number; in other words, how can you test a number to determine if it is real? One test: If the number is positive, negative, or zero, then it is a real number. Another test: Square the number; if the result is zero or positive, then the number is real. Recall the notation of inequalities: $>$, is greater than; $<$, is less than; $\geq$, is greater than or equal to; $\leq$, is less than or equal to. Using this notation, we can say that if $x > 0$, $x < 0$, or $x = 0$, then x is real. Also, if $x^2 \geq 0$, then x is real. Does it strike you that every number you have ever seen is real? That may, in fact, be true, at least until you study the last section of this chapter.

All the real numbers taken together can be thought of as the **set of real numbers**. Some special collections, or subsets, of real numbers are given names. Here are several such subsets of the set of real numbers.

1. **Natural numbers:** 1, 2, 3, 4, 5, 6, 7, . . .
   Note the use of three dots to specify continuation. The natural numbers are also called the **counting numbers**.
2. **Whole numbers:** 0, 1, 2, 3, 4, 5, 6, 7, . . .
3. **Integers:** . . . , -4, -3, -2, -1, 0, 1, 2, 3, . . .
   Positive integers: 1, 2, 3, 4, 5, 6, 7, . . .
   Negative integers: -1, -2, -3, -4, -5, . . .

Note. To say that x is positive means that $x > 0$. To say that x is negative means that $x < 0$.

4. **Rational numbers:** All real numbers that can be written in the form a/b, where a and b are integers. Of course, b cannot be zero because division by zero is not defined (see page 3).

Here are some examples of rational numbers and a/b forms for each.

$$\frac{3}{5} \longrightarrow \frac{3}{5} \qquad -\frac{1}{2} \longrightarrow \frac{-1}{2}$$

$$6 \longrightarrow \frac{6}{1} \qquad 0 \longrightarrow \frac{0}{7}$$

$$-5.2 \longrightarrow \frac{52}{-10} \qquad .333\overline{3} \longrightarrow \frac{1}{3}$$

The bar over the 3 in the last example specifies that the 3s repeat indefinitely. Any repeating decimal number is a rational number.

5. **Irrational numbers:** All real numbers that cannot be written in the form a/b, where a and b are integers and $b \neq 0$. The most common examples of irrational numbers are square roots of numbers that are not perfect squares, such as $\sqrt{2}$, $\sqrt{3}$, and $\sqrt{10}$, and cube roots of numbers that are not perfect cubes, such as $\sqrt[3]{7}$ and $\sqrt[3]{16}$. The number π, which is *approximately* 3.14, is also irrational; π is the ratio of the circumference of any circle to its diameter. We shall eventually see a need for the irrational number e, which is approximately 2.718.

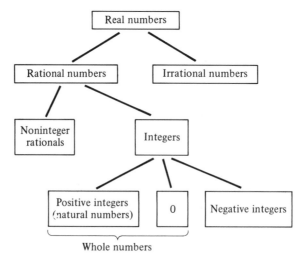

In summary, all real numbers are either rational or irrational. Furthermore, the rational numbers include integers and nonintegers.

All numbers used in this book are real numbers unless otherwise stated or implied by the nature of an equation.

A note on *division involving zero* is in order here. Normally when we add or subtract or multiply or divide real numbers, the outcome is a real number. The exception occurs when we divide by zero.

Division by zero does not produce a result; such division is said to be undefined.

In arithmetic division we reason that $10 \div 2 = 5$, since $2 \cdot 5 = 10$. Then what do you say about $10 \div 0$? The result would have to be a number x such that $0 \cdot x = 10$, which is impossible. Thus we conclude that you cannot divide by zero.

The section concludes with a brief review of three linear equations that will be solved to produce real-number solutions.

Example 1 *Solve the linear equation* $10x - 8 = 22$.

First add 8 to both sides of the equation $10x - 8 = 22$. This step will isolate the x term and produce $10x = 30$. Now divide both sides by the coefficient of x, which is 10. The result is $x = 3$; the solution is 3.

Example 2 *Solve the linear equation* $5(1 - 3y) + 2 = 19$.

Because the unknown for which we are trying to solve, y, is inside parentheses, multiply out to free the y term. This yields $5 - 15y + 2 = 19$. Next combine the 5 and 2 to produce $-15y + 7 = 19$. Then add -7 to both sides, which yields $-15y = 12$. Finally, divide both sides by -15. The result is $y = -\frac{12}{15}$, which reduces to $-\frac{4}{5}$.

Example 3 *Solve the linear equation* $8x - (3x - 5) = 9 + 12x$.

The minus in front of the parentheses has the effect of changing the signs of each term inside. The result is $8x - 3x + 5 = 9 + 12x$. When the x terms on the left side are combined, we have $5x + 5 = 9 + 12x$. Next add $-5x$ and -9 to both sides to produce $-4 = 7x$, from which we can get $x = -\frac{4}{7}$. The solution is $-\frac{4}{7}$.

EXERCISES 1.1

Answers to starred exercises are given in the back of the book.

1. For each real number listed, use as many of the following descriptions that apply: rational, irrational, integer, whole, natural.

   *(a) 6   (b) -9 *(c) $\dfrac{2}{5}$

   (d) $\dfrac{7}{-3}$ *(e) $\sqrt{3}$ (f) 1.962

   *(g) -17 (h) $-\sqrt{2}$ *(i) $\sqrt{1}$

   (j) 0   *(k) $\sqrt{\dfrac{9}{4}}$ (l) $3\frac{5}{16}$

   *(m) $.777\overline{7}$ (n) $.5161\overline{616}$ *(o) π

   (p) $-\dfrac{1}{4}$ *(q) $-\sqrt{144}$ (r) $\sqrt[3]{17}$

   *(s) $\sqrt[3]{20}$ (t) 3.14

2. Solve each linear equation.
   *(a) $3x + 2 = 14$ (b) $5x - 6 = 34$ *(c) $8m - 1 = 6$
   (d) $7y + 5 = 2$ *(e) $4x - 2 = -2$ (f) $12t + 2 = -10$

   *(g) $\dfrac{2}{3}h - 6 = 5$ (h) $\dfrac{5}{4}x + 2 = 18$ *(i) $-\dfrac{x}{6} + 2 = 7$

   (j) $-\dfrac{5x}{2} + 3 = -4$ *(k) $3 - \dfrac{x}{4} = -13$ (l) $5 + \dfrac{3x}{2} = 0$

3. Solve each linear equation.
   *(a) $4(1 - 5x) + 6 = -9$ (b) $5 - 8x = 3(2x + 1)$
   *(c) $9x - (2x - 7) = 4 + 3x$ (d) $3(x + 4) - 2(x - 6) = 17$
   *(e) $5(x - 4) - 3(x - 2) = 0$ (f) $17 - 2(1 - 8x) + x = 0$
   *(g) $5 - (3 - 2x)6 = 19$ (h) $5(2x + 7) = 2(1 - 3x)$

4. For each exercise, let x represent the unknown number. Then follow the words and establish an equation. Solve the equation to determine the value of the unknown number x.

   *(a) Six is added to a number. The sum is multiplied by 5. Finally, 7 is subtracted from the product. The result is 16. What was the original number?

   (b) The width of a rectangle is unknown. The length is twice the width. The perimeter (sum of all four sides) is 40 meters. How wide is the rectangle? How long is the rectangle?

   *(c) The size of an angle of a triangle is unknown. What is known, however, is that all three angles of the triangle are the same size. Furthermore,

in any triangle the sum of the angle is 180 degrees. Determine the size of the angle.

(d) The sum of four consecutive integers is 234. Determine the numbers.

*5. The Internal Revenue Service suggests that a common error on filed tax returns is the interchanging of two adjacent digits; for example, 2583 might be incorrectly written as 2853 or as 2538. Such an error is relatively easy to identify because the difference between the correct number and the incorrect number is divisible by 9. In other words,

$$\text{Correct} - \text{incorrect} = 9 \cdot (\text{some integer})$$

Consider a two-digit number whose digits are m and n. Represent the number and its incorrect form. Then prove that their difference is equal to nine times some integer.

6. Can you determine what is wrong with the following proof that $1 = 2$? Let $a = b$. Then $a^2 = ab$ and $a^2 - b^2 = ab - b^2$. So

$$(a + b)(a - b) = b(a - b)$$

or

$$a + b = b$$

By substitution,

$$b + b = b$$

which means $2b = b$ or $2b = 1b$. Thus $2 = 1$.

7. To demonstrate that they are indeed rational numbers, repeating decimals can be changed to fractions by the process demonstrated here. To change $x = .16161\overline{16}$ to a fraction, multiply it by 100 in order to align the repeating portions

$$x = .16161\overline{16}$$

$$100x = 16.16161\overline{16}$$

Next, subtract the smaller number x from the larger number $100x$. Since the repeating portions are aligned, the subtraction leaves simply

$$99x = 16, \quad \text{or} \quad x = \frac{16}{99}$$

Use this process to change each repeating decimal to a fraction.

*(a) .73737$\overline{73}$ (b) .555$\overline{5}$ *(c) .691$\overline{691}$

(d) .533$\overline{3}$ *(e) 1.21212$\overline{21}$ (f) 5.31616$\overline{16}$

1.2 FACTORING

Your knowledge of arithmetic and algebra includes an understanding of some basic properties that real numbers possess. There are two rather unusual properties, however, and they are explained next.

First let us consider the **closure properties**. The *closure property for addition* of real numbers says that if any two real numbers are added, then their sum is a unique real number. The *closure property for multiplication* says that if two real numbers are multiplied, their product is a unique real number. In a precalculus setting, you may have an expression such as $x + 3$. Assuming that x is a real number, then $x + 3$ is a real number (by the closure property.) This means that you can consider the expression $x + 3$ to be *one* number even though you see the two separate numbers x and 3 and may not know the specific value of $x + 3$. Our first application of the closure concept will appear shortly, in Example 6. Many others will follow throughout the book.

The second properties of interest here are the **distributive properties,** which state that for any real numbers a, b, and c,

1. $a(b + c) = ab + ac$
2. $(b + c)a = ba + ca$

When viewed from left to right, these properties are used to multiply. When viewed from right to left, these properties are used to factor.

Example 4 *Multiply $m(x + 4)$.*

$$m(x + 4) = m \cdot x + m \cdot 4 = mx + 4m$$

Example 5 *Factor $ty + xy$.*

$$ty + xy = (t + x)y$$

Example 6 *Factor $4(u + v) + 7(u + v)$.*

$$4(u + v) + 7(u + v) = (4 + 7)(u + v) = 11(u + v)$$

Notice how closure slipped into this factoring involving the distributive property. We considered $u + v$ to be one number, the a of the second distributive property.

Example 7 *Factor $m^2x + mx^2y + mx$.*

$$m^2x + mx^2y + mx = mx(m + xy + 1)$$

You should also recall *quadratic factoring*, as illustrated in the next examples.

Example 8   *Factor $x^2 + 7x$.*
Because there is no constant term, the variable x can be factored out of each term.

$$x^2 + 7x = x(x + 7)$$

Example 9   *Factor $x^2 + 5x - 14$.*
Because the coefficient of x^2 is 1, the form is $(x\quad)(x\quad)$ and we seek two numbers whose product is -14 (the constant term) and whose sum is 5 (the coefficient of x.) The numbers, found by trial and error, are $+7$ and -2. The factoring is

$$x^2 + 5x - 14 = (x + 7)(x - 2)$$

Example 10   *Factor $2m^2 - 4m - 30$.*
Note first the factor of 2 in each term and factor it out. Then complete the quadratic factoring by using the approach of Example 9.

$$2m^2 - 4m - 30 = 2(m^2 - 2m - 15)$$
$$= 2(m - 5)(m + 3)$$

Example 11   *Factor $6x^2 - 13x - 5$.*
Because the coefficient of x^2 is not 1 and cannot be factored out, the "sum" rule used in Example 9 does not apply. The form could be either $(6x\quad)(x\quad)$ or else $(3x\quad)(2x\quad)$. Trial and error yields the correct factoring

$$6x^2 - 13x - 5 = (3x + 1)(2x - 5)$$

Here next is the factoring for the difference of two squares.

$$\boxed{x^2 - y^2 = (x + y)(x - y)}$$

Example 12   *Factor $x^2 - 81$.*
This is $(x)^2 - (9)^2$, the difference of two squares. Thus the factoring is as follows.

$$x^2 - 81 = (x + 9)(x - 9)$$

Example 13   *Factor $t^2 - 4u^2$.*
This is $(t)^2 - (2u)^2$, the difference of two squares. The factoring is as follows.

$$t^2 - 4u^2 = (t + 2u)(t - 2u)$$

Example 14 *Factor $x^2 - 7$.*

Irrational numbers are needed to accomplish this factoring. Since 7 is $(\sqrt{7})^2$, $x^2 - 7$ can be considered the difference of two squares, as $(x)^2 - (\sqrt{7})^2$. The factoring is as follows.

$$x^2 - 7 = (x + \sqrt{7})(x - \sqrt{7})$$

Some cubic expressions can be readily factored by using two steps that resemble those we have already seen in previous examples.

Example 15 *Factor $x^3 + 7x^2 + 12x$.*

Note first that there is no constant term and there is an x in each term. The x can be factored out to produce $x(x^2 + 7x + 12)$. The quadratic that remains inside the parentheses can be factored. In steps,

$$x^3 + 7x^2 + 12x = x(x^2 + 7x + 12)$$
$$= x(x + 3)(x + 4)$$

The sum or difference of two cubes can be factored by remembering the formulas given next.

$$x^3 + y^3 = (x + y)(x^2 - xy + y^2)$$
$$x^3 - y^3 = (x - y)(x^2 + xy + y^2)$$

The formulas can be verified by multiplying out the factors on the right side of each equation and then simplifying.

Example 16 *Factor $m^3 - 8n^3$.*

This is the difference of two cubes, $(m)^3 - (2n)^3$. The factoring is

$$(m - 2n)(m^2 + 2mn + 4n^2)$$

Example 17 *Factor $27a^3 + b^3$.*

This is the sum of two cubes, $(3a)^3 + (b)^3$. The factoring is

$$(3a + b)(9a^2 - 3ab + b^2)$$

In elementary algebra you used factoring to solve quadratic equations in x, those of the form $ax^2 + bx + c = 0$. The basic procedure was to factor the quadratic expression and then set each linear factor equal to zero based on the fact that if $m \cdot n = 0$, then either $m = 0$ or $n = 0$.

Example 18 *Solve $x^2 - 7x + 12 = 0$.*

$$x^2 - 7x + 12 = 0$$
$$(x - 3)(x - 4) = 0$$

$x - 3 = 0$	$x - 4 = 0$
$x = 3$	$x = 4$

Example 19 *Solve $2x^2 + x - 6 = 0$.*

$$2x^2 + x - 6 = 0$$
$$(2x - 3)(x + 2) = 0$$

$2x - 3 = 0$	$x + 2 = 0$
$2x = 3$	$x = -2$
$x = \dfrac{3}{2}$	

Example 20 *Solve $6x^2 = 5 - 13x$.*

The quadratic equation must be changed into the form $ax^2 + bx + c = 0$. It can be done by adding $13x - 5$ to both sides.

$$6x^2 + 13x - 5 = 0$$
$$(3x - 1)(2x + 5) = 0$$

$3x - 1 = 0$	$2x + 5 = 0$
$x = \dfrac{1}{3}$	$x = -\dfrac{5}{2}$

Example 21 *Solve $x^2 = 25$.*

$$x^2 = 25$$
$$x^2 - 25 = 0$$
$$(x + 5)(x - 5) = 0$$

$x + 5 = 0$	$x - 5 = 0$
$x = -5$	$x = 5$

Thus $x = \pm 5$. The symbol $\pm$ is read *plus or minus*.

Can you see that if the equation were $x^2 - 81 = 0$, then the solutions would be $x = \pm 9$? In general, for $n > 0$:

$$\boxed{\text{If } x^2 = n, \text{ then } x = \pm \sqrt{n}.}$$

For example, if $x^2 = 121$, then $x = \pm 11$. If $x^2 = 5$, then $x = \pm\sqrt{5}$.

The boxed result shown suggests a method of solving quadratic equations when they cannot be solved readily by factoring. The technique is called **completing the square**. The equation $x^2 + 6x + 2 = 0$ cannot be solved by factoring involving integers; so completing the square will be used. First, the equation is written

$$x^2 + 6x = -2$$

The expression that is on the left side is nearly the square of $x + 3$. Specifically, $(x + 3)^2 = x^2 + 6x + 9$. The square of $x + 3$ is 9 more than $x^2 + 6x$. So if $x^2 + 6x$ is replaced by $(x + 3)^2$ on the left, then the left side is 9 more than it was. To compensate, 9 should be added to the right side. Thus

$$x^2 + 6x = -2$$

becomes

$$(x + 3)^2 = -2 + 9$$

or

$$(x + 3)^2 = 7$$

which leads to

$$x + 3 = \pm\sqrt{7}$$

and then

$$x = -3 \pm \sqrt{7}$$

A square of the form $x^2 + nx + \cdots$ can always be completed by noting that the square you will work with is $\left(x + \dfrac{n}{2}\right)^2$ and continuing from there. For example,

$$x^2 + 8x \cdots \longrightarrow (x + 4)^2$$
$$m^2 - 2m \cdots \longrightarrow (m - 1)^2$$
$$y^2 + 3y \cdots \longrightarrow \left(y + \frac{3}{2}\right)^2$$

Example 22 *Solve $2x^2 - 3x - 8 = 0$ by completing the square.*
We begin by dividing both sides of the equation by 2 in order to obtain the desired form $x^2 + nx + \cdots$. In other words, we must have a coefficient of 1 for

the x^2 term. The result is $x^2 - \frac{3}{2}x - 4 = 0$. We now complete the square in steps.

$$x^2 - \frac{3}{2}x = 4$$

$$\left(x - \frac{3}{4}\right)^2 = 4 + \left(-\frac{3}{4}\right)^2$$

$$\left(x - \frac{3}{4}\right)^2 = 4 + \frac{9}{16}$$

$$\left(x - \frac{3}{4}\right)^2 = \frac{73}{16}$$

$$x - \frac{3}{4} = \pm\sqrt{\frac{73}{16}}$$

$$x = \frac{3}{4} \pm \frac{\sqrt{73}}{4} = \frac{3 \pm \sqrt{73}}{4}$$

Although the process of completing the square will be needed in Chapter 8 to determine the center and radius of a circle and for other analytic geometry applications, its use in solving quadratic equations can be avoided by completing the square for the equation $ax^2 + bx + c = 0$ and obtaining a quadratic formula in terms of a, b, and c. That formula can then be used to solve all quadratic equations that cannot be solved by factoring involving integers.

To begin, divide both sides of $ax^2 + bx + c = 0$ by a in order to obtain a coefficient of 1 for x^2. (This means that a cannot be zero.)

$$x^2 + \frac{b}{a}x + \frac{c}{a} = 0$$

Next, add $-c/a$ to both sides of the equation in order to remove the constant term from the left side.

$$x^2 + \frac{b}{a}x = -\frac{c}{a}$$

The left side is the square of x plus half of b/a if $(b/2a)^2$ is added to both sides. Thus

$$\left(x + \frac{b}{2a}\right)^2 = \left(\frac{b}{2a}\right)^2 - \frac{c}{a}$$

or

$$\left(x + \frac{b}{2a}\right)^2 = \frac{b^2}{4a^2} - \frac{c}{a}$$

The fractions on the right can be combined.

$$\left(x + \frac{b}{2a}\right)^2 = \frac{b^2 - 4ac}{4a^2}$$

which leads to

$$x + \frac{b}{2a} = \pm\sqrt{\frac{b^2 - 4ac}{4a^2}}$$

or

$$x = -\frac{b}{2a} \pm \sqrt{\frac{b^2 - 4ac}{4a^2}}$$

The right side can be simplified, since $\sqrt{4a^2} = 2a$ when $a > 0$.

$$x = -\frac{b}{2a} \pm \frac{\sqrt{b^2 - 4ac}}{2a}$$

Finally

$$\boxed{x = \frac{-b \pm \sqrt{b^2 - 4ac}}{2a} \qquad a \neq 0}$$

if $ax^2 + bx + c = 0$ and $a > 0$. If $a < 0$, multiply the equation by -1 to make a positive before applying the formula.

Example 23 *Solve $x^2 - 7x + 4 = 0$.*

In $x^2 - 7x + 4 = 0$, a is 1, b is -7, and c is 4. Substituting these numbers into

$$x = \frac{-b \pm \sqrt{b^2 - 4ac}}{2a}$$

yields

$$x = \frac{-(-7) \pm \sqrt{(-7)^2 - 4(1)(4)}}{2(1)}$$

or

$$x = \frac{7 \pm \sqrt{33}}{2}$$

Example 24 *Solve $x^2 - 4x - 1 = 0$.*
Here a is 1, b is -4, and c is -1. Thus

$$x = \frac{-(-4) \pm \sqrt{(-4)^2 - 4(1)(-1)}}{2(1)}$$

or

$$x = \frac{4 \pm \sqrt{20}}{2}$$

Note that $\sqrt{20}$ can be simplified to $2\sqrt{5}$ and that such simplification will help to reduce the fraction ($\sqrt{20} = \sqrt{4 \cdot 5} = \sqrt{4}\sqrt{5} = 2\sqrt{5}$).†

$$x = \frac{4 \pm 2\sqrt{5}}{2}$$

$$= \frac{2(2 \pm \sqrt{5})}{2}$$

$$= 2 \pm \sqrt{5}$$

Example 25 *Solve $6x^2 + 5x = 4$.*
Change $6x^2 + 5x = 4$ to $ax^2 + bx + c = 0$ form, as

$$6x^2 + 5x - 4 = 0$$

So $a = 6$, $b = 5$, and $c = -4$. Now

$$x = \frac{-5 \pm \sqrt{(5)^2 - 4(6)(-4)}}{2(6)}$$

$$= \frac{-5 \pm \sqrt{121}}{12}$$

$$= \frac{-5 \pm 11}{12}$$

At this point, because no square root remains, pursue each case, plus and minus.

$$x = \frac{-5 + 11}{12} = \frac{6}{12} = \frac{1}{2}$$

$$x = \frac{-5 - 11}{12} = \frac{-16}{12} = -\frac{4}{3}$$

---

† A few such simplifications are given as exercises at the end of this section. However, this concept is covered in more detail in Section 1.6.

This equation could have been readily solved by factoring, as shown by the fact that there is no radical in the solution.

Example 26 *Solve $x^4 - 9x^2 + 14 = 0$.*

This equation is quadratic in x^2, as shown next.

$$(x^2)^2 - 9(x^2) + 14 = 0$$

We can proceed to solve the equation by factoring.

$$(x^2 - 7)(x^2 - 2) = 0$$

$x^2 - 7 = 0$	$x^2 - 2 = 0$
$x^2 = 7$	$x^2 = 2$
$x = \pm \sqrt{7}$	$x = \pm \sqrt{2}$

EXERCISES 1.2

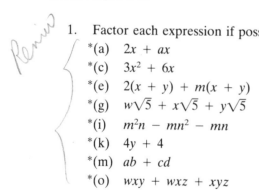

1. Factor each expression if possible.

    *(a) $2x + ax$
    *(c) $3x^2 + 6x$
    *(e) $2(x + y) + m(x + y)$
    *(g) $w\sqrt{5} + x\sqrt{5} + y\sqrt{5}$
    *(i) $m^2n - mn^2 - mn$
    *(k) $4y + 4$
    *(m) $ab + cd$
    *(o) $wxy + wxz + xyz$

    (b) $7b + ab$
    (d) $x^2 - 20x$
    (f) $a(a - b) - b(a - b)$
    (h) $y^3 - 7y^2$
    (j) $4a^2x^2 - 4ax + ax^2$
    (l) $8 + 40x^2$
    (n) $\pi r^2 + \pi rh$
    (p) $mnp - npq + mqr$

2. Factor each expression if possible.

    *(a) $y^2 + 5y - 14$
    *(c) $m^2 - 9m + 20$
    *(e) $2x^2 + 2x - 4$
    *(g) $4x^2 - 144$
    *(i) $5y^2 - 17y + 6$
    *(k) $5x^2 + 2x + 1$
    *(m) $a^5 - 9a^3$
    *(o) $n^3 - 4n^2 - 12n$
    *(q) $6x^2 - 5x - 6$

    (b) $x^2 + 7x + 6$
    (d) $2b^2 - 8$
    (f) $2x^2 + 13x + 15$
    (h) $m^2 - n^2$
    (j) $3x^2 - 15x - 42$
    (l) $4x^2 + 8x + 3$
    (n) $x(x^2 - 1) + 3(x^2 - 1)$
    (p) $3m^2 + 15m + 18$

(r) $x^4 - 1$ (Difference of two squares.)

*(s) $x^{2m} + 2x^m y^m + y^{2m}$ (*Note:* $x^{2m} = (x^m)^2$.)

3. Factor each expression completely.

*(a) $x^3 + 8$ (b) $m^3 - 27$ *(c) $a^3 - x^3$

(d) $8n^3 + 1$ *(e) $1 + x^6$ (f) $1 - x^6$

*(g) $27x^3 - 64y^3$ (h) $125u^3 - 8v^3$

Review 4. Solve each quadratic equation by factoring.

*(a) $x^2 + 5x + 4 = 0$ (b) $x^2 - 7x + 12 = 0$

*(c) $y^2 - 3y - 10 = 0$ (d) $x^2 - 8x + 16 = 0$

*(e) $x^2 + 5x = 14$ (f) $t^2 - 9 = 0$

*(g) $2m^2 + 7m + 6 = 0$ (h) $3x^2 + 13x - 10 = 0$

*(i) $5x^2 + 14x + 8 = 0$ (j) $2x^2 - 19x + 35 = 0$

*(k) $2x^2 = 15 - 7x$ (l) $4x^2 + 4x - 15 = 0$

*(m) $6x^2 - 5x - 6 = 0$ (n) $6x^2 - 11x + 4 = 0$

Review 5. Simplify each square root if possible. Recall the simplification shown in Example 24.

*(a) $\sqrt{8}$ (b) $\sqrt{24}$ *(c) $\sqrt{60}$

(d) $\sqrt{150}$ *(e) $\sqrt{250}$ (f) $\sqrt{72}$

*(g) $\sqrt{68}$ (h) $\sqrt{200}$

$\sqrt{250}$

6. Solve each quadratic equation by completing the square.

*(a) $x^2 + 6x + 5 = 0$ (b) $x^2 + 8x - 2 = 0$

*(c) $n^2 - 4n + 1 = 0$ *(d) $m^2 - 2m - 1 = 0$

*(e) $x^2 - 12x + 9 = 0$ (f) $y^2 + y - 1 = 0$

*(g) $x^2 - 3x - 8 = 0$ (h) $t^2 + 7t - \dfrac{1}{2} = 0$

*(i) $2x^2 + 3x = 4$ (j) $3x^2 - 4x + 1 = 0$

*(k) $4x^2 - 6x + 1 = 0$ (l) $5x^2 + 11x = 7$

7. Solve each quadratic equation by using the quadratic formula.

*(a) $t^2 - 2t - 1 = 0$ (b) $m^2 - 12m + 9 = 0$

*(c) $x^2 + 3x - 7 = 0$ (d) $x^2 - 5x = 8$

*(e) $x^2 + 4x + 3 = 0$ (f) $x^2 - 7x + 10 = 0$

*(g) $x^2 = 2x + 5$ (h) $2x^2 + 5x - 10 = 0$

*(i) $3x^2 - 9x + 2 = 0$ (j) $-x^2 + 7x - 2 = 0$

*(k) $-5x^2 + 3x + 1 = 0$ (l) $-2x^2 - 8x + 3 = 0$

8. Solve each equation (*See* Example 26).

*(a) $x^4 - 7x^2 + 12 = 0$ (b) $x^4 - 14x^2 + 45 = 0$

*(c) $4x^4 - 13x^2 + 9 = 0$ (d) $9x^4 - 46x^2 + 5 = 0$

1.3 THE BINOMIAL THEOREM

Two-term expressions, such as $a + b$, $x - y$, $6 + 5t$, and $x^2 + 34$, are called **binomials.** In elementary algebra you learned how to multiply binomials. For example,

$$(x + 5)(x - 8) = x^2 - 3x - 40$$

$$(a + b)(c + d) = ac + ad + bc + bd$$

For practice, some exercises of this type are provided at the end of the section. In this section you will learn a technique for multiplying out powers of binomials. The method is called the **binomial theorem.** To begin, let us study the results of raising the simple binomial $a + b$ to whole powers. These results can be obtained by actually multiplying, but we shall seek a pattern and a shortcut.

$(a + b)^0 = 1$ (*Note:* $x^0 = 1$. See page 25.)

$(a + b)^1 = a + b$

$(a + b)^2 = a^2 + 2ab + b^2$

$(a + b)^3 = a^3 + 3a^2b + 3ab^2 + b^3$

$(a + b)^4 = a^4 + 4a^3b + 6a^2b^2 + 4ab^3 + b^4$

$(a + b)^5 = a^5 + 5a^4b + 10a^3b^2 + 10a^2b^3 + 5ab^4 + b^5$

In each case the terms are written in order of decreasing powers of a (and increasing power of b). In each term the sum of the exponents of a and b equals the power to which the binomial is raised. For example, in $(a + b)^5$ the terms are as follows.

Terms	*Powers of a and b*
$1a^5b^0$	$5 + 0 = 5$
$5a^4b^1$	$4 + 1 = 5$
$10a^3b^2$	$3 + 2 = 5$
$10a^2b^3$	$2 + 3 = 5$
$5a^1b^4$	$1 + 4 = 5$
$1a^0b^5$	$0 + 5 = 5$

The coefficients of each term form a pattern, which was first recognized in the 1600s by Blaise Pascal, a French mathematician. The pattern is easy to see in **Pascal's triangle,** which is shown next.

$$
\begin{array}{ccccccccc}
 & & & & 1 & & & & \\
 & & & 1 & & 1 & & & \\
 & & 1 & & 2 & & 1 & & \\
 & 1 & & 3 & & 3 & & 1 & \\
1 & & 4 & & 6 & & 4 & & 1 \\
\end{array}
$$

and so on

Each row of Pascal's triangle begins and ends with 1. Any other term in any row can be obtained by adding the two terms above its position. For example, the 4 is obtained by adding the 1 and 3 above its position. Similarly, 6 comes from $3 + 3$. Generation of the next row of coefficients, for $(a + b)^5$, is shown next.

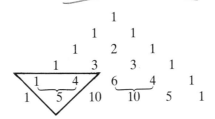

Note also that the number represented by all the digits in each of the first five rows that compose the triangle is a power of 11. The first row is 11^0, the next 11^1, then 11^2, 11^3, and 11^4. However, $11^5 \neq 15{,}101{,}051$.

Example 27 *Expand* $(x + 2y)^4$.

$$(x + 2y)^4 = [(x) + (2y)]^4$$

The expansion contains powers of x times powers of $2y$, with appropriate coefficients determined by Pascal's triangle. Those coefficients are 1, 4, 6, 4, and 1. Thus

$$
\begin{aligned}
[(x) + (2y)]^4 &= 1(x)^4(2y)^0 + 4(x)^3(2y)^1 + 6(x)^2(2y)^2 + 4(x)^1(2y)^3 + 1(x)^0(2y)^4 \\
&= 1 \cdot x^4 \cdot 1 + 4 \cdot x^3 \cdot 2y + 6 \cdot x^2 \cdot 4y^2 + 4 \cdot x \cdot 8y^3 + 1 \cdot 1 \cdot 16y^4 \\
&= x^4 + 8x^3y + 24x^2y^2 + 32xy^3 + 16y^4
\end{aligned}
$$

Example 28 *Expand* $(4m - n)^3$.

The binomial must be written as the sum $(+)$ of two terms. Thus

$$(4m - n)^3 = [(4m) + (-n)]^3$$

From Pascal's triangle the coefficients will be 1, 3, 3, and 1.

$$
\begin{aligned}
[(4m) + (-n)]^3 &= 1(4m)^3(-n)^0 + 3(4m)^2(-n)^1 + 3(4m)^1(-n)^2 + 1(4m)^0(-n)^3 \\
&= 1 \cdot 64m^3 \cdot 1 + 3 \cdot 16m^2 \cdot -n + 3 \cdot 4m \cdot n^2 + 1 \cdot 1 \cdot -n^3 \\
&= 64m^3 - 48m^2n + 12mn^2 - n^3
\end{aligned}
$$

Note: A general formula for $(a + b)^n$ will be given in Section 10.2.

EXERCISES 1.3

1. Expand each binomial by using the binomial theorem. Simplify completely.
   - *(a) $(c + d)^5$
   - (b) $(x + y)^4$
   - *(c) $(x + y)^6$
   - (d) $(a - b)^3$
   - *(e) $(p - q)^7$
   - (f) $(x + h)^5$
   - *(g) $(x + a)^8$
   - (h) $(x - a)^6$
   - *(i) $(2x + y)^5$
   - (j) $(x - 2y)^6$
   - *(k) $(2x - 3y)^5$
   - (l) $(x - y)^8$
   - *(m) $(x - y)^9$
   - (n) $(1 - x^2)^7$
   - *(o) $(x^3 + y^2)^3$
   - (p) $(t^4 + u)^5$
   - *(q) $(2 - x^3)^5$
   - (r) $(x^4 - 3)^4$
   - *(s) $\left(\dfrac{x}{2} + 1\right)^4$
   - (t) $\left(x + \dfrac{1}{x}\right)^5$
   - *(u) $\left(\dfrac{x}{2} + y\right)^6$
   - (v) $\left(\dfrac{x}{3} - y\right)^6$
   - *(w) $\left(x^2 - \dfrac{1}{x}\right)^4$
   - (x) $\left(2x - \dfrac{y}{3}\right)^4$

2. Multiply. Simplify when possible.
   - *(a) $(x + 1)(x + 4)$
   - (b) $(x + 3)(x + 2)$
   - *(c) $(a + 2)(a + 6)$
   - (d) $(m - 4)(m - 3)$
   - *(e) $(y - 8)(y - 2)$
   - (f) $(5 + m)(8 + m)$
   - *(g) $(2 + x)(7 - x)$
   - (h) $(1 + y)(1 - 2y)$
   - *(i) $(2x + 5)(x + 3)$
   - (j) $(5m + 2)(m - 6)$
   - *(k) $(3y - 5)(3y - 1)$
   - (l) $(5x + 3)(2x + 4)$
   - *(m) $(7x - 3)(2x - 5)$
   - (n) $(3x - 8)(5x - 1)$
   - *(o) $(x + y)(2x + y)$
   - (p) $(x - y)(2x - y)$

3. Multiply out $(a - b)^2$ and $(b - a)^2$ to verify the boxed statement shown.

$$\boxed{(a - b)^2 = (b - a)^2}$$

This says that the *square* of $a - b$ is the same as the *square* of $b - a$.

1.4 FRACTIONS

Addition, multiplication, division, and reduction of fractions are defined next. The numbers a, b, c, and d are real numbers. The presentation is a review; you should already be familiar with these operations.

1. $\dfrac{a}{d} + \dfrac{b}{d} = \dfrac{a + b}{d}$ Common denominators $\qquad d \neq 0$

2. $\dfrac{a}{b} \cdot \dfrac{c}{d} = \dfrac{ac}{bd}$ $\qquad b, d \neq 0$

3. $\dfrac{a}{b} + \dfrac{c}{d} = \dfrac{a}{b} \cdot \dfrac{d}{d} + \dfrac{c}{d} \cdot \dfrac{b}{b} = \dfrac{ad}{bd} + \dfrac{bc}{bd} = \dfrac{ad + bc}{bd}$ $\qquad b, d \neq 0$

4. $\dfrac{ac}{bc} = \dfrac{a}{b}$ $\qquad\qquad\qquad\qquad\qquad\qquad\qquad b, c \neq 0$

5. $\dfrac{a}{b} \div \dfrac{c}{d} = \dfrac{ad}{bc}$ $\qquad\qquad\qquad\qquad\qquad\qquad b, c, d \neq 0$

Example 29 *Combine* $\dfrac{3x}{5ab} + \dfrac{7}{4c}$.

The least common denominator is $5ab \cdot 4c$ or $20abc$. Thus

$$\dfrac{3x}{5ab} + \dfrac{7}{4c} = \dfrac{3x}{5ab} \cdot \dfrac{4c}{4c} + \dfrac{7}{4c} \cdot \dfrac{5ab}{5ab}$$

$$= \dfrac{12cx}{20abc} + \dfrac{35ab}{20abc}$$

$$= \dfrac{12cx + 35ab}{20abc}$$

Example 30 *Combine* $\dfrac{5}{2x - 8} + \dfrac{7}{x^2 - 2x - 8}$

$$\dfrac{5}{2x - 8} + \dfrac{7}{x^2 - 2x - 8} = \dfrac{5}{2(x - 4)} + \dfrac{7}{(x - 4)(x + 2)}$$

The least common denominator is $2(x - 4)(x + 2)$.

$$\dfrac{5}{2(x - 4)} + \dfrac{7}{(x - 4)(x + 2)} = \dfrac{5}{2(x - 4)} \cdot \dfrac{(x + 2)}{(x + 2)} + \dfrac{7}{(x - 4)(x + 2)} \cdot \dfrac{2}{2}$$

$$= \dfrac{5(x + 2) + 7 \cdot 2}{2(x - 4)(x + 2)}$$

$$= \dfrac{5x + 24}{2x^2 - 4x - 16}$$

Example 31 *Reduce* $\dfrac{x^2 + 7x + 12}{x^2 - x - 20}$.

The numerator and denominator can be factored and the common factor divided out according to Property 4, assuming $x \neq -4$.

$$\dfrac{x^2 + 7x + 12}{x^2 - x - 20} = \dfrac{(x + 3)(x + 4)}{(x - 5)(x + 4)} = \dfrac{x + 3}{x - 5}$$

Example 32 *Reduce* $\dfrac{3x - 3y}{y - x}$.

$$\frac{3x - 3y}{y - x} = \frac{3(x - y)}{(y - x)}$$

Now observe that $(x - y) = -1(y - x)$. This means

$$\frac{x - y}{y - x} = -1$$

and

$$\frac{3x - 3y}{y - x} = \frac{3(x - y)}{(y - x)} = 3(-1) = -3$$

Example 33 *Perform the indicated operation:* $\dfrac{x + 4}{5} \cdot \dfrac{2x + 1}{y}$.

$$\frac{x + 4}{5} \cdot \frac{2x + 1}{y} = \frac{(x + 4)(2x + 1)}{5y} = \frac{2x^2 + 9x + 4}{5y}$$

Often a factored form is more useful than a multiplied out form. The result here can be left as the fraction

$$\frac{(x + 4)(2x + 1)}{5y}$$

Example 34 *Perform the indicated operation:* $\dfrac{x^2 - 9}{x} \div \dfrac{2x + 6}{8}$.

$$\frac{x^2 - 9}{x} \div \frac{2x + 6}{8} = \frac{x^2 - 9}{x} \cdot \frac{8}{2x + 6}$$

$$= \frac{(x + 3)(x - 3)}{x} \cdot \frac{2 \cdot 4}{2(x + 3)} = \frac{(x - 3)4}{x}$$

Example 35 *Simplify the complex fraction*

$$\frac{\dfrac{a}{x} + 5}{3 + \dfrac{1}{y}}$$

As a first step in simplifying a complex fraction such as this one, examine all the fractions that make up the complex fraction (namely, a/x and $1/y$). Determine the least common denominator of these fractions (which is xy). Then multiply each term of the complex fraction by this least common denominator. In this instance, we multiply each term by xy. The effect is to eliminate all the fractions that compose the complex fraction. Here is the work.

$$\frac{\dfrac{a}{x} + 5}{3 + \dfrac{1}{y}} = \frac{xy \cdot \dfrac{a}{x} + xy \cdot 5}{xy \cdot 3 + xy \cdot \dfrac{1}{y}} = \frac{ay + 5xy}{3xy + x}$$

One final note on fractions: When an equation contains fractions, it is usually best to begin solving it by eliminating all the fractions. This can be done by multiplying both sides of the equation (all terms) by the least common denominator of all fractions involved. The resulting equation will contain no fractions and should be much easier to solve.

Example 36 *Solve* $\dfrac{5}{x + 1} - \dfrac{3}{20} = \dfrac{9}{5}$.

The least common denominator is $20(x + 1)$. If both sides of the equation are multiplied by $20(x + 1)$, we get

$$20(x + 1) \cdot \frac{5}{x + 1} - 20(x + 1) \cdot \frac{3}{20} = 20(x + 1) \cdot \frac{9}{5}$$

or

$$100 - 3(x + 1) = 36(x + 1)$$

or

$$100 - 3x - 3 = 36x + 36$$

Then

$$61 = 39x$$

Finally,

$$x = \frac{61}{39}$$

The number $\frac{61}{39}$ does check, although the check is not shown here. Whenever both sides of an equation are multiplied by a variable (as was done here, for example), the solution should be checked in the *original* equation. A number can be a solution of the altered equation even though it may not be a solution of the original equation.

EXERCISES 1.4

1. Combine the fractions. Simplify when possible.

*(a) $\dfrac{x}{a} + \dfrac{y}{b}$

(b) $\dfrac{x}{a} + \dfrac{a}{x}$

*(c) $\dfrac{5}{xy} + \dfrac{7x}{3y}$

(d) $\dfrac{4}{x + 2} - \dfrac{3}{x - 5}$

*(e) $\dfrac{3x}{x^2 - 25} + \dfrac{x + 1}{x^2 + 5x}$

(f) $\dfrac{2}{x^2 - 1} + \dfrac{5}{x^2 - 7x + 10}$

*(g) $\dfrac{5}{x^2 - 2x - 15} - \dfrac{9}{x^2 + 6x + 9}$

(h) $\dfrac{8}{x^2 - 4x + 4} - \dfrac{5}{2x^2 - 8}$

*(i) $\dfrac{8x}{3x^2 - 18x - 48} + \dfrac{x}{x^2 - 7x - 8}$

(j) $\dfrac{7x}{8x - 2x^2} - \dfrac{2x}{(4 - x)^2}$

2. Multiply or divide as specified and simplify.

*(a) $\dfrac{x}{y} \cdot \dfrac{2y}{x + 1}$

(b) $\dfrac{x + 3}{9} \cdot \dfrac{6x}{6x + 10}$

*(c) $\dfrac{x^2 - 16}{x^2 + 6x + 8} \cdot \dfrac{x^2 + 2x}{x^3}$

(d) $\dfrac{2x + 10}{4x - 12} \cdot \dfrac{x^2 - 8x + 15}{x^2 - 25}$

*(e) $\dfrac{3x}{2y} \div \dfrac{x + 1}{10y^2 + y}$

(f) $\dfrac{x - y}{y - x} \div \dfrac{x}{y}$

*(g) $\dfrac{x^2 + 2x}{5x} \div \dfrac{x^2 - 4}{10}$

(h) $\dfrac{x^2 - 6x + 9}{x^2 + 2x - 15} \div \dfrac{x^2 - 9}{5x}$

*(i) $\dfrac{1 - t^2}{1 - t} \cdot \dfrac{6t}{2t + 2}$

(j) $\dfrac{m^2 - 5m}{m^3} \div \dfrac{m^2 - 25}{5m}$

*(k) $\dfrac{a^2 - b^2}{ab} \div \dfrac{2b - 2a}{2b}$

(l) $\dfrac{2x^2 + x - 3}{10x + 15} \cdot \dfrac{30x}{3x^2 - 3}$

3. Simplify each complex fraction.

*(a) $\dfrac{2 + \dfrac{1}{x}}{3 - \dfrac{1}{x}}$

(b) $\dfrac{\dfrac{x}{y} + \dfrac{y}{x}}{\dfrac{x}{y}}$

*(c) $\dfrac{2 + \dfrac{x}{y}}{\dfrac{x}{y} + 4}$

(d) $\dfrac{\dfrac{n + 1}{n}}{\dfrac{2}{n} + 9}$

*(e) $\dfrac{\dfrac{2t+1}{t}+t}{\dfrac{1}{t}-t}$

(f) $\dfrac{\dfrac{m}{n}+\dfrac{n}{m}}{\dfrac{1}{n}-\dfrac{1}{m}}$

*(g) $\dfrac{\dfrac{1}{(x+h)-1}-\dfrac{1}{x-1}}{h}$

(h) $1-\dfrac{1}{1-\dfrac{1}{x}}$

*(i) $\dfrac{a-\dfrac{b}{c}}{\dfrac{d}{e}-f}$

(j) $\dfrac{\dfrac{ab}{cd}+\dfrac{ef}{gh}}{\dfrac{j}{k}+7}$

4. Solve each equation.

*(a) $\dfrac{9}{x}=10$

(b) $\dfrac{7}{x}=3$

*(c) $6+\dfrac{x}{7}=9$

(d) $\dfrac{3x+2}{5}+\dfrac{3}{4}=1$

*(e) $\dfrac{x}{4}+\dfrac{x+1}{3}=5$

(f) $\dfrac{x}{x+2}+\dfrac{1}{5}+\dfrac{5}{x+2}=0$

*(g) $\dfrac{3}{x-1}=\dfrac{5}{x+2}$

(h) $\dfrac{m}{m-3}+\dfrac{2}{7}=\dfrac{3}{2m-6}$

*(i) $\dfrac{x}{x+1}+\dfrac{x}{x+5}=2$

*5. If 3 is added to the reciprocal of a number x, the result is 17. Establish an equation and then solve it to determine x.

6. Consider a number x. Its reciprocal is multiplied by 6. Then 4 is subtracted from that result. The final result is 15. Determine x.

7. Show in steps how the fraction

$$\dfrac{-x^3}{x-4}$$

can be changed to the form $\dfrac{x^3}{4-x}$

1.5 INTEGER EXPONENTS

This section begins with a brief review of the notation and properties of exponents. The properties (given in boxes below) will be applied here only with positive integer exponents. However, later in the chapter they will be used with other real-number exponents as well. The properties hold for all real-number exponents.

Before we can state the properties of exponents, a definition is in order. If x is a real number and n is a positive integer, then

$$x^n = x \cdot x \cdot x \cdots x \qquad n \text{ factors of } x$$

Here then are some properties of exponents. All numbers used here (x, y, m, and n) can be any real numbers, although for now m and n are positive integers.

$$x^m \cdot x^n = x^{m+n}$$

$$(x^m)^n = x^{mn}$$

$$(x \cdot y)^m = x^m y^m$$

$$\left(\frac{x}{y}\right)^m = \frac{x^m}{y^m} \qquad y \neq 0$$

$$\frac{x^m}{x^n} = x^{m-n} \qquad x \neq 0$$

Here are some examples.

$$x^7 x^4 = x^{7+4} = x^{11}$$

$$(b^3)^5 = b^{3 \cdot 5} = b^{15}$$

$$(3x)^4 = 3^4 x^4 = 81x^4$$

$$\left(\frac{t}{u}\right)^{16} = \frac{t^{16}}{u^{16}}$$

$$\frac{x^8}{x^6} = x^{8-6} = x^2$$

$$(5x^3 y^2)(2x^8 y^7) = 5 \cdot 2 \cdot x^3 \cdot x^8 \cdot y^2 \cdot y^7 = 10x^{11} y^9$$

$$(x^2 y^5)^4 = (x^2)^4 (y^5)^4 = x^8 y^{20}$$

Example 37 *Factor $x^{2n} + x^n$.*

By the second exponent property, $x^{2n} = (x^n)^2$ or $x^n \cdot x^n$. Thus

$$x^{2n} + x^n = x^n \cdot x^n + x^n \cdot 1$$

$$= x^n(x^n + 1)$$

Example 38 *Factor $x^{2n} - 9$.*

Since $x^{2n} = (x^n)^2$, the expression $x^{2n} - 9$ is the difference of two squares and can be factored accordingly.

$$x^{2n} - 9 = (x^n)^2 - (3)^2$$
$$= (x^n + 3)(x^n - 3)$$

Use of the last boxed property

$$\frac{x^m}{x^n} = x^{m-n}$$

can produce a zero or negative exponent. For example, if $m = n$, the resulting exponent is zero.

$$\frac{x^m}{x^m} = x^{m-m} = x^0$$

But $x^m/x^m = 1$, since a number divided by itself equals one. This suggests the definition of x^0 as $x^0 = 1$.

$$\boxed{x^0 = 1 \qquad x \neq 0}$$

If n is larger than m, a negative exponent results. Consider

$$\frac{x^5}{x^9} = x^{5-9} = x^{-4}$$

But also,

$$\frac{x^5}{x^9} = \frac{xxxxx}{xxxxxxxxx} = \frac{1}{x^4}$$

which suggests that

$$x^{-4} = \frac{1}{x^4}$$

and, in general, for $x \neq 0$,

$$\boxed{x^{-n} = \frac{1}{x^n}}$$

Furthermore,

$$x^n = x^{-(-n)} = \frac{1}{x^{-n}}$$

$$\boxed{\frac{1}{x^{-n}} = x^n}$$

The next example shows that negative powers are not computed directly; they are changed to positive powers in order to be evaluated. Consequently, we will usually say that an expression is not simplified until all negative exponents have been removed.

Example 39 *Simplify 3^{-2}.*

$$3^{-2} = \frac{1}{3^2} = \frac{1}{9}$$

Example 40 *Simplify $\dfrac{(5x)^0 y^{10} z^9}{y^4 z^{12}}$.*

$$(5x)^0 = 1 \qquad \frac{y^{10}}{y^4} = y^6 \qquad \frac{z^9}{z^{12}} = \frac{1}{z^3}$$

so

$$\frac{(5x)^0 y^{10} z^9}{y^4 z^{12}} = \frac{y^6}{z^3}$$

Example 41 *Simplify $(x^2 x^{-7})^{-3}$.*

$$(x^2 x^{-7})^{-3} = (x^{-5})^{-3} = x^{15}$$

Example 42 *Simplify $(4x^0)^2 (x^{-2})^3$.*

$$(4x^0)^2(x^{-2})^3 = (4 \cdot 1)^2(x^{-6}) = 16 \cdot \frac{1}{x^6} = \frac{16}{x^6}$$

Example 43 *Simplify* $\dfrac{3x^{-2}y^5z^8}{6x^4y^3z^8}$.

$$\frac{3x^{-2}y^5z^8}{6x^4y^3z^8} = \frac{3}{6} \cdot \frac{x^{-2}}{x^4} \cdot \frac{y^5}{y^3} \cdot \frac{z^8}{z^8}$$

$$= \frac{1}{2} \cdot \frac{1}{x^6} \cdot \frac{y^2}{1} \cdot 1$$

$$= \frac{y^2}{2x^6}$$

Example 44 *Simplify* $\dfrac{x^{-1} - y^{-1}}{(xy)^{-2}}$.

Begin by changing to positive exponents.

$$\frac{x^{-1} - y^{-1}}{(xy)^{-2}} = \frac{\dfrac{1}{x} - \dfrac{1}{y}}{\dfrac{1}{(xy)^2}}$$

At this point you can either consider this a complex fraction to be simplified by multiplying each term by the least common denominator $(xy)^2$ or else you can simply rewrite the denominator fraction $1/(xy)^2$ as $(xy)^2$ in the numerator. The effect is the same, namely,

$$(xy)^2 \cdot \frac{1}{x} - (xy)^2 \cdot \frac{1}{y}$$

which simplifies to

$$xy^2 - x^2y$$

EXERCISES 1.5

1. Simplify each expression completely.
   - *(a) $x^{20}x^5$
   - (b) x^3x^{12}
   - *(c) $a^{17}a^{15}a$
   - (d) $b^6b^4b^2$
   - *(e) $6m^7m^8 \cdot 2m^2$
   - (f) $(3x^2)(-5x)(2x^8)$
   - *(g) $(4x^3y^5)(x^9y^2)$
   - (h) $(2x^4y)(-y^3z^7)^2$
   - *(i) $(x^4)^3(y^5)^6$
   - (j) $(5a^4)^2(b^4)^7$
   - *(k) $(x^2y^3)^4$
   - (l) $(3m^2n^5)^3$

*(m) $\left(\dfrac{a^4}{b^3}\right)^5$ (n) $\left(\dfrac{x^5}{3y^7}\right)^3$

*(o) $\dfrac{x^{40}y^{60}}{x^{10}y^{12}}$ (p) $\dfrac{a^{20}b^{15}c^{10}}{a^{11}b^4c^9}$

2. Simplify each expression completely. Eliminate all negative and zero exponents. In (s) through (v), assume that n is an integer 2 or larger.

*(a) $m^0 + 2^{-1}$ (b) $7(c^0d^4e^7)^0$

*(c) $(x^0 + 2^3)^2$ (d) $(1 - x^0)^7 + (2x^0)^5 + (x^0)^4$

*(e) $\left(\dfrac{a^0 - b^0}{a^0 + b^0}\right)^2$ (f) $\left(\dfrac{a^0 + b^0}{a^0 + b^0}\right)^{-2}$

*(g) $\dfrac{3^{-2}}{2^{-3}}$ (h) $4^0 + 4^{-1} + 4^{-2}$

*(i) $5 \cdot 2^{-3} + 2^{-4}$ (j) $7 \cdot 3^{-1} + 5 \cdot 3^{-2}$

*(k) $\dfrac{x^5y^{10}}{2x^{-3}y^4}$ (l) $\dfrac{14n^6p^{-2}}{2q^2r^{-5}s^{-2}}$

*(m) $\left(\dfrac{x^{-9}}{4x^2}\right)^3$ (n) $\left(\dfrac{x^3y^2}{x^5y}\right)^4$

*(o) $\left(\dfrac{3n^2}{4n^{-5}}\right)^{-2}$ (p) $(5x^{-3}y^2)^2$

*(q) $(x^{-3}y^{-2})(x^3y^{-1})$ (r) $(x^{-2}y^{-3})^{-5}$

*(s) $\dfrac{x^nx^{2n}x}{x^4}$ (t) $\dfrac{x^{3n}x^n}{x^{2n}}$

*(u) $\dfrac{x^{5n}x^{3n}}{x^5}$ (v) $\dfrac{x^{2n}x^nx^{3n}}{x^{4n}x^3}$

3. Write each expression as one reduced fraction.

*(a) $\dfrac{a^2}{b} + \dfrac{b^2}{a}$ (b) $c^{-3}d + c^2d^{-2}$

*(c) $a^{-1} + b^{-1}$ (d) $(a + b)(a^2 - b^2)^{-1}$

*(e) $\dfrac{\dfrac{1}{xy}}{x^{-1} + y^{-1}}$ (f) $(x^{-1} + y^{-1})^{-1}$

*(g) $\dfrac{x^{-1} + x^{-2}}{x}$ (h) $\dfrac{x^{-1}}{x^{-1} + x^{-2}}$

*(i) $(x + y^{-2})^{-1}$ (j) $\dfrac{x}{x^{-2} - x^{-1}}$

*(k) $\dfrac{x^2}{y^{-1}} + \dfrac{y}{x^{-2}}$ (l) $\left(\dfrac{x^{-2}}{y} + \dfrac{y^{-2}}{x}\right)^{-1}$

*(m) $(a^x + b^y)(a^{-x} - b^{-y})$ (n) $\dfrac{(x + 1)^{-1} + (x - 1)^{-1}}{x(x + 1)^{-1}}$

4. Factor.

*(a) $x^{n+1} + x^n$ (b) $x^{n-1} + x^n$ *(c) $x^{2n} + x^n$

(d) $y^{2n+1} + y^n$ *(e) $y^{n+1} + y^{n-1}$ (f) $x^{3n} + x^n$

*(g) $x^{2n} - 81$ (h) $a^{2n} - b^{2n}$ *(i) $x^{n+1} - x^{n-1}$

(j) $x^{3n} - x^n$

1.6 FRACTIONAL EXPONENTS AND RADICALS

The square root of a positive number x is the positive number $\sqrt{x}$ such that $\sqrt{x}\sqrt{x} = x$. In order to assign an exponent to x that corresponds to $\sqrt{x}$ and obeys the property $x^m \cdot x^n = x^{m+n}$, we define

$$\sqrt{x} = x^{1/2}$$

This is consistent because $\sqrt{x}\sqrt{x} = x$ and

$$x^{1/2} \cdot x^{1/2} = x^{1/2 + 1/2} = x^1 = x.$$

Similarly, for a cube root, $\sqrt[3]{x}\ \sqrt[3]{x}\ \sqrt[3]{x} = x$ leads to $\sqrt[3]{x} = x^{1/3}$. In general, the nth root of any positive number can be written

$$\boxed{\sqrt[n]{x} = x^{1/n}}$$

Example 45 *Simplify the expression $9^{1/2} + 64^{1/3}$.*

$$9^{1/2} + 64^{1/3} = \sqrt{9} + \sqrt[3]{64}$$

$$= 3 + 4$$

$$= 7$$

Fractional-exponent notation, such as $\tfrac{2}{3}$, has two equivalent interpretations, each of which is consistent with the property of exponents, $(x^m)^n = x^{mn}$.

$$x^{2/3} = x^{(1/3)\cdot 2} = (x^{1/3})^2$$

$$x^{2/3} = x^{2\cdot(1/3)} = (x^2)^{1/3}$$

In general, for m/n any positive rational number,

$$x^{m/n} = (x^{1/n})^m = (x^m)^{1/n}$$

For computations, it is generally easier to work with the first form.

Example 46 *Simplify the expression $64^{2/3} + 4^{7/2}$.*

$$\begin{aligned} 64^{2/3} + 4^{7/2} &= (64^{1/3})^2 + (4^{1/2})^7 \\ &= (4)^2 + (2)^7 \\ &= 16 + 128 \\ &= 144 \end{aligned}$$

Example 47 *Simplify $16^{-5/4}$.*

$$16^{-5/4} = \frac{1}{16^{5/4}} = \frac{1}{(16^{1/4})^5} = \frac{1}{(2)^5} = \frac{1}{32}$$

The properties of integer exponents also apply to any rational exponents. The property $(x \cdot y)^m = x^m \cdot y^m$ is useful in simplifying radicals. For example,

$$\sqrt{x \cdot y} = (x \cdot y)^{1/2} = x^{1/2} \cdot y^{1/2} = \sqrt{x}\sqrt{y}$$

Thus

$$\sqrt{x \cdot y} = \sqrt{x} \cdot \sqrt{y} \qquad \text{and, similarly,} \qquad \sqrt{\frac{x}{y}} = \frac{\sqrt{x}}{\sqrt{y}}$$

Similar properties hold for cube roots, fourth roots, and so on. For even roots (square root, fourth root, and so forth), x and y must be positive.

Example 48 *Simplify $\sqrt{75}$.*

$$\sqrt{75} = \sqrt{25 \cdot 3} = \sqrt{25}\sqrt{3} = 5\sqrt{3}$$

The square root of a number can be simplified in this manner whenever the number can be written as a perfect square times another positive integer.

Example 49   *Simplify* $\dfrac{x}{\sqrt{x}}$.

$$\frac{x}{\sqrt{x}} = \frac{\sqrt{x}\sqrt{x}}{\sqrt{x}} = \sqrt{x}$$

A cube root can be simplified in the manner of Example 48 whenever the number can be written as a perfect cube times another integer.

Example 50   *Simplify* $\sqrt[3]{320}$.

$$\sqrt[3]{320} = \sqrt[3]{64} \cdot \sqrt[3]{5}$$
$$= 4\sqrt[3]{5}$$

Simplification of radicals is sometimes easier when the radical notation is changed to exponent notation. The next example demonstrates such a procedure.

Example 51   *Express* $\sqrt{2}\ \sqrt[3]{5}$ *as one radical.*

$$\sqrt{2}\ \sqrt[3]{5} = 2^{1/2}5^{1/3} \qquad \text{obtaining fractional exponents}$$
$$= 2^{3/6}5^{2/6} \qquad \text{changing to common denominator}$$
$$= (2^3 5^2)^{1/6}$$
$$= \sqrt[6]{8 \cdot 25}$$
$$= \sqrt[6]{200}$$

It is sometimes desirable to eliminate irrational numbers from denominators of fractions, for example, when computations are forthcoming. It is simpler to divide a rational constant (often an integer) into an irrational number than to do the reverse of this process. For instance, using 1.414214 as an approximation of $\sqrt{2}$,

$$\frac{7}{\sqrt{2}} \approx \frac{7}{1.414214}$$

is a more difficult division than is

$$\frac{7\sqrt{2}}{2} \approx \frac{7(1.414214)}{2}$$

The symbol $\approx$ is used to mean *approximately equal to*. An irrational number can be removed from the denominator of a fraction by multiplying both numerator and denominator by an appropriate irrational number. Examples of such techniques are shown next.

Example 52 *Rationalize the denominator of* $\dfrac{6}{\sqrt{2}}$.

In this example rationalizing the denominator creates a simpler expression.

$$\frac{6}{\sqrt{2}} = \frac{6}{\sqrt{2}} \cdot \frac{\sqrt{2}}{\sqrt{2}} = \frac{6\sqrt{2}}{2} = 3\sqrt{2}$$

Example 53 *Rationalize the denominator of* $\dfrac{2\sqrt{5}}{\sqrt{8}}$.

Here the fraction has two radicals. Rationalizing the denominator will leave the fraction with only one radical. Although we could multiply both numerator and denominator by $\sqrt{8}$, it is simpler to multiply by $\sqrt{2}$, which is sufficient to produce a rational denominator.

$$\frac{2\sqrt{5}}{\sqrt{8}} = \frac{2\sqrt{5}}{\sqrt{8}} \cdot \frac{\sqrt{2}}{\sqrt{2}} = \frac{2\sqrt{10}}{4} = \frac{\sqrt{10}}{2}$$

Example 54 *Rationalize the denominator of* $\dfrac{5}{4 - \sqrt{3}}$.

$$\frac{5}{4 - \sqrt{3}} = \frac{5}{4 - \sqrt{3}} \cdot \frac{4 + \sqrt{3}}{4 + \sqrt{3}} = \frac{5(4 + \sqrt{3})}{16 - 3} = \frac{5(4 + \sqrt{3})}{13}$$

Do you see the application here of factoring the difference of two squares?

Example 55 *Rationalize the denominator of* $\dfrac{4}{\sqrt[3]{2}}$.

If the denominator is multiplied by $\sqrt[3]{2}\sqrt[3]{2}$, it will become 2 according to the definition of a cube root. Of course, we must multiply the numerator by $\sqrt[3]{2}\sqrt[3]{2}$, too.

$$\frac{4}{\sqrt[3]{2}} = \frac{4}{\sqrt[3]{2}} \cdot \frac{\sqrt[3]{2}\sqrt[3]{2}}{\sqrt[3]{2}\sqrt[3]{2}} = \frac{4\sqrt[3]{4}}{2} = 2\sqrt[3]{4}$$

The next two examples show simplification of expressions that arise when a particular calculus operation is applied to a product.

Example 56   *Factor completely* $(x^2 + 5)^4 \cdot 14(2x + 3)^6 + (2x + 3)^7 \cdot 8x(x^2 + 5)^3.$

   Note the factor $(x^2 + 5)^4$ in the first term and $(x^2 + 5)^3$ in the second term. The smaller power, $(x^2 + 5)^3$, can be factored out of each. Similarly, notice the factor $(2x + 3)^6$ in the first term and $(2x + 3)^7$ in the second term. The smaller power, $(2x + 3)^6$, can be factored out of each. Finally, with the factor 14 in the first term and $8x$ in the second term, a 2 can be factored out of each. Thus $2(x^2 + 5)^3(2x + 3)^6$ can be factored out of the expression. The result is

$$2(x^2 + 5)^3(2x + 3)^6 \, [7(x^2 + 5) + 4x(2x + 3)]$$

When the expression inside the brackets is multiplied out and like terms combined, the final result is

$$2(x^2 + 5)^3(2x + 3)^6(15x^2 + 12x + 35)$$

Example 57   *Simplify the expression* $x^4(x^2 + 10)^{-1/2} + 3x^2(x^2 + 10)^{1/2}.$

   Proceeding as in Example 56, note the factor x^4 in the first term and x^2 in the second term. The smaller power, x^2, can be factored out of each. Similarly, notice the factor $(x^2 + 10)^{-1/2}$ in the first term and $(x^2 + 10)^{1/2}$ in the second term. The smaller power, $(x^2 + 10)^{-1/2}$, can be factored out of each. The result of factoring out $x^2(x^2 + 10)^{-1/2}$ is

$$x^2(x^2 + 10)^{-1/2}[(x^2) + 3(x^2 + 10)]$$

or

$$x^2(x^2 + 10)^{-1/2}(x^2 + 3x^2 + 30)$$

or

$$x^2(x^2 + 10)^{-1/2}(4x^2 + 30)$$

A 2 can be factored from $4x^2 + 30$ to yield

$$2x^2(x^2 + 10)^{-1/2}(2x^2 + 15)$$

To eliminate negative exponents, the factor $(x^2 + 10)^{-1/2}$ can be written as $1/(x^2 + 10)^{1/2}$ or $1/\sqrt{x^2 + 10}$. The result is

$$\frac{2x^2(2x^2 + 15)}{\sqrt{x^2 + 10}}$$

This is a most useful form; yet the denominator is not rationalized. In calculus you will find that often the fraction with a rational numerator is the useful one.

Example 58   *Rationalize the numerator of* $\dfrac{\sqrt{5}}{6}$.

$$\frac{\sqrt{5}}{6} \cdot \frac{\sqrt{5}}{\sqrt{5}} = \frac{5}{6\sqrt{5}}$$

Equations that contain square roots can often be solved by squaring both sides of the equation—that is, multiplying both sides by equal quantities—themselves. If one side of the equation contains the sum (or difference) of two radicals or the sum (or difference) of a radical and another number, then manipulation to isolate the radical should be carried out first if possible. Otherwise it will be necessary to square both sides twice.

If the radical equation contains cube roots, then both sides must be cubed in order to simplify the equation.

Example 59   *Solve for x:* $\sqrt{6x - 1} = 2\sqrt{x}$.
After squaring both sides,

$$6x - 1 = 4x$$

or

$$x = \frac{1}{2}$$

Squaring both sides of an equation can introduce *extraneous roots*—that is, roots of the modified (squared) equation that are not solutions of the original equation. This means you should *always check* the solutions to such equations. Here $\frac{1}{2}$ checks in the original equation. On the other hand, the equation

$$\sqrt{3x + 1} + \sqrt{x - 1} = 0$$

has no solution. Although the mechanical problem-solving techniques produce $x = -1$ as a "solution," -1 does not check in the original equation and there is no solution.

Example 60   *Solve the equation* $\sqrt{x + 1} + 1 = \sqrt{2x}$.
Begin by squaring both sides of the equation.

$$(\sqrt{x + 1} + 1)^2 = (\sqrt{2x})^2$$
$$(x + 1) + 2\sqrt{x + 1} + 1 = 2x$$

After simplifying and isolating the radical, we have

$$2\sqrt{x + 1} = x - 2$$

Squaring both sides again yields

$$4(x + 1) = x^2 - 4x + 4$$

or

$$4x + 4 = x^2 - 4x + 4$$

This quadratic equation should be manipulated into the form $ax^2 + bx + c = 0$ and solved by factoring (if possible) or else by the quadratic formula. The equation will become

$$x^2 - 8x = 0$$

which is readily solved by factoring.

$$(x)(x - 8) = 0$$

Clearly the solutions of this quadratic equation are 0 and 8. But check these results in the original equation; you will find that 0 is an extraneous root. The only root of the original equation is 8.

EXERCISES 1.6

1. Simplify each expression.
    *(a) $144^{1/2}$
    (b) $100^{3/2}$
    *(c) $(9 + 16)^{1/2}$
    (d) $5^0 + 4^{3/2}$
    *(e) $32^{2/5}$
    (f) $(25^{1/2} + 27^{1/3})^{1/3}$
    *(g) $3 \cdot 4^{3/2} + 25^{3/2}$
    (h) $5 \cdot 4^{1/2}$
    *(i) $16^{-1/2}$
    (j) $81^{-3/4}$
    *(k) $125^{1/3} + 9^{1/2})^{-1/3}$
    (l) $(27x^{12}y^6)^{4/3}$
    *(m) $\sqrt[3]{64x^{18}}$
    (n) $\sqrt[5]{-32n^5}$
    *(o) $\sqrt[3]{-27x^3y^6}$
    (p) $\sqrt{16x^6y^4}$
    *(q) $(8m^{21}n^{12})^{2/3}$
    (r) $(49x^2y^2)^{3/2}$ $(x > 0, y > 0)$†
    *(s) $(125x^{18})^{4/3}$
    (t) $(81w^8)^{3/4}$ $(w > 0)$†
    *(u) $\left(\dfrac{8}{x^3}\right)^{2/3}$
    (v) $\left(\dfrac{64}{v^3}\right)^{2/3}$
    *(w) $\left(\dfrac{9x^4}{y^2}\right)^{3/2}$ $(y > 0)$†
    (x) $\left(\dfrac{4a^2}{9}\right)^{5/2}$ $(a > 0)$†
    *(y) $\left(\dfrac{x^3y^6}{27}\right)^{4/3}$
    (z) $\left(\dfrac{a^9b^6}{c^3}\right)^{4/3}$

_____

† No such restriction will be needed after absolute value is introduced in the next section.

2. Simplify each radical.

*(a) $\sqrt{20}$ (b) $\sqrt{72}$ *(c) $\sqrt{98}$

(d) $\sqrt{54}$ *(e) $\sqrt{48}$ (f) $\sqrt{150}$

*(g) $\sqrt{147}$ (h) $\sqrt{108}$ *(i) $\sqrt{126}$

(j) $\sqrt{300}$ *(k) $\sqrt{180}$ (l) $\sqrt{117}$

*(m) $\sqrt{162}$ (n) $\sqrt{363}$ *(o) $6\sqrt{28}$

(p) $5\sqrt{75}$ *(q) $\sqrt[3]{24}$ (r) $\sqrt[3]{128}$

*(s) $\sqrt[3]{54}$ (t) $\sqrt[3]{250}$ *(u) $\sqrt[3]{40}$

(v) $\sqrt[3]{270}$ *(w) $\sqrt{\dfrac{9}{4}}$ (x) $\sqrt{\dfrac{17}{16}}$

*(y) $\sqrt{\dfrac{7}{21}}$ (z) $\sqrt{\dfrac{1}{2}}$

3. Express as one radical in simplest form.

*(a) $\dfrac{\sqrt[3]{4}}{\sqrt{2}}$ (b) $\dfrac{\sqrt{6}}{\sqrt[3]{2}}$

*(c) $\sqrt[4]{3}\sqrt[3]{2}$ (d) $\sqrt[4]{5}\sqrt[8]{3}$

4. Rationalize the denominator of each fraction.

*(a) $\dfrac{3}{\sqrt{7}}$ (b) $\dfrac{5}{\sqrt{18}}$ *(c) $\dfrac{2\sqrt{5}}{\sqrt{6}}$

(d) $\dfrac{3}{1 - \sqrt{2}}$ *(e) $\dfrac{5}{2 + \sqrt{3}}$ (f) $\dfrac{5}{\sqrt{3} - \sqrt{2}}$

*(g) $\dfrac{w}{\sqrt{x} + \sqrt{y}}$ (h) $\dfrac{x}{\sqrt{a} - \sqrt{b}}$ *(i) $\dfrac{\sqrt{5} + 2}{\sqrt{5} - 2}$

(j) $\dfrac{\sqrt{6} - \sqrt{5}}{\sqrt{6} + \sqrt{5}}$ *(k) $\dfrac{7}{\sqrt{7}}$ (l) $\dfrac{x}{\sqrt{x}}$

5. Rationalize the denominator of each fraction.

*(a) $\dfrac{2}{\sqrt[3]{7}}$ (b) $\dfrac{13}{\sqrt[3]{10}}$ *(c) $\dfrac{5}{\sqrt[3]{32}}$

(d) $\dfrac{7}{\sqrt[3]{25}}$ *(e) $\dfrac{2}{\sqrt[3]{20}}$ (f) $\dfrac{4}{\sqrt[3]{16}}$

*(g) $\dfrac{5}{1 - \sqrt[3]{2}}$ (*Hint:* Difference of cubes.)   (h) $\dfrac{3}{2 + \sqrt[3]{5}}$

6. Rationalize the numerator of each fraction.

*(a) $\dfrac{\sqrt{7}}{3}$ (b) $\dfrac{\sqrt{6}}{4}$ *(c) $\dfrac{\sqrt{8}}{12}$

(d) $\dfrac{\sqrt{27}}{6}$ *(e) $\dfrac{1 + \sqrt{5}}{2}$ (f) $\dfrac{1 - \sqrt{6}}{5}$

$*$(g) $\dfrac{\sqrt[3]{4}}{3}$ (h) $\dfrac{\sqrt[3]{16}}{4}$ $*$(i) $\dfrac{\sqrt{11}}{11}$

(j) $\dfrac{\sqrt{m}}{m}$ $*$(k) $\dfrac{\sqrt{a+2}-\sqrt{a}}{2}$ (l) $\dfrac{\sqrt{x+h}-\sqrt{x}}{h}$

7. Factor each expression completely.

$*$(a) $(x^2 + 4)^3 \cdot 8x(2x + 1)^6 + (x^2 + 4)^4 \cdot 12(2x + 1)^5$

(b) $(x^2 + 7)^5 \cdot 12x(4x - 1)^4 + (x^2 + 7)^6 \cdot 16(4x - 1)^3$

$*$(c) $12(3x + 2)^3(x^2 - 3)^5 + 10x(3x + 2)^4(x^2 - 3)^4$

(d) $14x(1 + x^2)^6(x + 4)^{10} + 10(1 + x^2)^7(x + 4)^9$

$*$(e) $45(5x - 4)^8(3x + 1)^5 + 135(5x - 4)^9(3x + 1)^4$

8. Factor each expression completely and eliminate negative exponents if any.

$*$(a) $9x(x + 3)^{1/2} + 6(x + 3)^{3/2}$

(b) $9x^2(x^2 - 3)^{4/3} + 8x^4(x^2 - 3)^{1/3}$

$*$(c) $2(x + 1)^{1/2} + x(x + 1)^{-1/2}$

(d) $3x^2(3x^2 + 2)^{-1/2} + x(3x^2 + 2)^{1/2}$

$*$(e) $9x^2(1 - x^2)^{1/3} - 2x^4(1 - x^2)^{-2/3}$

(f) $5(x^2 + 9)^{2/5} + 4x^2(x^2 + 9)^{-3/5}$

$*$(g) $10(x^2 - 3)^{3/5} + 12x^2(x^2 - 3)^{-2/5}$

(h) $4x^3(x^2 - 1)^{-1/2} - 2x^5(x^2 - 1)^{-3/2}$

$*$(i) $15(x^2 + 2)^{-2/5} - 12x(x^2 + 2)^{-7/5}$

(j) $2x^2(x^2 + 1)^{-2/3} + 4x(x^2 + 1)^{1/3}$

9. Write each expression as one fraction without any negative exponents.

$*$(a) $2x^{-1/3} - 2$ (b) $x^{-1} + x^{-2}$ $*$(c) $3x^{-1/2} + x$

(d) $x^{-1/4} + x^{-1/3}$ $*$(e) $x^{2/3} + x^{-2/3}$ (f) $\dfrac{\sqrt{x}}{x} + \dfrac{1}{\sqrt{x}}$

$*$(g) $\dfrac{\sqrt[3]{x}}{x} + \dfrac{1}{\sqrt[3]{x}}$ (h) $1 - x^{-4/5}$ $*$(i) $x^{1/2} + \dfrac{1}{x^{1/2}}$

(j) $\dfrac{1}{x^{-1/2}} + \dfrac{1}{x^{-3/2}}$

10. Solve and check each equation.

$*$(a) $\sqrt{2x + 1} = 8$ (b) $\sqrt{5x - 9} = 3\sqrt{x}$

$*$(c) $\sqrt{4x - 3} = \sqrt{8 - 5x}$ (d) $\sqrt{x - 6} + 3 = \sqrt{x + 9}$

$*$(e) $\sqrt{2x + 3} + \sqrt{2x - 5} = 6$ (f) $(2x - 3)^{1/2} - 9 = 0$

$*$(g) $\sqrt{x + 2} + 1 = \sqrt{3x - 5}$ (h) $\sqrt{3x} = \sqrt{2x + 1} + 1$

$*$(i) $\sqrt{\sqrt{x + 4}} = 5$ (j) $(4x + 1)^{1/5} = 2$

$*$(k) $\sqrt[3]{3x + 5} - 4 = 0$ (l) $\sqrt[3]{4x - 6} = \sqrt[3]{2(4 - 3x)} + 5$

$*$(m) $3\sqrt{2x - 3} = \sqrt{x + 3}$

11. Use your knowledge of factoring and negative exponents to go, in steps, from

$$\frac{7}{3}\left(x + \frac{1}{x} + 2\right)(x^{-1/2} - x^{-3/2})$$

to

$$\frac{7(x + 1)^2(x - 1)}{3x^{5/2}}$$

1.7 ABSOLUTE VALUE

You may recall the concept of absolute value from elementary algebra. The *absolute value* of a number x, denoted by $|x|$, is defined as follows.

$$\boxed{|x| = \sqrt{x^2}}$$

In words, to find the absolute value of a number, square it and then take the positive square root of the result. Keep in mind that $\sqrt{}$ means the *positive* square root. Here are a few simple examples.

$$|+6| = \sqrt{(+6)^2} = \sqrt{36} = 6$$
$$|-6| = \sqrt{(-6)^2} = \sqrt{36} = 6$$
$$|0| = \sqrt{(0)^2} = \sqrt{0} = 0$$

Notice that $|+6| = 6$ and $|-6| = 6$. Consider the next example.

Example 61 *Solve the equation $|2x + 1| = 7$.*

$|2x + 1| = 7$ if $2x + 1 = 7$ *or* if $2x + 1 = -7$, since $|7| = 7$ and $|-7| = 7$. Consider both cases.

$$
\begin{array}{c|c}
2x + 1 = 7 & 2x + 1 = -7 \\
2x = 6 & 2x = -8 \\
x = 3 & x = -4
\end{array}
$$

The solutions are -4 and 3.

As suggested, $|x| \geq 0$ for all real numbers. In fact,

$$\boxed{\begin{array}{lll} |x| = & x & \text{if } x \geq 0 \\ |x| = & -x & \text{if } x < 0 \end{array}}$$

Note that the second statement in the box says that putting a minus in front of a negative number will create a positive number, its absolute value.

In view of absolute value, you should be particularly careful when simplifying square roots (or other even roots). Here is an example.

Example 62 *Simplify* $\sqrt{16x^2y}$.

$$\sqrt{16x^2y} = \sqrt{16}\sqrt{x^2}\sqrt{y} = 4|x|\sqrt{y}$$

Note: $\sqrt{x^2}$ is not necessarily equal to x; it would be $-x$ if the number x were negative. In the foregoing simplification, if $x < 0$, then $|x|$ could be replaced by $-x$ and the result would simplify to $-4x\sqrt{y}$. On the other hand, if $x > 0$, then $|x|$ could be replaced by x and the expression would become $4x\sqrt{y}$.

Example 63 *Simplify* $\dfrac{|x|}{x}$.

There are three possibilities, depending on the nature of the number x.

1. If $x > 0$, then $|x| = x$ and thus

$$\frac{|x|}{x} = \frac{x}{x} = 1$$

2. If $x < 0$, then $|x| = -x$ and thus

$$\frac{|x|}{x} = \frac{-x}{x} = -1$$

3. If $x = 0$, then $|x|/x$ is undefined, since division by zero is not defined.

Our conclusion here is that unless you know the nature of the x values involved, you cannot simplify the expression; it must remain $|x|/x$.

Here are three properties of absolute value that follow readily from the definition $|x| = \sqrt{x^2}$

$$|ab| = |a||b|$$
$$\left|\frac{a}{b}\right| = \frac{|a|}{|b|}$$
$$|-a| = |a|$$

The following steps show the proof of the first property.

$$|ab| = \sqrt{(ab)^2} \qquad \text{definition of absolute value}$$
$$= \sqrt{a^2 b^2} \qquad \text{property of exponents}$$
$$= \sqrt{a^2}\sqrt{b^2} \qquad \text{property of radicals}$$
$$= |a||b| \qquad \text{definition of absolute value}$$

Example 64   *Simplify* $\dfrac{|3 - x|}{|x - 3|}$, *assuming that* $x \neq 3$.

Observe that by the third property of absolute values, $|3 - x|$ is the same as $|-(3 - x)|$, or $|x - 3|$. Thus

$$\frac{|3 - x|}{|x - 3|} = \frac{|x - 3|}{|x - 3|} = 1$$

The quotient would not be defined for $x = 3$.

Example 65   *Simplify* $|x^4 + 5|$.

$$|x^4 + 5| = x^4 + 5$$

because $x^4 \geq 0$ for all real numbers; so $x^4 + 5 > 0$ for all real numbers. Thus $|x^4 + 5| = x^4 + 5$.

EXERCISES 1.7

1. Solve each equation if possible.
   *(a) $|3x + 1| = 16$ (b) $|4x - 8| = 5$
   *(c) $|6 - 5x| = 1$ (d) $|5 - 2x| = 2$
   *(e) $|8x - 7| = -1$ (f) $|-x + 7| = -4$
   *(g) $|-x| = 0$ (h) $|4x + 1| = 0$
   *(i) $|-x| = 6$ (j) $|-x| = -6$

2. Simplify whenever possible.
   *(a) $\sqrt{u^2}$ (b) $\sqrt{b^2}$
   *(c) $\sqrt{9m^2}$ (d) $\sqrt{81n^2}$
   *(e) $|-8|$ (f) $|\pi|$
   *(g) $|-y|$ (h) $|x^2|$

*(i) $\quad |-6x^2y|$

(j) $\quad |-5c^2|$

*(k) $\quad |x|$

(l) $\quad |x + 1|$

*(m) $\dfrac{w}{|w|}, \quad w > 0$

(n) $\quad |x + 9|, \quad x > 0$

*(o) $\quad |x - 9|, \quad x < 9$

(p) $\quad |x - 4|, \quad x > 4$

*(q) $\quad |x^2 + 1|$

(r) $\quad |-x^2|$

*(s) $\quad |3 - x|, x < 3$

(t) $\quad |3 - x|, x > 3$

*(u) $\quad |7 - x|$

(v) $\quad |x - 8|$

3. Simplify whenever possible.

*(a) $\dfrac{|7 - t|}{|t - 7|}, \quad t \neq 7$

(b) $\dfrac{w}{|w|}, \quad w < 0$

*(c) $\dfrac{|x + 4|}{x + 4}, \quad x > -4$

(d) $\dfrac{x - 5}{|x - 5|}, \quad x > 5$

*(e) $\dfrac{x - 3}{|x - 3|}, \quad x < 3$

(f) $\dfrac{|x + 6|}{x + 6}, \quad x < -6$

*(g) $\dfrac{|x + 1|}{x + 1}$

(h) $\dfrac{x - 1}{|x - 1|}$

1.8 FORMULA MANIPULATION

Equations are used in many fields of application, such as business, physics, engineering, geometry, genetics, statistics, and computer science. In some applications it is necessary to solve a given formula for one desired variable in terms of the others. The methods used to manipulate formulas are the same as those we saw earlier in the chapter. This section consists of a series of examples; in each example the steps of the manipulation are shown.

Example 66 *An amount of money p is invested at r percent per year simple interest for t years. The amount A after t years is A = p + prt. Solve this equation for t in terms of the other variables.*

$$A = p + prt$$

First, add $-p$ to both sides to isolate the t term.

$$A - p = prt$$

Next, divide both sides by pr, the coefficient of t.

$$\frac{A - p}{pr} = t, \quad \text{or} \quad t = \frac{A - p}{pr}$$

Example 67 *The area of a trapezoid is given by $A = \frac{1}{2}(b_1 + b_2)h$, where b_1 and b_2 are the lengths of the bases and h is the height. Solve this equation for b_1.*

First, notice the use of **subscripts** 1 and 2 in b_1 and b_2. The subscripts 1 and 2 are used only to distinguish two numbers that we wish to call by similar names, both b for *base*. The subscripts are *not* exponents.

If we begin by multiplying both sides by 2, then there will be no fraction.

$$A = \tfrac{1}{2}(b_1 + b_2)h$$

becomes

$$2A = (\overset{\downarrow}{b}_1 + b_2)h$$

Because the variable b_1 is inside parentheses, multiply to remove the parentheses and free the b_1 term.

$$2A = b_1 h + b_2 h$$

Now add $-b_2 h$ to both sides. Doing so will isolate the b_1 term.

$$2A - b_2 h = b_1 h$$

or

$$b_1 h = 2A - b_2 h$$

Finally, divide both sides by h.

$$b_1 = \frac{2A - b_2 h}{h} \qquad \text{answer}$$

This is the final result. But note that when we had $2A = (b_1 + b_2)h$, you could have divided both sides by h and then added $-b_2$ to both sides. The result would have been

$$b_1 = \frac{2A}{h} - b_2$$

If the number b_2 were then multiplied by h/h and subtracted from $2A/h$, the end result would be the same as the one labeled *answer* above.

Example 68   *The distance D of an image formed by a mirror is given by*

$$\frac{1}{d} + \frac{1}{D} = \frac{1}{f}$$

where d is the distance of the object from the mirror and f is the focal length of the mirror. Solve for D.

This is an equation containing fractions. Begin by multiplying both sides (all terms) by the least common denominator dDf. This step will eliminate all fractions.

$$dDf \cdot \frac{1}{d} + dDf \cdot \frac{1}{D} = dDf \cdot \frac{1}{f}$$

which simplifies to

$$Df + df = dD$$

Next, add $-Df$ to both sides so that both D terms will be together.

$$df = dD - Df$$

or

$$dD - Df = df$$

Now factor out D in order to obtain the coefficient of D.

$$(d - f)D = df$$

Finally, divide both sides by $d - f$, the coefficient of D. The result is

$$D = \frac{df}{d - f}$$

EXERCISES 1.8

Solve each formula for the variable indicated.

* 1. $V = lwh$ for h (volume of a box)

  2. $i = prt$ for r (simple interest)

* 3. $C = 2\pi r$ for r (circumference of a circle)

4. $V = \pi r^2 h$ for h (volume of a cylinder)

* 5. $S = \dfrac{1}{2}at^2$ for a (distance traveled by falling object)

6. $E = \dfrac{1}{2}mv^2$ for m (energy of a moving body)

* 7. $P = 2l + 2w$ for w (perimeter of a rectangle)

8. $V = \dfrac{1}{3}\pi r^2 h$ for h (volume of a cone)

* 9. $I = \dfrac{E}{R}$ for E (Ohm's law)

10. $I = \dfrac{E}{R}$ for R (Ohm's law)

*11. $v = \dfrac{s}{t}$ for t (velocity)

12. $S = \dfrac{a}{1 - r}$ for a (sum of a series)

*13. $A = p + prt$ for p (simple interest)

14. $F = \dfrac{m_1 m_2}{d^2}$ for m_1 (gravitational attraction)

*15. $S = \dfrac{n}{2}(a + l)$ for l (sum of terms)

16. $A = \dfrac{1}{2}(b_1 + b_2)h$ for h (area of trapezoid)

*17. $A = \dfrac{1}{2}(b_1 + b_2)h$ for b_2 (area of trapezoid)

18. $R = \dfrac{1}{2\pi fc}$ for c (capacitive reactance)

*19. $\dfrac{1}{R} = \dfrac{1}{R_1} + \dfrac{1}{R_2}$ for R_1 (resistance)

20. $\dfrac{1}{R} = \dfrac{1}{R_1} + \dfrac{1}{R_2} + \dfrac{1}{R_3}$ for R_1 (resistance)

*21. $P = I^2 R$ for I (power)

22. $s = \dfrac{1}{2}at^2$ for t (distance)

*23. $F = \dfrac{9}{5}C + 32$ for C (Celsius to Fahrenheit)

24. $C = \dfrac{5}{9}(F - 32)$ for F (Fahrenheit to Celsius)

*25. $\dfrac{a}{b} = \dfrac{c}{d}$ for d (proportion)

26. $\dfrac{P_1 V_1}{T_1} = \dfrac{P_2 V_2}{T_2}$ for V_2 (general gas law)

*27. $f = \dfrac{1}{2\pi}\sqrt{\dfrac{g}{l}}$ for l (frequency of a pendulum)

28. $y = C - \dfrac{C}{n}x$ for x (depreciation)

*29. $y = C - \dfrac{C}{n}x$ for C (depreciation)

30. $a = p(1 + rt)$ for t (simple interest)

*31. $S = 2\pi r(r + h)$ for h (surface area of cylinder)

32. $ct^2 + rt - v = 0$ for t (quadratic equation)

*33. $S = \dfrac{a}{1 - r}$ for r (sum of a series)

1.9 COMPLEX NUMBERS

All the numbers used so far in this book, and probably all the numbers you have ever used, are classified as real numbers. As you know, real numbers possess an important property: The square of any real number is either positive or zero. If a real number is squared, the result is never a negative number. Are there any numbers whose squares are negative numbers? Solving the quadratic equation $x^2 + 1 = 0$ leads to such a number, for x must be a number whose square is -1, since x^2 and 1 must have a sum of zero. The number whose square is -1 is an example of a so-called **imaginary number**. If we solve $x^2 + 1 = 0$ mechanically, we first get $x^2 = -1$ and then $x = \pm\sqrt{-1}$. The number $\sqrt{-1}$ is called i, for imaginary. The roots of the equation $x^2 + 1 = 0$ are $\pm i$.

$$i = \sqrt{-1} \qquad i^2 = -1$$

In general, for positive numbers a, $\sqrt{-a}$ is written $i\sqrt{a}$.

$$\sqrt{-a} = i\sqrt{a} \qquad \text{for } a > 0$$

Consider some other examples of imaginary numbers, $\sqrt{-4}$, $\sqrt{-5}$, $\sqrt{-75}$, and observe their simplification.

$$\sqrt{-4} = i\sqrt{4}$$
$$= i \cdot 2$$
$$= 2i$$

$$\sqrt{-5} = i\sqrt{5}$$

$$\sqrt{-75} = i\sqrt{75}$$
$$= i\sqrt{25}\sqrt{3}$$
$$= i \cdot 5\sqrt{3}$$
$$= 5i\sqrt{3}$$

Example 69 *Solve the equation $x^2 + 2x + 5 = 0$.*

Using the quadratic formula with $a = 1$, $b = 2$, and $c = 5$, we obtain

$$x = \frac{-b \pm \sqrt{b^2 - 4ac}}{2a}$$

$$= \frac{-2 \pm \sqrt{(2)^2 - 4(1)(5)}}{2(1)}$$

$$= \frac{-2 \pm \sqrt{4 - 20}}{2}$$

$$= \frac{-2 \pm \sqrt{-16}}{2}$$

$$= \frac{-2 \pm 4i}{2}$$

$$= \frac{2(-1 \pm 2i)}{2}$$

$$= -1 \pm 2i$$

We can determine the types of roots (that is, the nature of the roots) of a quadratic equation by examining $b^2 - 4ac$. The expression $b^2 - 4ac$ is called the **discriminant**.

$$x = \frac{-b \pm \sqrt{\boxed{b^2 - 4ac}}}{2a} \quad \text{——discriminant}$$

Case I. *Discriminant* $= 0$.

If $b^2 - 4ac = 0$, then $\sqrt{} = 0$ and the roots are $x = -b/2a$; that is, both roots are the same. The roots are, therefore, *real and equal.* As an example, in $x^2 + 6x + 9 = 0$, $a = 1$, $b = 6$, and $c = 9$. So $b^2 - 4ac$ is $6^2 - 4 \cdot 1 \cdot 9 = 36 - 36 = 0$. The roots of $x^2 + 6x + 9 = 0$ are real and equal. Note

$$x = \frac{-b \pm \sqrt{\text{discriminant}}}{2a}$$

$$= \frac{-6 \pm \sqrt{0}}{2(1)} = \frac{-6 \pm 0}{2} = -\frac{6}{2} = -3$$

Case II. *Discriminant* > 0.

If $b^2 - 4ac > 0$, then the number under the radical is positive. This means that the roots are real. Because of the $\pm$ sign, the roots are different. Thus the roots are *real and unequal.* As an example, the roots of $x^2 + 7x + 12 = 0$ are real and unequal because $b^2 - 4ac$ is $7^2 - 4 \cdot 1 \cdot 12 = 1$.

$$x = \frac{-b \pm \sqrt{\text{discriminant}}}{2a}$$

$$= \frac{-7 \pm \sqrt{1}}{2(1)} = \frac{-7 \pm 1}{2} = -3 \text{ and } -4$$

Case III. *Discriminant* < 0.

If $b^2 - 4ac < 0$, then the number under the radical is negative. This means that the roots are imaginary. Because of the $\pm$ sign, the roots are different. Thus the roots are *imaginary and unequal.* As an example, the roots of $x^2 + 3x + 7 = 0$ are imaginary and unequal, for $b^2 - 4ac = 3^2 - 4 \cdot 1 \cdot 7 = -19$

$$x = \frac{-b \pm \sqrt{\text{discriminant}}}{2a} = \frac{-3 \pm \sqrt{-19}}{2(1)} = \frac{-3 \pm i\sqrt{19}}{2}.$$

The solutions to the equation of Example 69 are $-1 + 2i$ and $-1 - 2i$. Each solution is a number, which is, in fact, a sum of two numbers—one real and one imaginary. The number $-1 + 2i$ is of the form $a + bi$, with a and b real numbers. Here $a = -1$ and $b = 2$. Numbers of the form $a + bi$, a and b real, are called **complex numbers**. Here are some other examples of complex numbers.

$$5 + i$$

$$7 - 3i$$

$$6i$$

$$12$$

The last two examples suggest that all real numbers are also complex numbers and that all imaginary numbers are also complex numbers. Both 12 and $6i$ are of the form $a + bi$. Specifically,

$$12 = 12 + 0i$$

$$6i = 0 + 6i$$

Two complex numbers $a + bi$ and $c + di$ are equal if $a = c$ and $b = d$. In other words, two complex numbers are equal if their real parts are equal and their imaginary parts are equal.

The sum of the two complex numbers $a + bi$ and $c + di$ is the number $(a + c) + (b + d)i$. For example,

$$(15 + 3i) + (8 + 9i) = 23 + 12i$$

The difference of $a + bi$ and $c + di$ is the number $(a - c) + (b - d)i$. For example,

$$(15 + 3i) - (8 + 9i) = 7 - 6i$$

Let us multiply $(a + bi)$ by $(c + di)$ in order to determine an appropriate definition for multiplication of complex numbers.

$$(a + bi)(c + di) = a \cdot c + a \cdot di + bi \cdot c + bi \cdot di$$

$$= ac + adi + bci + (-1)bd$$

$$= (ac - bd) + (ad + bc)i$$

The result is

$$\boxed{(a + bi)(c + di) = (ac - bd) + (ad + bc)i}$$

Unless you are doing a lot of multiplication with complex numbers, you might just as well multiply each as done in the preceding three-line process.

$$(3 + 4i)(5 - 2i) = 3 \cdot 5 + 3(-2i) + 4i \cdot 5 + 4i(-2i)$$

$$= 15 - 6i + 20i + 8$$

$$= 23 + 14i$$

The **complex conjugate** of the number $a + bi$ is the number $a - bi$. Here are some examples.

Number	Complex Conjugate
$5 + 3i$	$5 - 3i$
$1 - 7i$	$1 + 7i$
$+ 2i$	$- 2i$
9	9

The product of a complex number and its conjugate is a nonnegative real number. Specifically,

$$(a + bi)(a - bi) = a \cdot a + a(-bi) + bi(a) + bi(-bi)$$
$$= a^2 - abi + abi + b^2$$
$$= a^2 + b^2$$

As an example,

$$(2 + 3i)(2 - 3i) = 4 + 9 = 13$$

Conjugates can be used to eliminate a complex number with nonzero imaginary part from the denominator of a fraction. In a sense, the process is division of complex numbers. For instance, the division of $3i$ by $1 + i$ can be done by multiplying both numerator and denominator by the conjugate of $1 + i$. The result is a number of the form $a + bi$.

$$\frac{3i}{1 + i} = \frac{3i}{1 + i} \cdot \frac{1 - i}{1 - i} = \frac{3i + 3}{2}, \quad \text{or} \quad \frac{3}{2} + \frac{3}{2}i$$

In general,

$$\boxed{\frac{a + bi}{c + di} = \frac{ac + bd}{c^2 + d^2} + \frac{bc - ad}{c^2 + d^2}i}$$

As a final note, here is a brief look at powers of i.

$$i^1 = \sqrt{-1}$$
$$i^2 = -1$$
$$i^3 = i^2 \cdot i = (-1)(i) = -i$$
$$i^4 = i^2 \cdot i^2 = (-1)(-1) = 1$$

It can be shown that

$$i = i^5 = i^9 = i^{13} \cdots$$

$$i^2 = i^6 = i^{10} = i^{14} = \cdots$$

$$i^3 = i^7 = i^{11} = i^{15} = \cdots$$

$$i^4 = i^8 = i^{12} = i^{16} = \cdots$$

EXERCISES 1.9

1. Express each number in terms of i
   *(a) $\sqrt{-9}$ (b) $\sqrt{-25}$ *(c) $\sqrt{-3}$
   (d) $\sqrt{-5}$ *(e) $\sqrt{-100}$ (f) $\sqrt{-50}$
   *(g) $\sqrt{-45}$ (h) $\sqrt{-20}$ *(i) $\sqrt{-243}$
   (j) $\sqrt{-242}$

2. Solve each quadratic equation.
   *(a) $x^2 + x + 1 = 0$ (b) $x^2 - x + 4 = 0$
   *(c) $x^2 - 3x + 7 = 0$ (d) $x^2 - 2x + 5 = 0$
   *(e) $x^2 + 3x + 9 = 0$ (f) $2x^2 + 7x + 12 = 0$
   *(g) $3x^2 - 2x + 10 = 0$ (h) $-2x^2 + 3x - 4 = 0$
   *(i) $x^2 + 8 = 0$ (j) $5x^2 + 18 = 0$
   *(k) $x^2 = 2x - 9$ (l) $2x^2 + 6x = -8$

3. Check the discriminant to determine the nature of the roots of each quadratic equation. Do not actually solve the equations.
   *(a) $x^2 + 5x + 2 = 0$ (b) $m^2 - 3m + 1 = 0$
   *(c) $y^2 + 2y + 6 = 0$ (d) $x^2 - 3x + 2 = 0$
   *(e) $x^2 - 6x + 9 = 0$ (f) $x^2 - 6x - 9 = 0$
   *(g) $x^2 - 5 = 0$ (h) $n^2 + 5 = 0$
   *(i) $x^2 + 2x = 0$ (j) $3x^2 + 7x + 1 = 0$
   *(k) $5x^2 - 10x + 6 = 0$ (l) $x^2 = 3x + 10$
   *(m) $x^2 - 1 = x$ (n) $-x^2 + 7x + 2 = 0$
   *(o) $-x^2 + 6x - 9 = 0$ (p) $x^2 = 12x$

4. Perform each operation and leave the result in $a + bi$ form.
   *(a) $(2 + 3i) + (5 + i)$ (b) $(7 - 4i) + (1 + 6i)$
   *(c) $(9 - i) - (-4 + 2i)$ (d) $(-6 + 3i) - (5 - 9i)$
   *(e) $(8 - 3i) + (6)$ (f) $(7 + 3i) + (-5i)$
   *(g) $(3 + 5i)(2 + 3i)$ (h) $(3 + 5i)(2 - 3i)$
   *(i) $(8 + i)(8 + i)$ (j) $(i - 2)(3 - i)$
   *(k) $(1 - i)^2$ (l) $(2 + i)^3$

*(m) $\dfrac{2}{1 + i}$ (n) $\dfrac{-i}{1 - 2i}$

*(o) $\dfrac{i - 2}{3 + i}$ (p) $\dfrac{-5 + i}{2 + 3i}$

*(q) $\dfrac{1 + i}{2 - i}$ (r) $\dfrac{5 - 4i}{5 + 4i}$

*5. Prove that

$$\frac{a + bi}{c + di} = \frac{ac + bd}{c^2 + d^2} + \frac{bc - ad}{c^2 + d^2}i$$

6. Simplify each expression.

*(a) i^7 (b) i^{19} *(c) i^{20}

(d) i^{153} *(e) $i^{23} + i^{27} + i^{31}$ (f) $3i^2 - 2i^4 + 6$

REVIEW EXERCISES FOR CHAPTER 1

1. Solve each equation.

*(a) $5x - 2 = 6$ (b) $1 - \dfrac{x}{4} = 13$

*(c) $8(x - 4) = 6x$ (d) $1 - 9x = 2(x + 5)$

*(e) $x^2 - 3 = 0$ (f) $x^2 - 2x - 8 = 0$

*(g) $t^2 = 2t$ (h) $m^2 = 12 - m$

*(i) $\sqrt{1 - 2x} + 6 = 15$ (j) $\sqrt{x + 1} + 3 = x$

*(k) $\dfrac{9}{2x - 3} = 4$ (l) $x^2 + 5x - 2 = 0$

*(m) $x^2 - x + 7 = 0$ (n) $\dfrac{x}{9} + \dfrac{x + 2}{x} = 1$

*(o) $x(x + 1) - 3 = 2x$ (p) $\sqrt{3x + 4} = x$

*(q) $x^2 + 5 = 0$

2. Factor each expression if possible.

*(a) $x^2 - 14x + 13$ (b) $m^2 + m$

*(c) $x^2 + 16$ (d) $x^2 - 16$

*(e) $x^3 + 8$ (f) $x^3 - 8$

*(g) $x^3 - x$ (h) $x^2 - 6$

*(i) $14x - 7$ (j) $x^2 - 10x + 24$

*(k) $6x^2 - 6x - 12$ (l) $6x^2 - 31x + 5$

*(m) $x^4 - 16$ (n) $x^4 - 27x$

*(o) $x^{2n+1} + x^{2n}$ (p) $x^{2n+2} - x^{2n}$

*(q) $8(x + 3)^{1/2} - 2(x + 3)^{-1/2}$ (r) $7x^2(x - 2)^{-1/3} + x(x - 2)^{2/3}$

3. Expand.

*(a) $(m + n)^4$ (b) $(t - u)^6$

*(c) $(x - 2)^5$ (d) $(3x + y)^5$

4. Perform the indicated operations. Simplify when possible.

*(a) $\dfrac{m}{a^2bc} + \dfrac{n}{ac^2}$ (b) $\dfrac{3}{x^2} + \dfrac{1}{x^2 - 9} + \dfrac{2}{x + 3}$

*(c) $\dfrac{5x - 5y}{10x^2} \cdot \dfrac{x^2 - 9x}{x^2 - y^2}$ (d) $\dfrac{3a - 3b}{5b - 5a} \div \dfrac{7ab}{2c}$

*(e) $\dfrac{2 - 2x}{4x} \div \dfrac{1 - x^2}{x^2 + 2x + 1}$ (f) $\dfrac{5m}{5m + 10} \cdot \dfrac{m^2 + 7m + 10}{m^2 + 25}$

*(g) $\dfrac{9 - \dfrac{3}{x}}{\dfrac{5}{y} + 1}$ (h) $\dfrac{\dfrac{2}{a} + \dfrac{7}{b}}{4 - \dfrac{3}{c}}$

*(i) $\dfrac{(xy)^{-2}}{x^{-1} + y^{-1}}$ (j) $\dfrac{2 \cdot 9^{-1/2} + 3^{-1}}{5^0}$

5. Simplify.

*(a) $\left(\dfrac{a^{-2}}{3a^7}\right)^5$ (b) $\dfrac{b^n b^{8n}}{b}$ *(c) $(-6x^5y^4)(2xy^8)$

(d) $2[2^{-1} + 2^0 + 3^0]$ *(e) $\sqrt{120}$

(f) $(27)^{-5/3}$ *(g) $\dfrac{10}{\sqrt{5}}$ (h) $\dfrac{m}{\sqrt{m}}$

*(i) $\sqrt{25n^2}$ (j) $|-3x^2|$

6. Solve each equation for x in terms of the other quantities given.

*(a) $y = \dfrac{1}{1 + x}$ (b) $y = \dfrac{x}{1 - x}$

*(c) $m = \dfrac{1}{2}(1 + 5x)$ (d) $\dfrac{3}{x} - 7y + \dfrac{1}{2x} = y + 1$

*(e) $3x + t = a(1 - 2x)$ (f) $\dfrac{1}{y} = \dfrac{ax + b}{c}$

Preparation for Functions

2.1 INTRODUCTION

In Chapter 3 you will begin the study of functions. At this point you have already studied the fundamental mechanics and manipulations that you will need then. But the study of functions includes more than just algebraic manipulation. There is a lot of graphing, for example. So in this chapter we shall study the coordinate plane and straight lines and parabolas. Then in Chapter 3 you can broaden this foundation. In the study of functions you will also encounter inequalities that must be solved in order for you to define and describe functions. Because of this, a section on inequalities is included here.

Once you have mastered the topics covered in this chapter (and those of Chapter 1), you can focus your effort on understanding the concepts and applications encountered as you study functions.

2.2 THE CARTESIAN COORDINATE SYSTEM

The coordinate system described here is known as the **Cartesian coordinate system**, named for French mathematician René Descartes (1596–1650), who developed it in 1637 to link the studies of algebra and geometry. The system is also called the **rectangular coordinate system**.

To begin, consider that the real numbers consist of all numbers that are either positive, zero, or negative. The **real number line** is used to illustrate and compare real numbers. Positive numbers are located to the right of zero; negative numbers are located to the left of zero.

If two number lines are positioned perpendicular to each other and joined at their zeros, the result is the coordinate plane. Traditionally, the horizontal line is called the **x axis** and the vertical line is the **y axis**. Other letters are sometimes used. The point where the x and y axes intersect is called the **origin**.

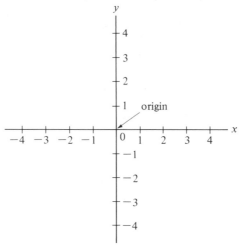

Points are specified by ordered pairs (x, y) of real numbers. To locate a point (x, y), begin at the origin and move first along the x axis according to the x coordinate. From there move up or down according to the y coordinate. The sign specifies the direction (for x: $+$ is right, $-$ is left; for y: $+$ is up, $-$ is down). The magnitude specifies the distance to be moved. To plot the point $(3, 5)$, begin at the origin and move right 3, and then up 5. Several points are shown plotted next.

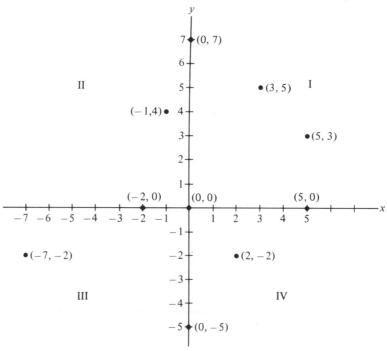

The quadrants are numbered I, II, III, and IV counterclockwise beginning in the top right quadrant.

Note that $(3, 5) \neq (5, 3)$. They are different points. Points are *ordered* pairs. The order in which the coordinates are written is critical.

The distance between any two points (x_1, y_1) and (x_2, y_2) can be determined by plotting the points, creating a triangle, and then using the Pythagorean theorem. To obtain a formula for the distance between two points, we begin by plotting the points and drawing the line segment that joins them.

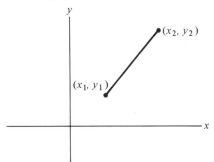

Consider the right triangle that includes these two points as vertices.

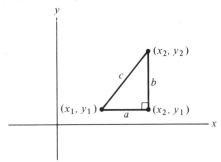

The sides are labeled *a, b,* and *c*. We seek a formula for *c*, the distance between (x_1, y_1) and (x_2, y_2). By the Pythagorean theorem, the hypotenuse *c* can be determined from

$$c^2 = a^2 + b^2$$

In this setting,

$$a = |x_2 - x_1|$$

and

$$b = |y_2 - y_1|$$

So

$$c^2 = |x_2 - x_1|^2 + |y_2 - y_1|^2$$

The absolute value signs are not needed, since the square of any real number cannot be negative. Thus

$$c^2 = (x_2 - x_1)^2 + (y_2 - y_1)^2$$

It follows that

$$c = \sqrt{(x_2 - x_1)^2 + (y_2 - y_1)^2}$$

Because it is traditional to use d for distance in this formula, we rewrite the formula as

$$d = \sqrt{(x_2 - x_1)^2 + (y_2 - y_1)^2}$$

Distance between (x_1, y_1) and (x_2, y_2)

Example 1   *Determine the distance between the points* $(2, -3)$ *and* $(6, 10)$.

It does not matter which point you call (x_1, y_1). So let us just call the first point (x_1, y_1) and the second point (x_2, y_2). This means that

$$(x_1, y_1) = (2, -3) \quad \text{and} \quad (x_2, y_2) = (6, 10)$$

Now substitute the two points into the formula

$$d = \sqrt{(x_2 - x_1)^2 + (y_2 - y_1)^2}$$

to get

$$d = \sqrt{(6 - 2)^2 + (10 - -3)^2}$$
$$= \sqrt{(4)^2 + (13)^2}$$
$$= \sqrt{16 + 169}$$
$$= \sqrt{185}$$

Thus the distance between the two points is $\sqrt{185}$, which is approximately 13.6.

The **midpoint** of a line segment is the point on the segment halfway between the endpoints of the segment. This means that the x coordinate of the midpoint is the average of the x coordinates of the endpoints. Similarly, the y coordinate of the midpoint is the average of the y coordinates of the endpoints. Thus if (x_1, y_1) and (x_2, y_2) are the endpoints of a line segment, then the midpoint of the segment $(\bar{x}, \bar{y})$, is given by

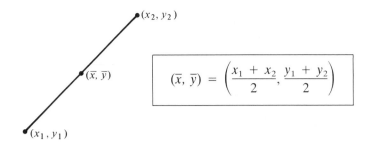

$$(\bar{x}, \bar{y}) = \left(\frac{x_1 + x_2}{2}, \frac{y_1 + y_2}{2} \right)$$

If this point $(\bar{x}, \bar{y})$ is indeed the midpoint of the segment joining (x_1, y_1) and (x_2, y_2), then the distance from (x_1, y_1) to $(\bar{x}, \bar{y})$ must equal the distance from $(\bar{x}, \bar{y})$ to (x_2, y_2). It is left for you to prove that those two distances are equal.

Example 2 *Find the midpoint of the line segment joining the points* $(4, 7)$ *and* $(8, 10)$.

$$\text{midpoint} = (\bar{x}, \bar{y}) = \left(\frac{4 + 8}{2}, \frac{7 + 10}{2} \right) = (6, 8\tfrac{1}{2})$$

EXERCISES 2.2

Answers to starred exercises are given in the back of the book.

1. Determine the distance between the points.
    *(a) (1, 1) and (5, 4)   (b) (4, 0) and (4, 12)
    *(c) (8, 2) and (10, 7)   (d) (6, 4) and (15, 8)
    *(e) (5, −2) and (8, 4)   (f) (−3, 6) and (5, 1)
    *(g) (6, −3) and (7, −7)   (h) (−4, −3) and (5, 2)
    *(i) (6, −4) and (−5, −8)   (j) (−3, −7) and (−1, −16)
    *(k) (−6, 0) and (0, −12)   (l) (0, −8) and (−4, −11)

2. Determine the midpoint of the line segment connecting each pair of points.
    *(a) (1, 4) and (3, 10)   (b) (6, 10) and (2, 34)
    *(c) (3, 5) and (1, 3)   (d) (0, 0) and (6, 18)
    *(e) (−2, 6) and (4, 0)   (f) (7, 1) and (4, −9)
    *(g) (−3, −6) and (−5, 13)   (h) (−5, 6) and (10, −11)
    *(i) (−8, 7) and (−5, 0)   (j) (−6, −8) and (−13, −1)

*3. First determine the midpoint of the line segment connecting (−3, 5) and (1, 9). Then determine the midpoint of the line segment connecting (1, 3) and (5, −1). Finally, determine the distance between the midpoints.

2.3 LINES AND SLOPES

The **graph** of an equation in two variables x and y can be made by obtaining points of the form (x, y), plotting them, and then drawing a curve through them. The points can be obtained by substituting values for one variable into the equation to obtain values for the other variable.

You should already be familiar with the equations and graphs of straight lines. For example, the graphs of such equations as $y = 2x + 3$, $x + 4y = 8$, $x = 6$, and $y = -2$ are straight lines. In fact, the equation of any straight line can be written in the form

$$ax + by + c = 0$$

in which a and b cannot both be zero simultaneously. Equations of lines are not always written this way, nor is this always a useful form in which to write such equations. But any line *can* be written this way. All lines fit this form. Thus manipulating an equation to fit this form will determine whether it is a line. Here are some equations of lines.

$$15x + 3y + 7 = 0$$

$$2x + y = 6$$

$$y = 9x + 14$$

$$x = -8$$

$$y - 12 = 0$$

The first line, $15x + 3y + 7 = 0$, is already in the standard form. The second line, $2x + y = 6$, can be changed to standard form by adding -6 to both sides of the equation. The result is $2x + y - 6 = 0$. The third line, $y = 9x + 14$, can be changed to standard form by adding $-9x$ and -14 to both sides of the equation. The result is $-9x + y - 14 = 0$ or $9x - y + 14 = 0$. The line $x = -8$ is changed by adding 8 to both sides in order to obtain $x + 8 = 0$. The equation $x + 8 = 0$ is in the standard form $ax + by + c = 0$; b is zero. The line $y - 12 = 0$ is already in standard form; a is zero.

In elementary algebra a line is usually graphed by obtaining two or more points, plotting them, and then drawing a straight line through them. Here we have used 0 and 1 for x, obtained two points, plotted them, and drawn a line through them.

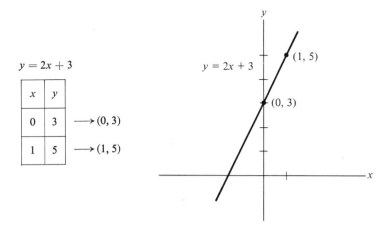

$y = 2x + 3$

x	y
0	3	$\longrightarrow (0, 3)$
1	5	$\longrightarrow (1, 5)$

In this book we shall look beyond merely plotting points and drawing a line through them. Our first concern will be the slope of a line.

The inclination or slant of a line with respect to the x axis is called the **slope** of the line. It is measured by comparing the change in the y coordinates with the change in the x coordinates for any two points on the line.† Specifically,

$$\text{Slope} = \frac{\text{change in } y}{\text{change in } x}$$

Using the letter m for *slope* and the symbol Δ (delta) for *change in*, this becomes

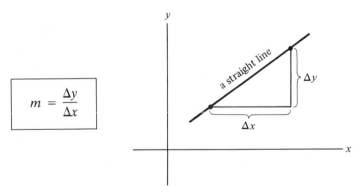

$$m = \frac{\Delta y}{\Delta x}$$

For the line $y = 2x + 3$, which we already sketched, we can use the two points $(0, 3)$ and $(1, 5)$ to compute the slope.

$$m = \frac{\Delta y}{\Delta x} = \frac{5 - 3}{1 - 0} = \frac{2}{1} = 2$$

---

† Proof that the numerical value of the slope of a line is independent of the two points chosen is given as Example 9 in Chapter 4, after the theorem for similar triangles is introduced.

The *slope of the line is* 2. Notice that the change in y is computed as the difference in the y coordinates and the change in x is computed as the difference in the x coordinates. To avoid getting the wrong sign when computing slope, it is necessary to be consistent when determining the difference in the y's and the difference in the x's. Subtract each coordinate of one point from the corresponding coordinate of the other point. If (x_1, y_1) represents one point and (x_2, y_2) represents the other, then

$$m = \frac{\Delta y}{\Delta x} = \frac{y_2 - y_1}{x_2 - x_1}$$

Example 3 *Find the slope of the line that passes through the points* (3, 7) *and* (5, 4).

It does not matter which point is called (x_1, y_1); so let (3, 7) be (x_1, y_1). Then (5, 4) is (x_2, y_2). The slope is computed as

$$m = \frac{\Delta y}{\Delta x} = \frac{y_2 - y_1}{x_2 - x_1} = \frac{4 - 7}{5 - 3} = \frac{-3}{2} = -\frac{3}{2}$$

The slope is $-\frac{3}{2}$, which demonstrates that slopes can be negative.

Let us draw the two lines just discussed to see what different slopes look like.

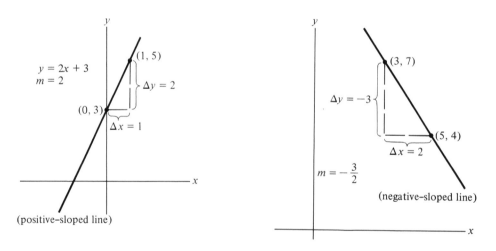

Notice that the line with positive slope rises as you go from left to right whereas the line with negative slope falls as you go from left to right.

Because the slope of the first line is 2, or $\frac{2}{1}$, another point on that line can be obtained by starting at (1, 5) and increasing x by 1 and y by 2. That point is (2, 7).

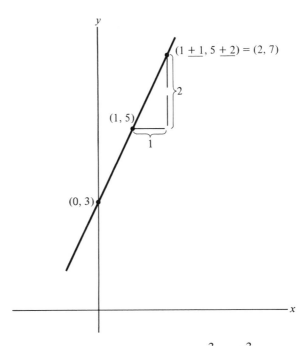

Similarly, since the slope of the second line is $-\dfrac{3}{2}$, or $\dfrac{-3}{2}$, another point on that line can be determined by starting at (5, 4) and increasing x by 2 and decreasing y by 3. That point is (7, 1).

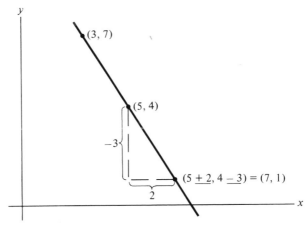

The slope of any **horizontal line** (such as $y = 3$, $y = -2$, and so on) is zero because the y coordinates of any two points used in the calculation of the slope are the same even though the x coordinates are different.

$$m = \frac{y_1 - y_1}{x_2 - x_1} = \frac{0}{x_2 - x_1} = 0$$

The slope of any **vertical line** (such as $x = 1, x = -5$, and so on) is undefined because the x coordinates of any two points used in the calculation of the slope are the same even though the y coordinates are different.

$$m = \frac{y_2 - y_1}{x_1 - x_1} = \frac{y_2 - y_1}{0}, \qquad \text{which is undefined}$$

As you know, the slope, m, of the line through points (x_1, y_1) and (x_2, y_2) can be computed as

$$m = \frac{y_2 - y_1}{x_2 - x_1}$$

If we use any point (x, y) instead of the specific point (x_2, y_2), the result is

$$m = \frac{y - y_1}{x - x_1}$$

If a specific value is supplied for slope m, then the preceding equation becomes the equation of the line with slope m that passes through the point (x_1, y_1).

Example 4   *Find the equation of the line with slope 3 that passes through the point* $(2, 4)$. Substitute 3 for m and $(2, 4)$ for (x_1, y_1) into

$$m = \frac{y - y_1}{x - x_1}$$

to obtain

$$3 = \frac{y - 4}{x - 2}$$

which can be simplified. First multiply both sides by $x - 2$.

$$3(x - 2) = y - 4$$

Then

$$3x - 6 = y - 4$$

or

$$y = 3x - 2$$

The form we have obtained, in which the equation states y in terms of x, is an important form and one we will see more of in this section and elsewhere. However, the equation could have been written as $3x - y - 2 = 0$ or even as an equation stating x in terms of y.

Perhaps you realize that each time such a problem is solved, it is necessary to multiply by $x - x_1$ in order to simplify the equation. Consequently, the formula

$$m = \frac{y - y_1}{x - x_1}$$

is usually written

$$\boxed{y - y_1 = m(x - x_1)}$$

This is the traditional form of the **point-slope formula.**

Example 5 *Find the equation of the line with slope $\frac{7}{2}$ that passes through the point* $(-3, 1)$.
   Use

$$y - y_1 = m(x - x_1)$$

with

$$m = \frac{7}{2}$$

$$x_1 = -3$$

$$y_1 = 1$$

The result is

$$y - 1 = \frac{7}{2}(x - -3)$$

or

$$y - 1 = \frac{7}{2}(x + 3)$$

Now multiply both sides by 2 to eliminate the fraction.

$$2y - 2 = 7(x + 3)$$
$$2y - 2 = 7x + 21$$
$$2y = 7x + 23$$
$$y = \frac{7}{2}x + \frac{23}{2}$$

Example 6 *Determine the equation of the line that passes through the points* $(1, 6)$ *and* $(3, 0)$.

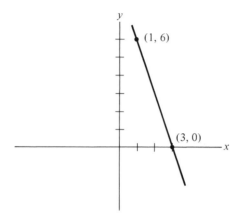

The slope of the line is computed as

$$m = \frac{y_2 - y_1}{x_2 - x_1} = \frac{0 - 6}{3 - 1} = \frac{-6}{2} = -3$$

Now use -3 for m and either point that was given—for example, $(3, 0)$—in the same way they were used in the preceding example.

$$y - y_1 = m(x - x_1)$$

becomes

$$y - 0 = -3(x - 3)$$

or

$$y = -3x + 9$$

Parallel lines have the same slope. They do not meet, because they are slanted or sloped the same. The inclination is the same for two lines that are parallel. The lines $y = 2x + 5$ and $y = 2x - 3$ are parallel, but $y = 2x + 5$ and $y = 5x + 2$ are not parallel.

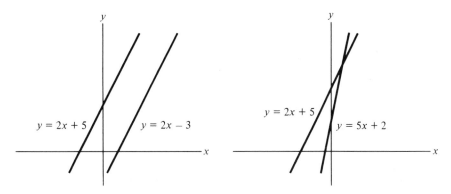

There is a relationship between the slopes of two **perpendicular lines.** If lines l_1 and l_2 are perpendicular and have slopes m_1 and m_2, respectively, then

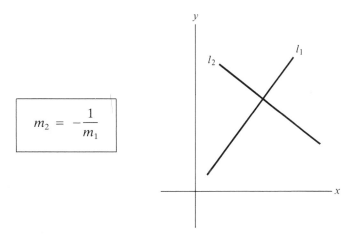

$$m_2 = -\frac{1}{m_1}$$

This relationship between the slopes of perpendicular lines is easy to prove with a little bit of trigonometry. We shall put off the proof until Chapter 7. For now, you can see that the lines must at least have slopes of opposite signs. As an example, if a line has slope 5, then any line perpendicular to it will have slope $-\frac{1}{5}$. Similarly, if a line has slope $-\frac{2}{3}$, then any line perpendicular to it will have slope $\frac{3}{2}$.

Example 7 *Determine the equation of the line that is the perpendicular bisector of the segment connecting* $(3, -4)$ *and* $(9, 10)$.

The perpendicular bisector must bisect the line segment connecting $(3, -4)$ and $(9, 10)$. That is, it must pass through the midpoint of that segment. And the midpoint of the segment is $(6, 3)$.

The perpendicular bisector must also be perpendicular to the line passing through the points $(3, -4)$ and $(9, 10)$. Its slope, then, is the negative of the reciprocal of the slope of the line through $(3, -4)$ and $(9, 10)$.

$$m_{\text{segment}} = \frac{10 - (-4)}{9 - (3)} = \frac{14}{6} = \frac{7}{3}$$

$$m_\perp = -\frac{1}{\frac{7}{3}} = -\frac{3}{7}$$

So the perpendicular bisector of the original segment has a slope of $-\frac{3}{7}$ and passes through the point (6, 3). The equation of the perpendicular bisector can now be readily obtained from the formula $y - y_1 = m(x - x_1)$. The equation becomes

$$y - 3 = -\frac{3}{7}(x - 6)$$

or

$$y = -\frac{3}{7}x + \frac{18}{7} + 3$$

Finally,

$$y = -\frac{3}{7}x + \frac{39}{7}$$

Knowing the **intercepts** of the graph of a straight line or curve is helpful in drawing the graph. An intercept is a point where the graph crosses an axis. Consider the line $y = \frac{1}{2}x - 1$, drawn next.

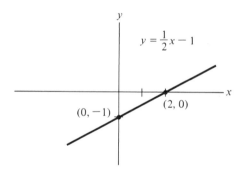

Each of the two points identified on the graph is one where the line crosses an axis. Those two points are the intercepts. So the **y intercept** is the point where $x = 0$; it is where the graph crosses the y axis.† For the line $y = \frac{1}{2}x - 1$, graphed above, the y intercept is (0, −1). For line $y = 3x - 2$, the y intercept is (0, −2) because when $x = 0$, $y = -2$. Similarly, the y intercept of the line $y = 7x + 9$ is (0, 9).

---

† Some mathematicians say that the y intercept is the y value when x is 0.

Note that if lines are written in the form $y = mx + b$, then mx is equal to zero when $x = 0$; so $(0, b)$ is always the y intercept. Earlier, lines were described by $y - y_1 = m(x - x_1)$. All lines except those parallel to the y axis must cross the y axis. Thus, all such lines have a y intercept and it occurs at the point $(0, b)$. If $(0, b)$ is substituted for (x_1, y_1) in $y - y_1 = m(x - x_1)$, the result is

$$y - b = m(x - 0)$$

or

$$y - b = mx$$

or

$$y = mx + b$$

This shows that if a line is written in the form $y = mx + b$, then m is the slope and $(0, b)$ is the y intercept. The form $y = mx + b$ is called the **slope-intercept** form of a line.

$$y = mx + b$$
$$m = \text{slope}$$
$$(0, b) = y \text{ intercept}$$

Example 8 *Find the slope and y intercept of the line $y = 12x + 5$.*
   $y = 12x + 5$ is already in $y = mx + b$ form. Here $m = 12$ and $b = 5$. So the slope is 12 and the y intercept is $(0, 5)$.

Example 9 *Find the slope and y intercept of the line $2y - 3x = -5$*
   The line $2y - 3x = -5$ is not in $y = mx + b$ form; so you cannot read the slope and y intercept directly. Change it to $y = mx + b$ (slope-intercept) form.
   Add $3x$ to both sides to isolate the y term.

$$
\begin{array}{rcl}
2y - 3x & = & -5 \\
\underline{ 3x} & & \underline{3x } \\
2y & = & 3x - 5
\end{array}
$$

Next, multiply by $\frac{1}{2}$ to get $y = mx + b$ form. The result is

$$y = \tfrac{1}{2} \cdot (3x - 5)$$
$$y = \tfrac{3}{2}x - \tfrac{5}{2}$$

In this form we now see that $m = \frac{3}{2}$ and $b = -\frac{5}{2}$. So the slope is $\frac{3}{2}$ and the y intercept is $(0, -\frac{5}{2})$.

Example 10 *Sketch the graph of the line with slope 2 and y intercept (0, 1).*

The *y* intercept (0, 1) is a point. So begin by plotting that point. Then use the fact that the slope is 2.

$$m = 2 = \frac{2}{1} = \frac{\Delta y}{\Delta x}$$

Beginning at the point (0, 1), increase *x* by 1 and *y* by 2. This will give you a second point, (1, 3), on the line. The line can now be drawn through the two points (0, 1) and (1, 3).

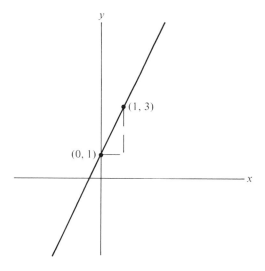

Example 11 *Determine the equation of the line that passes through the points (1, 6) and (3, 0) and write it in y = mx + b form.*

This is the same problem that was worked in Example 6. We are, however, taking a different approach this time. After we have finished, you might like to reread Example 6 and select the method you prefer. This time we are going to use the *y* = *mx* + *b* form. First determine the slope of the line through points (1, 6) and (3, 0).

$$m = \frac{\Delta y}{\Delta x} = \frac{6 - 0}{1 - 3} = \frac{6}{-2} = -3$$

Now substitute -3 for *m* in *y* = *mx* + *b*. Doing so yields

$$y = -3x + b$$

The two points (1, 6) and (3, 0) must satisfy the equation of the line on which they lie; so take either point and substitute the x and y values into $y = -3x + b$. This will determine b. Let us use $(1, 6)$.

$$y = -3x + b$$

becomes

$$6 = -3(1) + b$$

or

$$9 = b$$

Finally, substitute 9 for b in the equation $y = -3x + b$. The result is the equation of the line:

$$y = -3x + 9$$

Also of some interest is the **x intercept**, the point where the graph crosses the x axis. In other words, the x intercept is the point where $y = 0$.

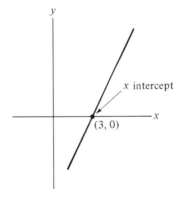

It should be pointed out that except for those lines parallel to an axis, lines have one x intercept and one y intercept. But we shall soon encounter graphs that have more than one x intercept or more than one y intercept.

Example 12   *Find the x intercept of $y = 5x - 1$.*
To get the x intercept, let $y = 0$ in $y = 5x - 1$.

$$0 = 5x - 1$$
$$5x = 1$$
$$x = \tfrac{1}{5}$$

The x intercept is $(\tfrac{1}{5}, 0)$.

1. Rewrite the equation of each line in the form $ax + by + c = 0$.
   - *(a) $4x + 3y = -5$
   - (b) $4x - 8 = 7y$
   - *(c) $7y + 2 = x$
   - (d) $5x = 2y + 15$
   - *(e) $x = 4 - 9y$
   - (f) $y = 17$
   - *(g) $3x = 1$
   - (h) $3y - 2x = 9$
   - *(i) $y = 6x - 4$
   - (j) $y = 8 - 3x$

2. Find the slope of the line through each pair of points.
   - *(a) $(5, 7)$ and $(3, 6)$
   - (b) $(10, 8)$ and $(6, 4)$
   - *(c) $(4, 2)$ and $(6, 8)$
   - (d) $(5, 1)$ and $(6, 0)$
   - *(e) $(0, 0)$ and $(1, 5)$
   - (f) $(7, 0)$ and $(4, 3)$
   - *(g) $(-5, 7)$ and $(-3, 1)$
   - (h) $(2, -3)$ and $(-7, 4)$
   - *(i) $(8, -2)$ and $(-5, -3)$
   - (j) $(-5, -3)$ and $(-3, -1)$
   - *(k) $(7, 3)$ and $(7, -9)$
   - (l) $(-3, 2)$ and $(4, 2)$

3. Determine the equation of the line that passes through the given point and has the given slope. Use point-slope formula, $y - y_1 = m(x - x_1)$.
   - *(a) $(4, 9)$, $m = 2$
   - (b) $(2, 11)$, $m = 3$
   - *(c) $(3, 7)$, $m = 5$
   - (d) $(2, 5)$, $m = 4$
   - *(e) $(1, 4)$, $m = -3$
   - (f) $(-1, 3)$, $m = -2$
   - *(g) $(-2, 7)$, $m = -6$
   - (h) $(-4, 11)$, $m = -5$
   - *(i) $(8, 3)$, $m = 1/2$
   - (j) $(10, 17)$, $m = 3/2$
   - *(k) $(-6, -2)$, $m = -1/3$
   - (l) $(4, -3)$, $m = -1/2$

4. Determine the equation of the line through each pair of points.
   - *(a) $(1, 6)$ and $(2, 9)$
   - (b) $(2, 7)$ and $(4, 13)$
   - *(c) $(0, 6)$ and $(1, 4)$
   - (d) $(4, 5)$ and $(1, 11)$
   - *(e) $(-1, 5)$ and $(2, 8)$
   - (f) $(-3, -2)$ and $(-2, -3)$
   - *(g) $(6, 4)$ and $(9, 6)$
   - (h) $(1, 8)$ and $(5, 10)$
   - *(i) $(3, -4)$ and $(5, -5)$
   - (j) $(7, 6)$ and $(2, 10)$

5. Which of the following points are on the line $y = 4x - 3$?
   - (a) $(0, -3)$
   - (b) $(1, -1)$
   - (c) $(-1, 1)$
   - (d) $(0, 4/3)$
   - (e) $(-11, -2)$
   - (f) $(2, 5)$

*6. What is the equation of the x axis and what is its slope?

7. What is the equation of the y axis and what is its slope?

8. Write the equation of the line that passes through the given point and is parallel to the given line.
   - *(a) $(5,3)$, $y = 2x + 3$
   - (b) $(1, 7)$, $y = 3x - 5$
   - *(c) $(1, -2)$, $y = -x + 7$
   - (d) $(-4, 6)$, $y = -4x + 9$

*(e) (3, 4), $y = 7 - 4x$ (f) (4, -7), $y = 9 - 5x$
*(g) (2, 5), $y = \frac{1}{2}x - 8$ (h) (-1, 6), $y = \frac{1}{4}x + 15$
*(i) (4, 7), $3x + 2y = 12$ (j) (6, 2), $5x - 2y = 10$

9. Determine the slope and y intercept of each line by first writing the equation in $y = mx + b$ form.

*(a) $y = 2x - 1$ (b) $y = -x + 4$
*(c) $y - 2 = x$ (d) $y = -3x + 2$
*(e) $y = 3(x + 1)$ (f) $x + y = 0$
*(g) $2x - y = 6$ (h) $2x + 5y = 6$
*(i) $x = 3y - 4$ (j) $x = \frac{y}{2}$
*(k) $y - 2x + 3 = 0$ (l) $4x = 2y + 8$
*(m) $2x = 3y + 18$ (n) $3x + y = 5$
*(o) $3(x + y) - 1 = x$ (p) $y = 4x + 5y - 8$

10. Sketch the graph of each line, using the given slope and point.

*(a) $m = 2$, (3, 7)   (b) $m = 3$, (6, 2)
*(c) $m = \frac{2}{3}$, (4, 5)   (d) $m = \frac{5}{4}$, (7, 1)
*(e) $m = -3$, (2, 1)   (f) $m = -4$, (2, 9)
*(g) $m = -\frac{3}{4}$, (5, 7)   (h) $m = -\frac{3}{2}$, (-4, 2)
*(i) $m = -1$, (5, 0)   (j) $m = -\frac{2}{3}$, (1, 0)
*(k) $m = 1\frac{1}{2}$, (0, -4)   (l) $m = 1\frac{1}{4}$, (0, 6)

11. Redo Exercise 3 by using the slope-intercept formula, $y = mx + b$.

12. Determine the equation of one line that is perpendicular to the line $3x + 5y - 6 = 0$.

*13. Find the equation of the line passing through the point (3, -1) and perpendicular to the line $y = 6 - 2x$.

14. Write the equation of the line that is the perpendicular bisector of the segment connecting the points.

*(a) (1, 2) and (5, 10)   (b) (2, 3) and (4, 4)
*(c) (1, 2) and (4, 5)   (d) (6, 3) and (4, 5)
*(e) (0, 8) and (-3, 9)   (f) (0, 0) and (7, 0)

*15. Prove that the line

$$\frac{x}{a} + \frac{y}{b} = 1$$

has x intercept $(a, 0)$ and y intercept $(0, b)$.

16. Show that if a line is of the form $y = mx + b$, then the x intercept is $(-b/m, 0)$.

2.4 PARABOLAS

The graph of any equation of the form $y = ax^2 + bx + c$ $(a \neq 0)$ is a curve called a **parabola**. The equation is a quadratic equation. Parabolas have some interesting properties and applications. And there are shortcuts that make graphing them simpler than by using just a lot of points.

We shall begin, however, with two examples in which we obtain points, plot them, and draw a smooth curve through them. The points are obtained by substituting values for x and computing the corresponding y values.

x	$y = x^2 - 2x - 8$	(x, y)
0	$y = (0)^2 - 2(0) - 8$	$(0, -8)$
1	$y = (1)^2 - 2(1) - 8$	$(1, -9)$
2	$y = (2)^2 - 2(2) - 8$	$(2, -8)$
3	$y = (3)^2 - 2(3) - 8$	$(3, -5)$
4	$y = (4)^2 - 2(4) - 8$	$(4, 0)$
5	$y = (5)^2 - 2(5) - 8$	$(5, 7)$
-1	$y = (-1)^2 - 2(-1) - 8$	$(-1, -5)$
-2	$y = (-2)^2 - 2(-2) - 8$	$(-2, 0)$
-3	$y = (-3)^2 - 2(-3) - 8$	$(-3, 7)$

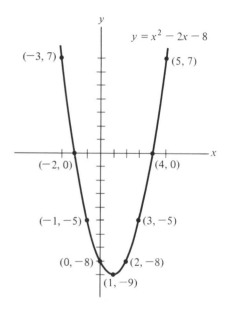

x	$y = -x^2 + 4x - 3$	(x, y)
0	$y = -(0)^2 + 4(0) - 3$	$(0, -3)$
1	$y = -(1)^2 + 4(1) - 3$	$(1, 0)$
2	$y = -(2)^2 + 4(2) - 3$	$(2, 1)$
3	$y = -(3)^2 + 4(3) - 3$	$(3, 0)$
4	$y = -(4)^2 + 4(4) - 3$	$(4, -3)$
5	$y = -(5)^2 + 4(5) - 3$	$(5, -8)$
-1	$y = -(-1)^2 + 4(-1) - 3$	$(-1, -8)$

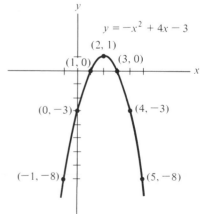

Notice that the first graph opens upward and has a minimum (lowest) point. By contrast, the second graph opens downward and has a maximum (highest) point. Let us see how these facts could have been determined in advance—that is, before obtaining any points or doing any graphing. As the values of x used increase in magnitude, the values of y determined tend to resemble the ax^2 term. For example, in $y = x^2 - 2x - 8$, if $x = 100$, $y = (100)^2 - 2(100) - 8 = 10{,}000 - 208 = 9792$. Clearly the x^2 term dominates the overall value of the expression. Similarly, in $y = -x^2 + 4x - 3$, if $x = 100$, $y = -(100)^2 + 4(100) - 3 = -10{,}000 + 397 = -9603$. Again the x^2 term dominates the overall value of the expression. So if the a of ax^2 is positive, then ax^2 is positive, which means that the curve will go upward as x gets larger in magnitude. Thus for $a > 0$, the curve opens upward and has a minimum point. On the other hand, if $a < 0$, then ax^2 is negative and the curve will go downward as x gets larger in magnitude. Thus for $a < 0$, the curve opens downward and has a maximum point. In summary.

Parabolas

$$y = ax^2 + bx + c \qquad a \neq 0$$

$a > 0$:   Opens upward, has minimum.

$a < 0$:   Opens downward, has maximum.

If you were to pass a vertical line through the maximum or minimum point of either parabola we graphed, the two segments of the curve produced would be mirror images of one another. We say the curve is **symmetric** with respect to that line. In view of the symmetry, this vertical line must be halfway between any two points on the parabola with the same y coordinate. Let us observe this situation

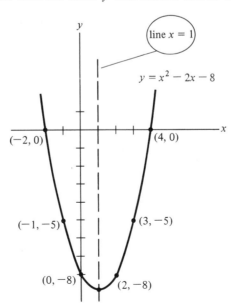

in the first parabola, $y = x^2 - 2x - 8$. Here the minimum point is $(1, -9)$. So the vertical line about which the curve is symmetric is the line $x = 1$. Notice the pairs of points that have the same y coordinates—$(0, -8)$ and $(2, -8)$, $(-1, -5)$ and $(3, -5)$, $(-2, 0)$ and $(4, 0)$, and so on. Each point of a pair is the same distance from the vertical line as the other point of that pair. Knowing this fact makes graphing easier.

We can also apply our knowledge to obtain a formula for the x coordinate of the maximum or minimum point. Consider $y = ax^2 + bx + c$. If $x = 0$, then $y = c$. So $(0, c)$ is one point of a pair that is the same distance from the vertical line about which the graph is symmetric. The other point of the pair must have the same y coordinate: c. Thus the other point is (x, c). The x value can be determined by substituting c for y in $y = ax^2 + bx + c$. If

$$c = ax^2 + bx + c$$

then

$$ax^2 + bx = 0$$

or

$$(x)(ax + b) = 0$$

This leads to $x = 0$ (which we know already) and to $ax + b = 0$. The solution of $ax + b = 0$ is $-b/a$. This means the other point is $(-b/a, c)$. Thus the x coordinate of the maximum or minimum point is halfway between the x coordinates of $(0, c)$ and $(-b/a, c)$. This means the x coordinate we seek is

$$x = \frac{-\dfrac{b}{a} + 0}{2} = -\frac{b}{2a}$$

The x coordinate of the maximum or minimum point of the parabola $y = ax^2 + bx + c$ is

$$x = -\frac{b}{2a}$$

Example 13 *Determine the minimum point of the parabola $y = 2x^2 + 3x + 2$.*

First of all, you can tell that the parabola has a minimum point rather than a maximum point because $a = 2 > 0$. The x coordinate of the minimum point is

$$x_{min} = -\frac{b}{2a} = -\frac{3}{2(2)} = -\frac{3}{4}$$

The corresponding y coordinate is determined from $y = 2x^2 + 3x + 2$ as

$$y_{min} = 2(-\tfrac{3}{4})^2 + 3(-\tfrac{3}{4}) + 2 = \tfrac{7}{8}$$

Thus the minimum point of this parabola is $(-\tfrac{3}{4}, \tfrac{7}{8})$.

Example 14 *If a company's revenue on the sale of x units is $R = -x^2 + 50x - 23$ dollars, what is the maximum revenue possible and how many units should be sold to realize that revenue?*

Because the expression that represents revenue is quadratic and because $a = -1 < 0$, there will be a maximum R value. The x value for which R is maximum is

$$x_{max} = -\frac{b}{2a} = -\frac{50}{2(-1)} = 25$$

This means 25 units should be sold to maximize revenue. The maximum revenue, which is R for $x = 25$, is

$$R = -(25)^2 + 50(25) - 23 = 602$$

The maximum revenue is $602.

Just as intercepts are helpful in graphing straight lines, they can also be helpful in graphing parabolas. The y intercept of $y = ax^2 + bx + c$ is the point where $x = 0$. Clearly, when $x = 0$ in $y = ax^2 + bx + c$, $y = c$. Thus $(0, c)$ is the y intercept, the point where the parabola crosses the y axis.

> The y intercept of $y = ax^2 + bx + c$ is $(0, c)$.

The x intercepts of $y = ax^2 + bx + c$ are the points where $y = 0$. So solve $0 = ax^2 + bx + c$ to determine them. From your work with quadratic equations in Chapter 1 you know that a quadratic equation can have two, one, or no real solutions. If there are two real solutions, then the graph has two x intercepts and thus crosses the x axis twice. Such is the case in both examples at the beginning of this section. If there is only one real solution, then the graph has only one x intercept, which means it merely touches the x axis with its maximum or minimum point. If there are no real solutions, then the graph has no x intercept, which means it neither touches nor crosses the x axis. The discriminant $b^2 - 4ac$ can be used to determine the number of x intercepts of $y = ax^2 + bx + c$.

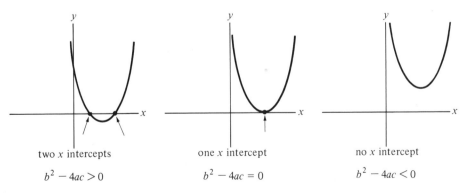

two x intercepts   one x intercept   no x intercept

$b^2 - 4ac > 0$ $b^2 - 4ac = 0$ $b^2 - 4ac < 0$

Example 15 *Sketch the graph of* $y = x^2 - 4x + 5$.

The y intercept is $(0, 5)$. The x coordinate of the minimum point (minimum, since $a = 1 > 0$) is

$$x_{min} = -\frac{b}{2a} = -\frac{-4}{2(1)} = 2$$

The corresponding y, computed by using 2 for x in $y = x^2 - 4x + 5$, is 1. Thus the minimum point is $(2, 1)$. So far we have

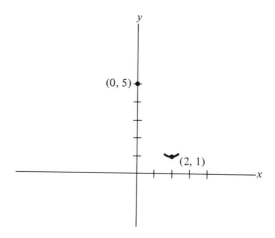

If we let $x = 1$, we get the point $(1, 2)$.

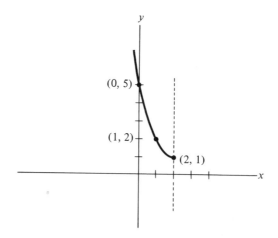

Using symmetry, we know that the mirror image is on the other side of the line $x = 2$ (the vertical line through the minimum point), which tells us that two other points of this parabola are $(3, 2)$ and $(4, 5)$.

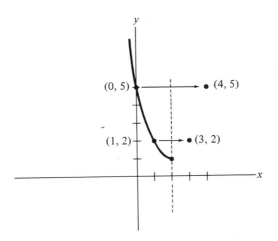

So the graph will appear as

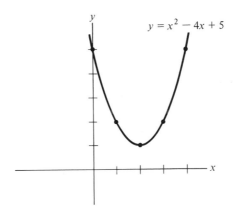

$y = x^2 - 4x + 5$

As it happens, this graph has no x intercepts.

Example 16   *A ball is thrown straight upward and travels so that its distance from the ground after t seconds is s = −16t² + 80t + 144 feet. When does the ball strike the ground?*

The ball strikes the ground when its distance (s) from the ground is 0. So we must solve the equation

$$0 = -16t^2 + 80t + 144$$

First, divide through by -16, which will produce the simpler equation

$$t^2 - 5t - 9 = 0$$

This equation can be solved by the quadratic formula as

$$t = \frac{5 \pm \sqrt{25 - 4(1)(-9)}}{2(1)} = \frac{5 \pm \sqrt{61}}{2}$$

Using Appendix Table VI or a calculator, we obtain $\sqrt{61} \approx 7.810$. So

$$t \approx \frac{5 \pm 7.810}{2}$$

$$\approx \frac{12.810}{2} \quad \text{or} \quad \frac{-2.810}{2}$$

$$\approx 6.405 \quad \text{or} \quad -1.405$$

Since t represents time, we reject the negative root and have $t \approx 6.405$ seconds as the time at which the ball strikes the ground.

Example 17 *Determine the x intercepts of* $y = x^2 - 12x + 36$.
  The x intercepts are the points where $y = 0$. So we solve the equation $0 = x^2 - 12x + 36$.

$$x^2 - 12x + 36 = 0$$

$$(x - 6)(x - 6) = 0$$

$$x = 6 \mid x = 6$$

At this point you can see there is only one x intercept, $(6, 0)$. The curve merely touches the x axis at $(6, 0)$.

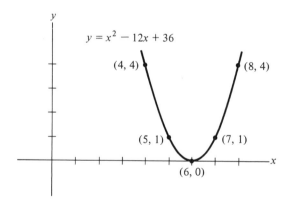

In this section we have taken an algebraic view of parabolas by studying $y = ax^2 + bx + c$. In Chapter 8 we shall use a geometric definition of parabola to obtain a different form for the equation of a parabola. The applications presented there will also reflect a geometric interpretation.

EXERCISES 2.4

1. Sketch the graph of the parabola associated with each equation given. Proceed by obtaining the extreme point (maximum or minimum), the y intercept, and another point or two; use symmetry.

*(a) $y = x^2 + 2x - 15$ (b) $y = x^2 - 2x - 15$

*(c) $y = x^2 - 8x + 12$ (d) $y = x^2 + 6x + 8$

*(e) $y = -x^2 + 6x - 5$ (f) $y = -x^2 - 8x - 7$

*(g) $y = x^2 - 8x$ (h) $y = -x^2 - 4x$

*(i) $y = 3 + x^2$ (j) $y = 2 - x^2$

*(k) $y = x^2 - 8x + 1$ (l) $y = x^2 + 6x - 5$

*(m) $y = -x^2 + 2x - 11$ (n) $y = 1 - 4x - x^2$

*(o) $y = 2x^2 - 7x - 15$ (p) $y = 3x^2 - 20x + 12$

*(q) $y = -3x^2 - 10x - 6$ (r) $y = -2x^2 - 5x + 3$

*(s) $y = x^2 - 3x + 1$ (t) $y = -x^2 + 5x - 2$

2. Determine the x intercepts of each parabola.

*(a) $y = x^2 - x - 20$ (b) $y = x^2 + 7x - 30$

*(c) $y = 2x^2 + 3x - 14$ (d) $y = 5x^2 - 11x - 12$

*(e) $y = x^2 - 3x + 7$ (f) $y = -x^2 + 3x + 17$

*(g) $y = 5 - 3x - x^2$ (h) $y = 1 - 8x^2$

*(i) $y = -7x^2 + 41x + 6$ (j) $y = -4x^2 + 3x - 19$

*3. A company's revenue on the sale of x items is $R = -2x^2 + 200x + 135$ dollars. What is the maximum revenue possible and how many units should be sold to realize that revenue?

4. A ball thrown straight upward travels so that its distance from the ground in t seconds is $s = -16t^2 + 56t + 120$ feet. When does the ball strike the ground?

*5. A rocket shot straight upward travels so that its distance from the ground in t seconds is $s = -16t^2 + 640t + 150$ feet. When does it reach its maximum height and what is that maximum height?

6. When a frog leaps, its path through the air is a parabola. Suppose that a particular frog's path is $y = 2x - \frac{1}{4}x^2$, where y is the frog's height in flight and x is the horizontal distance from where it began to leap. All measurements are in feet.

   (a) How high does the frog leap?

   (b) How far (horizontally) does the frog leap?

   (c) Sketch the graph of the frog's path during a leap.

*7. The area of a rectangular garden of length x meters and width $400 - x$ meters is $A = x(400 - x)$ square meters. What is the largest possible area for the garden?

2.5   SETS AND INTERVALS

Your first real encounter with the use of sets in mathematics will come in Chapter 3 when we define and explain the concept of a function. The ideas and notation of functions are basic to the study of calculus. In this section we provide brief coverage of set notation and terminology. We also present interval notation.

A **set** is a collection of things. The things that make up the set are called *elements* or *members* of the set. The elements of the set of integers between one and ten inclusive are 1, 2, 3, 4, 5, 6, 7, 8, 9, and 10. Such a set will be written as {1, 2, 3, 4, 5, 6, 7, 8, 9, 10}. Braces, { }, are used to specify a set. The elements of the set are placed inside the braces and are separated by commas. It does not matter in what order the elements are written. That is, the sets {1, 2, 3, 4, 5} and {3, 2, 1, 5, 4} are the same.

The symbol $\in$ is used to mean "is an element of" or "is in." For example, $5 \in \{2, 3, 5, 9, 17\}$ is read as 5 *is in* the set consisting of 2, 3, 5, 9, 17 or as 5 *is an element of* that set. The symbol $\notin$ means *is not an element of* or *is not in*. Thus the statement 7 *is not an element of* {1, 2, 3, 6} can be written $7 \notin \{1, 2, 3, 6\}$.

If every element of set A is also an element of set B, then A is called a *subset* of B, written $A \subseteq B$. The set {2, 3, 4, 6} is a subset of the set {1, 2, 3, 4, 5, 6}. It is also a subset of itself. In fact, $A \subseteq A$ for any set A.

The set containing no elements is called the *empty set* or *null set* and is denoted by $\varnothing$ or { }.

Sometimes three dots (. . .) are used to indicate a "continuation in the same manner." The notation is used to avoid writing all the members of the set explicitly. Thus the set of whole numbers {1, 2, 3, 4, 5, 6, 7, 8, 9, 10, 11, 12, 13} can be written {1, 2, 3, 4, . . ., 13}. The set {14, 16, 18, 20, 22, 24, 26, 28, 30, 32, 34, 36} of all the even whole numbers between 14 and 36 inclusive can be written as {14, 16, 18, . . . , 36}. The set of all whole numbers greater than 13 can be written as {14, 15, 16, 17, . . .}.

The set {2, 4, 6, 8, 10, . . .} is the set of all positive even integers. It can also be written $\{x \mid x$ positive, even integer$\}$, which is read as "the set of all numbers x such that x is a positive, even integer." The vertical line $\mid$ is read as *such that*. This is particularly useful notation for some statements about sets. For example, how could we represent the set of *all* real numbers that are greater than zero? Using the new notation, we simply write this as $\{x \mid x$ real, $x > 0\}$, the set of all real numbers x such that x is greater than zero.

Example 18   *Indicate the set of all real numbers less than* 17.

$$\{x \mid x \text{ real}, x < 17\}$$

Example 19   *Write the set of all odd numbers greater than 7.*

$$\{n \mid n \text{ odd}, n > 7\}$$

The odd numbers greater than 7 are 9, 11, 13, 15, 17, and so on. So the set could also be written

$$\{9, 11, 13, 15, 17, \ldots\}$$

To compare Example 19 with Example 18, note that the set of Example 18 cannot be written by listing the elements. There is no way to write down a list or pattern of all the real numbers less than 17. Remember, all the reals include all the rational numbers (fractions, terminating decimals, and repeating decimals—not just integers) as well as all the irrational numbers.

Example 20   *Represent the set of all real numbers that are between 3 and 5 exclusive—that is, all numbers that are both greater than 3 and less than 5.*

$$\{y \mid y \text{ real}, 3 < y < 5\}$$

Notice how the inequalities $y > 3$ (which is the same as $3 < y$) and $y < 5$ were combined as $3 < y < 5$.

The set in Example 20 represents an interval between two real numbers. An abbreviated **interval notation** is often used to write such a set. Here is a table that demonstrates how to write such sets in interval notation. Also included is the (illustrated) number-line form. A few comments follow the table. Be sure to read them, especially if you have any questions about the table.

Set Notation	Interval Notation	Number-Line Form
$\{x \mid 2 < x < 3\}$	$(2, 3)$	
$\{x \mid 2 \leq x \leq 3\}$	$[2, 3]$	
$\{x \mid 2 \leq x < 3\}$	$[2, 3)$	
$\{x \mid 2 < x \leq 3\}$	$(2, 3]$	
$\{x \mid x > 2\}$	$(2, \infty)$	
$\{x \mid x \leq 3\}$	$(-\infty, 3]$	

Several observations should be made. A parenthesis is used to specify that the endpoint is not included and a bracket indicates that the endpoint is included. The symbol ∞ is used to represent the right end of an interval that continues infinitely far in the positive direction. The symbol −∞ represents the left end of an interval that continues infinitely far in the negative direction. On the number line, circles (large dots) specify the ends of the interval. A circle is darkened in to specify that the endpoint is included or else left open to specify that the endpoint is not included in the set. The interval between the endpoints is darkened to distinguish it from the rest of the number line. An arrowhead is used to specify cases in which the interval continues infinitely far in one direction.

An interval [a, b] that includes both endpoints is called a **closed interval**. An interval (a, b) that excludes both endpoints is called an **open interval**. Intervals [a, b) and (a, b] are called **half-open intervals**.

EXERCISES 2.5

1. Indicate which of the following statements are true and which are false.
   *(a) $x \in \{a, b, c, x, y, z\}$ (b) $x \notin \{a, b, c, x, y, z\}$
   *(c) $5 \in \{2, 4, 6, 8, 10\}$ (d) $5 \in \{1, 3, 15, 17, 19\}$
   (e) $d \in \{a, e, q, r\}$ (f) $ \notin \{\square, \triangle, *, \$\}$
   *(g) $-19 \in \{\text{integers}\}$ (h) $x \notin \{R, S, T, U, V\}$
   *(i) $341 \notin \{\text{odd numbers}\}$ (j) $5.6 \in \{\text{whole numbers}\}$

2. Use the *such that* notation to represent each set consisting of the elements described.
   *(a) All real numbers greater than 13.
   (b) All real numbers less than $\frac{1}{2}$.
   *(c) All real numbers not less than zero.
   (d) The real numbers between −5 and 16, inclusive.
   *(e) The nonzero real numbers between, but not including, −50 and 400.
   (f) All real numbers between 6 and 50, excluding 6 but including 50.
   *(g) All real numbers between −7 and 2, including −7 but excluding 2.
   (h) All nonzero real numbers.
   *(i) All the positive numbers.
   (j) All the negative numbers.
   *(k) All the real numbers with absolute value greater than 17.
   (l) All the real numbers with squares not exceeding 75.
   *(m) All the real numbers between 7 and 100 (inclusive) in absolute value.

3. Represent each set two ways: once by using *such that* notation and once by listing the elements. See Example 19.
   *(a) The odd numbers greater than 10.

(b)   The even numbers between 3 and 95.

*(c)   All even numbers between and including 4 and 300.

(d)   The integers between -600 and 700 inclusive.

*(e)   All the positive integers.

(f)   All the whole numbers.

*(g)   All the negative integers.

(h)   The odd numbers less than zero.

*(i)   All positive even numbers.

4.   Represent each set by using both interval notation and the number-line form.

*(a) $\{x \mid -2 \leq x < 6\}$ (b) $\{x \mid x > 3\}$

*(c) $\{x \mid x \leq -7\}$ (d) $\{x \mid 5 < x \leq 10\}$

*(e) $\{t \mid t \geq -2\}$ (f) $\{t \mid t < 4\}$

*(g) $\{x \mid -9 \leq x \leq -4\}$ (h) $\{x \mid x > -9\}$

*(i) $\{x \mid 5 < x < 6\}$ (j) $\{n \mid n < -15\}$

5.   Represent each interval by using *such that* notation and by the number-line form.

*(a)   [4, 10]   (b)   (3, 5)

*(c) $(-2, 6)$ (d)   [0, 12]

*(e)   (5, 8]   (f) $[-1, 6)$

*(g) $(2, \infty)$ (h) $[-3, \infty)$

*(i) $(-\infty, 5)$ (j) $(-\infty, -4)$

*(k) $(-\infty, 10]$ (l) $[0, \infty)$

*6.   For each interval in Exercises 5(a)-(f), determine whether it is open, closed, or half open.

2.6   INEQUALITIES

You should recall from your previous algebra course that you solved linear inequalities in one variable in much that same way as you solved linear equations. There is but one essential difference in the mechanics of solving.

> If you multiply or divide both sides of an inequality by a negative number, the direction of the inequality is reversed:
> $>$ becomes $<$ and $<$ becomes $>$

As you follow the next three examples, notice how the method of solving these inequalities is similar to the method of solving linear equations.

Example 21 *Solve* $2x + 5 < 9$.

Add -5 to both sides to get the x term alone.

$$\begin{array}{rcr} 2x + 5 < & 9 \\ -\;5 & -5 \\ \hline 2x \quad\; < & 4 \end{array}$$

Now divide both sides by 2 (or, equivalently, multiply by $\frac{1}{2}$) to get a coefficient of 1 for x.

$$x < 2$$

This means that any number less than 2 satisfies the original inequality.

Note: If desired, we could write the solution $x < 2$ in interval notation, as $(-\infty, 2)$.

Example 22 *Solve* $5x + 2 - 9x \geq 17$.

Combining like terms on the left side produces

$$-4x + 2 \geq 17$$

Next, add -2 to both sides to get the x term alone.

$$-4x \geq 15$$

Now divide both sides by -4 to get a coefficient of 1 for x.

$$x \leq -\frac{15}{4}$$

Note that division by -4, a *negative* number, reverses the direction of the inequality; $\geq$ becomes $\leq$.

Example 23 *Solve* $3(x + 1) - 7 < 8x + 9$.

Distribute the 3 to eliminate parentheses.

$$3x + 3 - 7 < 8x + 9$$

Combine the like terms on the left side.

$$3x - 4 < 8x + 9$$

To get the x term alone, first add $+4$ to both sides.

$$3x < 8x + 13$$

Then add $-8x$ to both sides.

$$-5x < 13$$

Obtain a coefficient of 1 for x.

$$x > -\frac{13}{5}$$

Note that we divided both sides by -5 and consequently changed $<$ to $>$.

Now we shall consider some nonlinear inequalities. Techniques for solving such inequalities that contain products and quotients will be presented by means of a series of examples.

Example 24 *Solve $(x + 1)(x + 3) > 0$.*

The product $(x + 1)(x + 3)$ is positive when both factors are positive or when both factors are negative. Clearly $x + 1 > 0$ when $x > -1$ and $x + 1 < 0$ when $x < -1$. Using a *sign chart* (which resembles a number line), we can illustrate where $x + 1$ is positive and where it is negative.

$$x + 1: \quad \underset{\underset{-1}{|}}{\overline{- - - - - - - - - - - \ + + + + + + +}}$$

Similarly, we can produce a sign chart for the other factor, $x + 3$.

$$x + 3: \quad \underset{\underset{-3}{|}}{\overline{- - - - + + + + + + + + + + + + +}}$$

When the two lines are combined, we have the sign chart shown next.

$$x + 1: \quad \underset{\underset{-1}{|}}{\overline{- - - - - - - - - \ + + + +}}$$

$$x + 3: \quad \underset{\underset{-3}{|}}{\overline{- - - + + + + + + + + + +}}$$

The drawing shows that $(x + 1)(x + 3) > 0$ when $x < -3$ (because both $x + 1$ and $x + 3$ are negative then) or when $x > -1$ (because both $x + 1$ and $x + 3$ are positive then). Thus $(x + 1)(x + 3) > 0$ when $x < -3$ or $x > -1$. The word *or* is used because x cannot be simultaneously less than -3 and greater than -1. Note, too, that the inequality $(x + 1)(x + 3) > 0$ could have been given originally as $x^2 + 4x + 3 > 0$, in which case factoring would have been the first step toward a solution.

Example 25 *Solve $x^2 - 3x - 10 \le 0$.*

To begin, $x^2 - 3x - 10 \le 0$ is the same as

$$(x - 5)(x + 2) \le 0$$

The product is negative when one factor is negative and the other factor is positive. Using a sign chart, we have

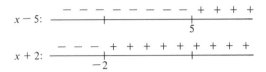

Clearly $(x - 5)(x + 2)$ is negative for x between -2 and 5. The product *equals* zero at 5 and at -2. Thus $x^2 - 3x - 10 \le 0$ when $-2 \le x \le 5$.

The same solution can also be obtained by graphing. If values are supplied for x to get values for the expression $x^2 - 3x - 10$, then points of the form $(x, x^2 - 3x - 10)$ are obtained. The graph of all such points is shown next. You can see that $x^2 - 3x - 10 \le 0$ between -2 and 5.

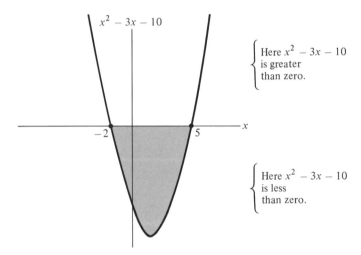

Example 26 *Solve* $\dfrac{(x - 1)}{(x + 2)(x - 3)} > 0.$

The quotient is positive when all three factors are positive or when two are negative and one is positive. The sign chart is

Thus

$$\frac{(x - 1)}{(x + 2)(x - 3)} > 0$$

when $-2 < x < 1$ or when $x > 3$.

Example 27 *Solve* $\dfrac{2}{x + 2} < 4$.

We will *not* multiply both sides by $x + 2$ because we don't know whether $x + 2$ is positive or negative; so we don't know if the direction should be changed. Instead note that if -4 is added to both sides, the inequality will be compared to zero, thus resembling the inequalities of Examples 24 through 26.

$$\frac{2}{x + 2} - 4 < 0$$

The left side can now be written as one fraction.

$$\frac{2 - 4(x + 2)}{x + 2} < 0$$

or

$$\frac{-4x - 6}{x + 2} < 0$$

The fraction is less than zero when the numerator and denominator are of opposite sign, that is, one positive and one negative. Here is the sign chart (noting that $-4x - 6 > 0$ when $x < -\frac{3}{2}$).

$$-4x - 6: \quad \overset{+\ +\ +\ +\ +\ +\ +\ +\ \ -\ -\ -\ -}{\rule{6cm}{0.4pt}}$$
$$-\frac{3}{2}$$

$$x + 2: \quad \overset{-\ -\ -\ -\ -\ +\ +\ +\ +\ +\ +\ +\ +}{\rule{6cm}{0.4pt}}$$
$$-2$$

The fraction is less than zero for x less than -2 and for x greater than $-\frac{3}{2}$. Thus

$$\frac{2}{x + 2} < 4$$

when $x < -2$ or $x > -\frac{3}{2}$.

With a number line in mind, the absolute value of a number can be thought of as the distance of the number from 0.

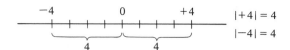

$|+4| = 4$

$|-4| = 4$

Consider the inequality $|x| < 5$. What numbers have absolute value less than 5? Obviously any positive number less than 5 will satisfy this inequality. Zero also satisfies $|x| < 5$. Do all negative numbers satisfy $|x| < 5$? No, only negative numbers greater than -5. Numbers such as -5, -6, -7, and so on fail to satisfy $|x| < 5$ because their absolute values are not less than 5.

$$x = -5 \qquad |x| = |-5| = 5$$
$$x = -6 \qquad |x| = |-6| = 6$$
$$x = -7 \qquad |x| = |-7| = 7$$

Thus only numbers between -5 and 5 satisfy $|x| < 5$. The solution to $|x| < 5$ is $-5 < x < 5$.

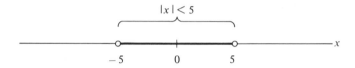

In general, for $a > 0$,

$$\text{If } |x| < a,$$
$$\text{then } -a < x < a.$$

Example 28 *Solve $|x| < 9$.*

$$|x| < 9 \quad \text{means} \quad -9 < x < 9$$

Example 29 *Solve $|2x| < 12$.*

$$|2x| < 12 \quad \text{means} \quad -12 < 2x < 12$$

But we want x, not $2x$; so we divide by 2.

$$-12 < 2x < 12$$

becomes

$$-6 < x < 6$$

If you prefer, you can separate the inequality $-12 < 2x < 12$ into the two inequalities $-12 < 2x$ and $2x < 12$, get $-6 < x$ and $x < 6$, and put them back together as $-6 < x < 6$.

Example 30   *Solve* $|x + 9| < 15$.

$$|x + 9| < 15 \quad \text{means} \quad -15 < x + 9 < 15$$

Add -9 to all parts of the inequality to get x alone. This process yields the inequality $-24 < x < 6$ as the solution.

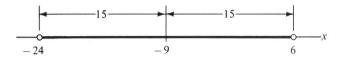

Note that this absolute value inequality may be interpreted to mean that the distance between -9 and x must be less than 15 units on either side of -9.

Example 31   *Solve* $|-2x + 7| < 13$.

$$|-2x + 7| < 13 \quad \text{means} \quad -13 < -2x + 7 < 13$$

Add -7 to each part of the inequality to get

$$-20 < -2x < 6$$

Finally, divide through by -2 and change the direction of the inequality.

$$10 > x > -3$$

Example 32   *Show that if* $|5x - 15| < \varepsilon$, *then* $|x - 3| < \dfrac{\varepsilon}{5}$.

$$|5x - 15| < \varepsilon$$
$$|5(x - 3)| < \varepsilon$$
$$|5||x - 3| < \varepsilon$$
$$5|x - 3| < \varepsilon$$
$$|x - 3| < \frac{\varepsilon}{5}$$

The symbol ε is the Greek letter "epsilon."

So far we have worked with absolute values that were *less than* some number; for example,

$$|x| < 9$$

$$|x + 9| < 15$$

$$|-2x + 7| < 13$$

Now let us consider an example where the absolute value is *greater than* some number. Suppose that $|x| > 2$. Clearly any number greater than 2 satisfies this inequality. What negative numbers satisfy $|x| > 2$? Any number whose absolute value is greater than 2 satisfies this inequality. For example, -5, -12, and $-13\frac{1}{2}$ satisfy $|x| > 2$. Any negative number less than -2 satisfies the inequality. Thus $|x| > 2$ is satisfied by positive numbers greater than 2 and negative numbers less than -2.

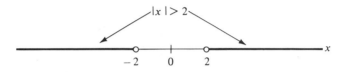

Thus $|x| > 2$ means that

$$x > 2 \quad \text{or} \quad x < -2$$

Using the distance interpretation, the distance between zero and x must always be greater than 2 units on either side of zero.

In general, for $a \geq 0$,

If $|x| > a$,

then $x > a$ or $x < -a$.

The inequalities $x > a$ or $x < -a$ are *not written* combined as $a < x < -a$ or as $-a > x > a$ because those forms suggest that x is greater than a and less than $-a$, which is not possible for $a \geq 0$.

Example 33 *Solve* $|x| > 6$.
 If $|x| > 6$, then

$$x > 6 \quad \text{or} \quad x < -6$$

Example 34 *Solve* $|3x| > 27$.
 $|3x| > 27$ means that

$$3x > 27 \quad \text{or} \quad 3x < -27$$

$$x > 9 \quad \text{or} \quad x < -9$$

Example 35 *Solve* $|x - 8| > 6$.
$|x - 8| > 6$ means that

$$x - 8 > 6 \quad \text{or} \quad x - 8 < -6$$
$$x > 14 \quad \text{or} \quad x < 2$$

Example 36 *Solve* $|5x + 3| > 1$.
$|5x + 3| > 1$ means that

$$5x + 3 > 1 \quad \text{or} \quad 5x + 3 < -1$$
$$5x > -2 \quad \text{or} \quad 5x < -4$$
$$x > -\frac{2}{5} \quad \text{or} \quad x < -\frac{4}{5}$$

Example 37 *Solve* $|-2x + 1| > 7$.
$|-2x + 1| > 7$ means that

$$-2x + 1 > 7 \quad \text{or} \quad -2x + 1 < -7$$
$$-2x > 6 \quad \text{or} \quad -2x < -8$$
$$x < -3 \quad \text{or} \quad x > 4$$

EXERCISES 2.6

1. Solve each linear inequality.
    *(a) $x + 1 < 6$
    *(c) $2x + 3 < 6$
    *(e) $3x - 4 \leq -8$
    *(g) $3x + 1 - x \geq 13$
    *(i) $2x - 7 - 9x \leq 6$
    *(k) $3(x + 1) + 5 < 5$
    *(m) $2(3 + 2x) - 4 > 7x$
    *(o) $4x + 3 + 2x < 5 - 2x$
      (b) $x - 3 \leq 10$
      (d) $5x + 1 > 7$
      (f) $2x - 9 > -3$
      (h) $5x + 3 + 2x < -4$
      (j) $2(x + 3) - 6 \geq 9$
      (l) $4(x - 2) - 3 > x$
      (n) $5x + 1 < 2(3x - 4) + 3$
      (p) $4x + 2(3 + x) \geq 6x + 7$

2. Solve each nonlinear inequality.
    *(a) $(x - 5)(x + 2) \geq 0$
    *(c) $(x - 3)(x - 1) < 0$
      (b) $(x + 4)(x + 7) > 0$
      (d) $(x + 6)(x - 8) \leq 0$

*(e) $x^2 + 7x + 12 > 0$ (f) $x^2 - 10x + 16 < 0$

*(g) $x^2 - 3x \leq 0$ (h) $x^2 + 5x > 0$

*(i) $x^2 - 1 > 0$ (j) $x^2 - 9 < 0$

*(k) $x^2 - 7 < 0$ (l) $x^2 - 5 \geq 0$

*(m) $\dfrac{x + 5}{x - 3} < 0$ (n) $\dfrac{x - 7}{x + 4} > 0$

*(o) $\dfrac{x - 9}{x - 4} > 0$ (p) $\dfrac{x + 5}{x + 1} \leq 0$

*(q) $(2x + 1)(x - 3) < 0$ (r) $(3x - 1)(x + 7) < 0$

*(s) $\dfrac{5x - 2}{x + 1} > 0$ (t) $\dfrac{4x + 3}{x - 9} > 0$

3.   Solve each nonlinear inequality.

*(a) $\dfrac{7}{x - 6} < 8$ (b) $\dfrac{3}{x + 4} > 2$

*(c) $\dfrac{-3}{x - 7} > 6$ (d) $\dfrac{-5}{x + 7} < 4$

*(e) $(x - 2)(x + 3)(x - 4) < 0$ (f) $(x + 5)(x + 1)(x - 6) > 0$

*(g) $\dfrac{x^2 - 9x + 20}{x + 3} \geq 0$ (h) $\dfrac{x - 1}{x^2 - 16} \leq 0$

*(i) $\dfrac{2x + 1}{x - 3} < 1$ (j) $\dfrac{3x + 8}{x - 2} < 1$

*(k) $\dfrac{x}{x - 4} > 3$ (l) $\dfrac{5x + 9}{2x + 5} > 2$

4.   Solve each inequality. Assume the numbers a and m are positive constants.

*(a) $|x| < 6$ (b) $|x| < 19$

*(c) $|4n| < 16$ (d) $|5t| < 20$

*(e) $|7x| < 13$ (f) $|2x| < 11$

*(g) $|m + 2| < 6$ (h) $|x - 17| < 6$

*(i) $|x - 4| \leq 12$ (j) $|4y - 2| < 10$

*(k) $|3x + 5| < 10$ (l) $|7 + 2x| < 15$

*(m) $|4 - 7z| \leq 12$ (n) $|35 - x| < 10$

*(o) $|8 - 9x| < 24$ (p) $|x + 7| < a$

*(q) $|x - 6| < a$ (r) $|x - a| < m$

5.   Solve each inequality.

*(a) $|x| > 7$ (b) $|x| > 65$

*(c) $|5w| > 35$ (d) $|4x| > 86$

*(e) $|x - 9| > 45$ (f) $|x + 16| \geq 6$

*(g) $|2x - 7| > 16$ (h) $|4x - 3| > 30$

*(i) $|5x + 9| > 20$ (j) $|2x + 12| > 5$

6. Solve each inequality *if possible*. Watch for shortcuts and use facts you know; for example, if x is a real number, then $x^2 \geq 0$ and $|x| \geq 0$ for all real x.

*(a) $|7x + 2| < -1$

(b) $|2x - 5| < -10$

*(c) $|5x - 3| > -2$

(d) $|1 - 8x| > -5$

*(e) $|x + 5| \leq 0$

(f) $|x - 7| \leq 0$

*(g) $\dfrac{3}{x - 2} > 0$

(h) $\dfrac{4}{x + 1} < 0$

*(i) $\dfrac{x^2}{x - 7} < 0$

(j) $\dfrac{3x + 2}{x^2} > 0$

*(k) $|x^2 + 3| > 2$

(l) $\dfrac{1}{x^2 + 5} > 3$

*(m) $x^2(x - 9) > 0$

(n) $\dfrac{x - 2}{x^4} < 0$

7. Verify each statement.

(a) If $|3x - 12| < \varepsilon$, then $|x - 4| < \dfrac{\varepsilon}{3}$.

(b) If $|6x - 18| < \varepsilon$, then $|x - 3| < \dfrac{\varepsilon}{6}$.

(c) If $|5x + 20| < \varepsilon$, then $|x + 4| < \dfrac{\varepsilon}{5}$.

REVIEW EXERCISES FOR CHAPTER 2

*1. What is the distance between the points $(6, -2)$ and $(1, 8)$?

2. What is the midpoint of the line segment connecting the points $(-7, 0)$ and $(4, 17)$?

3. Determine the slope of each line.
   *(a) It passes through $(7, -1)$ and $(3, 1)$.
   (b) It is parallel to the line $2x - 5y = 19$.
   *(c) It is perpendicular to the line $3x + 7y = 4$.

4. Determine the equation of each line.
   *(a) It passes through $(-1, 4)$ and $(5, 3)$.
   (b) It passes through $(5, -1)$ and has slope 6.
   *(c) It passes through $(7, 3)$ and has slope -2.
   (d) It passes through $(2, 15)$ and is parallel to the line $y = 5x - 1$.
   *(e) It passes through $(-1, -4)$ and is perpendicular to the line $y = -3x + 17$.

*5. Sketch the graph of the line that passes through the point (3, 2) and has a slope of $-\frac{4}{5}$.

6. Sketch the graph of each equation.
   *(a) $y = 4x - 3$ (b) $2x - 5y = 10$
   *(c) $y = x^2 - 5x + 3$ (d) $y = -x^2 - 6x + 1$

7. Solve each inequality.
   *(a) $7(5x - 2) - x \le 16$ (b) $x^2 - 4x - 12 < 0$
   *(c) $\dfrac{x - 2}{x + 5} > 0$ (d) $|4x - 7| < 17$
   *(e) $|5x - 16| > 3$

8. Determine the maximum value of y.
   *(a) $y = -x^2 + 8x - 32$ (b) $y = -2x^2 - 200x + 1000$

9. Determine the minimum value of y.
   *(a) $y = x^2 - 10x + 1$ (b) $y = 3x^2 + 3x + 2$

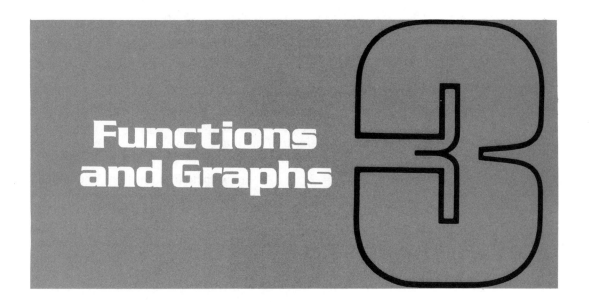

Functions and Graphs

3.1 INTRODUCTION

Up to this point you have been reviewing and extending your basic knowledge of algebra. Now you will have the opportunity to apply your understanding to the theory of functions, which is presented in this chapter. While there are some applications in this chapter, a wide variety of applications is presented in Chapter 4. But before we can begin, you must be introduced to the idea of a correspondence between real numbers. This, then, is the topic of the next paragraph.

Consider the equation $y = 2x + 1$. For every real number x, there is a corresponding real number y that makes the equation true. The pairs of x's and corresponding y's determined from the equation $y = 2x + 1$ are an example of a *relation* involving two sets of real numbers. Since the relation includes all real numbers x and y that satisfy the equation, it includes all ordered pairs that could be graphed by using the equation to determine points. Set notation can be used to express the relation as $\{(x,y) \mid y = 2x + 1\}$. Note that the pairs are *ordered pairs*, which means that the order in which the numbers are written is important. For example, the pair (2, 5) is different from the pair (5, 2).

We can think of a relation as a set of ordered pairs, a set of points. Accordingly, we can then define a **relation** as a subset of the set of points that compose the *xy* plane.

3.2 DOMAIN AND RANGE

The concept of function involves three things: domain, range, and rule of correspondence. The **domain** D is the set of all values that the first coordinate can take on. The domain is usually a subset of the set of real numbers. The **range** R is the set of all values that the second coordinate can take on. The range is usually a subset of the set of real numbers.† The rule of correspondence specifies how to pair elements of the range with elements of the domain.

> A **function** *is a set of ordered pairs of real numbers (a relation) such that to each element of the domain there corresponds exactly one element of the range.*

The relation $\{(x, y) \mid y = 2x + 1\}$ is an example of a function. The domain D is the set of all real numbers that can be used for x. The range R is the set of all real numbers that can be used for y. The rule of correspondence between the x's and the y's is as follows: Multiply x by 2 and then add 1 to the product to obtain y. A graph of this function shows that the domain is the set of all real numbers: $D = \{x \mid x \in \text{Reals}\}$. It is also apparent that $R = \{y \mid y \in \text{Reals}\}$; the range, too, is the set of all real numbers.

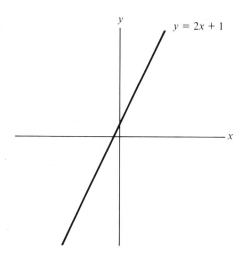

Techniques other than graphing are often used to determine the domain and range of a function, and these methods will be presented in the examples that follow. Throughout the book the following assumption is made: *Unless otherwise stated, the domain and range of a function (or relation) will be the domain and range implied by the rule of correspondence.* This is the largest possible domain and corresponding range. Whenever restrictions are intended, they will be stated explicitly.

If all relations were functions, there would be no need for defining both words. Not all relations are functions. The relation

$$\{(1, 3), (2, 5), (2, 4), (3, -7)\}$$

---

† An exception occurs when trigonometric points are introduced in Chapter 7.

is not a function, because corresponding to the element 2 of the domain are two different elements (5 and 4) of the range.

Graphically, if any vertical line can be passed through two or more points of the relation, then the relation is *not* a function, because this means that there are two *y* values for some *x* value.

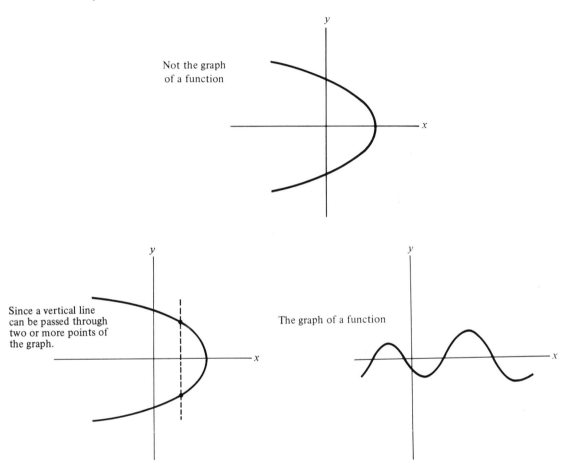

Not the graph
of a function

Since a vertical line
can be passed through
two or more points of
the graph.

The graph of a function

Example 1 *Determine the domain and range of the function below.*

$$\{(1, 2), (2, 5), (3, 17), (5, -3)\}$$

The domain is $\{1, 2, 3, 5\}$, since these are the values that the first coordinate may assume.

The range is $\{2, 5, 17, -3\}$, since these are the values that the second coordinate takes on.

The function in Example 1 was given as a list of points. In reality, most relations and functions are given as equations (such as $y = 2x + 1$) rather than as lists of specific points. There are usually an infinite number of real numbers in both the domain and range of such functions. In view of this, it is easier to determine which real numbers are *not* in the domain or range. Here is the key to determining what numbers are not in the domain of a relation.

> A real number (x) is *not* in the domain of a relation if there is no corresponding real number (y). This can happen four different ways, as shown in the four keys below.

Key 1. *A real number is not in the domain of a relation if that number creates division by zero, because such division is not defined.*

Example. In $y = \dfrac{1}{x}$, x cannot be 0, since 1/0 is not defined; thus there is no y for $x = 0$. Therefore 0 is not in the domain of this relation; all other real numbers are in the domain.

Example. In $y = \dfrac{x^2 - 9}{x + 3}$, x cannot be -3, since 0/0 is not defined. Thus the domain is all the real numbers except -3.

Key 2. *A real number is not in the domain of a relation if the number creates an even root ($\sqrt{}$, $\sqrt[4]{}$, $\sqrt[6]{}$, and so on) of a negative number, because even roots of negative numbers are not real numbers.*

Example. In $y = \sqrt{x - 2}$, x cannot be less than 2, for if $x < 2$, then $x - 2 < 0$ and $\sqrt{x - 2}$ is not a real number. This means there is no real number y corresponding to any number less than 2. The domain is $x \geq 2$.

Key 3. *A real number is not in the domain of a relation if the definition of the relation excludes the number from the domain.*

Example. In the two-part function

$$y = \begin{cases} 3x + 1 & 2 \leq x < 9 \\ x^2 & 9 \leq x \leq 20 \end{cases}$$

the value of y is determined as follows:

$$\begin{cases} y = 3x + 1 & \text{when} \quad 2 \leq x < 9 \\ y = x^2 & \text{when} \quad 9 \leq x \leq 20 \end{cases}$$

For example, if x is 5, then $y = 3(5) + 1 = 16$. In other words, since 5 is between 2 and 9, y is computed as $3x + 1$. On the other hand, if x is 13, then $y = (13)^2 = 169$. That is, since 13 is between 9 and 20, the y

value is computed as x^2. *But if x is 1, there is no rule for determining y.* This means that 1 is not in the domain of this relation. Similarly, if x is 32, there is no corresponding y. So 32 is not in the domain. As you can see from the function itself, the domain includes only the real numbers between 2 and 20 inclusive; that is, the domain is the set of all x such that $2 \leq x \leq 20$. This domain is not implied; it is explicitly stated in the first lines of this example.

Key 4. *An application may naturally exclude certain numbers from the domain.*

Example. The volume (V) of a cube with sides of length x is given by $V = x^3$. Certainly x cannot be negative (or even zero) for this application; a side of a cube cannot have a negative length. Thus the domain is $x > 0$.

Example 2 *Determine the implied domain of $y = \sqrt{x + 4}$.*

We must ensure that $x + 4 \geq 0$, since the square root of a negative number is not a real number (see Key 2). And since $x + 4 \geq 0$ whenever $x \geq -4$, we must insist that $x \geq -4$. Thus the domain is all real numbers x such that $x \geq -4$.

Example 3 *Determine the implied domain of $y = \dfrac{5}{x - 2}$.*

We must ensure that $x - 2 \neq 0$, since division by zero is undefined and thus does not produce a real number (see Key 1). Since $x - 2 \neq 0$ when $x \neq 2$, we insist that $x \neq 2$. Thus the domain is all real numbers x such that $x \neq 2$. In other words, the domain is all real numbers except 2.

Example 4 *Determine the domain of the function given here.*

$$y = \begin{cases} 5x & 1 \leq x < 6 \\ 1 - 2x & 6 \leq x \leq 75 \end{cases}$$

For any real number between 1 and 75, a method is given for obtaining a corresponding y. Thus the domain is $1 \leq x \leq 75$ (see Key 3).

Example 5 *Chirps of a cricket.*

The number of chirps (y) per minute made by a cricket depends on the temperature (x) in degrees Fahrenheit. The relationship is known to be $y = 4x - 160$. Because the number of chirps cannot be less than zero, the formula is valid only when $4x - 160 \geq 0$, that is, when $x \geq 40$. Crickets do not chirp when the temperature is below 40°F. We have seen, then, that the domain of this function is $x \geq 40$ (see Key 4).

The next three examples present three different methods that can be used to determine the domain and range. In each example the function used is $y = x^2$.

Example 6 *Determine the implied domain and range of the function $y = x^2$ by examining the equation.*

For any real value of x supplied, we obtain a real value for y. So there is no restriction on x. The domain of the function is all the real numbers.

Since the y values are obtained by *squaring* the real x values, y can never be negative. And any nonnegative number (y) can be obtained by squaring the proper x. Thus the range of the function is all real $y \geq 0$.

Example 7 *Determine the implied domain and range of the function $y = x^2$ from its graph.*

Here is the graph of $y = x^2$.

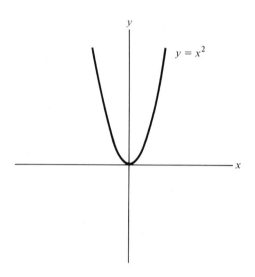

Observe that as you go along the x axis, there is a y corresponding to every x value. This means that x can be any real number; so the domain is all the real numbers. On the other hand, as you go along the y axis, there are no x values corresponding to negative y values. This means y cannot be negative; the range is $y \geq 0$.

Example 8 *Determine the implied range of $y = x^2$ by algebraic manipulation.*

To determine the range, solve for x in terms of y and then see what y values, if any, will not produce a corresponding real number for x.

$$y = x^2$$
$$x^2 = y$$
$$x = \pm\sqrt{y}$$

If y is negative, no real number will be produced as a corresponding x value (see Key 2). Thus the range is $y \geq 0$.

Example 9 *Find the implied domain and range of the function* $y = 2x + 1$.

Note that x can be any real number, since for every real number x there is a corresponding y. Thus the domain is all the real numbers. To find the range, solve for x in terms of y and see what y values, if any, do not produce a corresponding x.

$$y = 2x + 1$$

becomes

$$y - 1 = 2x$$

or

$$x = \frac{y - 1}{2}$$

Now you can see that any real number can be substituted for y in order to produce a corresponding x. So y can be any real number. In other words, the range is all the real numbers. Earlier we determined that the domain was all the real numbers.

In Example 9 we could also have determined the range by examining the function or by graphing it and looking at the graph. But often relations and functions are not written in a form that permits you to determine easily the domain and range by examination or by graph. In such instances, algebraic manipulation is used. The following examples show various techniques for getting $y = \dots$ (solving for y) in order to determine the domain and for getting $x = \dots$ (solving for x) in order to determine the range.

Note that for all relations given in this chapter, when both x and y appear, it is assumed that the domain includes all possible values of x and the range includes all possible values of y. In other words, points will always be (x, y)—never (y, x). On our graphs the x axis will always be horizontal and the y axis will be vertical.

Example 10 *Determine the implied domain and range of* $xy = 1$.

Solve for y by dividing both sides of $xy = 1$ by x. This step yields

$$y = \frac{1}{x}$$

The relation is not defined for $x = 0$. Any other x value is acceptable. Thus the domain is all the real numbers except 0; $D = \{x \mid x \text{ real}, x \neq 0\}$. Furthermore, you can now see that the relation is a function because for any x value supplied there corresponds only one y value.

If the equation $xy = 1$ is solved for x by dividing both sides by y, the result is

$$x = \frac{1}{y}$$

So, similarly, the range is all real numbers y except 0; that is, $R = \{y \mid y \text{ real}, y \neq 0\}$.

Example 11 *Determine the implied domain and range of $y^2 - x = 0$.*

To find the range, solve for x by adding x to both sides of $y^2 - x = 0$. Doing so produces

$$x = y^2$$

It is now clear that any real number can be substituted for y. Thus the range is all the real numbers, or $R = \{y \mid y \in \text{Reals}\}$.

To find the domain, solve for y by first adding x to both sides of the equation $y^2 - x = 0$. This yields

$$y^2 = x$$

Then

$$y = \pm\sqrt{x}$$

The domain includes all $x \geq 0$, or $D = \{x \mid x \text{ real}, x \geq 0\}$. The square root of any $x < 0$ is not a real number. Note that the relation is not a function, since the $\pm$ indicates that for an x value supplied (for instance, $x = 9$), there are two y values ($y = \pm 3$).

Example 12 *Determine the implied domain of $y = \sqrt{\dfrac{x + 3}{x - 8}}$.*

Clearly $x \neq 8$, or division by zero will be implied. Also, we insist that

$$\frac{x + 3}{x - 8} \geq 0$$

in order to avoid $\sqrt{\text{negative}}$. Here is the sign chart for solving this inequality.

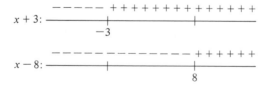

We conclude that

$$\frac{x + 3}{x - 8} > 0$$

when $x < -3$ or when $x > 8$. Note, too, that -3 is acceptable for x because it makes the fraction equal to zero. However, as stated earlier, 8 is not acceptable for x because it creates division by zero. Thus the domain of this function is $D = \{x \mid x \text{ real}, x \leq -3 \text{ or } x > 8\}$.

Example 13 *Determine the implied domain and range of $y = 2 + \sqrt{x}$ by examining the equation as given.*

The domain is $\{x \mid x \text{ real}, x \geq 0\}$, since the square root of any $x < 0$ is not a real number, but the square root of any $x \geq 0$ *is* a real number.

To determine the range, note that when a number is used for x, the y value determined is $2 + \sqrt{x}$. The smallest y value possible is 2, which results when x is 0. And any number greater than 2 can be produced as y by using an appropriate positive value of x. Thus $y \geq 2$; the range is $\{y \mid y \text{ real}, y \geq 2\}$.

Note: Do not square both sides of an equation when seeking domain or range, since squaring may expand the domain and range. In Example 13, $y = 2 + \sqrt{x}$ or $\sqrt{x} = y - 2$, the squared result is $x = y^2 - 4y + 4$. In this result y can be any real number and still produce a corresponding real x. Yet we saw in Example 13 that y cannot be less than 2. Clearly, squaring both sides of the equation expanded the range and produced an error.

Example 14 *Use algebraic manipulation to determine the implied domain and range of $x^2y^2 + y^2 - 9 = 0$.*

To determine the domain, we need to solve for y in terms of x. The equation has two y^2 terms in it and no other y terms. So to solve for y, begin by eliminating the -9 and then factor out the y^2.

$$x^2y^2 + y^2 - 9 = 0$$

becomes

$$x^2y^2 + y^2 = 9$$

and then

$$y^2(x^2 + 1) = 9$$

Now divide both sides by $x^2 + 1$ in order to get y^2 alone.

$$y^2 = \frac{9}{x^2 + 1}$$

Finally,

$$y = \pm\sqrt{\frac{9}{x^2 + 1}}$$

There is no value of x that can be substituted in this form to cause division by zero or the square root of a negative number. So $D = \{x \mid x \in \text{Reals}\}$.

To determine the range, we need to solve for x in terms of y. The equation $x^2y^2 + y^2 - 9 = 0$ has only one term with x in it; so begin by eliminating the y^2 and -9. Add $-y^2 + 9$ to both sides of the equation. The result is

$$x^2y^2 = 9 - y^2$$

Now divide both sides by y^2.

$$x^2 = \frac{9 - y^2}{y^2}$$

Note that y^2 cannot be 0 in the form being created, since you cannot divide by 0. Also, substitute 0 for y in the original equation to see if there can be a corresponding x.

$$x^2(0)^2 + (0)^2 - 9 = 0$$
$$-9 = 0$$

There is no x that can make this statement true. So $y^2 \neq 0$, which means $y \neq 0$. Continuing, we obtain

$$x = \pm \sqrt{\frac{9 - y^2}{y^2}}$$

The fraction

$$\frac{9 - y^2}{y^2}$$

must not be negative, since the square root of a negative number is not a real number. Because y^2 is always positive, our only concern is that $9 - y^2$ not be negative. In other words, exclude from the range all values of y such that

$$9 - y^2 < 0$$

or

$$9 < y^2$$

or

$$y^2 > 9$$

If $y > 3$ or $y < -3$, then $y^2 > 9$. Thus the range is all real numbers y except $y = 0$, $y > 3$, $y < -3$. In other words,

$$R = \{y \mid y \text{ real}, -3 \le y \le 3, y \neq 0\}$$

or

$$R = \{y \mid y \text{ real}, \mid y \mid \leq 3, y \neq 0\}$$

Example 15 *Determine the implied domain and range of $x^2y + xy + 7 = 0$.*
First determine the domain by solving for y in terms of x. Observing that there are two y terms, proceed by eliminating the 7 and then factoring out the y.

$$x^2y + xy + 7 = 0$$
$$x^2y + xy = -7$$
$$y(x^2 + x) = -7$$
$$y = \frac{-7}{x^2 + x}$$

or

$$y = -\frac{7}{x(x + 1)}$$

If $x = 0$ or $x = -1$, then the fraction is not defined. Furthermore, when 0 or -1 is used for x in the original equation, there is no corresponding y. All other x values have corresponding y values. The domain is therefore $\{x \mid x \text{ real}, x \neq 0, x \neq -1\}$.
Now solve for x in terms of y in order to determine the range. The original relation, $x^2y + xy + 7 = 0$, is a quadratic equation in x; that is, it is of the form $ax^2 + bx + c = 0$. Note that it can be rewritten to make this more apparent.

$$yx^2 + yx + 7 = 0$$

where

$$a = y \quad \text{(the coefficient of } x^2)$$
$$b = y \quad \text{(the coefficient of } x)$$
$$c = 7 \quad \text{(the non-}x \text{ term)}$$

The quadratic formula can be used to solve for x, since the equation is quadratic in x. From

$$x = \frac{-b \pm \sqrt{b^2 - 4ac}}{2a}$$

we obtain

$$x = \frac{-y \pm \sqrt{y^2 - 4 \cdot y \cdot 7}}{2y} \qquad y \neq 0$$

or

$$x = \frac{-y \pm \sqrt{y^2 - 28y}}{2y} \qquad y \neq 0$$

If $y = 0$, then the original equation $yx^2 + yx + 7 = 0$ is not quadratic and therefore must not be solved by the quadratic formula. Furthermore, returning to the original equation, a value of 0 for y yields the nonsense equation $7 = 0$. This means, of course, that there is no corresponding x for $y = 0$. So 0 is not in the range of the relation.

The expression $y^2 - 28y$ cannot be negative; otherwise we would have the square root of a negative number. So only y values such that $y^2 - 28y \geq 0$ can be in the range. The expression is equal to zero if $y = 0$ or $y = 28$; y can be 28, but it cannot be zero, as explained above. Now consider that

$$y^2 - 28y > 0$$

if

$$(y)(y - 28) > 0$$

The sign chart is

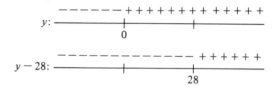

We can see that $(y)(y - 28) > 0$ when $y < 0$ or when $y > 28$. Therefore the range is $\{y \mid y \text{ real}, y < 0 \text{ or } y \geq 28\}$.

Example 16 *Determine the implied domain and range of $x^2y^2 + 5y^2 + 2 = 0$.*

First solve for y in terms of x in order to determine the domain. Although this is a quadratic equation, the two terms with y in them are both y^2 terms. So do not use the quadratic formula. The formula would be used if there were a y^2 term and a y term. With two y^2 terms and no y term, factoring can be used after the constant 2 is eliminated from the left side of the equation.

$$x^2y^2 + 5y^2 + 2 = 0$$
$$x^2y^2 + 5y^2 = -2$$
$$y^2(x^2 + 5) = -2$$
$$y^2 = \frac{-2}{x^2 + 5}$$
$$y = \pm\sqrt{\frac{-2}{x^2 + 5}}$$

Since $x^2 \geq 0$ for all real numbers x, then $x^2 + 5 \geq 0$ for all real numbers x. This means that $\dfrac{-2}{x^2 + 5}$ is negative for all real numbers x. And since this fraction is under a radical indicating square root, there are no x values that produce real y values. The "domain" is the empty set. It follows that the range is also the empty set, for there are no y values. In fact, the equation $x^2y^2 + 5y^2 + 2 = 0$ does not define a relation, since there are no ordered pairs (x, y).

EXERCISES 3.2

Answers to starred exercises are given in the back of the book.

1. Determine which of the following are functions.
    *(a) $y = x + 3$ (b) $\{(1, 2)\}$
    *(c) $\{(0, 1), (1, 0)\}$ (d) $\{(1, 0), (1, 1)\}$
    *(e) $\{(1, 2), (3, 4), (-1, -2)\}$ (f) $y = x^2$
    *(g) $x^2 + y^2 = 25$ (h) $y^2 = 81 - x^2$

    *(i) $y = \pm x$ (j) $y = \dfrac{x + 8}{x - 2}$

2. Determine the implied domain of each function.
    *(a) $y = 3x + 2$ (b) $y = 5 - x$
    *(c) $y = x^2 + 7x - 2$ (d) $y = x^2 - 8x$
    *(e) $y = \sqrt{x}$ (f) $y = \sqrt{x - 8}$
    *(g) $y = \sqrt{3x + 2}$ (h) $y = \sqrt{1 - 2x}$
    *(i) $y = \sqrt{x^2 + 3}$ (j) $y = \sqrt{x^2 - 36}$

    *(k) $y = \dfrac{x + 1}{x}$ (l) $y = \dfrac{10}{x}$

    *(m) $y = \dfrac{x}{5 - x}$ (n) $y = \dfrac{3x}{x + 2}$

    *(o) $y = \dfrac{x + 1}{x^2 - 9}$ (p) $y = \dfrac{x - 2}{x^2 - 4}$

    *(q) $y = 5 - \sqrt{x - 8}$ (r) $y = \dfrac{1}{x^2 + 3} - \sqrt{18 + x^2}$

    *(s) $y = \sqrt{x} + \dfrac{1}{x - 1}$ (t) $y = \sqrt{x + 1} + \dfrac{1}{x}$

    *(u) $y = \dfrac{x + 1}{x^2 - 7x + 12}$ (v) $y = \dfrac{x - 5}{x^2 + 2x - 15}$

3. Determine the domain of each function.
    *(a) $y = \begin{cases} 3x + 7 & 0 \leq x < 9 \\ 1 - 8x & 9 \leq x \leq 50 \end{cases}$

(b) $\quad y = \begin{cases} \sqrt{x + 5} & -5 \le x < 0 \\ \sqrt{x + 2} & 0 \le x \le 7 \end{cases}$

*(c) $\quad y = \begin{cases} x^2 & -10 \le x < 0 \\ x^3 & 0 \le x \end{cases}$

(d) $\quad y = \begin{cases} x^2 + 3 & x \le 0 \\ 9x - 4 & 0 < x \end{cases}$

*(e) $\quad y = \begin{cases} 2x & 0 \le x < 2 \\ 5x & 2 \le x < 5 \\ 9x & 5 \le x < 9 \end{cases}$

(f) $\quad y = \begin{cases} x^3 & 1 \le x < 3 \\ x^2 & 3 \le x < 9 \\ x & 9 \le x < 27 \end{cases}$

*(g) $\quad y = \begin{cases} \dfrac{3}{x + 1} & 0 \le x \le 5 \\ \sqrt{\dfrac{x^2 + 7}{x^2}} & 5 < x < 8 \end{cases}$

(h) $\quad y = \begin{cases} 1 - x & 0 \le x \le 6 \\ x & 10 \le x \le 12 \end{cases}$

*(i) $\quad y = \begin{cases} 3x & 1 \le x \le 8 \\ x^2 & 11 \le x \le 15 \end{cases}$

4. Determine the domain of the relation that is suggested by the application setting.

   *(a) The area A of a square with sides of length x is given by $A = x^2$.

   (b) When an object is dropped, the distance s it falls in t seconds is given by $s = 16t^2$. Consider here that s is a function of t; that is, let t be the first coordinate.

   *(c) If you earn \$4.00 an hour at work, then your gross income y for working x hours is $y = 4x$ dollars.

   (d) If the length of a rectangle is x units and the width is $x - 5$, then the perimeter is $P = 4x - 10$. Such a function gives the perimeter for any rectangle in which the width is 5 units less than the length.

   *(e) The number of degrees D in each interior angle of a regular polygon of n sides is

   $$D = \left(\frac{n - 2}{n}\right) 180$$

   By polygons we mean triangles, rectangles, pentagons, hexagons, and so on.

5. Determine the domain and range of each relation by studying the graph. Notice that arrows are used here to indicate that the curve continues indefinitely in a particular direction. Each mark indicates one unit.

*(a)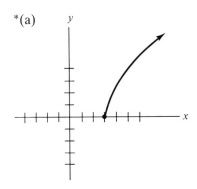

(b)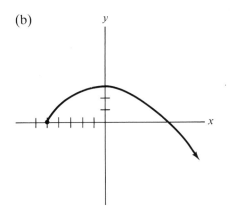

*(c)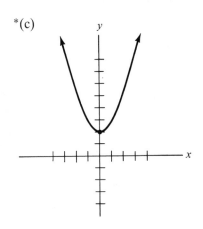

(d)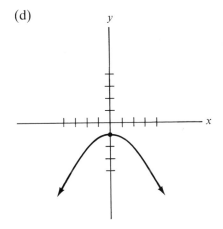

*(e)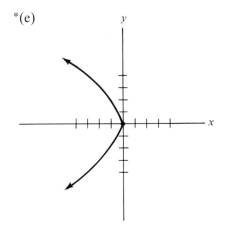

(f)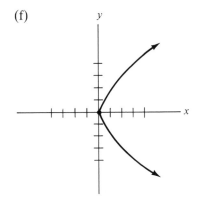

*(g)

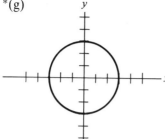

(h)

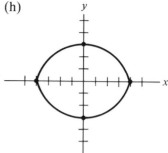

*(i)

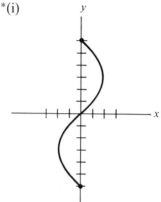

(j)

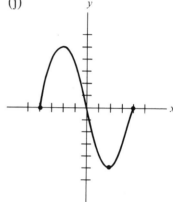

6. Determine the implied domain of each function.

*(a) $y = \sqrt{\dfrac{x - 5}{x + 2}}$

(b) $y = \sqrt{\dfrac{x + 1}{x + 4}}$

*(c) $y = \sqrt{x^2 + 5x - 14}$

(d) $y = \sqrt{x^2 - 4x - 12}$

*(e) $y = \sqrt{\dfrac{x^2}{x + 1}}$

(f) $y = \sqrt{\dfrac{x - 7}{x^2}}$

7. Determine the implied domain and range of each relation. Do not square both sides of any equation, because that process often does not produce equivalent equations.

*(a) $x + y = 8$

(b) $x = 7y + 2$

*(c) $3xy = 7$

(d) $y = \sqrt{x} + 3$

*(e) $y = -\sqrt{x}$

(f) $y = -\sqrt{x - 6}$

*(g) $x^3 - y = 0$

(h) $y = x^2 + 1$

*(i) $y^2 - 4x = 0$

(j) $x = y^2$

*(k) $x + xy - 4y = 5$

(l) $3x - xy + y = 1$

*(m) $xy + y - x = 0$

(n) $xy - x + 1 = 0$

*(o) $y = \sqrt{-x}$

(p) $y = \sqrt[3]{-x}$

*(q) $y = x^{1/3}$ (r) $y = 5x^{1/3} + 2$
*(s) $y = x^{3/2}$ (t) $y = 5 + x^{3/2}$
*(u) $y = x^{1/2} + 1$ (v) $y = x^{1/2} - 2$
*(w) $y = 5 - x^{3/2}$ (x) $y = x^{3/2} - 5$

8. Determine the implied domain and range of each relation. Do not square both sides of any equation because often that process does not produce equivalent equations (as noted on page 103).

*(a) $x^2 + y^2 = 16$ (b) $x^2 + y^2 + 9 = 0$
*(c) $x^2 - y^2 = 16$ (d) $4x^2 + 9y^2 = 36$
*(e) $y = -\sqrt{x^2 - 1}$ (f) $x = -\sqrt{9 - y^2}$
*(g) $x^2y + 9y = 6$ (h) $x^2y^2 + y^2 - 13 = 0$
*(i) $xy^2 - 2x - 16 = 0$ (j) $x^2y - 3y - 12 = 0$
*(k) $x^2y + xy - 4 = 0$ (l) $xy^2 - 4x + 7y = 0$
*(m) $x^2y^2 - 9x^2 - 4y^2 = 0$ (n) $x^2y^2 - 16x^2 - 9y^2 = 0$
*(o) $xy^2 + 3x - 7y = 0$ (p) $x^2y^2 - 4y^2 = 7x$
*(q) $x^2y^2 + 16xy - 4 = 0$ (r) $x^2y^2 - 9xy + 16 = 0$
*(s) $y = x^2 + 5x + 4$ (t) $y = x^2 + 7x + 6$

3.3 FUNCTION NOTATION

We have considered the definition and concept of function and we have determined the domain and range of functions. In many calculus situations, you will also need the special notation of functions, which is presented next.

To begin, functions are named by letters. The letter f is most popular when one function is being discussed; f and g are often used when two functions are presented together. Other letters can be used. In Chapter 4 you will see the use of function names that fit the application, such as P for profit, R for revenue, C for cost, and v for velocity.

A function f associates with each element of its domain exactly one element of its range. The notation $f(x)$ is frequently used to denote the second element of the ordered pair whose first element is x. Thus, ordered pairs take the form $(x, f(x))$. The notation $f(x)$ is read "f of x" or "f at x." It is the *value of f at x.* The correspondence can be seen as

$$x \xrightarrow{\ f\ } f(x)$$

If the function $y = 2x + 1$ is written as $f(x) = 2x + 1$, then

$$f(x) = 2(x) + 1$$

so for $x = 3$,

$$f(3) = 2(3) + 1 = 7$$

Symbolically,

$$3 \xrightarrow{f} 7$$

or

$$(3) \xrightarrow{f} 2(3) + 1 = 7$$

Note that $f(3)$ is the value of f at 3; here $f(3)$ means the same as "the y value in $y = 2x + 1$ when x is 3."

Example 17 *If $f(x) = 3x^2 + 5x + 2$, find $f(0)$, $f(1)$, $f(-1)$, $f(x + 1)$, and $f(r - 2)$.*

$$f(x) = 3(x)^2 + 5(x) + 2$$
$$f(0) = 3(0)^2 + 5(0) + 2 = 2$$
$$f(1) = 3(1)^2 + 5(1) + 2 = 10$$
$$f(-1) = 3(-1)^2 + 5(-1) + 2 = 0$$
$$f(x + 1) = 3(x + 1)^2 + 5(x + 1) + 2$$
$$= 3(x^2 + 2x + 1) + 5x + 5 + 2$$
$$= 3x^2 + 11x + 10$$

$$f(r - 2) = 3(r - 2)^2 + 5(r - 2) + 2$$
$$= 3(r^2 - 4r + 4) + 5r - 10 + 2$$
$$= 3r^2 - 7r + 4$$

Example 18 *Let $f(x) = x^2 + 2x + 5$. Let h represent a positive number. Find each value.*

(a) $f(x + h)$ (b) $f(x + h) - f(x)$ (c) $\dfrac{f(x + h) - f(x)}{h}$

(a) $f(x + h) = (x + h)^2 + 2(x + h) + 5$
$$= x^2 + 2xh + h^2 + 2x + 2h + 5$$

(b) $f(x + h) - f(x) = [x^2 + 2xh + h^2 + 2x + 2h + 5] - [x^2 + 2x + 5]$
$$= x^2 + 2xh + h^2 + 2x + 2h + 5 - x^2 - 2x - 5$$
$$= 2xh + h^2 + 2h$$

(c)
$$\frac{f(x + h) - f(x)}{h} = \frac{2xh + h^2 + 2h}{h}$$

$$= \frac{h(2x + h + 2)}{h}$$

$$= 2x + h + 2$$

Note that the division by h can be done because h is a positive number and therefore not equal to zero.

Example 19   *Given $f(x) = x^2$ and $a = 3$, find the value of*

$$\frac{f(x) - f(a)}{x - a} \qquad x \neq a$$

We must assume that $x \neq a$, that is, that $x \neq 3$. Otherwise division by zero will be suggested.

$$\frac{f(x) - f(a)}{x - a} = \frac{(x^2) - (3^2)}{x - 3}$$

$$= \frac{x^2 - 9}{x - 3}$$

$$= \frac{(x + 3)(x - 3)}{(x - 3)}$$

$$= x + 3$$

Two functions can be added, subtracted, multiplied, or divided for all values in the domain common to both functions. Here are the notation and definition of the operations.

Addition:	$(f + g)(x) = f(x) + g(x)$
Subtraction:	$(f - g)(x) = f(x) - g(x)$
Multiplication:	$(f \cdot g)(x) = f(x) \cdot g(x)$
Division:	$(f \div g)(x) = \dfrac{f(x)}{g(x)} \qquad g(x) \neq 0$

In each case, the domain of the resulting function consists of all numbers common to the domains of f and g, except in the case of $(f \div g)(x)$, where x values for which $g(x) = 0$ are excluded.

Example 20 Let $f(x) = x^2$ and $g(x) = \sqrt{x}$. Determine $f + g$, $f - g$, $f \cdot g$, and $f \div g$.

$$(f + g)(x) = f(x) + g(x) = x^2 + \sqrt{x}$$

$$(f - g)(x) = f(x) - g(x) = x^2 - \sqrt{x}$$

$$(f \cdot g)(x) = f(x) \cdot g(x) = x^2\sqrt{x} = x^2 x^{1/2} = x^{5/2}$$

$$(f \div g)(x) = \frac{f(x)}{g(x)} = \frac{x^2}{\sqrt{x}} = \frac{x^2}{x^{1/2}} = x^{3/2} \qquad (x \neq 0)$$

Since the implied domain of f is all the real numbers and the implied domain of g is all the nonnegative real numbers, the domains of $f + g$, $f - g$, and $f \cdot g$ are $\{x \mid x \geq 0\}$. But $g(x) = 0$ when $x = 0$; so the domain of $f \div g$ is $\{x \mid x > 0\}$.

EXERCISES 3.3

*1. If $f(x) = 3x - 5$, find each value.
   (a) $f(1)$ (b) $f(2)$
   (c) $f(0)$ (d) $f(-5)$
   (e) $f(a)$ (f) $f(\tfrac{1}{2})$
   (g) $f(-\tfrac{1}{2})$ (h) $f(3m)$
   (i) $f(x + 1)$ (j) $f(x - 5)$

2. If $f(x) = x^2 + 8x - 1$, find each value.
   *(a) $f(2)$ (b) $f(3)$
   *(c) $f(10)$ (d) $f(0)$
   *(e) $f(-1)$ (f) $f(-3)$
   *(g) $f(t)$ (h) $f(\tfrac{1}{2})$
   *(i) $f(-\tfrac{1}{4})$ (j) $f(x + 2)$

3. Compute the specified functional value and then simplify the result.
   *(a) Let $F(x) = x^2 - \dfrac{2}{x}$. Determine $F(\sqrt{2})$.

   (b) Let $F(x) = \dfrac{8}{\sqrt{x}}$. Determine $F(2)$.

   *(c) Let $G(x) = x^3 - x^2 + x + 1$. Determine $G(\sqrt{7})$.

   (d) Let $G(x) = \dfrac{x + 1}{x - 1}$. Determine $G\left(\dfrac{3}{2}\right)$.

   *(e) Let $g(x) = x^{3/2} + x^{2/3}$. Determine $g(64)$.

4. Compute $f(x + h)$ for each function and simplify. Use the binomial theorem when appropriate.
   *(a) $f(x) = 7x + 1$ (b) $f(x) = 5x - 3$

*(c) $f(x) = x^2 + 3x - 4$ (d) $f(x) = x^2 - 5x + 2$

*(e) $f(x) = x^3$ (f) $f(x) = x^4$

*(g) $f(x) = x^5$ (h) $f(x) = x^6$

5. For each function below, compute and simplify the value of

$$\frac{f(x + h) - f(x)}{h} \qquad h \neq 0$$

*(a) $f(x) = x$ (b) $f(x) = 6x + 7$

*(c) $f(x) = x^2 + 3x + 7$ (d) $f(x) = x^2 - 2x + 4$

*(e) $f(x) = 3x^2 + 5x - 1$ (f) $f(x) = 1 - 7x - 2x^2$

*(g) $f(x) = x^3$ (h) $f(x) = x^3 + 3x^2 + 4x - 7$

*(i) $f(x) = \dfrac{1}{x}$ (j) $f(x) = \dfrac{3}{x}$

*(k) $f(x) = \dfrac{1}{2x}$ (l) $f(x) = \dfrac{2}{x - 1}$

*(m) $f(x) = 12$ (n) $f(x) = -10x$

6. For each function, compute and simplify the value of

$$\frac{f(x) - f(a)}{x - a} \qquad x \neq a$$

*(a) $f(x) = x;\ a = 6$ (b) $f(x) = 3x + 4;\ a = 2$

*(c) $f(x) = x^2 - 3;\ a = 5$ (d) $f(x) = 2x^2 + 3x + 4;\ a = 5$

*(e) $f(x) = x^3;\ a = 4$ (f) $f(x) = 5x^2 - 8;\ a = 3$

7. Determine the implied domain of each function.

*(a) $f(x) = \dfrac{5}{x + 2}$ (b) $f(x) = \dfrac{7}{1 - 8x}$

*(c) $f(x) = 6x^{1/2}$ (d) $f(x) = -x^{3/2}$

*(e) $g(x) = x^2 - 19$ (f) $g(x) = \sqrt[3]{x} - 2$

*(g) $g(x) = \dfrac{x}{x^2 - 9}$ (h) $g(x) = \dfrac{\sqrt{x}}{x^2 - 9}$

*(i) $h(x) = \sqrt{-x}$ (j) $h(x) = \sqrt{1 - x}$

8. Determine $f + g$, $f - g$, $f \cdot g$, and $f \div g$. Specify the implied domain of each of the four new functions.

*(a) $f(x) = x,\ g(x) = 3$

(b) $f(x) = x^2,\ g(x) = x + 1$

*(c) $f(x) = x + 2,\ g(x) = x^2 + 9$

(d) $f(x) = 5x^2,\ g(x) = \sqrt{x}$

*(e) $f(x) = \sqrt{x},\ g(x) = \sqrt[3]{x}$

(f) $f(x) = \dfrac{1}{x}, g(x) = \dfrac{1}{x + 1}$

*(g) $f(x) = \dfrac{\sqrt{x}}{x - 3}, g(x) = \dfrac{x - 7}{\sqrt{x}}$

*9. Hooke's law states that if a spring is stretched x inches beyond its natural length, then the force pulling back the spring is kx pounds. The number k is constant for a given spring. Writing F for force, we have the function

$$F(x) = kx$$

Suppose that a spring has a natural length of 15 inches and that a force of 6 pounds is required to stretch the spring 2 inches.

(a) Determine the constant k.

(b) Write the function.

(c) What force is required to stretch the spring 4 inches beyond its natural length?

(d) What force is required to stretch the spring from its natural length to a length of 22 inches?

(e) A force of 36 pounds is applied to stretch the spring. What is the length of the stretched spring?

3.4 GRAPHS

In Chapter 2 we graphed straight lines and parabolas. If function notation and terminology are applied to the equations that yield lines and parabolas, we obtain two important classes of functions. But except for the new name and notation, we know these functions.

> **Linear functions**
> $f(x) = mx + b$

The graph of a linear function is a straight line with slope m and y intercept $(0, b)$. If $m = 0$, the function becomes $f(x) = b$, a **constant function,** the graph of which is a horizontal line. The domain of any linear function is all the reals. The range (except for constant functions) is all the reals.†

> **Quadratic functions**
> $f(x) = ax^2 + bx + c \qquad a \neq 0$

---

† Equations of the form $x = c$ ($c =$ constant) are not functions; their graphs are *vertical* lines.

The graph of a quadratic function is a parabola. If $a > 0$, it opens upward from minimum point at $x = -b/2a$. If $a < 0$, it opens downward from maximum point at $x = -b/2a$. The y intercept is $(0, c)$. The graph crosses the x axis where $ax^2 + bx + c = 0$. The domain of any quadratic function is all the reals. The range is $y \geq f(-b/2a)$ if $a > 0$ or $y \leq f(-b/2a)$ if $a < 0$. This is illustrated by the graphs shown here.

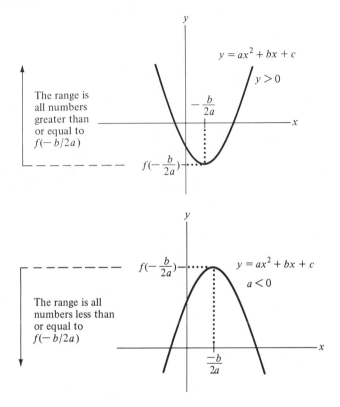

The preceding statement, that the graph of $f(x) = ax^2 + bx + c$ crosses the x axis where $ax^2 + bx + c = 0$, suggests the general idea of the *zeros of a function*.

> The **zeros of a function** $y = f(x)$ are the numbers for which $f(x) = 0$.

Example 21 *Determine the zeros of the linear function $f(x) = 3x + 2$ and the quadratic function $g(x) = x^2 + 7x + 2$.*

For $f(x) = 3x + 2$, the zeros are the values of x for which $3x + 2 = 0$. Solving this equation yields $x = -\frac{2}{3}$; so $-\frac{2}{3}$ is the only zero of f.

For $g(x) = x^2 + 7x + 2$, the zeros are all of the values of x for which

$x^2 + 7x + 2 = 0$. The expression $x^2 + 7x + 2$ cannot be factored by the usual means; so we use the quadratic formula to obtain the two zeros.

$$x = \frac{-7 \pm \sqrt{41}}{2}$$

Now let us consider some kinds of functions we have not graphed before.

Absolute value function
$$f(x) = |x|$$

The domain of $f(x) = |x|$ is all the reals. The range is all the nonnegative reals, because $|x| \geq 0$ for all x. Here is a graph of the function, obtained by selecting several values for x and obtaining corresponding values for $f(x)$.

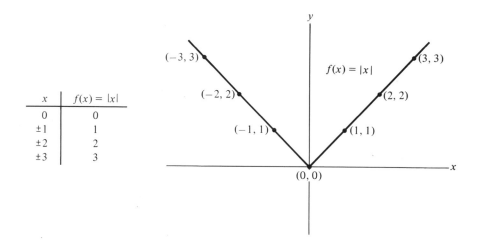

x	$f(x) = |x|$
0	0
± 1	1
± 2	2
± 3	3

In Exercise 6 you will have an opportunity to obtain the graph of $y = |x|$ by using a definition of $|x|$ suggested in Section 1.7.

Square root function
$$f(x) = \sqrt{x}$$

The domain of $f(x) = \sqrt{x}$ is $x \geq 0$ only. The range is $y \geq 0$. The graph is sketched next.

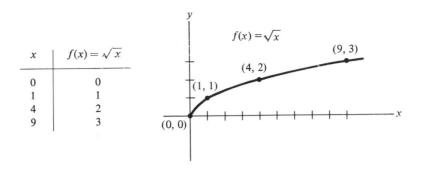

x	$f(x) = \sqrt{x}$
0	0
1	1
4	2
9	3

Greatest integer function
$$f(x) = [\![x]\!]$$

The notation $[\![x]\!]$ means the greatest integer not exceeding x. So $f(x) = [\![x]\!]$ is the **greatest integer function**. For each value of x supplied, the value of $f(x)$ obtained is the largest integer not exceeding x. This function is used extensively in computer programming, where truncation to the lower integer often occurs rather than rounding off to the nearer integer. A roundoff can be obtained using the greatest integer function by specifying $[\![x + .5]\!]$.

Note that $[\![-0.4]\!]$ is -1, not 0. Zero is greater than -0.4 whereas -1 is not greater than -0.4. Thus -1 is the greatest integer not exceeding -0.4. Similarly, $[\![-1.3]\!]$ is -2 rather than -1.

The domain of $f(x) = [\![x]\!]$ is the set of all real numbers. The range is the set of integers.

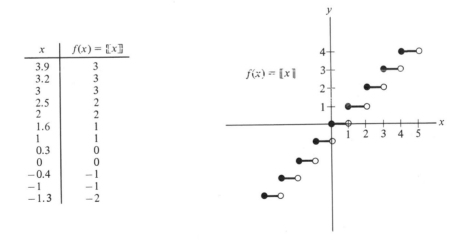

x	$f(x) = [\![x]\!]$
3.9	3
3.2	3
3	3
2.5	2
2	2
1.6	1
1	1
0.3	0
0	0
-0.4	-1
-1	-1
-1.3	-2

Notice the use of open circles to specify points that are not included, for example, $(1, 0)$ and $(2, 1)$.

Cube function
$$f(x) = x^3$$

The domain of $f(x) = x^3$ is all the reals. The range is also all the reals. The graph is sketched next.

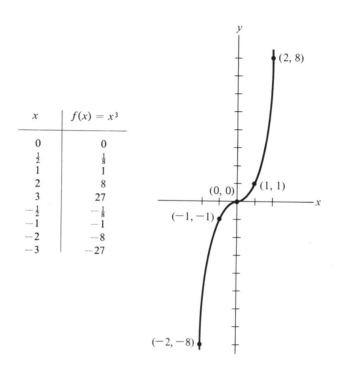

x	$f(x) = x^3$
0	0
$\frac{1}{2}$	$\frac{1}{8}$
1	1
2	8
3	27
$-\frac{1}{2}$	$-\frac{1}{8}$
-1	-1
-2	-8
-3	-27

In Section 3.2 we introduced two-part and three-part functions as examples of functions whose definitions excluded numbers from the domain. The next two examples include graphs of such functions.

Example 22 *Sketch the graph of the function*

$$f(x) = \begin{cases} 2x & x \geq 3 \\ 6 & 0 \leq x < 3 \end{cases}$$

For $x \geq 3$, the values of $f(x)$ are computed as $f(x) = 2x$. For $0 \leq x < 3$, $f(x)$ is 6. The function is only defined for $x \geq 0$. Thus the domain is $x \geq 0$. The range is, from the graph, $f(x) \geq 6$.

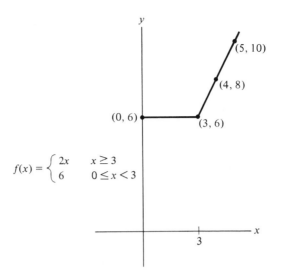

$$f(x) = \begin{cases} 2x & x \geq 3 \\ 6 & 0 \leq x < 3 \end{cases}$$

Example 23   *Sketch the graph of the function*

$$f(x) = \begin{cases} -x - 2 & -2 \leq x \leq -1 \\ x & -1 < x \leq 1 \\ 2 - x & 1 < x \leq 2 \end{cases}$$

The domain is $-2 \leq x \leq 2$, since the function is only defined for x between -2 and 2. The range, from the graph, is $-1 \leq f(x) \leq 1$.

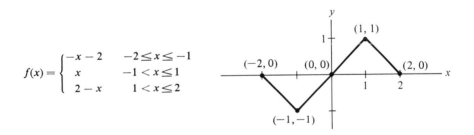

Example 24   *Sketch the graph of the function*

$$f(x) = \begin{cases} 3 & 0 \leq x < 4 \\ x & 4 \leq x \leq 7 \end{cases}$$

The graph:

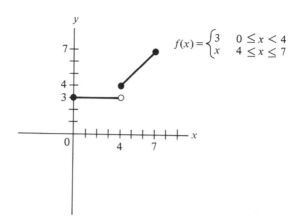

$$f(x) = \begin{cases} 3 & 0 \le x < 4 \\ x & 4 \le x \le 7 \end{cases}$$

From $x = 0$ to $x = 4$ (but excluding 4) the graph is of the line $y = 3$. Then at $x = 4$ the graph jumps up to 4 (for y) and continues on as the graph of the line $y = x$ from $x = 4$ to $x = 7$. An open circle is used to show that the point $(4, 3)$ is excluded.

The next example features a graph of a *hyperbola*. Hyperbolas will be studied in detail in Chapter 8.

Example 25   *Graph* $g(x) = \dfrac{1}{x}$.

Immediately we note that $x \ne 0$; the domain includes all the real numbers except 0.

The points shown in the following table were obtained by using for x the numbers 1, 2, 3, 4, $\frac{1}{2}$, $\frac{1}{3}$, and $\frac{1}{4}$. Too, if x values of -1, -2, -3, -4, $-\frac{1}{2}$, $-\frac{1}{3}$, and $-\frac{1}{4}$ are supplied, then $g(x)$ will be -1, $-\frac{1}{2}$, $-\frac{1}{3}$, $-\frac{1}{4}$, -2, -3, and -4, respectively.

x	$g(x) = 1/x$
1	1
2	1/2
3	1/3
4	1/4
1/2	2
1/3	3
1/4	4

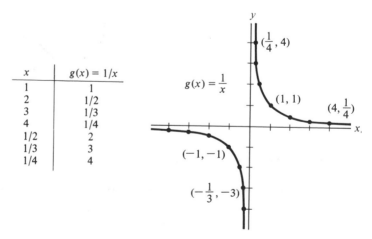

Note that as the magnitude of x gets larger, the graph of function g gets closer to the line $y = 0$ (the x axis). However, the curve never actually reaches the line $y = 0$. We call the line $y = 0$ an **asymptote** of the curve $g(x) = 1/x$; it is a line that the curve approaches. Similarly, as the magnitude of $g(x)$ gets larger, the curve approaches the line $x = 0$ (the y axis). This means that the line $x = 0$ is also an asymptote of $g(x) = 1/x$.

From the graph you can see that the range includes all the real numbers except 0.

The section ends with a most interesting type of function and its graph.

Example 26   *Graph* $f(x) = \dfrac{(x + 2)(x - 3)}{(x - 3)}$.

For all values of x except 3, the factor of $x - 3$ can be divided out to reduce $f(x)$ to $x + 2$. When $x = 3$, the function is not defined. The graph is a line with a hole in it, the hole being the missing point $(3, 5)$. The domain of f is all the real numbers except 3. The range is all the reals except 5.

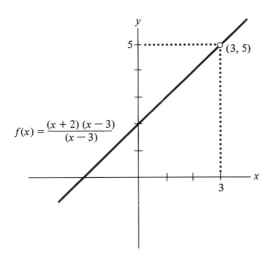

If the function definition is extended to let $f(3) = 5$, then the graph will have no gap in it. The domain and range will both be all the reals. *But*, this would be a *different function* because the domain and range are not the same as those of f; so give this new function a different name, such as h.

$$h(x) = \begin{cases} \dfrac{(x + 2)(x - 3)}{(x - 3)} & x \neq 3 \\[2mm] 5 & x = 3 \end{cases}$$

Note that the original function could have been given as

$$f(x) = \frac{x^2 - x - 6}{x - 3}$$

in which case factoring would have been the first step.

Note on graphs:

It is assumed that a graph continues indefinitely in each direction, *unless* it is made to begin or end by the use of a closed or open circular dot. For example,

1. The graph in Example 23 begins at $(-2, 0)$ and ends at $(2, 0)$.
2. The graph in Example 22 begins at $(0, 6)$ but does not end. Notice how it passes through $(5, 10)$ and continues.
3. The graph in Example 25 continues indefinitely in four directions.
4. The graph in Example 26 continues indefinitely in two directions.

Some people prefer to use *arrows* at the "ends" of their graph sketches when the graph continues indefinitely.

EXERCISES 3.4

1. Graph each linear function.
    *(a) $f(x) = 3x + 2$
    *(c) $f(x) = -x - 3$
    *(e) $f(x) = 5$
    *(g) $f(x) = -4$
    (b) $f(x) = 2x - 7$
    (d) $f(x) = 1 - 8x$
    (f) $f(x) = 0$
    (h) $f(x) = -x$

2. Graph each quadratic function.
    *(a) $f(x) = x^2$
    *(c) $f(x) = x^2 + 4x + 1$
    *(e) $f(x) = -x^2$
    *(g) $f(x) = 1 - x^2$
    *(i) $f(x) = x^2 + 3x$
    *(k) $f(x) = 2x^2 - 6x + 5$
    (b) $f(x) = x^2 + 2$
    (d) $f(x) = x^2 - 6x + 3$
    (f) $f(x) = -x^2 + 8x + 2$
    (h) $f(x) = 5 + x^2$
    (j) $f(x) = x^2 - 4x$
    (l) $f(x) = -3x^2 - 12x + 1$

3. Determine the zeros of each function. Do not graph.
    *(a) $f(x) = 3x + 17$
    *(c) $f(x) = 1 - 3x$
    *(e) $f(x) = 7$
    *(g) $f(x) = x^2 - 16$
    *(i) $f(x) = x^2 + 25$
    (b) $f(x) = 5x - 2$
    (d) $f(x) = 5 - 4x$
    (f) $f(x) = -9$
    (h) $f(x) = x^2 - 3$
    (j) $f(x) = x^2 - 8x$

*(k) $f(x) = 5x - x^2$ (l) $f(x) = (x - 7)(x + 3)$

*(m) $f(x) = x(x - 1)(x + 5)$ (n) $f(x) = x^2$

*(o) $f(x) = \sqrt{x - 6}$ (p) $f(x) = \sqrt{3x + 10}$

*(q) $f(x) = \sqrt{x^2 - 4}$ (r) $f(x) = \sqrt{6 - x^2}$

*(s) $f(x) = \dfrac{x - 7}{x + 3}$ (t) $f(x) = \dfrac{3x + 5}{2x - 9}$

*(u) $f(x) = \dfrac{1 + 7x}{3x - 4}$ (v) $f(x) = \dfrac{9 - 2x}{8x + 5}$

*(w) $f(x) = x^{1/3} - 2x^{4/3}$ (x) $f(x) = 2x^{1/3} - 2$

*(y) $f(x) = 2x^{1/2} - 6x^{3/2}$ (z) $f(x) = 6x^{1/2} - 3x^{3/2}$

4.   Graph each function and give its domain and range. Write the equations of asymptotes whenever they occur.

*(a) $f(x) = |x + 2|$ (b) $f(x) = |x - 1|$

*(c) $f(x) = 3|x|$ (d) $f(x) = -|x|$

*(e) $f(x) = \dfrac{1}{x^2}$ (f) $f(x) = \dfrac{1}{x - 2}$

*(g) $f(x) = \dfrac{1}{x + 1}$ (h) $f(x) = x^3$

*(i) $f(x) = \sqrt{x}$ (j) $f(x) = \sqrt{x - 2}$

*(k) $f(x) = \dfrac{(x + 5)(x + 2)}{(x + 2)}$ (l) $f(x) = \dfrac{(x - 4)(x + 1)}{(x - 4)}$

*(m) $f(x) = \dfrac{x^2 - 5x + 4}{x - 1}$ (n) $f(x) = \dfrac{x^2 + 8x + 15}{x + 3}$

*(o) $f(x) = \dfrac{x^3}{x^2}$ (p) $f(x) = \dfrac{x - 2}{x - 2}$

*(q) $f(x) = \dfrac{x^3}{x}$ (r) $f(x) = \dfrac{(x - 1)^3}{(x - 1)^2}$

*(s) $f(x) = [\![\,|x|\,]\!]$ (t) $g(x) = |[\![x]\!]|$

5.   Graph each function and give its domain and range.

*(a) $f(x) = \begin{cases} 2 & x \geq 0 \\ x + 2 & -3 \leq x < 0 \end{cases}$

(b) $f(x) = \begin{cases} x & x \geq 0 \\ -x & -4 \leq x < 0 \end{cases}$

*(c) $h(x) = \begin{cases} -x & x \geq 0 \\ x & x < 0 \end{cases}$

(d) $g(x) = \begin{cases} x^2 & x > 0 \\ 0 & x = 0 \\ -x^2 & x < 0 \end{cases}$

*(e) $\quad F(x) = \begin{cases} [\![x]\!] & x \geq 0 \\ -[\![x]\!] & x < 0 \end{cases}$

(f) $\quad G(x) = \begin{cases} |x| & x \geq 0 \\ -|x| & x < 0 \end{cases}$

*(g) $\quad f(x) = \begin{cases} |x - 1| & 0 \leq x \leq 4 \\ 4 & x < 0 \end{cases}$

(h) $\quad g(x) = \begin{cases} \dfrac{1}{x} & x > 0 \\ x^3 & x < 0 \end{cases}$

*(i) $\quad g(x) = \begin{cases} \sqrt{x} & x \geq 0 \\ x^2 & x < 0 \end{cases}$

(j) $\quad f(x) = \begin{cases} x & 0 \leq x < 3 \\ x + 1 & 3 \leq x \leq 5 \end{cases}$

*(k) $\quad g(x) = \begin{cases} x + 1 & 0 \leq x < 2 \\ x^2 & 2 \leq x \leq 3 \end{cases}$

(l) $\quad G(x) = \begin{cases} x & 0 \leq x < 1 \\ x - 1 & 1 \leq x < 2 \\ x - 2 & 2 \leq x < 3 \\ x - 3 & 3 \leq x < 4 \end{cases}$

*(m) $\quad F(x) = \begin{cases} 1 & x < 1 \\ 2 - x & 1 \leq x \leq 3 \\ -1 & 3 < x \leq 5 \\ x - 6 & 5 < x \leq 8 \\ 2 & x > 8 \end{cases}$

(n) $\quad h(x) = \begin{cases} x + 2 & -2 \leq x \leq -1 \\ -x & -1 < x \leq 1 \\ x - 2 & 1 < x \leq 3 \\ 4 - x & 3 < x \leq 4 \end{cases}$

6. The graph of $y = |x|$ can be obtained by recalling the definition of absolute value from Section 1.7—namely,

$$|x| = \begin{cases} x & x \geq 0 \\ -x & x < 0 \end{cases}$$

Use this definition to sketch the graph of $y = |x|$.

3.5 COMPOSITION OF FUNCTIONS

The **composite function** $(f \circ g)(x)$, read "f circle g of x," "f composition g of x," or "f of g of x," is defined by

$$(f \circ g)(x) = f(g(x))$$

The domain of $f \circ g$ contains all numbers x in the domain of g for which $g(x)$ is in the domain of f.

Example 27   If $f(x) = 7x + 1$ and $g(x) = x^2 - 4$, determine $(f \circ g)(3)$.

$$(f \circ g)(3) = f(g(3))$$
$$= f(3^2 - 4)$$
$$= f(5)$$
$$= 7(5) + 1$$
$$= 36$$

Example 28   If $f(x) = x + 5$ and $g(x) = \sqrt{x}$, determine $(f \circ g)(x)$ and $(g \circ f)(x)$.

$$(f \circ g)(x) = f(g(x))$$
$$= f(\sqrt{x})$$
$$= \sqrt{x} + 5$$

and

$$(g \circ f)(x) = g(f(x))$$
$$= g(x + 5)$$
$$= \sqrt{x + 5}$$

Note that $(f \circ g)(x) \neq (g \circ f)(x)$ in the example just completed. Occasionally $(f \circ g)(x) = (g \circ f)(x)$, but usually not. In the next section we shall see cases where $(f \circ g)(x) = (g \circ f)(x)$.

Example 29   If $f(x) = x^2 + 5x + 3$ and $g(x) = 4x - 3$, determine $(f \circ g)(x)$ and $(g \circ f)(x)$.

$$(f \circ g)(x) = f(g(x))$$
$$= f(4x - 3)$$
$$= (4x - 3)^2 + 5(4x - 3) + 3$$
$$= 16x^2 - 4x - 3$$

and

$$(g \circ f)(x) = g(f(x))$$
$$= g(x^2 + 5x + 3)$$
$$= 4(x^2 + 5x + 3) - 3$$
$$= 4x^2 + 20x + 9$$

Clearly $(f \circ g)(x) \neq (g \circ f)(x)$ in this example.

Example 30 *Express $h(x) = (5x + 2)^7$ as the composition of two functions f and g.*
If

$$g(x) = 5x + 2$$

and

$$f(x) = x^7$$

then

$$(f \circ g)(x) = f(g(x)) = f(5x + 2) = (5x + 2)^7$$

EXERCISES 3.5

1. Determine $(f \circ g)(x)$ and $(g \circ f)(x)$ for each problem. Simplify whenever possible.

*(a) $f(x) = x^2$, $g(x) = x + 3$

(b) $f(x) = \sqrt{x}$, $g(x) = x - 1$

*(c) $f(x) = \dfrac{1}{x}$, $g(x) = x^2$

(d) $f(x) = x^2 + 2x + 5$, $g(x) = x + 2$

(e) $f(x) = \dfrac{x}{x + 1}$, $g(x) = 2 - x$

(f) $f(x) = |x|$, $g(x) = 2x + 5$

*(g) $f(x) = [\![x + 1]\!]$, $g(x) = x^2$

(h) $f(x) = \dfrac{3}{x + 2}$, $g(x) = \dfrac{1}{x}$

*(i) $f(x) = \dfrac{1}{x + 1}$, $g(x) = \dfrac{5}{x^2 - 3}$

(j) $f(x) = \dfrac{x + 2}{x - 2}$, $g(x) = \dfrac{1}{x}$

2. Let $f(x) = 5x - 2$, $g(x) = x^2 + 1$, and $h(x) = \sqrt[3]{x + 1}$. Determine the numerical value of each expression.

*(a) $f(g(3))$ (b) $f(g(0))$

*(a) $f(g(3))$

(b) $f(g(0))$

*(c) $(g \circ f)(1)$

(d) $(g \circ f)(2)$

*(e) $(f \circ h)(0)$

(f) $(f \circ h)(7)$

*(g) $h(f(0))$

(h) $h(f(3))$

*(i) $g(h(6))$

(j) $g(h(7))$

*(k) $h(g(2))$

(l) $(h \circ g)(3)$

3. Let $f(x) = x^2 + 7$ and $g(x) = 3x - 2$. Determine each requested composition.

*(a) $f(g(x))$

(b) $g(f(x))$

*(c) $(g \circ f)(x + 1)$

(d) $(f \circ g)(x + 1)$

*(e) $f(g(x - 1))$

(f) $g(f(x - 1))$

*(g) $f(g(x^2))$

(h) $g(f(x^2))$

4. Express h as the composition of two functions f and g. Call the composition $f \circ g$ and specify the functions f and g.

*(a) $h(x) = (9x + 1)^5$

(b) $h(x) = (1 - 3x)^8$

*(c) $h(x) = (x^2 + 3)^{2/3}$

(d) $h(x) = (2x + 1)^{4/3}$

*(e) $h(x) = \sqrt{5x^2 + 9}$

(f) $h(x) = \sqrt[3]{x^2 + 6}$

*5. Determine the function g in each case.

(a) $f(x) = x^3 + 1$ and $(g \circ f)(x) = x$

(b) $f(x) = x^3 + 1$ and $(f \circ g)(x) = x$

*6. Let $f(x) = x^2 + 3x$, $g(x) = 2x - 1$, and $h(x) = 8x$. Determine each composition.

(a) $f(g(h(x)))$

(b) $h(g(f(x)))$

3.6 INVERSE FUNCTIONS

Recall that a relation is a set of ordered pairs. If we interchange the first and second coordinates of each ordered pair of a relation, we obtain the **inverse** of the relation. The domain of the relation becomes the range of the inverse relation. The range of the original relation is the domain of the inverse relation.

Example 31 *Let $A = \{(1, 2), (3, 4), (5, 6)\}$.*

If $A = \{(1, 2), (3, 4), (5, 6)\}$, then the domain of A is $\{1, 3, 5\}$ and the range of A is $\{2, 4, 6\}$.

The inverse of A is $\{(2, 1), (4, 3), (6, 5)\}$. The domain of the inverse is $\{2, 4, 6\}$ and the range is $\{1, 3, 5\}$.

If the relation is in the form of an equation, then the inverse is readily obtained by interchanging the variables in the equation.

Example 32   *Find the inverse of y = 2x − 7.*
Interchange x and y to obtain the inverse relation.

$$\text{Relation:}\quad y = 2x - 7$$
$$\text{Inverse:}\quad x = 2y - 7$$

The inverse is usually manipulated to solve for y in terms of x. Here $x = 2y - 7$ becomes $2y = x + 7$ and then

$$y = \frac{x + 7}{2}$$

The points (a, b) and (b, a) are symmetric with respect to the line $y = x$.

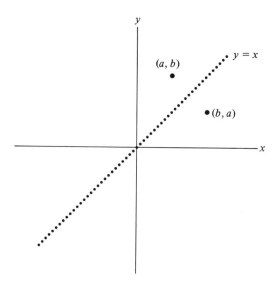

This means the graphs of a relation and its inverse are symmetric with respect to the line $y = x$. In other words, if the graph of the relation is reflected across the line $y = x$, then the graph of the inverse is obtained. In view of this, an inverse can be sketched directly from the graph of the original relation by using the line $y = x$. Here is the graph of $y = 2x - 7$ and its inverse $y = \dfrac{x + 7}{2}$.

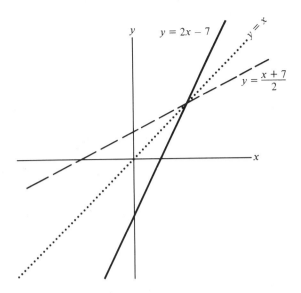

If the inverse of a relation satisfies the definition of function, then it is called the **inverse function** of the original relation. If no two distinct ordered pairs of a relation have the same second coordinate, then no two distinct ordered pairs of the inverse will have the same first coordinate. Thus the inverse of such a relation is a function. Consider the relation $y = x^2$.

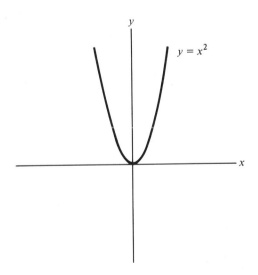

Although $y = x^2$ is itself a function, it has distinct ordered pairs with the same second coordinate, such as $(2, 4)$ and $(-2, 4)$. So its inverse will not be a function. Its inverse is $y = \pm\sqrt{x}$, shown next.

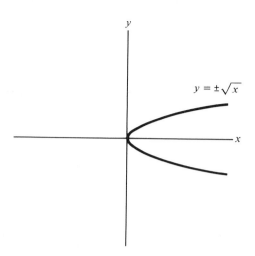

$y = \pm\sqrt{x}$

The implied domain D of $y = x^2$ includes all the real numbers. If that domain is restricted to either $D_1 = \{x \mid x \geq 0\}$ or $D_2 = \{x \mid x \leq 0\}$, then the inverse will be a function. Here are the two functions, their inverses, and their graphs. Note the use of the notation $\mathbf{f}^{-1}$ for the function that is the inverse of f. The -1 is *not an exponent*; it merely denotes the inverse; $f^{-1} \neq \dfrac{1}{f}$.

$f_1(x) = x^2$
$D_1 = \{x \mid x \geq 0\}$
$f_1^{-1}(x) = \sqrt{x}$

$f_2(x) = x^2$
$D_2 = \{x \mid x \leq 0\}$
$f_2^{-1}(x) = -\sqrt{x}$

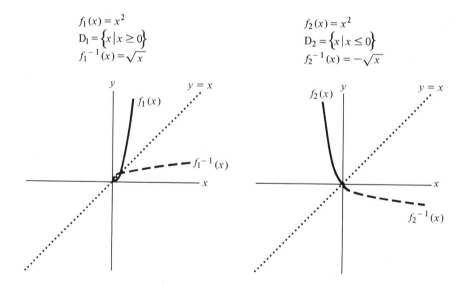

Recall that a relation is a function only if no vertical line can be passed through two or more points of the graph. Considering inverses, this means that the inverse is a function if no *horizontal* line can be passed through two or more points of the graph of the original relation. For $y = x^2$, a horizontal line can be passed through two points of its graph. This means that the inverse of $y = x^2$ is not a function.

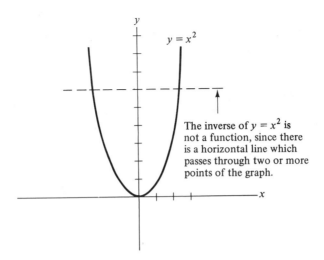

The inverse of $y = x^2$ is not a function, since there is a horizontal line which passes through two or more points of the graph.

We have just seen that in order for a function to have an inverse that is also a function, the function can have only one x value for each y value. (Graphically, no horizontal line can be passed through two or more points.) Functions satisfying this condition are called "one to one." Thus *a* **one-to-one function** *is a function such that for every y value there is only one x value.* So for every x there is one y and for every y there is one x. Two observations can be made.

1. If a function is one to one, its inverse is a function.
2. If no horizontal line can be passed through two or more points of the graph of a function, then the function is one to one.

Example 33   *Given $f(x) = x^3 - 7$, determine $f^{-1}(x)$.*

$$\text{The function:}\quad y = x^3 - 7$$

$$\text{Its inverse:}\quad x = y^3 - 7$$

Now solve $x = y^3 - 7$ for y. The result is

$$y = \sqrt[3]{x + 7}$$

Thus

$$f^{-1}(x) = \sqrt[3]{x + 7}$$

Example 34   *Given $f(x) = \dfrac{x + 4}{2x}$, determine $f^{-1}(x)$.*

$$\text{The function:}\quad y = \frac{x + 4}{2x}$$

$$\text{The inverse:}\quad x = \frac{y + 4}{2y}$$

To solve for y in terms of x, begin by multiplying both sides by $2y$ in order to eliminate the fraction. The result is

$$2xy = y + 4$$

Next, collect the y terms on the same side.

$$2xy - y = 4$$

Factor out the y.

$$(2x - 1)y = 4$$

Finally,

$$y = \frac{4}{2x - 1}$$

or

$$f^{-1}(x) = \frac{4}{2x - 1}$$

Suppose that there is a function such that $f(4) = 7$ and suppose also that f has an inverse f^{-1}. Then, using arrows to denote the correspondence,

$$4 \xrightarrow{\ f\ } 7$$

and

$$7 \xrightarrow{\ f^{-1}\ } 4$$

Putting these two statements together yields

$$4 \xrightarrow{\ f\ } 7 \xrightarrow{\ f^{-1}\ } 4$$

In the usual notation of functions, this correspondence appears as

$$f(4) = 7$$
$$f^{-1}(7) = 4$$

and

$$f^{-1}(f(4)) = 4$$

Also, from $7 \xrightarrow{f^{-1}} 4 \xrightarrow{f} 7$ we have $f(f^{-1}(7)) = 7$. In fact,

f^{-1} is the inverse of f if and only if
$f(f^{-1}(x)) = x$ and $f^{-1}(f(x)) = x$

Example 35 *Verify* $f(f^{-1}(x)) = x$ *and* $f^{-1}(f(x)) = x$ *for the functions in Example 32.*

$$f(x) = 2x - 7 \quad \text{and} \quad f^{-1}(x) = \frac{x + 7}{2}$$

$$f(f^{-1}(x)) = f\left(\frac{x + 7}{2}\right)$$

$$= 2\left(\frac{x + 7}{2}\right) - 7$$

$$= x + 7 - 7$$

$$= x$$

$$f^{-1}(f(x)) = f^{-1}(2x - 7)$$

$$= \frac{(2x - 7) + 7}{2}$$

$$= \frac{2x}{2}$$

$$= x$$

EXERCISES 3.6

1. Determine the inverse of each relation and indicate whether the inverse is a function. In (d) through (s), be sure to write the inverse as y in terms of x. Do not graph the relations.

    *(a) $\{(0, 3), (1, 4), (2, 8), (-3, 6)\}$ (b) $\{(1, 2), (1, 4), (1, 8)\}$
    *(c) $\{(3, 2), (4, -8), (6, -2), (10, 2)\}$ (d) $y = 5x - 3$

    *(e) $y = 9x + 2$ (f) $y = \dfrac{2}{x}$

    *(g) $y = x^2$ (h) $y = x^2 - 3$
    *(i) $y = x^3$ (j) $y = x^3 + 1$

    *(k) $y = \dfrac{x + 5}{3x}$ (l) $y = \dfrac{3}{x - 2}$

*(m) $x^2 + y^2 = 25$ (n) $y = \pm \sqrt{5 + x}$

*(o) $y = 4x^2 + x$ (p) $xy^2 + x = 3$

*(q) $y = x^2 + 3x + 5$ (r) $x^2y + x = 3$

*(s) $y = x^2 - 7x + 11$

2. For each function f, determine its inverse f^{-1}.

   *(a) $f(x) = 7x - 4$ (b) $f(x) = 1 + 6x$

   *(c) $f(x) = x^3 + 1$ (d) $f(x) = 3 - x^3$

   *(e) $f(x) = \dfrac{9}{x + 2}$ (f) $f(x) = \dfrac{3}{x - 5}$

   *(g) $f(x) = \dfrac{x + 3}{x - 6}$ (h) $f(x) = \dfrac{x - 4}{x + 1}$

   *(i) $y = \dfrac{x + 5}{3x}$ *(j) $y = \dfrac{7x}{x - 2}$

3. Use $f(f^{-1}(x)) = x$ and $f^{-1}(f(x)) = x$ as a check in all parts of Exercise 2.

4. Sketch the graph of each relation. Then sketch the inverse by reflecting the graph across the line $y = x$.

   *(a) $y = 4x + 1$ (b) $y = 2x - 1$

   *(c) $y = x^2 + 1$ (d) $y = x^2 - 3$

   *(e) $y = |x|$ (f) $y = \dfrac{1}{x}$

   *(g) $y = x^3$ (h) $y = \sqrt{x}$

   *(i) $y = -2x + 3$ (j) $y = |x + 2|$

   *(k) $y = \sqrt{x - 4}$ (l) $y = |x - 3|$

   *(m) $y = -|x|$ (n) $y = \dfrac{1}{x - 2}$

*5. Apply the horizontal line test to determine which functions are one to one.

   (a) $f(x) = x^2$ (b) $f(x) = x^2 + 1$

   (c) $f(x) = x^3$ (d) $f(x) = |x|$

   (e) $f(x) = \dfrac{1}{x}$ (f) $f(x) = [\![x]\!]$

   (g) $f(x) = \sqrt{x}$

6. Prove that f and g are inverses of each other by showing that $f(g(x)) = x$ and $g(f(x)) = x$.

   (a) $f(x) = 6x + 1, \; g(x) = \dfrac{x - 1}{6}$

   (b) $f(x) = \tfrac{1}{2}x - 5, \; g(x) = 2x + 10$

   (c) $f(x) = x^2 + 3, \; x \geq 0; \; g(x) = \sqrt{x - 3}$

   (d) $f(x) = \dfrac{5}{x + 2}, \; g(x) = \dfrac{5 - 2x}{x}$

3.7 SYMMETRY

In the preceding section it was noted that the graphs of a relation and its inverse are symmetric with respect to the line $y = x$. This fact made it very easy to sketch the graph of the inverse once the graph of the relation had been sketched. Recognition of certain kinds of symmetry can be used to simplify the graphing of some relations themselves. This section presents some examples of symmetry and ways to discover it.

If you look at the graph of $y = x^2$, shown next, you will see that it is symmetric with respect to the y axis.

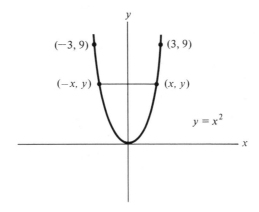

This means that every point of the graph has a corresponding point of the graph that is its reflection across the y axis. For every point (x, y) on the curve, there is a corresponding point $(-x, y)$. For example, corresponding to $(3, 9)$ is $(-3, 9)$. We can test for *symmetry with respect to the y axis* as follows.

Substitute $-x$ for x in the original equation. If this new equation is the same as (or can be made the same as) the original, then the graph is **symmetric with respect to the y axis**.

Example 36 *Test for symmetry with respect to the y axis.*
(a) $y = x^2 - 9$ (b) $y = x^2 + 3x + 1$

(a) Upon substituting $-x$ for x in $y = x^2 - 9$, we get

$$y = (-x)^2 - 9$$

or

$$y = x^2 - 9$$

The new equation is the same as the original; this means the graph of $y = x^2 - 9$ is symmetric with respect to the y axis.

(b)   Upon substituting $-x$ for x in $y = x^2 + 3x + 1$, we get

$$y = (-x)^2 + 3(-x) + 1$$

or

$$y = x^2 - 3x + 1$$

The new equation is not the same as the original; this means the graph of $y = x^2 + 3x + 1$ is not symmetric with respect to the y axis.

If you look at the graph of $x = y^2 + 1$, shown next, you will see that it is symmetric with respect to the x axis.

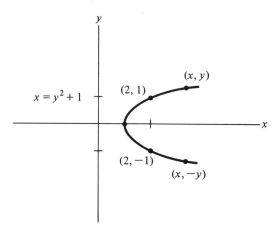

This means that every point of the graph has a corresponding point of the graph that is its reflection across the x axis. For every point (x, y) on the curve, there is a corresponding point $(x, -y)$. For example, corresponding to $(2, 1)$ is $(2, -1)$. We can test for *symmetry with respect to the x axis* as follows.

> Substitute $-y$ for y in the original equation. If this new equation is the same as (or can be made the same as) the original, then the graph is **symmetric with respect to the x axis.**

Example 37   *Test for symmetry with respect to the x axis.*
(a) $x^2 + y^2 = 12$ (b) $y = x^4 + 5$

(a)   On substituting $-y$ for y in $x^2 + y^2 = 12$, we get

$$x^2 + (-y)^2 = 12$$

or

$$x^2 + y^2 = 12$$

The new equation is the same as the original, which means the graph of $x^2 + y^2 = 12$ is symmetric with respect to the x axis.

(b)   On substituting $-y$ for y in $y = x^4 + 5$, we get

$$-y = x^4 + 5$$

or

$$y = -x^4 - 5$$

The new equation is not the same as the original; which means the graph of $y = x^4 + 5$ is not symmetric with respect to the x axis.

The next graph shown, that of $y = 1/x$, is symmetric with respect to the origin. In other words, if the graph is rotated 180° (half a turn) in either direction, the figure would look the same as before it was rotated. (The 180° rotation can also be accomplished by reflecting the graph about the y axis and that result about the x axis or vice versa.)

Another way of visualizing symmetry with respect to the origin is to observe that a straight line through the origin intersects the graph at equal distances from the origin in both directions.

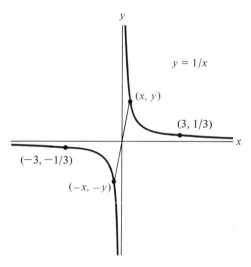

For every point (x, y) on the curve there is a corresponding point $(-x, -y)$. For example, corresponding to $(3, \frac{1}{3})$ is $(-3, -\frac{1}{3})$. We can test for *symmetry with respect to the origin* as follows.

> Substitute $-x$ for x and $-y$ for y in the original equation. If this new equation is the same as (or can be made the same as) the original, then the graph is **symmetric with respect to the origin.**

Example 38 *Test for symmetry with respect to the origin.*
(a) $x^2 + y^2 = 12$ (b) $y - x^2 = 17$

(a) On substituting $-x$ for x and $-y$ for y in $x^2 + y^2 = 12$, we get

$$(-x)^2 + (-y)^2 = 12$$

or

$$x^2 + y^2 = 12$$

The new equation is the same as the original, which means the graph of $x^2 + y^2 = 12$ is symmetric with respect to the origin.

(b) On substituting $-x$ for x and $-y$ for y in $y - x^2 = 17$, we get

$$-y - (-x)^2 = 17$$

or

$$-y - x^2 = 17$$

The new equation is not the same as the original, which means the graph of $y - x^2 = 17$ is not symmetric with respect to the origin.

EXERCISES 3.7

1. Test each relation for symmetry. Then graph the relation, using symmetry when available.

*(a) $y = x^2 + 4$ (b) $y = x^2 - 1$
*(c) $y = x^3$ (d) $y = x^3 + 1$
*(e) $y = x^4$ (f) $y = x^4 + 1$
*(g) $y = |x|$ (h) $y = |x - 1|$
*(i) $y^2 = x$ (j) $x^2 = y$
*(k) $xy = 1$ (l) $y = -x$
*(m) $y = \sqrt{x}$ (n) $y = \sqrt[3]{x}$
*(o) $y = x^2 + 4x - 1$ (p) $y = x^2 - 6x + 2$
*(q) $y = \pm x$ (r) $y = \pm\sqrt{x}$

2. Test each relation for symmetry. Do not graph.

*(a) $x^2 + y^2 = 4$ (b) $x^2 + y = 7$
*(c) $x^2 - y^2 = 2$ (d) $y^2 - x^2 = 9$
*(e) $3x^2 + 5y^2 = 20$ (f) $8x^2 - 3y^2 = 1$

*(g) $x^2 - xy + y^2 = 6$ (h) $y = \dfrac{x}{x + 1}$

*(i) $y = \dfrac{5 - x}{5 + x}$ (j) $x^2y + xy - y^2 = 1$

*(k) $x^4 + y^3 = 10$ (l) $x^2 + y^3 = 16$

*(m) $x^3y + x^2y^2 + xy^3 = 3$ (n) $y^3 = x^5$

3. A function is said to be **even** if $f(-x) = f(x)$ for all x in its domain. A function is **odd** if $f(-x) = -f(x)$ for all x in its domain. Determine which functions are even, which are odd, and which are neither.

*(a) $f(x) = x$ (b) $f(x) = x^2$

*(c) $f(x) = x^3$ (d) $f(x) = x^4$

*(e) $f(x) = 5x + 2$ (f) $f(x) = 8$

*(g) $f(x) = x^2 - x$ (h) $f(x) = x^2 + 4$

*(i) $f(x) = x^2 + 3$ (j) $f(x) = x^2 - 3x + 5$

*(k) $f(x) = x^3 + x$ (l) $f(x) = x^3 - 5$

4. (a) What kind of symmetry, if any, do the graphs of all even functions possess? (See Exercise 3.)

    (b) What kind of symmetry, if any, do the graphs of all odd functions possess? (See Exercise 3.)

5. (a) If a graph is symmetric with respect to the x axis and symmetric with respect to the y axis, is it necessarily symmetric with respect to the origin?

    (b) If a graph is symmetric with respect to the origin, is it necessarily symmetric with respect to the x axis or y axis or both?

3.8 TRANSLATION

Compare the graphs of $f(x) = x^2$, $g(x) = x^2 + 1$, and $h(x) = x^2 - 2$.

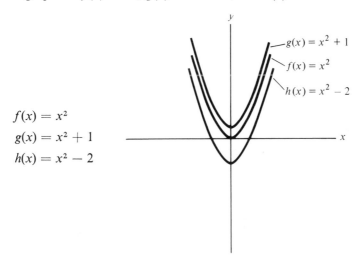

$$f(x) = x^2$$
$$g(x) = x^2 + 1$$
$$h(x) = x^2 - 2$$

Point for point, the graph of $g(x) = x^2 + 1$ is one unit above the graph of $f(x) = x^2$. The graph of $h(x) = x^2 - 2$ is two units below $f(x) = x^2$. In general,

The graph of $f(x) + c$ is:
1. c units above the graph of f if c is positive.
2. c units below the graph of f if c is negative.

Example 39   *Compare the graphs of $g(x) = 5x - 3$ and $h(x) = 5x + 7$ with the graph of $f(x) = 5x$.*

The graph of $g(x) = 5x - 3$ is 3 units below the graph of $f(x) = 5x$. The graph of $h(x) = 5x + 7$ is 7 units above the graph of $f(x) = 5x$.

Next let us compare the graphs of $f(x) = x^2$, $g(x) = (x + 1)^2$, and $h(x) = (x - 2)^2$.

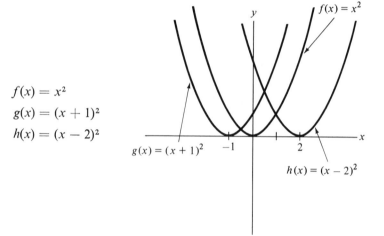

$f(x) = x^2$
$g(x) = (x + 1)^2$
$h(x) = (x - 2)^2$

Point for point, the graph of $g(x) = (x + 1)^2$ is one unit to the left of the graph of $f(x) = x^2$. The graph of $h(x) = (x - 2)^2$ is two units to the right of $f(x) = x^2$. In general,

The graph of $f(x + c)$ is:
1. c units to the left of the graph of f if c is positive.
2. c units to the right of the graph of f if c is negative.

Example 40   *Compare the graphs of $g(x) = \sqrt{x + 4}$ and $h(x) = \sqrt{x - 3}$ with the graph of $f(x) = \sqrt{x}$.*

The graph of function $g(x) = \sqrt{x + 4}$ is 4 units to the left of the graph of $f(x) = \sqrt{x}$. The graph of $h(x) = \sqrt{x - 3}$ is 3 units to the right of the graph of $f(x) = \sqrt{x}$.

Example 41   *Sketch the graph of the function* $y = (x - 1)^2 + 3$ *by using horizontal and vertical translations.*

The desired graph can be obtained from the graph of $f(x) = x^2$ by translating it right 1 unit and then up 3 units. In steps,

$$f(x) = x^2$$
$$g(x) = (x - 1)^2$$
$$h(x) = (x - 1)^2 + 3$$

The graph:

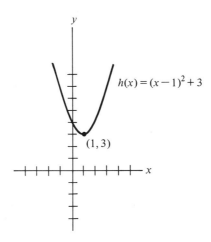

$h(x) = (x - 1)^2 + 3$

$(1, 3)$

EXERCISES 3.8

1. For each problem, sketch the graph of function f. Then graph functions m, n, s, and t by using the principles of vertical and horizontal translation suggested in this section.

*(a) $f(x) = x^2$

$m(x) = x^2 - 7$

$n(x) = (x - 7)^2$

$s(x) = x^2 + 5$

$t(x) = (x + 5)^2$

(b) $f(x) = |x|$

$m(x) = |x + 3|$

$n(x) = |x| - 4$

$s(x) = |x| + 7$

$t(x) = |x - 1|$

*(c) $f(x) = \sqrt{x}$

$m(x) = \sqrt{x} + 2$

$n(x) = \sqrt{x + 2}$

$s(x) = \sqrt{x - 3}$

$t(x) = \sqrt{x} - 3$

(d) $f(x) = x^3$

$m(x) = (x - 1)^3$

$n(x) = (x + 5)^3$

$s(x) = x^3 + 2$

$t(x) = x^3 - 4$

*(e)　　$f(x) = [\![x]\!]$

$m(x) = [\![x]\!] + 3$

$n(x) = [\![x + 3]\!]$

$s(x) = [\![x]\!] - 2$

$t(x) = [\![x - 2]\!]$

(f)　　$f(x) = \dfrac{1}{x}$

$m(x) = \dfrac{1}{x + 2}$

$n(x) = \dfrac{1}{x - 5}$

$s(x) = \dfrac{1}{x} + 4$

$t(x) = \dfrac{1}{x} - 3$

2.　Sketch the graph of the given function by combining horizontal and vertical translations.

*(a)　$y = (x - 2)^2 + 1$

*(c)　$y = (x + 3)^2 - 1$

*(e)　$f(x) = \sqrt{x - 3} + 1$

*(g)　$f(x) = \dfrac{1}{x + 1} + 2$

(b)　$y = (x - 4)^2 + 2$

(d)　$y = (x + 1)^2 - 5$

(f)　$f(x) = \sqrt{x + 2} - 4$

(h)　$f(x) = \dfrac{1}{x - 2} + 1$

3.9 STRETCHING, SHRINKING, AND REFLECTION

Consider three functions,

$$y = x^2$$

$$y = 2x^2$$

$$y = \tfrac{1}{2}x^2$$

We shall tabulate some points for the functions.

x	$y = x^2$	$y = 2x^2$	$y = \tfrac{1}{2}x^2$
0	$(0, 0)$	$(0, 0)$	$(0, 0)$
± 1	$(\pm 1, 1)$	$(\pm 1, 2)$	$(\pm 1, \tfrac{1}{2})$
± 2	$(\pm 2, 4)$	$(\pm 2, 8)$	$(\pm 2, 2)$
± 3	$(\pm 3, 9)$	$(\pm 3, 18)$	$(\pm 3, 4\tfrac{1}{2})$

From the table you can see that for the same x, the y coordinate of $y = 2x^2$ is 2 times that of $y = x^2$. The y coordinate of $y = \tfrac{1}{2}x^2$ is $\tfrac{1}{2}$ that of $y = x^2$. The graphs are:

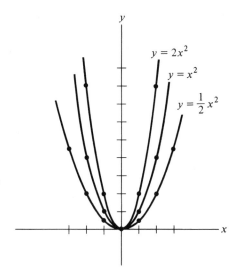

The graph shows the points of $y = 2x^2$ to be higher than those of $y = x^2$; it gets higher faster and thus is "thinner" than the graph of $y = x^2$. The points of $y = \frac{1}{2}x^2$ are lower than those of $y = x^2$; it is "wider" than the graph of $y = x^2$.

The graph of $y = 2x^2$ is called a *stretching* of the graph of $y = x^2$. The graph of $y = \frac{1}{2}x^2$ is called a *shrinking* of the graph of $y = x^2$.

> The graph of $y = cf(x)$ is:
>
> 1. a **stretching** of the graph of $y = f(x)$ if $c > 1$.
> 2. a **shrinking** of the graph of $y = f(x)$ if $0 < c < 1$.

Example 42 *Apply the stretching concept to the graph of $y = |x|$ in order to sketch the graph of $y = 3|x|$.*

First graph $y = |x|$. Then sketch a graph in which the y coordinates are 3 times as large as those of $y = |x|$.

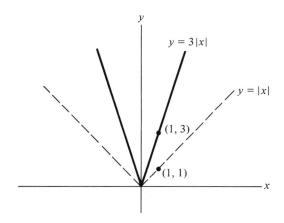

Example 43 *Apply the shrinking concept to the graph of $y = |x|$ in order to sketch the graph of $y = \frac{1}{2}|x|$.*

First graph $y = |x|$. Then sketch a graph in which the y coordinates are $\frac{1}{2}$ as large as those of $y = |x|$.

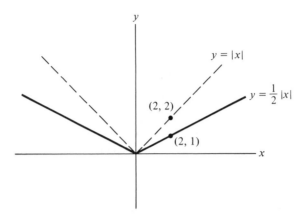

Next, consider the graphs of $y = x^2$ and $y = -x^2$. Points for the graph of $y = -x^2$ can be obtained from points for the graph of $y = x^2$ by changing the sign of the y coordinates. Such a change in sign creates a graph that is a reflection across the x axis.

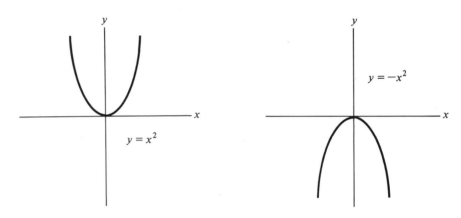

> Multiplying a function by -1 has the effect of **reflecting** its graph across the x axis.

Example 44 *Use the concepts of this section to sketch the graph of $y = -2|x|$.*

The graph of $y = -2|x|$ can be obtained from the graph of $y = |x|$ as follows. First apply a stretching that multiplies all y coordinates by 2; then reflect the graph across the x axis.

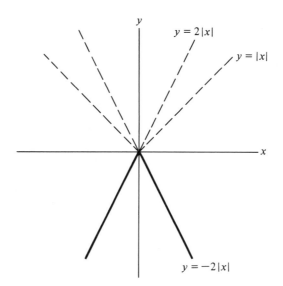

Example 45 *Combine the concepts of this chapter to sketch the graph of* $y = -x^2 + 5$.
The graph of this function can be based on the graph of $y = x^2$. First, the graph of $y = -x^2$ is a reflection across the x axis of the graph of $y = x^2$. Next, the graph of $y = -x^2 + 5$ is 5 units above the graph of $y = -x^2$.

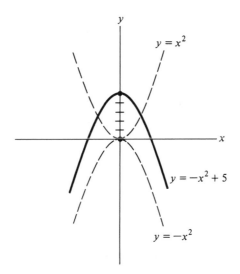

Note: The graph of $y = -(x^2 + 5)$ is different from the function just graphed, $y = -x^2 + 5$. Both graphs do apply an upward translation and a reflection. However, in $y = -(x^2 + 5)$ the parentheses indicate that the translation upward 5 units is done first. *Then* the graph is reflected across the x axis. Here is the graph.

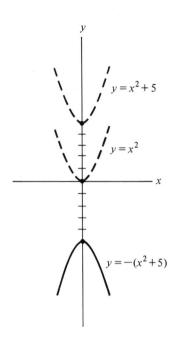

$y = x^2 + 5$

$y = x^2$

$y = -(x^2 + 5)$

EXERCISES 3.9

1. Apply the concepts of this section to sketch the graph of each function.

*(a) $y = 3x^2$

(b) $y = \dfrac{1}{3} x^2$

*(c) $y = \dfrac{1}{3} |x|$

(d) $y = 2|x|$

*(e) $f(x) = 2\sqrt{x}$

(f) $f(x) = \dfrac{1}{2} \sqrt{x}$

*(g) $f(x) = \dfrac{3}{2} \sqrt{x}$

(h) $f(x) = \dfrac{3}{2} |x|$

*(i) $f(x) = \dfrac{3}{2} x^2$

(j) $f(x) = \dfrac{2}{3} x^2$

*(k) $f(x) = 2[\![x]\!]$

(l) $f(x) = \dfrac{1}{2} [\![x]\!]$

2. Apply the concepts of this section to sketch the graph of each function.

*(a) $y = -3|x|$

(b) $y = -2x^2$

*(c) $y = -\sqrt{x}$

(d) $y = -2\sqrt{x}$

*(e) $f(x) = -\dfrac{1}{2}\sqrt{x}$

(f) $f(x) = -\dfrac{1}{x}$

*(g) $f(x) = -[\![x]\!]$

(h) $f(x) = -\dfrac{1}{2} |x|$

*(i) $f(x) = -\dfrac{1}{2}x^2$

(j) $f(x) = -\dfrac{3}{2}\sqrt{x}$

3.   Combine the concepts of this chapter (emphasizing Sections 3.4, 3.7, 3.8, and 3.9) in order to sketch the graph of each function.

*(a) $f(x) = 2x^2 + 3$

(b) $f(x) = 2x^2 - 1$

*(c) $f(x) = -x^2 + 1$

(d) $f(x) = -x^2 - 3$

*(e) $f(x) = -2x^2 - 4$

(f) $f(x) = -2x^2 + 5$

*(g) $f(x) = -\dfrac{1}{2}x^2 + 5$

(h) $f(x) = \dfrac{1}{2}x^2 - 3$

*(i) $f(x) = 2|x| + 1$

(j) $f(x) = -|x| + 5$

*(k) $f(x) = -\dfrac{1}{2}|x| + 4$

(l) $f(x) = -2|x| - 1$

*(m) $f(x) = -\sqrt{x} + 3$

(n) $f(x) = 2\sqrt{x} - 4$

*(o) $f(x) = 3\sqrt{x} - 1$

(p) $f(x) = -3\sqrt{x} + 1$

*(q) $f(x) = (x - 1)^2 + 2$

(r) $f(x) = (x + 3)^2 - 1$

*(s) $f(x) = |x + 2| - 1$

(t) $f(x) = |x - 1| + 5$

*(u) $f(x) = 5|x - 3|$

(v) $f(x) = -|x + 3|$

*(w) $f(x) = \sqrt{x - 2} + 3$

(x) $f(x) = -2\sqrt{x + 1}$

*(y) $f(x) = 3\sqrt{x - 1}$

(z) $f(x) = -\sqrt{x + 5}$

4.   Combine the concepts of this chapter (emphasizing Sections 3.4, 3.7, 3.8, and 3.9) in order to sketch the graph of each function.

*(a) $y = -x^4 + 3$

(b) $y = (x - 1)^4$

*(c) $y = (x + 2)^3 - 1$

(d) $y = \dfrac{1}{2}(x - 1)^3$

*(e) $y = \dfrac{1}{2}x^4 + 5$

(f) $y = 1 - x^4$

*(g) $y = (x + 1)^4 - 2$

(h) $y = 3 - 2(x + 1)^3$

*(i) $y = \dfrac{3}{x - 2}$

(j) $y = \dfrac{3}{x} - 2$

REVIEW EXERCISES FOR CHAPTER 3

1.   Determine the implied domain of each function.

*(a) $y = \dfrac{x^2}{x + 5}$

(b) $y = \sqrt{x^2 - 10}$

*(c) $y = \dfrac{1}{\sqrt{x}}$

(d) $y = \dfrac{x^2 + 7x + 10}{x^2 + 9}$

*(e) $f(x) = \dfrac{\sqrt{2x + 1}}{x - 9}$

(f) $f(x) = 5x^{1/2} - 2$

2. Determine the implied domain and range of each relation.
   *(a) $y^3 - x = 0$ (b) $x = y^2 + 3$
   *(c) $x^2 + y^2 = 9$ (d) $x^2 - y^2 = 9$
   *(e) $xy^2 + 7x = 5$ (f) $y = x^2 + 7x$

3. Determine $f(1)$, $f(-2)$, $f(\frac{2}{3})$, and $f(x + h)$.

   *(a) $f(x) = x^2 - 3x + 5$ (b) $f(x) = \dfrac{1}{x + 1}$

4. If $f(x) = 2x + 7$ and $g(x) = \dfrac{3}{1 - x}$, determine $f + g$, $f - g$, $f \cdot g$, and
   $f \div g$. Also, give the domain of each of the four new functions created.

5. Graph each function and give its domain and range.
   *(a) $f(x) = 4x - 2$ (b) $f(x) = x^2 - 9x + 1$

   *(c) $f(x) = -x^3$ (d) $f(x) = \dfrac{1}{x + 4}$

   *(e) $f(x) = \sqrt{x + 1}$ (f) $f(x) = \begin{cases} -x^2 & x \le 0 \\ 3 & x > 0 \end{cases}$

   *(g) $f(x) = \dfrac{x^2 - 9}{x + 3}$ (h) $f(x) = |x - 2|$

6. Determine the zeros of each function.
   *(a) $f(x) = x^2 - 3x - 10$ (b) $f(x) = \sqrt{3 - x^2}$

7. Determine $f \circ g$ and $g \circ f$ for the given functions.
   *(a) $f(x) = x^2 + 9x + 3$, $g(x) = 5x$

   (b) $f(x) = \dfrac{7}{x}$, $g(x) = \dfrac{x}{x - 2}$

8. Determine the inverse of each function.

   *(a) $y = 3x - 2$ (b) $y = \dfrac{x}{x - 3}$

   *(c) $f(x) = \dfrac{x^2}{x + 1}$ (d) $f(x) = x^2 - 8x + 2$

9. Graph each relation by using the concepts of this chapter.
   *(a) $f(x) = 3x^2 + 1$ (b) $f(x) = -x^3 + 1$
   *(c) $y = 1 - |x|$ (d) $y = -\sqrt{x - 2}$
   *(e) $y = 3\sqrt{x} + 2$ (f) $y = 3|x| - 4$
   *(g) $y = -x^4 + 2$ (h) $y = (x + 2)^3 + 1$

   *(i) $y = (x - 2)^4 - 1$ (j) $y = 1 - \dfrac{2}{x}$

Applications of Functions 4

4.1 INTRODUCTION

In Chapter 3 you were introduced to the concept and notation of functions. Now it is time to see some applications in which it is desirable to use function notation. In Section 4.2 you will see the use of function notation in settings involving basic geometric concepts, algebraic manipulation, and substitution. In Section 4.3 the use of functions in economics is considered. In Section 4.4 you will examine distance and velocity functions.

There are many types of functions we have not yet studied, so applications involving them must wait until later in the book. Such functions include exponential functions, logarithmic functions, trigonometric functions, rational functions, and many polynomial functions. Keep in mind that new and interesting applications will be presented as you study these other types of functions.

4.2 GEOMETRIC APPLICATIONS

In this section, manipulative techniques of algebra are applied to problems involving geometry. The techniques include substitution, simplification of radicals, solution of quadratic equations, and equation manipulation. Many applied calculus problems involve settings and manipulations similar to those shown in the examples and exercises of this section.

Example 1   *The area of a circular region is given by $A = \pi r^2$, where r is the radius.*
(a) *Express the radius as a function of the area.*
(b) *Express the diameter of the circle as a function of the area.*

(a) To express the radius as a function of area, solve $A = \pi r^2$ for r.

$$A = \pi r^2$$

$$\frac{A}{\pi} = r^2 \quad \text{after dividing both sides by } \pi$$

$$\sqrt{\frac{A}{\pi}} = r$$

or

$$r = \sqrt{\frac{A}{\pi}}$$

The $\pm$ is omitted from in front of the radical because a radius cannot be negative. We conclude that the $+$ case is correct in this geometric setting.

(b) The diameter of a circle is twice the radius.

$$d = 2r$$

Now, since

$$r = \sqrt{\frac{A}{\pi}}$$

and

$$2r = 2\sqrt{\frac{A}{\pi}}$$

it follows that

$$d = 2\sqrt{\frac{A}{\pi}}$$

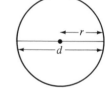

Example 2   *The volume contained by a cone is $V = \frac{1}{3}\pi r^2 h$, where r is the radius and h is the height. If the radius is equal to $\frac{2}{5}$ of the height,*
(a) determine the volume V as a function of h;
(b) determine the volume V as a function of r.

(a)   We have

$$V = \tfrac{1}{3}\pi r^2 h$$

and

$$r = \tfrac{2}{5}h$$

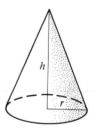

At this point, V is a function of two variables, r and h. In order to get V as a function of h alone, eliminate r by substituting $\frac{2}{5}h$ for r. When this is done,

$$V = \tfrac{1}{3}\pi r^2 h$$

becomes

$$V = \tfrac{1}{3}\pi(\tfrac{2}{5}h)^2 h \quad \text{after substituting } \tfrac{2}{5}h \text{ for } r$$

Then

$$V = \tfrac{1}{3}\pi \tfrac{4}{25}h^2 h$$

Finally,

$$V = \frac{4\pi h^3}{75}$$

We could write V as $V(h)$ to emphasize that V is a function of h.

$$V(h) = \frac{4\pi h^3}{75}$$

(b) To get V as a function of r, eliminate h. Since $r = \frac{2}{5}h$, then $h = \frac{5}{2}r$. Thus

$$V = \tfrac{1}{3}\pi r^2 h$$

becomes

$$V = \tfrac{1}{3}\pi r^2(\tfrac{5}{2}r)$$

which simplifies to

$$V = \frac{5\pi r^3}{6}$$

or

$$V(r) = \frac{5\pi r^3}{6}$$

Example 3 *A piece of wire length 23 units is to be cut into two pieces. One of the pieces will be bent into a square; the other will be bent into a circle. If the length of the piece used for the square is x, express the total area of the square and circular regions formed in terms of x.*

If one piece is of length x, then the other is of length $23 - x$.

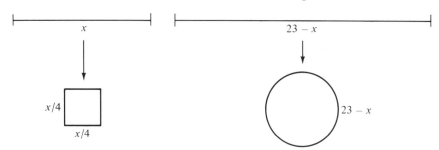

The square has sides of length $x/4$. Its area is any side squared.

$$A_\square = \left(\frac{x}{4}\right)^2 = \frac{x^2}{16}$$

The circle has a circumference of $23 - x$, where $C = 2\pi r$. To find the area of the circular region, we need to know the length of the radius, since $A = \pi r^2$. Using

$$C = 2\pi r$$

and knowing that $C = 23 - x$, we obtain

$$23 - x = 2\pi r$$

or

$$r = \frac{23 - x}{2\pi}$$

Now that we have r in terms of x, substitute the expression for r into

$$A_\circ = \pi r^2$$

The result is

$$A_\circ = \pi \cdot \left(\frac{23 - x}{2\pi}\right)^2$$

$$= \frac{\pi(23 - x)^2}{4\pi^2}$$

$$= \frac{(23 - x)^2}{4\pi}$$

So the total area is

$$A_\square + A_\circ = \frac{x^2}{16} + \frac{(23 - x)^2}{4\pi}$$

or

$$\text{area} = f(x) = \frac{x^2}{16} + \frac{(23 - x)^2}{4\pi}$$

Note that x can only be between 0 and 23. In other words, the domain of f is restricted to x such that $0 < x < 23$. This is because the piece cut for the square must be greater than zero, but cannot be as long as the whole wire (23).

The **Pythagorean theorem** is often useful when working in geometric settings. The theorem was first proved by the Greek mathematician Pythagoras in the sixth century B.C. It states that in any right triangle the square of the length of the hypotenuse equals the sum of the squares of the lengths of the legs. (The hypotenuse is the side opposite the right angle.)

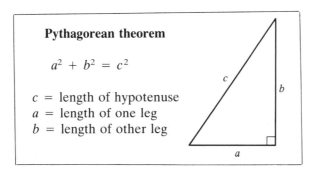

Pythagorean theorem

$a^2 + b^2 = c^2$

$c =$ length of hypotenuse
$a =$ length of one leg
$b =$ length of other leg

Example 4 shows an application of the Pythagorean theorem.

Example 4   *Find the area of an equilateral triangle in terms of its side s.*
An equilateral triangle is one in which all three sides are equal in length.

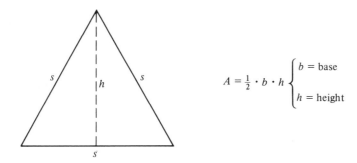

$$A = \frac{1}{2} \cdot b \cdot h \begin{cases} b = \text{base} \\ \\ h = \text{height} \end{cases}$$

The base is s, but we must find the height as a function of s in order to determine the area in terms of s. To do so, we shall now focus attention on half the triangle.

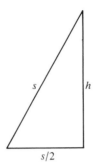

By the Pythagorean theorem, we can establish a relationship between s and h.

$$s^2 = h^2 + \left(\frac{s}{2}\right)^2$$

or

$$s^2 = h^2 + \frac{s^2}{4}$$

Now we will solve this equation for h in terms of s. First,

$$s^2 - \frac{s^2}{4} = h^2$$

The terms on the left can be combined by changing s^2 to a fraction with a denominator of 4.

$$\frac{4s^2}{4} - \frac{s^2}{4} = h^2$$

or

$$\frac{3s^2}{4} = h^2$$

Finally,

$$h = \sqrt{\frac{3s^2}{4}}$$

The term on the right can be simplified, if desired, by noting that $\sqrt{s^2} = s$ (because $s > 0$) and $\sqrt{4} = 2$.

$$h = \frac{s\sqrt{3}}{2}$$

Thus

$$A = \frac{1}{2} \cdot b \cdot h$$

becomes

$$A = \frac{1}{2} \cdot s \cdot \frac{s\sqrt{3}}{2}$$

or

$$A = \frac{s^2\sqrt{3}}{4}$$

Some effort could have been saved by using a theorem about $30°-60°-90°$ triangles. Such a theorem is presented in Chapter 7.

Similar triangles sometimes appear in geometric settings. Two triangles are **similar** if the three angles of one triangle are each equal to the three angles of the other. Thus similar triangles will have the same shape, although one may be larger than the other. Here is a drawing of two similar triangles.

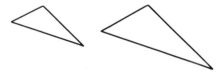

The following theorem for similar triangles is particularly useful.

> **Theorem for similar triangles**
>
> If two triangles are similar, their corresponding sides are in proportion.

As an example, consider these two similar triangles, where a, b, c, x, y, and z represent the lengths of the sides.

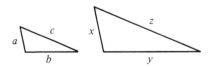

Several proportions can be written. Here are four such proportions.

$$\frac{a}{b} = \frac{x}{y}, \quad \frac{y}{x} = \frac{b}{a}, \quad \frac{a}{x} = \frac{c}{z}, \quad \frac{y}{b} = \frac{x}{a}$$

Example 5 *Solve for x. Assume that the triangles are similar.*

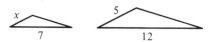

By the theorem for similar triangles, corresponding sides of the triangles are in proportion. One such proportion is

$$\frac{x}{7} = \frac{5}{12}$$

We can solve for x by multiplying both sides by 7.

$$x = 7 \cdot \frac{5}{12} = \frac{35}{12}$$

Example 6 *Given the following triangle, write x as a function of y.*

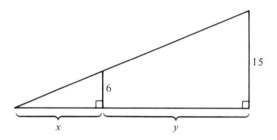

Note the following similar triangles that appear in the given triangle.

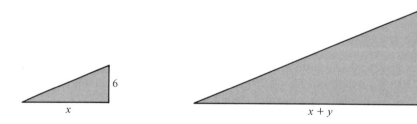

Because corresponding sides of similar triangles are in proportion, we can set up the proportion

$$\frac{x}{6} = \frac{x + y}{15}$$

which becomes

$$15x = 6(x + y)$$

Next, proceed to multiply out the expression on the right and then collect x terms on the left side.

$$15x = 6x + 6y$$

$$9x = 6y$$

$$x = \frac{6y}{9}$$

$$x = \frac{2y}{3}$$

Example 7 *A man 6 feet tall has been walking away from a streetlight. When he is 10 feet from the light, he stops.*
(a) If his shadow is 11 feet long, how high is the streetlight?
(b) If his shadow is x feet long, express the length (x) of his shadow as a function of the height (y) of the streetlight.

(a) Here is a drawing of the situation.

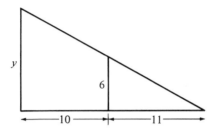

Observe that the large right triangle with side y is similar to the smaller right triangle (within) with side 6. A proportion can be established and solved for y, the height of the streetlight.

$$\frac{y}{21} = \frac{6}{11}$$

from which

$$y = 21 \cdot \frac{6}{11} = \frac{126}{11}$$

(b) Here is a drawing of the situation.

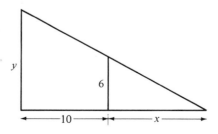

The larger right triangle with side y is similar to the smaller right triangle with side 6. This enables us to establish a proportion involving both x and y. One such proportion is

$$\frac{y}{10 + x} = \frac{6}{x}$$

Now we must manipulate this equation into a form that gives x as a function of y, as required by the statement of the problem. To begin, multiply both sides of the equation by the common denominator $(10 + x)(x)$. This step will eliminate the fractions from the equation. The result is

$$xy = (10 + x)6$$

or

$$xy = 60 + 6x$$

Next, add $-6x$ to both sides to get the x terms together on the same side.

$$xy - 6x = 60$$

Factor out an x from both terms. The result is

$$x(y - 6) = 60$$

Finally, divide both sides by $y - 6$.

$$x = \frac{60}{y - 6}$$

Since the streetlight must be taller than the man, $y > 6$. (Furthermore, if $y < 6$, then shadow length x is negative. If $y = 6$, x is not defined.) The shadow length must be positive; so $x > 0$.

As you will see, Example 8 is fairly complex and it involves another theorem from geometry. The theorem:

> An angle inscribed in a semicircle is a right angle.

In the following diagrams the angles labeled C are inscribed in semicircles and so each is a right angle.

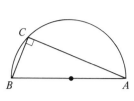

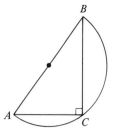

Example 8 also uses the fact that the two shaded triangles shown are similar. Here angle C is assumed to be a right angle.

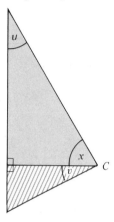

To see that the triangles are similar, observe that since C is a right angle, we have $v + x = 90°$. In the top triangle the sum of the angles is $180°$, of course. Thus $90° + u + x = 180°$, or $u + x = 90°$. This means that $u = v$.

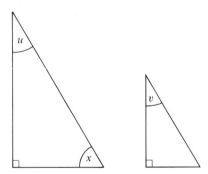

Clearly the two triangles are similar: the right angles are equal, angle u equals angle v, and angle x must equal the third angle of the other triangle (since the sum of the angles in each triangle is $180°$).

Example 8 *Consider a right circular cone inscribed within a sphere of radius r. Express the height h of the cone in terms of the radius r of the sphere and the radius R of the cone.*

The sphere: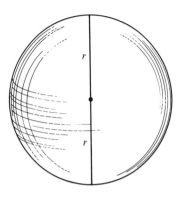   The cone: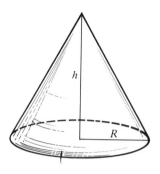

The cone inscribed within the sphere:

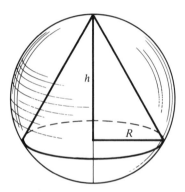

We can focus on

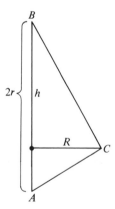

Angle C is a right angle because it is inscribed in a semicircle. The two right triangles formed with common side R are similar; so their corresponding sides are in proportion.

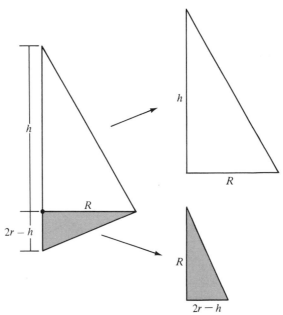

One proportion that can be written is

$$\frac{h}{R} = \frac{R}{2r - h}$$

Multiply both sides of this equation by the common denominator $R(2r - h)$. The result is

$$R \cdot R = h(2r - h)$$
$$R^2 = 2rh - h^2$$
$$h^2 - 2rh + R^2 = 0$$

This is a quadratic equation in h, of form $ah^2 + bh + c = 0$, with $a = 1$, $b = -2r$, and $c = R^2$. Thus by the quadratic formula,

$$h = \frac{-(-2r) \pm \sqrt{(-2r)^2 - 4(1)(R^2)}}{2(1)}$$

$$= \frac{2r \pm \sqrt{4r^2 - 4R^2}}{2}$$

$$= \frac{2r \pm \sqrt{4(r^2 - R^2)}}{2}$$

$$= \frac{2r \pm 2\sqrt{r^2 - R^2}}{2}$$

$$= \frac{2(r \pm \sqrt{r^2 - R^2})}{2}$$

Finally,

$$h = r \pm \sqrt{r^2 - R^2}$$

Example 9 *Use the theorem for similar triangles to prove that the value of the slope of a line is independent of the two points chosen to compute it.*

Consider the line passing through four points, as shown next.

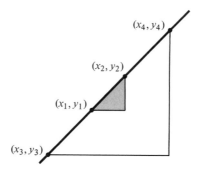

Using points (x_1, y_1) and (x_2, y_2), we see that the slope is

$$\frac{y_2 - y_1}{x_2 - x_1}$$

Using points (x_3, y_3) and (x_4, y_4), we see that the slope is

$$\frac{y_4 - y_3}{x_4 - x_3}$$

We want to show that these two slopes are indeed equal. Note that the smaller triangle (shaded) and the larger triangle are similar. The length of the vertical side of the smaller triangle is $y_2 - y_1$. The length of the horizontal side is $x_2 - x_1$.

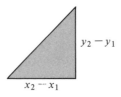

Similarly the length of the vertical side of the larger triangle is $y_4 - y_3$ and the length of the horizontal side is $x_4 - x_3$.

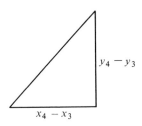

Since the triangles are similar, their corresponding sides are in proportion. Specifically,

$$\frac{y_2 - y_1}{x_2 - x_1} = \frac{y_4 - y_3}{x_4 - x_3}$$

which is what we wanted to prove.

Formulas

$$C = \text{circumference}$$
$$A = \text{area}$$
$$P = \text{perimeter}$$
$$V = \text{volume}$$
$$S = \text{surface area}$$

1. Circle.

$$C = 2\pi r$$
$$A = \pi r^2$$

2. Rectangle.

$$A = lw$$
$$P = 2l + 2w$$

3. Triangle.

$$A = \tfrac{1}{2}bh$$

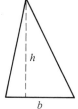

4. Trapezoid.

$$A = \tfrac{1}{2}(b_1 + b_2)h$$

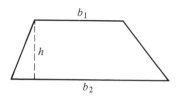

5. Rectangular solid.

$$V = lwh$$

$$S = 2lh + 2lw + 2hw$$

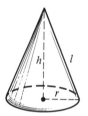

6. Cone.

$$V = \tfrac{1}{3}\pi r^2 h$$

$$S = \pi rl \qquad \text{curved portion only}$$

7. Cylinder.

$$V = \pi r^2 h$$

$$S = 2\pi rh \qquad \text{curved side only}$$

$$S = \pi r^2 \qquad \text{top } or \text{ bottom } only$$

8. Sphere.

$$V = \tfrac{4}{3}\pi r^3$$

$$S = 4\pi r^2$$

EXERCISES 4.2

Answers to starred exercises are given in the back of the book.

*1. In each exercise you are asked to make a manipulation or substitution (or both) in order to express one variable as a function of another variable.

(a) The circumference of a circle is $C = 2\pi r$. Express the radius as a function of the circumference.

(b) Express the diameter of a circle as a function of the circumference.

(c) The volume of a cone is $V = \frac{1}{3}\pi r^2 h$. If the height is six times the radius, determine V as a function of r.

(d) Repeat part (c), except determine V as a function of h.

(e) Given $V = \frac{4}{3}\pi r^3$ for a sphere of radius r, express V as a function of diameter d rather than radius r.

(f) A cone has a radius equal to twice its height. Express the volume in terms of height—that is, without the radius.

(g) The volume of a cylinder is given by $V = \pi r^2 h$. Express the volume as a function of r if r is twice h.

(h) Express the volume of a cylinder as a function of the *diameter* of its base if its height and radius of base are the same length.

2. Determine length x in each triangle.

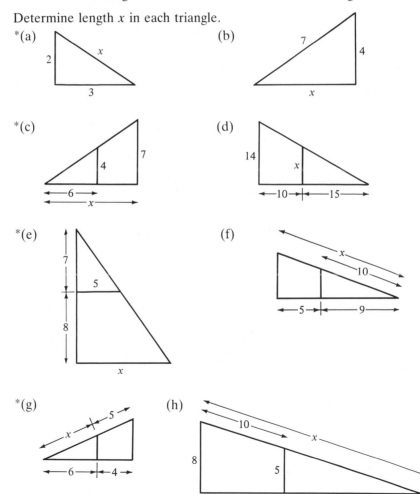

* 3. Suppose there are two numbers whose sum is 100. Call one number x.
   (a) Express the other number in terms of x.
   (b) Express the product of the two numbers in terms of x.

4. Suppose there are two numbers whose product is 50. Call one number x.
   (a) Express the other number in terms of x.
   (b) Express the sum of the two numbers in terms of x.

*5. A closed box has a base that is a square, x units by x units. The height of the box is y units. Express the area of the surface of the box in terms of x and y. (*Note:* The surface area is the combined area of the four sides and the top and bottom.)

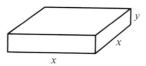

6. A circular disc of radius x is cut out from a square piece of cardboard. Express the area of the waste as a function of x.

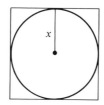

*7. A wire 252 centimeters long will be bent into the shape of a right triangle whose sides are in the ratio of 3: 4: 5. How long is the hypotenuse of the triangle?

8. A homeowner plans to use 100 feet of fence to enclose a patio area behind her house. The width of the patio is x feet.
   (a) Express the length in terms of x.
   (b) Express the area to be enclosed as a function of x.
   (c) Determine how long the patio should be if the area to be enclosed is 1200 square feet.

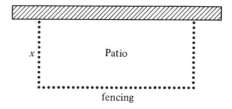

*9. A fence of length 200 feet will be used to enclose a rectangular area. If the length of the rectangle is x feet, express the width w as a function of x.

10. Express the distance between the batter (home plate) and the runner as a function of x. All four sides of the diamond (square) are 90 feet.

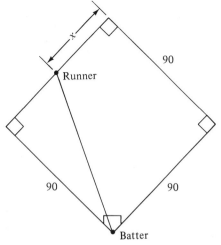

*11. A tent is made in the shape of a cone and has no floor. The surface area can be computed as $S = \pi r l$, where l is the slant height (see diagram).

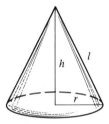

(a) If the height h is 7 feet, express S as a function of l. (*Hint:* To obtain S as a function of l, you need to eliminate r. So obtain a relationship involving r and l and solve it for r.)

(b) Suppose instead that the slant height l is 10 feet. Express the volume of the cone as a function of radius r.

12. Express the area of each rectangle in terms of x.

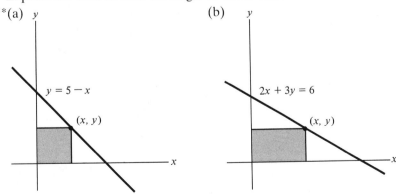

*13. Express the area of the given right triangle as a function of x.

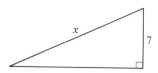

*14. Express the area of the given right triangle as a function of t alone (that is, without u).

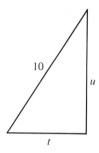

*15. Determine the area of the shaded triangle.

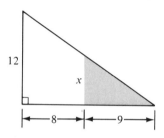

16. Determine the number of square units in the rectangle.

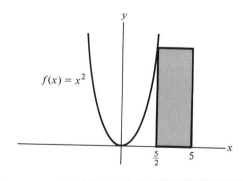

*17. Consider the parabola below and the shaded rectangle within it.

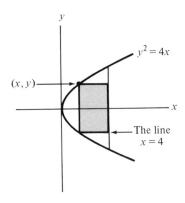

(a) Express the length (vertical) of the rectangle as a function of y.

(b) Express the width (horizontal) of the rectangle as a function of x.

(c) Express the area of the rectangle as a function of y.

18. Two posts are placed 50 feet apart. One is 12 feet high; the other is 9 feet high. Then a stake is placed x feet from the shorter post. A rope runs from the top of one post to the stake and then on to the top of the other post. Express the total length of the rope as a function of x.

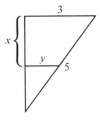

(*Note:* These are *not* similar triangles.)

*19. A rectangle of length 10 and width 4 is inscribed in a circle. How long is the radius of the circle? (*Hint:* Draw a useful radius.)

20. For the figure, express y in terms of x.

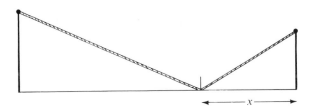

*21. A rectangle has length x, width y, and area 25. Express the perimeter of the rectangle as a function of x.

22. A rancher plans to fence in a rectangular-shaped area of 300 square feet. If the length of the region is x feet, express the perimeter of the region as a function of x.

*23. A person plans to swim from point A to point B and then run from point B to point C (see diagram). Assume that it is 2 miles from A to D and 8 miles from D to C. Express the distance traveled (swimming plus running) in terms of x, where x is the distance from D to B.

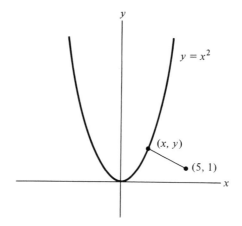

24. Express the distance between the point (5, 1) and the curve $y = x^2$ as a function of x. (See page 56 for the distance formula.)

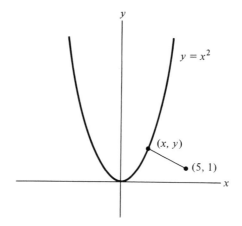

*25. Express the area A of a circle as a function of its circumference C.

*26. Suppose that the sides of a square are of length x. Then each side is increased by an amount h.
    (a) Express the area of the original square as a function of x.
    (b) Express the area of the new square as a function of x and h.
    (c) Express the increase in the area of the square in terms of x and h.

*27. The radius of the semicircle shown is 7 inches. Let y represent the length of a vertical side of the rectangle. Express the area of the rectangle as a function of y. (*Hint:* Draw a useful radius.)

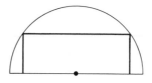

28. Given a right triangle with base b and height h of equal size and hypotenuse of length $\sqrt{1 + 8x^2}$, express the area of the triangle as a function of x—without b or h.

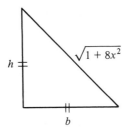

*29. A closed box is to be constructed so that its base is a square (x by x) and its volume is 1000 cubic centimeters. Express the area of the surface of the box as a function of x.

*30. The volume of a cylindrical can ($V = \pi r^2 h$) is 50 cubic inches. Express the area of the surface of the can as a function of radius r. Notice that the surface area consists of two circular regions (top and bottom) each with area πr^2 and a curved side with area $2\pi rh$.

*31. A trapezoid is inscribed in a semicircle of radius 7. Express the area of the trapezoid as a function of x.

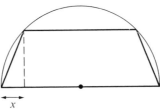

32. A child 4 feet tall walks away from a streetlight that is 11 feet high. How far (x) is he from the light if his shadow is 9 feet long?

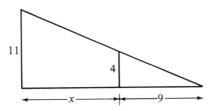

*33. A boy 5 feet tall walks away from a streetlight that is 14 feet high. How long is his shadow when he is 12 feet from the light?

34. Express the area of an equilateral triangle in terms of its perimeter. Use A for area and P for perimeter.

*35. A cylinder of radius r is inscribed in a sphere of radius 7. Let the height of the cylinder be h.
   (a) Determine a relationship (equation) involving h and r. A well-chosen radius of the sphere will help.
   (b) Use the relationship determined in part (a) to express the volume of the cylinder as a function of h.
   (c) Express the volume of the cylinder as a function of r.

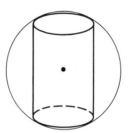

36. An open box (that is, one without a top) has a square base x centimeters by x centimeters. It is made from 228 square centimeters of material. Express the volume of the box as a function of x. Note that the material used is the surface area of the box.

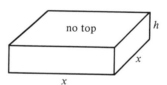

*37. A rectangular piece of cardboard 30 centimeters by 40 centimeters is used to make an open box with a rectangular base. This is done by cutting out a small square from each corner and then bending up the sides. Express the volume of the box created as a function of x.

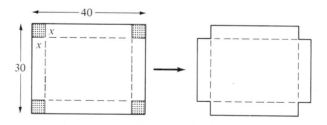

38. A man has a square sheet of paper 10 inches by 10 inches. Squares of size x by x are cut from each corner of the sheet. The four flaps that are left

after cutting are then folded up to form a box without a top. Express the volume of the box in terms of x.

*39. A rectangular sheet of paper with an area of 150 square inches will include a rectangular printed area and margins of 2 inches at the top and bottom and 1 inch on each side. Let x be the width of the sheet and express the area of the printed region in terms of x.

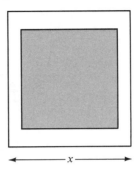

*40. Consider the right triangle here.
   (a) Determine the value of x.
   (b) Determine the value of y.

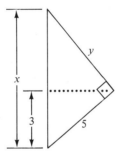

*41. In the triangle shown, assume that C is a right angle. In each case, express y as a function of x.
   (a) If AD is 7 and BD is y.
   (b) If AD is 7 and AB is y.
   (c) If AD is y and BD is 7.
   (d) If AD is y and AB is 7.

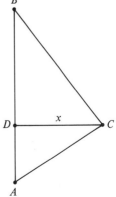

42. A rectangle is inscribed in a circle of radius r. The length l of the rectangle is twice the width w. Express r as a function of w.

*43. A conical drinking cup is constructed so that the height of the fluid in it is always three times the radius of the fluid (the radius of the fluid being measured at the top of the fluid). The radius of the cup is 3 centimeters and its height is 9 centimeters.

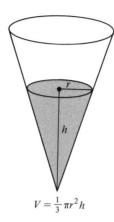

$$V = \tfrac{1}{3}\pi r^2 h$$

(a) Express r as a function of h.
(b) Determine the volume of the fluid when the height of the fluid is half that of the cup.
(c) Determine the height of the fluid when the volume of the fluid is half the capacity of the cup.
(d) Determine the radius of the fluid when the volume of the fluid is half the capacity of the cup.

44. A window is formed by placing a semicircular piece of glass above a rectangular piece. The perimeter of the entire window is 16. If the radius of the semicircular piece is r, express the area of the entire window in terms of r.

*45. The isosceles triangle shown here has a height of 70 centimeters and a base of 40 centimeters. A rectangle of width x centimeters and length y

centimeters is inscribed in the triangle. Express the area of the rectangle in terms of x. (*Hint:* Look for similar triangles.)

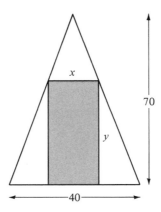

46. A wire of length 32 units will be cut into two pieces—one to be bent into a square, the other into an equilateral triangle. If the length of the piece used for the triangle is x, express the total area of the square and triangular regions as a function of x.

4.3 FUNCTIONS IN ECONOMICS

Basic economic theory includes relationships between supply and demand. Cost, revenue, and profit involve supply and demand. Supply, demand, cost, revenue, and profit can all be expressed in terms of the number of units (call it x) that are produced or sold. So we are involved with supply functions, demand functions, and others.

A **supply function** expresses an average price per unit at which x units can be supplied. We shall use S to denote supply functions. Some manufactured products, such as stereo equipment, can be supplied at a lower price if more can be made. This is due to the lower cost per unit when the product can be mass produced. The supply function $S(x) = 1000 - x$ suggests that one stereo unit can be supplied at $999, two units at an average of $998 *each*, and 100 units at an average of $900 *each*. Note

$$S(x) = 1000 - x$$

$$S(1) = 1000 - 1 = 999$$

$$S(2) = 1000 - 2 = 998$$

$$S(100) = 1000 - 100 = 900$$

This function might only be good for x up to 200 or 300. It surely is not accurate for $x = 990$, since $S(990) = 10$ says that if 990 units can be produced, they can be supplied at $10 each. Some products are supplied at a higher price if more are made, perhaps because the resources needed are scarce or in great demand.

A **cost function** expresses the total cost at which x units can be supplied. We will use C to denote cost functions. The cost of x units is always x times the average cost per unit. This statement can be expressed as

$$C(x) = x \cdot S(x)$$

A supply function for stereos was given as $S(x) = 1000 - x$. The cost of x units is $C(x) = x \cdot S(x)$. Thus, $C(x) = x \cdot (1000 - x)$ or $C(x) = 1000x - x^2$ for stereos. The cost of 10 stereos is $C(10)$.

$$C(10) = 10 \cdot (1000 - 10)$$
$$= 10 \cdot 990$$
$$= \$9900$$

A **demand function** expresses an average price per unit at which x units can be sold. The demand is, in effect, how much people are willing to pay per unit. We shall use D to denote demand functions.† If stereos can be sold at an average of $1200 each, regardless of how many, then $D(x) = 1200$.

A **revenue function** expresses the total revenue received if x units are sold. We shall use R to denote revenue functions. The revenue from x units is always x times the average price per unit. This statement can be expressed as

$$R(x) = x \cdot D(x)$$

For the stereos example,

$$D(x) = 1200$$
$$R(x) = x \cdot 1200 \quad \text{or} \quad R(x) = 1200x$$

The revenue from the sale of 10 stereos is $R(10)$.

$$R(10) = 1200(10) = \$12,000$$

The *profit* from the sale of x units can be computed as revenue minus cost.

---

† The equation showing the relationship between price and quantity is called the **demand equation**. It can be solved for price as a function of quantity. We call this latter function $D(x)$ (D for demand) rather than $P(x)$ (P for price) because we shall use $P(x)$ for the profit function.

If P represents profit—that is, a **profit function**—then

$$P(x) = R(x) - C(x)$$

Since profit is given by

$$P(x) = R(x) - C(x)$$

we have for the stereo example

$$P(x) = 1200x - (1000x - x^2)$$

which simplifies to

$$P(x) = x^2 + 200x$$

Next, let us consider some specific values of P, that is, a few specific profit figures from the sale of stereos. Consider $x = 0, 1, 2,$ and 10 stereos.

$$P(0) = \$0$$
$$P(1) = \$201$$
$$P(2) = \$404$$
$$P(10) = \$2100$$

A product is said to reach a state of **equilibrium** when the supply equals the demand.

Example 10 *If $S(x) = 2x + 3$ and $D(x) = 51 - 4x$, for what quantity x will equilibrium exist?*

Equilibrium exists when supply equals demand—that is, when $S(x) = D(x)$. In this example, $S(x) = 2x + 3$ and $D(x) = 51 - 4x$; so equilibrium exists when

$$2x + 3 = 51 - 4x$$

or

$$6x = 48$$

or

$$x = 8$$

Thus equilibrium exists when the number of units is 8.

When more units are supplied than are demanded (at a particular price), then there is a **surplus**. When more units are demanded than are supplied (at a particular price), then there is a **shortage**.

Example 11 *Surplus and shortage.*

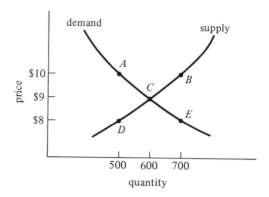

Let us consider this graph of supply and demand functions and make some observations. First, the point C represents a state of equilibrium because that is where supply and demand are equal. The price at that point is $9 and the quantity is 600 units. Next, note that when the price is $10, the quantity supplied is 700 (point B), but the quantity demanded is only 500 (point A). This means that at $10 per unit there is a *surplus* of 200 units ($700 - 500 = 200$). By contrast, when the price is $8, the quantity supplied is 500 (point D) whereas the quantity demanded is 700 (point E). This means that at $8 per unit there is a *shortage* of 200 units.

We have seen that the cost per unit or revenue per unit can depend on the number of units. A manufacturer may want to halt production if the cost per unit becomes too large or if the revenue per unit becomes too small. This means it is quite reasonable to calculate the cost of the 100th unit or 1000th unit, for example, or the revenue from the sale of the 100th unit or 1000th unit.

Example 12 *Determine the cost of the 50th unit if* $C(x) = \dfrac{x^2}{10} + x$ *dollars.*

The cost of the 50th unit is *not* $C(50)$ because $C(50)$ is the cost of 50 units— the first 50. Consider that $C(49)$ is the cost of the first 49 units. If $C(49)$ is subtracted from $C(50)$, the result will be the cost of the 50th unit alone.

$$\text{Cost of 50th unit} = C(50) - C(49)$$

$$= \left(\frac{50^2}{10} + 50\right) - \left(\frac{49^2}{10} + 49\right)$$

$$= (250 + 50) - (240.10 + 49)$$

$$= 10.90$$

The cost of the 50th unit is $10.90.

We have seen that the cost of supplying units depends on how many units are to be supplied. There are usually, however, certain costs in a business that are not affected by the number of units that are produced. The rent on a building and the cost of machinery are two examples of such **overhead** costs. As a result, we could define overhead as the cost of supplying zero units. In other words,

$$\boxed{\text{Overhead} = C(0)}$$

Example 13   *If $C(x) = x^2 - 3x + 500$ dollars, what is the overhead?*

$$\text{Overhead} = C(0)$$
$$= (0)^2 - 3(0) + 500$$
$$= 500$$

The overhead is $500.

EXERCISES 4.3

1.   Answer each question. Assume that the monetary unit is dollars.
   *(a)   If $R(x) = 7 + 3x$, what is the revenue from the sale of 15 units?
   (b)   If $P(x) = x^2 + 10x - 1200$, what is the profit from the sale of 40 units?
   *(c)   If $S(x) = 500 - 8x$, what is the average price per unit at which 7 units can be supplied?
   (d)   If $D(x) = \dfrac{72}{x} + 5$, what is the average price per unit at which 12 units can be sold?
   *(e)   If $C(x) = x^2 + 7x$ and $R(x) = 8 + 30x$, what is the profit from the sale of 20 units?
   (f)   If $S(x) = 5x - 24$ and $D(x) = \dfrac{100}{x} + 35$, what is the profit from the sale of 7 units?

2.   For each supply and demand function given, determine the cost, revenue, and profit functions.
   *(a) $S(x) = 200 + x$, $D(x) = 300$
   (b) $S(x) = \dfrac{3}{x} + 5$, $D(x) = x^2 - 8$

*(c) $S(x) = 1 - x^2, \quad D(x) = 7x$

(d) $S(x) = 3x + 15, \quad D(x) = \dfrac{20}{x} + 17$

*(e) $S(x) = 7x - 20, \quad D(x) = 3 + \dfrac{50}{x}$

*3.   Let $S(x) = 2x + 3$ and $D(x) = \dfrac{20}{x} + 5$. Determine the profit on the sale of 3 units and of 10 units. Compare and comment on the two values determined.

4.   Determine the quantity x for which equilibrium will exist.
   *(a) $S(x) = 5x + 1, \quad D(x) = 22 - 2x$
   (b) $S(x) = 7x - 3, \quad D(x) = 150 - 2x$
   *(c) $S(x) = 8, \quad D(x) = \dfrac{200}{x}$
   (d) $S(x) = 6, \quad D(x) = \dfrac{100}{x} + 1$

*5.   Consider the graph shown and answer the questions based on it.

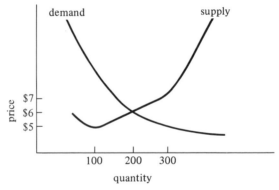

(a)   For what quantity does equilibrium exist?
(b)   When the price is $7, what is the approximate quantity demanded and the approximate quantity supplied? Is there a surplus or shortage?
(c)   When the price is $5, what is the approximate quantity demanded and the approximate quantity supplied? Is there a surplus or shortage?

6.   Let $C(x) = x^2 + 8x$.
   (a)   What is the cost of 10 units?
   (b)   What is the cost of 9 units?
   (c)   What is the cost of the tenth unit?

*7.   Let $R(x) = 100 + 2x$.
   (a)   What is the revenue from the sale of 15 units?

(b)   What is the revenue from the sale of 14 units?

(c)   What is the revenue from the sale of the 15th unit?

(d)   What is the revenue from the sale of the 12th unit?

8.   Let $S(x) = x + 10$ and $D(x) = \dfrac{110}{x} + 60$. What is the profit from the sale of the 11th unit?

9.   Determine the overhead.

   *(a) $C(x) = x^2 - 16x + 350$

   (b) $C(x) = 1.5x^2 - 18x + 23.50$

   *(c) $C(x) = \dfrac{x + 15}{5} - 1.80x + 2.50$

   (d) $C(x) = x^2 + 19x$

4.4 DISTANCE AND VELOCITY

This section presents the application of functions to the study of projectile motion in the vertical direction. We shall shoot rockets straight up, drop stones off cliffs, and so on, and use the functions that describe their motion. We shall not use the usual "example" format, but rather a question-and-answer approach, because of the nature of the applications.

Suppose that a ball is thrown vertically upward from the roof of a building. The person throwing it reaches over the edge so that the ball will not hit the building when it comes back down.

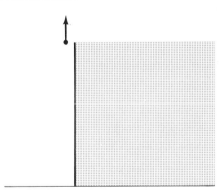

We shall assume that the ball travels according to certain equations (functions of time t) and then see what else we can determine about its travel. We shall use the following variables:

      t for *time* (in seconds)

      s for *distance* from the ground (in feet)

      v for *velocity* (in feet per second)

We shall assume that the ball travels according to these formulas:

$$s = s(t) = -16t^2 + 80t + 96$$

$$v = v(t) = -32t + 80$$

These equations contain a lot of information about the situation we have described. Let us obtain some of that information by answering a few basic questions.

Question. *How tall is the building?*

Answer. The height of the building is, in fact, the same as the distance of the ball from the ground in the beginning. In other words, the height of the building is s when $t = 0$. That height is $s(0)$, which we compute next.

$$s(0) = -16(0)^2 + 80(0) + 96 = 96$$

The building is 96 feet tall.

Question. *When does the ball strike the ground?*

Answer. The ball strikes the ground when its distance from the ground is 0—that is, when $s = 0$. Thus we determine when $s = -16t^2 + 80t + 96$ is 0.

$$0 = -16t^2 + 80t + 96$$

After dividing both sides by -16, the equation is

$$t^2 - 5t - 6 = 0$$

or

$$(t - 6)(t + 1) = 0$$

The solutions of this equation are

$$t = 6, \qquad t = -1$$

Thus the ball strikes the ground 6 seconds after it is thrown. Notice that we reject $t = -1$ because a negative value of t (time) makes no sense.

Question. *With what velocity does the ball strike the ground?*

Answer. We have just determined that the ball strikes the ground when $t = 6$. So we compute $v(6)$, the velocity of the ball when t is 6. From the equation $v(t) = -32t + 80$ we obtain

$$v(6) = -32(6) + 80 = -112$$

The ball strikes the ground with a velocity of -112 feet per second.

Note on sign. The minus in -112 feet per second indicates that the ball is traveling downward. The ball begins with a velocity of 80 feet per second in the upward direction, which is $+80$. As it travels, its velocity decreases until it reaches 0 (which we shall find happens when $t = \frac{5}{2}$). Then it begins to fall and its velocity is negative on the entire flight downward to the ground. Thus the sign of the velocity specifies the direction in which the ball is traveling: $+$ is upward, $-$ is downward.

The acceleration due to gravity ($a = -32$ feet per second per second) is in the downward direction and thus is negative.

If the ball were thrown downward rather than upward, then its initial velocity would be negative rather than positive.

Finally, it should be noted that the formulas for s and v that we have assumed since the beginning are easily derived by using elementary calculus.

Question. *With what velocity is the ball thrown; that is, what is its initial velocity?*

Answer. We want v when $t = 0$.

$$v(0) = -32(0) + 80 = 80$$

The initial velocity of the ball is 80 feet per second.

Question. *When does the ball reach its maximum height, and how high is it at that time?*

Answer. First, consider the nature of the ball's travel. It starts out fast and gradually slows down because the force of gravity pulls against it in the downward direction. So eventually the ball will stop in midair (for an instant) and begin to fall downward toward the ground. It is at the instant when it is stopped that its height is maximum. It has gone as high as it will go. So the maximum height occurs when the velocity is zero. To determine when (for what t value) this occurs, let $v = 0$ in

$$v = -32t + 80$$

The result is

$$0 = -32t + 80$$

from which $t = \frac{80}{32}$, or $\frac{5}{2}$. Thus, the ball reaches its maximum height $2\frac{1}{2}$ seconds after being thrown.

To determine the maximum height, compute $s(\frac{5}{2})$, the height when $t = 2\frac{1}{2}$, when the ball reaches its maximum height.

$$
\begin{aligned}
s(\tfrac{5}{2}) &= -16(\tfrac{5}{2})^2 + 80(\tfrac{5}{2}) + 96 \\
&= -16 \cdot \tfrac{25}{4} + 200 + 96 \\
&= -100 + 200 + 96 \\
&= 196
\end{aligned}
$$

Thus the maximum height attained is 196 feet.

EXERCISES 4.4

In all exercises, assume that t is time in seconds, s is distance in feet, and v is velocity in feet per second.

*1. A rocket is shot vertically upward from the edge of a cliff and travels according to

$$s = s(t) = -16t^2 + 352t + 768$$
$$v = v(t) = -32t + 352$$

Here s is the distance from the ground.
(a) How high is the cliff?
(b) When does the rocket strike the ground?
(c) With what velocity does the rocket strike the ground?
(d) What is the initial velocity of the rocket?
(e) When does the rocket reach its maximum height?
(f) What is the maximum height attained by the rocket?
(g) Determine the velocity 7 seconds after launch and 15 seconds after launch. Explain the similarity and the difference in the two velocities you have calculated.
(h) How many seconds after launch does it take before the rocket passes the top of the cliff on the way down?

2. A rocket is shot vertically upward so that its distance from the ground t seconds after launch is $s = -16t^2 + 480t$ feet. Its velocity t seconds after launch is $v = -32t + 480$ feet per second.
(a) When will the rocket reach its maximum height?
(b) How high will the rocket travel?
(c) From what height was the rocket launched?
(d) What was the rocket's velocity at the instant it was launched?
(e) With what velocity does the rocket strike the ground upon its return?

*3. A ball thrown directly downward from the top of a building travels so that its distance from the ground is $s = -16t^2 - 8t + 224$ and its velocity is $v = -32t - 8$.
(a) With what initial velocity is the ball thrown downward?
(b) How high is the building?
(c) When does the ball strike the ground?
(d) How fast is the ball going when it strikes the ground?

4. A stone is dropped from the top of a cliff of unknown height h feet. It travels according to $s = -16t^2 + h$ and $v = -32t$.
(a) If it takes 5 seconds for the stone to hit the lake below, how high is the cliff?

(b) What is the velocity of the stone at the instant it hits the lake?

*5. The acceleration due to gravity of the *moon* is less than that of the earth ($a \approx -5.3$ feet per second per second rather than $a \approx -32$ feet per second per second). Consequently, a ball thrown upward on the surface of the moon will go higher and take longer to return. Consider a ball thrown upward from the surface of the moon and a ball thrown upward from the surface of the earth—both with the same initial velocity.

$$\text{Moon:} \quad \begin{aligned} s &= -2.65t^2 + 106t \\ v &= -5.3t + 106 \end{aligned}$$

$$\text{Earth:} \quad \begin{aligned} s &= -16t^2 + 106t \\ v &= -32t + 106 \end{aligned}$$

(a) What is the initial velocity in each case?

(b) How high does the ball go on the moon and on the earth? Answers should be to the nearest tenth of a foot.

(c) How long does it take the ball to reach the ground on the moon and on the earth? Answers should be to the nearest tenth of a second.

Polynomials and Rational Functions

5.1 INTRODUCTION AND FUNDAMENTALS

Most of this chapter is devoted to the study of polynomials. What, then, is a polynomial?

> A **polynomial function** in x is any function of the form
>
> $$p(x) = a_n x^n + a_{n-1} x^{n-1} + \cdots + a_2 x^2 + a_1 x + a_0$$
>
> where n is a nonnegative integer and $a_n, a_{n-1}, a_{n-2}, \ldots, a_1, a_0$ are real numbers.

Thus a polynomial function consists of a sum of terms in which each term is a real constant times a nonnegative integer power of the variable. The **degree** of a polynomial is the highest power of the variable; that is, if $p(x) = a_n x^n + a_{n-1} x^{n-1} + \cdots + a_2 x^2 + a_1 x + a_0$ and $a_n \neq 0$, polynomial p has degree n. The coefficient of the variable in the term of highest degree is called the **leading coefficient.** Here are some examples of polynomial functions.

$$f(x) = x^5 + 3x^4 - x^3 + 2x + 7 \qquad \text{degree 5}$$

$$p(x) = 4x^7 - \frac{3x^4}{5} + x^2 + 1 \qquad \text{degree 7}$$

$$q(x) = x^2 - 5x - \sqrt{7} \qquad \text{degree 2}$$

$$g(x) = 3x + 2 \qquad \text{degree 1}$$

$$t(x) = 7 = 7x^0 \qquad \text{degree 0}$$

The leading coefficient of the polynomial $f(x) = x^5 + 3x^4 - x^3 + 2x + 7$ is 1, the coefficient of the x^5 term. The leading coefficient of polynomial $g(x) = 3x + 2$ is 3.

The following functions are not polynomials in x:

$$f(x) = x^5 - \frac{1}{x^2} + 4 \qquad \text{since } \frac{1}{x^2} = x^{-2}$$

$$g(x) = x^2 + 3\sqrt{x} + 4x - 9 \qquad \text{since } \sqrt{x} = x^{1/2}$$

The domain of any polynomial function is the set of all real numbers.

Polynomial functions of small degree are named. Polynomials of first degree, $f(x) = ax + b$, are called linear polynomial functions or simply **linear functions**. Polynomials of degree two, $f(x) = ax^2 + bx + c$, are **quadratic functions**. Polynomials of degree three, $f(x) = ax^3 + bx^2 + cx + d$, are **cubic functions**. Polynomials of degree four are called **quartic functions**.

In Chapter 3 we determined the zeros of linear functions, quadratic functions, and others. As you know, linear functions have one zero and quadratic functions have two zeros. A theorem of algebra states that:

> A polynomial function of degree n has exactly n zeros (not necessarily distinct).

This statement is consistent with linear functions (polynomials of degree 1) having one zero and quadratic functions (polynomials of degree 2) having two zeros. Here is an example illustrating a *cubic* function (degree 3) and its *three* zeros.

$$p(x) = x^3 - 5x^2 - 14x$$

$$x^3 - 5x^2 - 14x = 0$$

$$(x)(x^2 - 5x - 14) = 0$$

$$(x)(x - 7)(x + 2) = 0$$

$$x = 0 \mid x = 7 \mid x = -2$$

The preceding cubic expression was readily factored because there was no constant term; that is, an x could be factored from each term to leave a quadratic expression. In the next section we shall factor cubic and quartic polynomial expressions that do have constant terms.

The polynomial function $p(x) = x^2 + 2x + 1$ has two zeros and they are not distinct.

$$p(x) = x^2 + 2x + 1$$

$$x^2 + 2x + 1 = 0$$

$$(x + 1)(x + 1) = 0$$

$$x = -1, \qquad x = -1$$

We say that -1 is a **double zero** of polynomial p. (If the polynomial had three factors the same, such as $(x - 4)(x - 4)(x - 4)$, then we would say that 4 is a **triple zero** or **zero of multiplicity 3** and so on.)

EXERCISES 5.1

Answers to starred exercises are given in the back of the book.

*1. Determine which functions are polynomials.
 (a) $f(x) = x^4 + 5x^3 - 4x^2 + 3x + 1$

 (b) $f(x) = -x^3 + \dfrac{5}{3}x - 15$

 (c) $f(x) = x^2 - x + \sqrt{11}$
 (d) $f(x) = 5x^{-3} + 7x^2 + 3x - 1$
 (e) $f(x) = x^5 + 3x^4 - 2\sqrt{x} + x$

 (f) $f(x) = \dfrac{5}{x^3} - 6x^2 + 5x - 2$

 (g) $f(x) = 1 - x^7$
 (h) $f(x) = (x + 3)(x + 5)$

*2. Determine the degree and leading coefficient of each polynomial.
 (a) $p(x) = 3x^4 + 2x^3 + x^2 + 7$
 (b) $p(x) = x^2 - 8x + 14$
 (c) $f(x) = 1 - x^2 - 2x^3$
 (d) $g(x) = -x^3 + 7x^2 - 3x + 4$
 (e) $p(x) = (5x^2 + 3)(2x + 1)$

3. Determine all zeros of each polynomial function.
 *(a) $p(x) = 5x - 2$
 (b) $f(x) = -7x - 8$
 *(c) $g(x) = x^2$
 (d) $f(x) = x^2 - 4x - 12$
 *(e) $p(x) = x^2 + 7x - 18$
 (f) $p(x) = x^2 + 9x - 1$

*(g) $f(x) = x^2 - 7x + 2$

(h) $p(x) = 2x^2 + 8x - 5$

*(i) $f(x) = x^3 - 7x^2 + 12x$

(j) $p(x) = x^3 - 2x^2 - 15x$

*(k) $q(x) = x^3 + 7x^2 + 3x$

(l) $p(x) = x^3 - 5x^2 - 2x$

*(m) $p(x) = 2x^3 + 5x^2 - x$

(n) $p(x) = -x^3 + 3x^2 - 11x$

5.2 FACTORS AND ZEROS

Factoring a cubic expression is more complicated than factoring a quadratic, since there are three factors instead of two. Expressions of still higher degree are even more complicated. The approach to factoring cubic expressions is to determine one factor first. When that factor is divided into the original cubic expression, the result is a quadratic expression, which can be handled as before. Here is an example of the long-division process:

$$x - 3 \overline{)x^3 - 5x^2 + 7}$$

First, note that the x term is missing from the dividend, $x^3 - 5x^2 + 7$. Accordingly, insert $+0x$ in the expression to serve as a placeholder.

$$x - 3 \overline{)x^3 - 5x^2 + 0x + 7}$$

Begin the division by dividing $x - 3$ into $x^3 - 5x^2$. This is done by dividing x into x^3. The result is x^2.

$$\begin{array}{r} x^2 \\ x - 3 \overline{)x^3 - 5x^2 + 0x + 7} \end{array}$$

Now multiply the x^2 by $x - 3$ and subtract that product from $x^3 - 5x^2$. Then bring down the next term, $+0x$.

$$\begin{array}{r} x^2 \\ x - 3 \overline{)x^3 - 5x^2 + 0x + 7} \\ \underline{x^3 - 3x^2} \downarrow \\ -2x^2 + 0x \end{array}$$

Next, divide $x - 3$ into $-2x^2 + 0x$ by dividing x into $-2x^2$. The result is $-2x$.

$$\begin{array}{r} x^2 - 2x \\ x - 3 \overline{)x^3 - 5x^2 + 0x + 7} \\ \underline{x^3 - 3x^2} \\ -2x^2 + 0x \end{array}$$

Multiply the $-2x$ by $x - 3$, subtract the product from $-2x^2 + 0x$, and then bring down the next term, $+7$.

$$
\begin{array}{r}
x^2 - 2x \\
x - 3\overline{)x^3 - 5x^2 + 0x + 7} \\
\underline{x^3 - 3x^2} \\
-2x^2 + 0x \\
\underline{-2x^2 + 6x} \\
-6x + 7
\end{array}
$$

Finally, divide $x - 3$ into $-6x + 7$ by dividing x into $-6x$. The result is -6. Multiplying the -6 by $x - 3$ produces $-6x + 18$. A remainder of -11 is left after the subtraction.

$$
\begin{array}{r}
x^2 - 2x - 6 \\
x - 3\overline{)x^3 - 5x^2 + 0x + 7} \\
\underline{x^3 - 3x^2} \\
-2x^2 + 0x \\
\underline{-2x^2 + 6x} \\
-6x + 7 \\
\underline{-6x + 18} \\
-11 \quad \text{R} \qquad \text{remainder}
\end{array}
$$

Since the division is complete and the remainder is not zero, we conclude that $x - 3$ is not a factor of $x^3 - 5x^2 + 7$.

If desired, this division and result can be written as

$$
\frac{x^3 - 5x^2 + 7}{x - 3} = x^2 - 2x - 6 + \frac{-11}{x - 3}
$$

More will be said about this later in the chapter.

As you can see, the long-division process is time consuming. You would not want to divide $x^3 - 5x^2 + 7$ by $x - 3$ only to find out in the end that $x - 3$ is not a factor. So rather than divide by $x - 3$ just to determine if $x - 3$ is a factor, employ instead a concept used previously with quadratics: $x - 3$ is a factor of the expression if 3 is a zero of the function. (Also, if $x - 3$ is a factor, then 3 is a zero.) This idea is known formally as the **factor theorem**.

Factor theorem

If $x - r$ is a factor of polynomial $p(x)$, then $p(r) = 0$.
Also, if $p(r) = 0$, then $x - r$ is a factor of $p(x)$.

So before you carry out long division by $x - 3$, you check that $f(3) = 0$ first. In this example, where $p(x) = x^3 - 5x^2 + 7$, $p(3) = (3)^3 - 5(3)^2 + 7 \neq 0$. So $x - 3$ is not a factor of the expression and you do not have to waste time dividing in order to determine that.

Zero	Corresponding Factor
2	$x - 2$
-3	$x + 3$
4	$x - 4$

Example 1 *Find all the zeros of $f(x) = x^3 + 9x^2 + 17x + 6$.*

By trying different numbers for x, it is eventually determined that $f(-2) = 0$. Thus -2 is a zero of $f(x)$, and $(x + 2)$ is a factor of the polynomial expression $x^3 + 9x^2 + 17x + 6$. When $x + 2$ is divided into the cubic expression, the result is a quadratic expression, $x^2 + 7x + 3$. Because $x + 2$ is a factor, there is no remainder in the division by $x + 2$.

$$
\begin{array}{r}
x^2 + 7x + 3 \\
x + 2 \overline{) x^3 + 9x^2 + 17x + 6} \\
\underline{x^3 + 2x^2} \\
7x^2 + 17x \\
\underline{7x^2 + 14x} \\
3x + 6 \\
\underline{3x + 6} \\
0 \quad R
\end{array}
$$

The expression $x^2 + 7x + 3$ cannot be readily factored; so the roots of the equation $x^2 + 7x + 3 = 0$ are obtained by using the quadratic formula.

$$ x = \frac{-7 \pm \sqrt{49 - 12}}{2} = \frac{-7 \pm \sqrt{37}}{2} $$

We have determined that the zeros of the function are

$$ -2 \quad \text{and} \quad \frac{-7 \pm \sqrt{37}}{2} $$

You are probably wondering how many trials it took to come up with -2 as a zero of the previous function or how you should decide what numbers to test. Here is the key to the trial-and-error approach for polynomials of degree n in which the coefficient of x^n is 1.

Theorem

If a polynomial is of the form

$$p(x) = x^n + a_{n-1}x^{n-1} + \cdots + a_1 x + a_0$$

where $a_{n-1}, \ldots, a_1, a_0$ are integers, then the only possible rational zeros are the integer factors of the constant a_0.

In the preceding polynomial, $f(x) = x^3 + 9x^2 + 17x + 6$, the only possible rational zeros are $+6$, -6, $+3$, -3, $+2$, -2, $+1$, and -1. These numbers are the only integer factors of $+6$; so they are the only possible rational zeros of the polynomial. A quick look at the function shows that all connecting signs are positive. This means that $+6$, $+3$, $+2$, and $+1$ cannot be zeros. Why? Because there is no way that a sum of all positive numbers will be equal to 0. Thus -6, -3, -2, and -1 are the only numbers worth testing.

$$f(-6) = (-6)^3 + 9(-6)^2 + 17(-6) + 6 = 12$$

$$f(-3) = (-3)^3 + 9(-3)^2 + 17(-3) + 6 = 9$$

$$f(-2) = (-2)^3 + 9(-2)^2 + 17(-2) + 6 = 0$$

$$f(-1) = (-1)^3 + 9(-1)^2 + 17(-1) + 6 = -3$$

Only -2 is a zero; -2 is the only rational zero of the function. From this analysis we conclude that the other zeros are either irrational or imaginary. (In Example 1 they were found to be irrational.)

Before continuing on to apply the theorem in Example 2, note how the theorem is an extension of the approach used to factor quadratics. Consider the expression $x^2 - 8x + 15$. To fill in the factored form $(x \quad)(x \quad)$, you begin by considering numbers whose product is 15; that is, you consider factors of 15. Here 15 is the a_0 of the theorem.

Example 2 *Determine all the zeros of $p(x) = x^3 + 4x^2 - 7x - 10$.*
    The only possible rational zeros are the factors of -10, namely, ± 10, ± 5, ± 2, ± 1. After a few tries we discover that $f(-5) = 0$.

$$f(-5) = (-5)^3 + 4(-5)^2 - 7(-5) - 10 = 0$$

Because -5 is a zero of the function, $x + 5$ must be a factor of the expression $x^3 + 4x^2 - 7x - 10$. After dividing the polynomial expression by $x + 5$, we obtain

$x^2 - x - 2.$

$$
\begin{array}{r}
x^2 - x - 2 \\
x + 5 \overline{)x^3 + 4x^2 - 7x - 10} \\
\underline{x^3 + 5x^2} \\
- x^2 - 7x \\
\underline{- x^2 - 5x} \\
-2x - 10 \\
\underline{-2x - 10} \\
0
\end{array}
$$

The remaining quadratic expression, $x^2 - x - 2$, can be factored into $(x - 2)(x + 1)$, yielding 2 and -1 as the other zeros. Thus the zeros of the function are -5, 2, and -1.

Example 3   *Factor the polynomial expression $x^3 + 5x^2 + 2x - 8$.*

To find a zero (and then the corresponding factor), we should make the expression into a function by naming it; we shall use p. Thus we create

$$p(x) = x^3 + 5x^2 + 2x - 8$$

The only possible rational zeros are the factors of -8, namely, $\pm 8, \pm 4, \pm 2, \pm 1$. Because the first two terms are $x^3 + 5x^2$, it seems unlikely that $+8$, $+4$, or $+2$ would be zeros. So try -4, -2, ± 1, or even -8. We shall try $+1$. We compute $p(+1) = (+1)^3 + 5(+1)^2 + 2(+1) - 8$, which is, in fact, 0. So $+1$ is a zero of the function. This makes $x - 1$ a factor of the expression. Next, we shall use long division to determine the quadratic expression that remains when $x - 1$ is factored out.

$$
\begin{array}{r}
x^2 + 6x + 8 \\
x - 1 \overline{)x^3 + 5x^2 + 2x - 8} \\
\underline{x^3 - x^2} \\
6x^2 + 2x \\
\underline{6x^2 - 6x} \\
8x - 8 \\
\underline{8x - 8} \\
0
\end{array}
$$

Thus

$$x^3 + 5x^2 + 2x - 8 = (x - 1)(x^2 + 6x + 8)$$

The quadratic expression factors easily, and the result is

$$x^3 + 5x^2 + 2x - 8 = (x - 1)(x + 4)(x + 2)$$

If the original polynomial is of degree four, then division by the first factor obtained will reduce the quartic expression to cubic. Thus, another zero (and its associated factor) must be found and another division performed before a quadratic expression is produced.

Example 4 *Determine the zeros of* $p(x) = x^4 - 2x^3 - 9x^2 + 2x + 8$.

The only possible zeros of p are the factors of 8, namely, $\pm 8, \pm 4, \pm 2, \pm 1$. By trial and error, we find that $p(1) = 0$. Thus 1 is a zero and $x - 1$ is a factor of the expression. When $x^4 - 2x^3 - 9x^2 + 2x + 8$ is divided by $x - 1$, the result is $x^3 - x^2 - 10x - 8$. The next thing to do is to factor this remaining cubic expression. Using the same trial-and-error procedure, we find that 4 is a zero and $x - 4$ is a factor. Dividing $x^3 - x^2 - 10x - 8$ by $x - 4$ yields $x^2 + 3x + 2$. This remaining quadratic expression factors as $(x + 1)(x + 2)$. Thus the four zeros of p are $-1, -2, 1$, and 4.

If the coefficient of the highest-degree term is not 1, then the following theorem should be used to aid the search for zeros. It is an extension of the preceding theorem regarding rational zeros.

Theorem

If a polynomial is of the form

$$p(x) = a_n x^n + a_{n-1} x^{n-1} + \cdots + a_1 x + a_0$$

where $a_n, a_{n-1}, \ldots, a_1, a_0$ are integers, the only possible rational zeros are the fractions formed by using the factors of a_0 as numerators and the factors of a_n as denominators ($a_n \neq 0$).

If the zero you find turns out to be a fraction, then before doing the long division you should change the form of the factor to one that has no fraction in it. To do so, multiply the factor by the denominator of the fraction involved. Here is a table of examples.

Zero	Factor	Factor Ready for Long Division
$\frac{1}{2}$	$x - \frac{1}{2}$	$2x - 1$
$\frac{3}{5}$	$x - \frac{3}{5}$	$5x - 3$
$-\frac{7}{3}$	$x + \frac{7}{3}$	$3x + 7$

Example 5 *Find all the zeros of* $f(x) = 2x^3 + x^2 + 5x - 3$.

The only possible rational zeros have factors of -3 as their numerators and factors of 2 as their denominators. The possibilities are:

$$\pm\frac{3}{1}, \quad \pm\frac{3}{2}, \quad \pm\frac{1}{1}, \quad \pm\frac{1}{2}$$

It is natural to try ± 1 first, and then ± 3 if neither $+1$ nor -1 is a zero. Unfortunately, all four of these numbers fail to be zeros. But $f(\frac{1}{2}) = 0$; so $\frac{1}{2}$ is a zero of the function. The linear factor that produces $\frac{1}{2}$ as a zero is $2x - 1$, since the equation $2x - 1 = 0$ leads to $x = \frac{1}{2}$. The division:

$$
\begin{array}{r}
x^2 + x + 3 \\
2x - 1 \overline{)2x^3 + x^2 + 5x - 3} \\
\underline{2x^3 - x^2} \\
2x^2 + 5x \\
\underline{2x^2 - x} \\
6x - 3 \\
\underline{6x - 3} \\
0
\end{array}
$$

The remaining quadratic expression cannot be factored. However, when the quadratic formula is applied to $x^2 + x + 3 = 0$, the result is

$$x = \frac{-1 \pm \sqrt{-11}}{2} = \frac{-1 \pm i\sqrt{11}}{2}$$

The zeros of the function are $\frac{1}{2}$, $(-1 + i\sqrt{11})/2$, and $(-1 - i\sqrt{11})/2$.

Perhaps you noticed that there were two complex zeros of the polynomial function here: $(-1 + i\sqrt{11})/2$ and $(-1 - i\sqrt{11})/2$. In general, *if $f(x)$ is a polynomial with real coefficients and if $a + bi$ is a zero of $f(x)$, then $a - bi$ is also a zero of $f(x)$.* Imaginary zeros always come in complex-conjugate pairs.

Not all cubic and quartic polynomial functions have rational zeros. A cubic polynomial could have three irrational zeros or one irrational zero and two imaginary zeros, for example. If you test all possible rational zeros and none is indeed a zero, then the polynomial has no rational zeros (see Exercise 5).

EXERCISES 5.2

1.   Perform each long division.
  *(a)   Divide $x^3 + 2x^2 - 13x - 6$ by $x - 3$.
   (b)   Divide $x^3 - x^2 - 25x + 25$ by $x - 5$.

*(c)   Divide $x^3 + 3x^2 - 2x - 3$ by $x - 2$.
(d)   Divide $x^3 + 7x^2 + 13x + 6$ by $x + 2$.
*(e)   Divide $x^3 + 3x^2 - 5x - 39$ by $x + 3$.
(f)   Divide $x^3 - 2x^2 + 4x + 1$ by $x + 2$.
*(g)   Divide $2x^4 - 3x^2 - 7x + 3$ by $x - 2$.
(h)   Divide $3x^4 + 14x^3 + x^2 - 11x + 3$ by $3x - 1$.
*(i)   Divide $2x^4 + x^3 - 2x - 1$ by $2x + 1$.
(j)   Divide $x^4 - 2x + 1$ by $x + 2$.
*(k)   Divide $x^3 - 1$ by $x - 1$.
(l)   Divide $x^4 - 81$ by $x - 3$.
*(m)   Divide $x^5 - 32$ by $x - 2$.

2.   Factor each cubic polynomial expression completely.
   *(a) $x^3 - 4x^2 + x + 6$ (b) $x^3 - 9x^2 + 20x$
   *(c) $x^3 + 4x^2 + x - 6$ (d) $x^3 + x^2 - 16x - 16$
   *(e) $x^3 + 11x^2 + 39x + 45$ (f) $x^3 - x^2 - x + 1$
   *(g) $2x^3 + 19x^2 + 49x + 20$ (h) $2x^3 - 5x^2 - x + 6$
   *(i) $3x^3 + 11x^2 - 14x - 40$ (j) $3x^3 - 14x^2 + 17x - 6$

3.   Determine all the zeros of each polynomial function.
   *(a) $p(x) = x^3 - x^2 - 9x + 9$
   (b) $p(x) = x^3 - 5x^2 + x - 5$
   *(c) $f(x) = x^3 - 7x^2 - x + 7$
   (d) $g(x) = x^3 - 7x - 6$
   *(e) $f(x) = x^3 + 8$
   (f) $q(x) = x^3 + 8x^2 + 14x - 5$
   *(g) $f(x) = x^3 + 7x^2 + 15x + 25$
   (h) $g(x) = 2x^3 + 5x^2 - 4x - 3$
   *(i) $h(x) = x^4 - 5x^3 + 7x^2 - 15x + 12$
   (j) $r(x) = x^4 + 3x^3 + 11x^2 + 27x + 18$
   *(k) $s(x) = 4x^3 - 11x^2 + x + 1$
   (l) $f(x) = 2x^4 - 3x^3 - 4x^2 + 3x + 2$
   *(m) $m(x) = x^4 - 16$
   (n) $p(x) = x^4 + 7x^3 + 13x^2 + x - 6$
   *(o) $p(x) = 4x^4 + 4x^3 + 3x^2 - x - 1$
   (p) $f(x) = 2x^4 + 3x^3 - 19x^2 + 6x + 8$
   *(q) $f(x) = x^4 - x^3 - 7x^2 + x + 6$

4.   Find all roots of the following polynomial equations.
   *(a) $x^3 - 4x^2 + x + 6 = 0$ (b) $x^3 - 2x^2 + 5x - 10 = 0$
   *(c) $x^3 + 7x^2 + 13x + 6 = 0$ (d) $2x^4 + x^3 - 2x - 1 = 0$
   *(e) $2x^3 - 11x^2 + 20x - 12 = 0$

5. Show that each polynomial function has no rational zeros.
   *(a) $f(x) = x^3 + 2$ (b) $g(x) = x^3 + 2x^2 + 5x + 1$
   (c) $h(x) = x^4 + x^2 + 2x + 6$ (d) $n(x) = x^4 - x + 17$
   (e) $t(x) = x^5 + x^3 + 9$

6. The theorem for determining zeros of polynomial functions does not apply directly in cases where a_0 (the constant term) is 0. In such instances you must factor out x or whatever power of x is common to all terms. The theorem can then be applied to the remaining polynomial expression. Of course, 0 will be a zero of any such polynomial function. For example, in

$$p(x) = x^5 + 3x^4 - x^3 - 3x^2$$

begin by factoring out x^2.

$$p(x) = (x^2)(x^3 + 3x^2 - x - 3)$$

The expression $x^3 + 3x^2 - x - 3$ can now be factored by using the theorem. The result is

$$p(x) = (x^2)(x + 1)(x - 1)(x + 3)$$

The zeros are 0, ± 1, -3. Determine the zeros of each polynomial function.
   *(a) $p(x) = x^4 - 2x^3 - 5x^2 + 6x$
   (b) $p(x) = x^5 - x^4 + 4x^3 - 4x^2$
   *(c) $f(x) = x^5 + 2x^4 + x^3 + 2x^2$

7. *(a)   Determine the three cube roots of -27 by solving the polynomial equation $x^3 = -27$.
   (b)   Determine the three cube roots of -64 by solving the polynomial equation $x^3 = -64$.

5.3   SYNTHETIC DIVISION

Synthetic division is a shortcut method for dividing a polynomial in x by an expression of the form $x - a$, where a is a constant. Thus synthetic division offers a shortcut to determining factors and zeros of polynomials.

Before presenting the mechanics of synthetic division, it seems in order to issue a warning. In a sense, the use of synthetic division is controversial. Although it is both efficient and mathematically sound, your instructor may not want you to become *dependent* on it. And even though the process resembles long division, some signs and arithmetic used are just the opposite of those used in long division. Consequently, using both long division and synthetic division can be confusing. But the real problem is that many students opt for synthetic division, forget how to do long division, and are later in trouble in calculus where long division is needed and synthetic division does not apply. In calculus the divisor is often a quadratic expression. Furthermore, the concern is usually that of determining a quotient and remainder—not a zero or factor.†

We begin now to explain the mechanics of synthetic division by means of an example. Let us carry out the division below synthetically.

$$x - 3\overline{)2x^3 - 5x^2 + 23}$$

To divide by $x - 3$, we use 3. (If we were dividing by $x + 2$, we should use -2.) The coefficients of each term of the dividend polynomial $2x^3 - 5x^2 + 0x + 23$ are listed. We begin then by writing

$$\underline{3|}\quad 2\quad -5\quad 0\quad 23$$

Bring down the leading coefficient, 2.

$$\underline{3|}\quad 2\quad -5\quad 0\quad 23$$
$$\qquad 2$$

Next, multiply the 3 by the 2 and write the product below the next coefficient (-5).

$$\underline{3|}\quad 2\quad -5\quad 0\quad 23$$
$$\qquad\qquad 6$$
$$\qquad 2$$

Now *add* the two numbers (-5 and 6) and write the sum below the line.

$$\underline{3|}\quad 2\quad -5\quad 0\quad 23$$
$$\qquad\qquad 6$$
$$\qquad 2\quad 1$$

Continue the process by multiplying the 3 by 1 and writing that product below the next coefficient (0).

$$\underline{3|}\quad 2\quad -5\quad 0\quad 23$$
$$\qquad\qquad 6\quad 3$$
$$\qquad 2\quad 1$$

---

† When done synthetically, division by a linear expression $ax + b$ ($a \neq 1$) introduces fractions unnecessarily. Too, handling the remainder in such cases requires extra care.

Now add the 0 and 3 and write the sum below the line.

$$
\begin{array}{r|rrrr}
3 & 2 & -5 & 0 & 23 \\
  &   & 6 & 3 & \\
\hline
  & 2 & 1 & \mathbf{3} &
\end{array}
$$

Next, multiply the 3 by 3 and write that product below the next coefficient (23).

$$
\begin{array}{r|rrrr}
3 & 2 & -5 & 0 & 23 \\
  &   & 6 & 3 & \mathbf{9} \\
\hline
  & 2 & 1 & 3 &
\end{array}
$$

Finally, add the 23 and 9 and place the sum below the line.

$$
\begin{array}{r|rrrr}
3 & 2 & -5 & 0 & 23 \\
  &   & 6 & 3 & 9 \\
\hline
  & 2 & 1 & 3 & \mathbf{32}
\end{array}
$$

At this point, the division is complete and we must interpret the result. The last number, 32, is the remainder in the division. The other numbers below the line—2, 1, 3—are the coefficients of the quotient polynomial of degree one less than that of the original dividend polynomial. Thus the quotient is $2x^2 + x + 3$. For comparison purposes, here is the synthetic division side by side with long division. Notice how much shorter synthetic division is than long division.†

$$
\begin{array}{r|rrrr}
3 & 2 & -5 & 0 & 23 \\
  &   & 6 & 3 & 9 \\
\hline
  & 2 & 1 & 3 & 32
\end{array}
$$

$2x^2 + x + 3 \qquad R: 32$

$$
\begin{array}{r}
2x^2 + x + 3 \\
x - 3 \overline{\smash{)}2x^3 - 5x^2 + 0x + 23} \\
\underline{2x^3 - 6x^2 } \\
x^2 + 0x \\
\underline{x^2 - 3x } \\
3x + 23 \\
\underline{3x - 9} \\
32 \leftarrow R
\end{array}
$$

---

† To avoid errors, synthetic division is performed by using addition whereas in long division you use subtraction. So in synthetic division, we change the sign of the divisor at the beginning (we used 3 rather than -3) in order to make the process equivalent to that of long division.

Another advantage of synthetic division is that you use it to determine a zero instead of having to evaluate the function directly to determine a zero. It takes about the same length of time and in the process of finding the zero you automatically get the quotient.

Example 6   *Use synthetic division to show that* -2 *is a zero of the polynomial* $p(x) = x^3 - 3x^2 - 9x + 2$ *and to produce the quotient when* $p(x)$ *is divided by the factor* $x + 2$.

To determine if -2 is a zero, divide by $x + 2$. In other words, use -2 as a "divisor" in the synthetic division.

$$
\begin{array}{r|rrrr}
-2 & 1 & -3 & -9 & 2 \\
   &   & -2 & +10 & -2 \\
\hline
   & 1 & -5 & +1 & 0
\end{array}
$$

Because the remainder is 0, we see that -2 is indeed a zero of the polynomial. The quotient is $x^2 - 5x + 1$. Also,

$$p(x) = x^3 - 3x^2 - 9x + 2 = (x + 2)(x^2 - 5x + 1)$$

You can use synthetic division to evaluate a function at a number because of the following theorem. In the theorem, x and a are real numbers.

Remainder theorem

The remainder in the division of polynomial $p(x)$ *by* $x - a$ *is* $p(a)$.

The Remainder theorem is easy to prove. If polynomial $p(x)$ is divided by $x - a$, the result is a quotient $q(x)$ and a remainder R. This can be written

$$p(x) = (x - a)q(x) + R$$

Since x can be any real number, let x be a. Then

$$
\begin{aligned}
p(a) &= (a - a)q(a) + R \\
     &= 0 \cdot q(a) + R \\
     &= R
\end{aligned}
$$

This shows that the remainder is $p(a)$.

Example 7   *Use the synthetic division process to determine the value of* $p(4)$, *where* $p(x) = x^3 - 7x^2 + 6x - 5$.

$$\begin{array}{r|rrrr} 4 & 1 & -7 & 6 & -5 \\ & & 4 & -12 & -24 \\ \hline & 1 & -3 & -6 & \big| -29 \end{array}$$

The remainder in the division is -29. Thus $p(4) = -29$.

EXERCISES 5.3

1. Use synthetic division to determine the quotient and remainder.
    *(a) Divide $3x^3 - 6x^2 + x - 8$ by $x - 3$.
    (b) Divide $2x^3 - 3x^2 + 4x - 6$ by $x - 2$.
    *(c) Divide $-x^3 + 2x^2 + 22x - 8$ by $x + 4$.
    (d) Divide $-2x^3 + 7x^2 - 2x + 7$ by $x - 1$.
    *(e) Divide $2x^4 + 5x^3 - 2x^2 + x - 8$ by $x + 3$.
    (f) Divide $x^5 - 3x^3 + 6x^2 + 7x + 5$ by $x + 1$.
    *(g) Divide $-2x^3 + 13x^2 - 3x - 5$ by $2x + 1$.†
    (h) Divide $2x^3 - 5x^2 + 4x - 1$ by $2x - 1$.
    *(i) Divide $-3x^3 - 25x^2 + 30x - 8$ by $3x - 2$.

2. Use synthetic division as an aid in determining the zeros of each polynomial function.
    *(a) $p(x) = x^3 + 2x^2 - 5x - 6$
    (b) $p(x) = x^3 + 2x^2 - 12x + 8$
    *(c) $f(x) = x^3 - 5x^2 + 7x - 2$
    (d) $g(x) = x^3 - x^2 - 8x - 16$
    *(e) $y = 2x^3 + x^2 - 7x - 6$
    (f) $y = x^3 + 2x^2 - 23x - 60$
    *(g) $p(x) = x^4 - 16x^2 + 63$
    (h) $p(x) = -x^4 - 3x^3 + 8x^2 + 12x - 16$
    *(i) $q(x) = 2x^4 - x^3 - 20x^2 + 13x + 30$
    (j) $f(x) = x^4 + x^3 - 2x^2 + 4x - 24$

3. Use synthetic division to determine the value of $p(a)$ for the given polynomial p and the given a.
    *(a) $p(x) = x^3 - 2x^2 + 5x - 11, a = 2$
    (b) $p(x) = x^4 + 5x^3 - 6x^2 + x - 50, a = -3$
    *(c) $p(x) = 3x^4 - 7x^3 + 2x^2 - 13x - 6, a = -4$
    (d) $p(x) = -x^4 + 6x^3 + 7x^2 - 5x + 14, a = 5$

---

† To divide, write $2x + 1$ as $2(x + \frac{1}{2})$. Then divide synthetically by $-\frac{1}{2}$ (from $x + \frac{1}{2}$) and then divide the result by 2. In general, to divide by $ax + b$ ($a \neq 1$), write $ax + b$ as $a(x + b/a)$, divide synthetically by $-b/a$ and divide that result by a.

*(e) $p(x) = 2x^3 + 3x^2 - 7x + 1, a = \dfrac{1}{2}$

(f) $p(x) = 4x^3 - 6x^2 + x - 16, a = -\dfrac{1}{2}$

*(g) $p(x) = 3x^4 - x^3 + x^2 + 5x - 10, a = -\dfrac{2}{3}$

(h) $p(x) = 4x^3 + 5x^2 - 6x + 9, a = \dfrac{3}{4}$

5.4 GRAPHS OF POLYNOMIAL FUNCTIONS

In Chapter 2 we graphed straight lines (polynomials of degree 1) and parabolas (polynomials of degree 2). Such graphs were not difficult to obtain and they were accurate. By contrast, most higher-degree polynomials are more difficult to sketch and some calculus is needed for real accuracy in the sketch. For example, the graph of most cubic polynomials (degree 3) will look like one of these two forms.†

The high and low points (marked H and L) are really determined by calculus methods. We can only approximate them in this presentation. The number of high and low points (two in each graph above) of a polynomial of degree n may be as many as $n - 1$ or as few as one (if the degree is even) or zero (if the degree is odd).

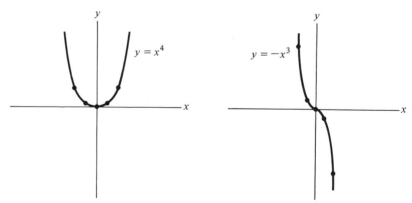

In this section we shall sketch graphs of cubic polynomials by obtaining points and passing a smooth curve through them. But before doing so, it seems appropriate to note that just by looking at a cubic polynomial $p(x) = ax^3 + bx^2 + cx + d$ you can tell whether it will appear as one of these

---

† The only other form is that shown for $y = x^3$ (see page 120) or the mirror image of that graph with respect to the y axis (see $y = -x^3$ on this page).

or as one of these.

If ax^3 is factored out of $ax^3 + bx^2 + cx + d$, then we have

$$p(x) = ax^3 \left(1 + \frac{b}{ax} + \frac{c}{ax^2} + \frac{d}{ax^3}\right)$$

If the magnitude of x is very large, the terms b/ax, c/ax^2, and d/ax^3 will be very small in magnitude (nearly zero). So for very large magnitude x,

$$p(x) \approx ax^3(1 + 0 + 0 + 0)$$

or

$$p(x) \approx ax^3$$

At the left portion of the graph, large-magnitude x values are negative. Consequently, x^3 will be a large-magnitude negative number. So if $a > 0$, then $ax^3 < 0$; and if $a < 0$, then $ax^3 > 0$. For the right portion of the graph, the large-magnitude x values are positive. This means that x^3 will be a large-magnitude positive number. So if $a > 0$, then $ax^3 > 0$; and if $a < 0$, then $ax^3 < 0$. Graphically,

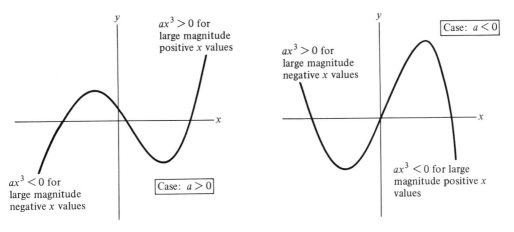

In conclusion,

The graph of $p(x) = ax^3 + bx^2 + cx + d$ *appears as*

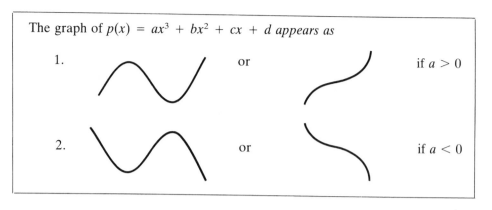

1.　　　　　　　　　　or　　　　　　　　　　if $a > 0$

2.　　　　　　　　　　or　　　　　　　　　　if $a < 0$

Example 8 *Sketch the graph of $f(x) = x^3 - 3x^2 + 5$.*
　　　First, we obtain some points by selecting values for x and then computing corresponding functional values.

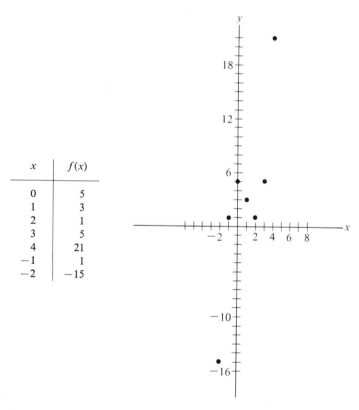

x	$f(x)$
0	5
1	3
2	1
3	5
4	21
−1	1
−2	−15

Now draw a smooth curve through the points, keeping in mind that since $a > 0$ it will look like a curve of Case 1 (see preceding box).

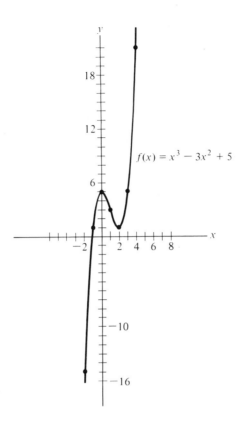

$f(x) = x^3 - 3x^2 + 5$

Example 9 *Sketch the graph of* $f(x) = -(x - 1)(x + 2)(x - 2)$.

Because the polynomial is factored, we can obtain the zeros immediately. The zeros are 1, -2, and 2. This means that we know three points, all of which are x intercepts: $(1, 0)$, $(-2, 0)$, and $(2, 0)$.

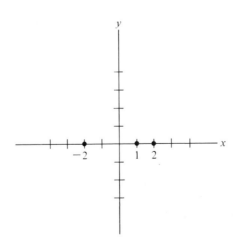

Furthermore, because f is cubic and $a < 0$, we know that its form is

So let us obtain some points by using $x = -3, -1, 0, \frac{3}{2}$, and 3 (all are near the three x values already used), plot the points, and sketch the graph.

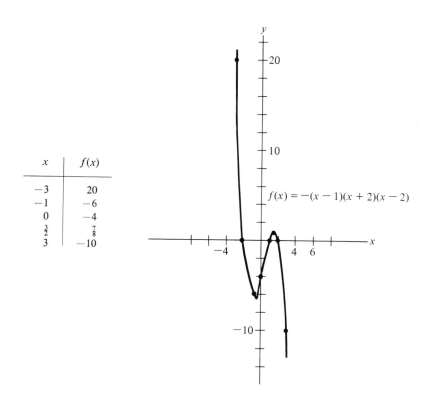

x	$f(x)$
-3	20
-1	-6
0	-4
$\frac{3}{2}$	$\frac{7}{8}$
3	-10

$f(x) = -(x - 1)(x + 2)(x - 2)$

The section concludes with a graph-related theorem concerning the real zeros of a polynomial function.

Theorem

If f is a polynomial function and if a and b are real numbers for which $f(a)$ and $f(b)$ have opposite signs, then there is at least one real number c between a and b such that $f(c) = 0$.

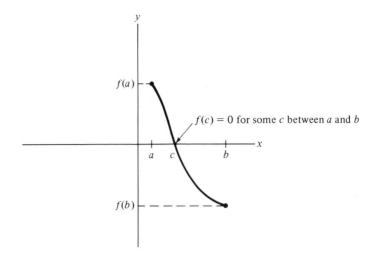

Consider, for example, the function $f(x) = x^3 - 5x^2 + 2x + 1$. We calculate

$$f(0) = +1$$
$$f(1) = -1$$

Because $f(0)$ and $f(1)$ have opposite signs, there is at least one real zero between 0 and 1.

EXERCISES 5.4

---

1. Sketch the graph of each polynomial function.
    *(a) $f(x) = x^3 - x^2 - 2x$
    (b) $p(x) = x^3 - 7x - 6$
    *(c) $y = x^3 - x^2 - x + 1$
    (d) $y = x^3 + x^2 + 6x - 6$
    *(e) $f(x) = -x^3 + x^2 + 2x$
    (f) $p(x) = -x^3 + 6x - 5$
    *(g) $f(x) = x^3 - 3x^2 - 9x + 7$
    (h) $y = x^3 + x^2 - 2x - 2$
    *(i) $y = -x^3 + 4x^2 - 4$
    (j) $y = 2x^3 - 3x + 1$
    *(k) $f(x) = (x - 2)(x - 4)(x + 1)$
    (l) $f(x) = (x - 3)(x + 4)(x + 1)$
    *(m) $p(x) = x(x + 3)(x - 1)$
    (n) $p(x) = x^3 - 2x^2 - 3x + 5$

$*(o)$ $y = x^3 - 3x^2 + x - 3$

(p) $y = x(x - 5)(x + 3)$

$*(q)$ $f(x) = -x^3 + 2x^2 + 4x + 2$

(r) $f(x) = x^3 + 3x^2 - 2x - 6$

$*(s)$ $f(x) = 2x^3 + x^2 + x - 3$

(t) $y = -x^3 + x^2 - 2x + 5$

2. For the given polynomial function f, determine whether there is a real zero between the two numbers given or whether you cannot tell.

$*(a)$ $f(x) = x^3 - 8x^2 + x + 2$.   Between 0 and 1

(b) $f(x) = 2x^3 - 3x^2 - 3x + 1$.   Between 2 and 3

$*(c)$ $f(x) = 4x^3 + 4x^2 - 8x - 2$.   Between -1 and 0

(d) $f(x) = x^4 - 50x^2 + 3x - 5$.   Between -2 and -1

$*(e)$ $f(x) = x^4 + 15x + 20$.   Between -3 and -2

5.5   RATIONAL FUNCTIONS

A function consisting of the quotient of two polynomials is called a **rational function**. In other words, if $p(x)$ and $q(x)$ are polynomial functions, then

$$f(x) = \frac{p(x)}{q(x)}$$

is a rational function. Furthermore, since the domain of any polynomial function is the set of all real numbers, the domain of any rational function $f(x) = p(x)/q(x)$ is the set of all real numbers except those for which $q(x)$ is zero.

Example 10   *Determine the domain of the rational function f.*

$$f(x) = \frac{5x + 2}{x^3 - 3x^2 - 10x}$$

The domain includes all the real numbers except those for which the denominator $x^3 - 3x^2 - 10x$ is zero. So we shall solve the equation $x^3 - 3x^2 - 10x = 0$ to determine which real numbers are not in the domain of f.

$$x^3 - 3x^2 - 10x = 0$$

$$(x)(x^2 - 3x - 10) = 0$$

$$(x)(x - 5)(x + 2) = 0$$

$$x = 0 \mid x = 5 \mid x = -2$$

The domain of f is all the real numbers except -2, 0, and 5.

Example 11 *Determine the zeros of the rational function f.*

$$f(x) = \frac{x^2 - 16}{x^3 + 6x^2 + 2x + 7}$$

A fraction is zero when its numerator is zero (provided that its denominator is not zero, too). So the only possible zeros are the roots of $x^2 - 16 = 0$—namely, 4 and -4. And because the denominator is not zero for either 4 or -4, both numbers are indeed zeros of the function.

Example 12 *Determine the zeros of the rational function f.*

$$f(x) = \frac{x^2 - 1}{x^2 + 6x + 5}$$

The only possible zeros are the roots of $x^2 - 1 = 0$, namely, 1 and -1. However, the *denominator* $x^2 + 6x + 5$ is also zero when x is -1. Thus, $f(-1) = 0/0$, meaning that f is not defined at -1 and so -1 is not a zero of f. For $x = 1$, we have $f(1) = 0/12 = 0$. So 1 is a zero of f, the only zero of f.

In arithmetic, a fraction is called *improper* if the numerator is greater than or equal to the denominator. Such fractions as $\frac{8}{5}, \frac{9}{9}$, and $\frac{6}{3}$ are examples of improper fractions.

In algebra, a rational expression $p(x)/q(x)$ is called **improper** if the degree of numerator $p(x)$ is greater than or equal to the degree of denominator $q(x)$. Here are two examples of rational expressions that are improper fractions.

$$\frac{3x^4 + 5x^3 + 6x^2 + x - 15}{10x^3 - 8x^2 + 3x - 4} \qquad \begin{cases} \text{Degree of numerator (4) is greater than} \\ \text{the degree of the denominator (3).} \end{cases}$$

$$\frac{x^2 - 9x + 2}{2x^2 + 6x - 19} \qquad \begin{cases} \text{Degree of numerator (2) equals degree} \\ \text{of denominator (2).} \end{cases}$$

Improper fractions such as those just given can be simplified (made proper) by means of long division.

Example 13 *Simplify the improper fraction*

$$\frac{x^3 + x^2 + 50x + 17}{x^2 - 8}$$

Using long division, we get

$$
\begin{array}{r}
x + 1 \\
x^2 - 8\overline{)x^3 + x^2 + 50x + 17} \\
\underline{x^3 - 8x} \\
x^2 + 58x + 17 \\
\underline{x^2 - 8} \\
58x + 25
\end{array}
$$

The division process ends at this point because what remains, $58x + 25$, has lower degree than the divisor, $x^2 - 8$.

Since the purpose of the division is to obtain an alternate form of the fraction, place the remainder $58x + 25$ over the divisor $x^2 - 8$ and add it to the quotient. The result is

$$
\frac{x^3 + x^2 + 50x + 17}{x^2 - 8} = x + 1 + \frac{58x + 25}{x^2 - 8}
$$

Example 14 *Simplify the improper fraction*

$$
\frac{x^2 + 7x - 10}{x^2 - 5x + 1}
$$

By long division,

$$
\begin{array}{r}
1 \\
x^2 - 5x + 1\overline{)x^2 + 7x - 10} \\
\underline{x^2 - 5x + 1} \\
12x - 11
\end{array}
$$

Thus

$$
\frac{x^2 + 7x - 10}{x^2 - 5x + 1} = 1 + \frac{12x - 11}{x^2 - 5x + 1}
$$

One special type of rational function was presented in Chapter 3 (Example 26). The function

$$
f(x) = \frac{(x + 2)(x - 3)}{(x - 3)}
$$

was discussed and graphed. The function simplifies to $f(x) = x + 2$ for $x \ne 3$; so the graph of f is a straight line with a point missing. Since 3 is not in the domain, there can be no point $(3, f(3))$—which would be $(3, 5)$ if the function were the entire line $y = x + 2$.

The example just reviewed is unusual. For most rational functions the numerator and denominator do not have common factors, so when the denominator is zero, the numerator usually is not zero. Let us consider some rational function $f(x) = p(x)/q(x)$ in which the denominator is zero when $x = c$ (that is, $q(c) = 0$) and the numerator is not zero at c (that is, $p(c) \neq 0$). Now as x gets closer and closer to c, the denominator gets closer and closer to 0 and the functional values will get larger and larger in magnitude. In such a case, the line $x = c$ is called a *vertical asymptote* of the function. The graph of the function gets closer and closer to the line $x = c$ but never reaches it.

The line $x = c$ is a **vertical asymptote** of the rational function

$$f(x) = \frac{p(x)}{q(x)}$$

if $q(c) = 0$ and $p(c) \neq 0$.

Here is a drawing showing two vertical asymptotes, $x = -1$ and $x = 2$.

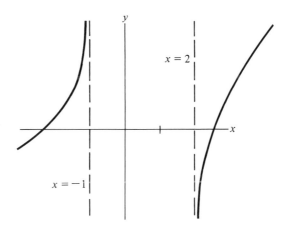

Example 15 *Determine the vertical asymptotes of the function*

$$f(x) = \frac{x^2 - 7x + 12}{x^2 + 5x - 14}$$

First, factor the numerator and denominator. The result is

$$f(x) = \frac{(x - 3)(x - 4)}{(x + 7)(x - 2)}$$

The denominator is zero when x is -7 and when x is 2. And in each case the numerator is not zero. Thus the vertical asymptotes of this function are the lines $x = -7$ and $x = 2$.

It can happen that the graph of a function tends toward a line as the magnitude of x increases.

A *horizontal asymptote* of $y = f(x)$ is a line toward which the function tends as the magnitude of x gets larger and larger. Here are two illustrations of horizontal asymptotes.

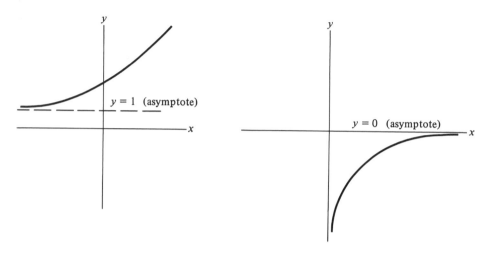

To study the behavior of a rational function $f(x) = p(x)/q(x)$ as the magnitude of x increases without bound, recall from Section 5.4 that in any polynomial the highest-degree term dominates the function for large-magnitude x. This can be extended to rational functions in which the degree of the numerator is different from the degree of the denominator. Consider the following examples.

$$\frac{x^2 + 1}{x} \quad \text{and} \quad \frac{x}{x^2 + 1}$$

In the first fraction, if x gets very large, the numerator will be much larger than the denominator. If x becomes infinitely large, so will the fraction become infinitely large. In the second fraction, if x gets very large, the denominator will become much larger than the numerator and so the fraction will have a small magnitude. If x becomes infinitely large, the fraction will tend toward zero.

One other case is possible: the degree of the numerator and denominator could be the same. In such a case, when x becomes infinitely large, the functional values tend toward the number formed as the quotient of the coefficients of the highest powers of x. This can be shown by dividing each term (numerator and denominator) by the highest power of x. Here it is done for two specific cubic polynomials.

$$\frac{-5x^3 + 4x^2 + 7x + 18}{7x^3 - 2x^2 + 3x - 11} = \frac{\dfrac{-5x^3}{x^3} + \dfrac{4x^2}{x^3} + \dfrac{7x}{x^3} + \dfrac{18}{x^3}}{\dfrac{7x^3}{x^3} - \dfrac{2x^2}{x^3} + \dfrac{3x}{x^3} - \dfrac{11}{x^3}}$$

$$= \frac{-5 + \dfrac{4}{x} + \dfrac{7}{x^2} + \dfrac{18}{x^3}}{7 - \dfrac{2}{x} + \dfrac{3}{x^2} - \dfrac{11}{x^3}}$$

Clearly, as x becomes infinitely large, the six fractions tend to zero and all that remains is $\dfrac{-5}{7}$, or $-5/7$.

Here is a summary of our results.

The **horizontal asymptote** of rational function

$$f(x) = \frac{p(x)}{q(x)} = \frac{a_n x^n + a_{n-1} x^{n-1} + \cdots + a_0}{b_m x^m + b_{m-1} x^{m-1} + \cdots + b_0}$$

is

1. $y = 0$ if the degree of q is larger.
2. $y = a_n/b_m$ if p and q have the same degree.
3. No horizontal asymptote if the degree of p is larger.

Example 16 *Determine the horizontal asymptote of*

$$f(x) = \frac{5x^2 + 8x - 17}{x^3 - 7x^2 + 6x}$$

Since the degree of the denominator is greater than the degree of the numerator, the function tends toward 0 as x becomes infinitely large. Thus the horizontal asymptote is $y = 0$. This is Case 1.

Example 17 *Determine the horizontal asymptote of*

$$f(x) = \frac{x^3 - 7x^2 + 6x}{5x^2 + 8x - 17}$$

Since the degree of the numerator is greater than the degree of the denominator, the function becomes infinitely large as x becomes infinitely large. There is no horizontal asymptote. This is Case 3.

Example 18 *Determine the horizontal asymptote of*

$$f(x) = \frac{3x^4 + 7x - 9}{x^4 + 6x^3 - 5x^2 + 2x - 8}$$

Since the degree of the numerator is the same as the degree of the denominator, the horizontal asymptote is $y = \frac{3}{1}$, or $y = 3$. This is Case 2.

The next two examples demonstrate the use of asymptotes in sketching graphs of rational functions. The use of domain, range, intercepts, and symmetry is also shown.

Example 19 *Sketch the graph of*

$$y = \frac{6}{x^2 + 1}$$

We will determine domain, range, intercepts, symmetry, asymptotes, and (if needed to determine the graph) a few additional points.

Domain

Here x can be any real number.

Range

The equation

$$y = \frac{6}{x^2 + 1}$$

can be solved for x as

$$x^2 y + y = 6$$

$$x = \pm \sqrt{\frac{6 - y}{y}} \qquad y \neq 0 \text{ here or in the original equation.}$$

We insist that $(6 - y)/y \geq 0$, since the square root of a negative number is not a real number; $(6 - y)/y = 0$ when $y = 6$. To see when the expression is positive, use a sign chart.

$$6 - y: \quad \frac{+ \ + \ + \ + \ + \ + \ + \ + \ + \quad - \ - \ - \ -}{\underset{6}{\qquad\qquad\qquad\qquad\qquad\qquad}}$$

$$y: \quad \frac{- \ - \ - \quad + \ + \ + \ + \ + \ + \ + \ + \ +}{\underset{0}{\qquad\qquad\qquad\qquad\qquad\qquad}}$$

We conclude that $(6 - y)/y \geq 0$ when $0 < y \leq 6$. This means that the range is $\{y \mid 0 < y \leq 6\}$.

Intercepts

Since $y \neq 0$, there are no x intercepts. The curve crosses the y axis when $x = 0$, and $y = \dfrac{6}{x^2 + 1} = 6$ when $x = 0$. This means that $(0, 6)$ is the (only) y intercept.

Symmetry

The graph is symmetric with respect to the y axis, because when $-x$ is substituted for x, the resulting equation is the same as the original. The other symmetry tests fail.

Asymptotes

This is a rational function in which the degree of the denominator (degree 2) is greater than the degree of the numerator (degree zero). Thus $y = 0$ is a horizontal asymptote of the function.

    Since the denominator cannot be zero, this functioin has no vertical asymptote.

Using the Information

We already have enough information to make a rough sketch of the function. We know that the point $(0, 6)$ is the highest point of the curve, because the range is $\{y \mid 0 < y \leq 6\}$. And because $y = 0$ is an asymptote, the curve must come down toward the x axis from $(0, 6)$. Its behavior is the same on both sides of the y axis, since the curve is symmetric with respect to the y axis. There are no points below the x axis, since $y > 0$. The only remaining question is how gently or sharply does the curve fall from $(0, 6)$. Obtaining two additional points, $(1, 3)$ and $(2, 1\frac{1}{5})$, will enable us to make a fairly refined drawing.

The Sketch

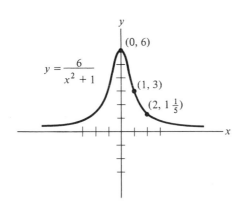

Example 20 *Sketch the graph of*

$$y = \frac{x^2}{x^2 - 9}$$

Domain

$$\{x \mid x \neq \pm 3\}$$

Range

The equation

$$y = \frac{x^2}{x^2 - 9}$$

can be solved for x as

$$x^2 y - 9y = x^2$$
$$x^2 y - x^2 = 9y$$
$$x^2(y - 1) = 9y$$
$$x = \pm \sqrt{\frac{9y}{y - 1}} \qquad y \neq 1 \text{ here or in the original equation.}$$

We insist that $(9y)/(y - 1) \geq 0$. Clearly the expression equals zero when $y = 0$. By the sign chart, we see that $(9y)/(y - 1) > 0$ when $y < 0$ or $y > 1$.

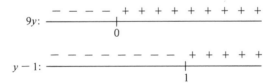

Thus the range is $\{y \mid y \leq 0, y > 1\}$.

Intercepts

When $x = 0$, $y = 0$. The origin $(0, 0)$ is the only intercept.

Symmetry

The graph is symmetric with respect to the y axis.

Asymptotes

This is a rational function in which the degree of the numerator and of the denominator are the same (each is degree 2). So $y = \frac{1}{1}$, or $y = 1$, is a horizontal asymptote. (The 1s are the coefficients of the second-degree terms in the numerator and denominator.)

Since the denominator is zero when x is 3 or -3 (while the numerator is not zero then), $x = 3$ and $x = -3$ are the vertical asymptotes.

Using the Information

In order to sketch the graph, first draw the three asymptotes $y = 1$, $x = 3$, and $x = -3$. Plot the intercept $(0, 0)$. Keep in mind the symmetry with respect to the y axis and work on the right portion of the curve (where $x > 0$). There are no y values between 0 and 1; so there will be a top portion ($y > 1$) and a bottom portion ($y \leq 0$). Obtain a few points by using positive values for x. Doing so will give you an idea of how the curve will flow and how it will approach its asymptotes. Some points are $(1, -\frac{1}{8})$, $(2, -\frac{4}{5})$, $(4, 2\frac{2}{7})$, $(5, 1\frac{9}{16})$.

The Sketch

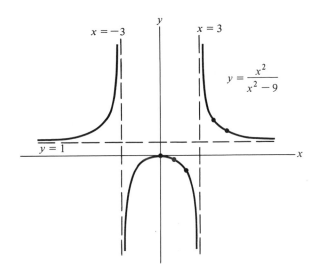

EXERCISES 5.5

1.   Determine the domain of each rational function.

   *(a) $f(x) = \dfrac{5x}{3x - 2}$

   (b) $f(x) = \dfrac{9}{9 + 2x}$

   *(c) $g(x) = \dfrac{3x - 4}{x^2 + 15}$

   (d) $g(x) = \dfrac{7x}{x^2 - 3x - 10}$

   *(e) $y = \dfrac{x^2 + 1}{2x^2 - 7x + 5}$

   (f) $y = \dfrac{x^2 - 9}{8x + 5x^2}$

   *(g) $y = \dfrac{x^2 - 5x + 1}{3x^2 - 12x + 12}$

   (h) $y = \dfrac{11 - x^7}{7x + 6x^2}$

*(i) $\quad f(x) = \dfrac{x^2 - 3x + 2}{x^3 - 5x^2 + 2x + 8}$ (j) $\quad f(x) = \dfrac{x^3 + 7x^2 + 12x}{x^3 + 3x^2 - 4x - 12}$

2. Determine the real zeros of each rational function.

*(a) $\quad f(x) = \dfrac{5 + x}{x}$ (b) $\quad f(x) = \dfrac{3x}{7 - x}$

*(c) $\quad g(x) = \dfrac{x^2 + 7}{x^2 + 6x + 8}$ (d) $\quad g(x) = \dfrac{x^2 - 9}{x^2 + 9}$

*(e) $\quad y = \dfrac{x^2 - 8x + 15}{x^2 - 5x}$ (f) $\quad y = \dfrac{1 - 2x^2}{1 - x}$

*(g) $\quad y = \dfrac{5x^2 - 9}{x^2 + 16}$ (h) $\quad y = \dfrac{5x}{6x}$

*(i) $\quad f(x) = \dfrac{x^2 - 3x + 2}{x^3 - 5x^2 + 2x + 8}$ (j) $\quad f(x) = \dfrac{x^2 + 2x - 15}{x^3 + 3x^2 - 4x - 12}$

3. Simplify each improper fraction. (See Example 13.)

*(a) $\quad \dfrac{x^3 + 4x^2 + 3x + 9}{x^2 + 3x + 2}$ (b) $\quad \dfrac{x^3 + 7x^2 - 2x + 6}{x^2 - 3x + 5}$

*(c) $\quad \dfrac{x^2 + 6x - 9}{x^2 + x + 1}$ (d) $\quad \dfrac{5x^2 + 3x - 2}{x^2 - x + 4}$

*(e) $\quad \dfrac{x^3 + 5x^2 + 3x - 4}{x^2 + 1}$ (f) $\quad \dfrac{2x^3 - 7x^2 + 5x + 11}{x^2 - 2}$

*(g) $\quad \dfrac{x^4 - 8}{x + 1}$ (h) $\quad \dfrac{x^5 + 16}{x - 1}$

*(i) $\quad \dfrac{x^5 + x^3 + x}{x^2 - 3}$ (j) $\quad \dfrac{6x^4 - 5x^2 + 2}{2x^2 + 3}$

4. Determine the vertical asymptote(s) of each function.

*(a) $\quad f(x) = \dfrac{17}{x - 5}$ (b) $\quad f(x) = \dfrac{x + 2}{x + 4}$

*(c) $\quad f(x) = \dfrac{5(x + 2)}{(x + 2)(x - 4)}$ (d) $\quad f(x) = \dfrac{7(x - 3)}{(x + 3)(x + 4)}$

*(e) $\quad y = \dfrac{3x + 5}{x^2 - 2x - 8}$ (f) $\quad y = \dfrac{19 - 15x}{x^2 + 14x + 13}$

*(g) $\quad y = \dfrac{x^2 - 25}{2x^2 + 7x - 15}$ (h) $\quad y = \dfrac{x^2 - 5x + 4}{3x^2 - x - 2}$

*(i) $\quad g(x) = \dfrac{9x - 4}{x^2 + 6x - 2}$ (j) $\quad g(x) = \dfrac{3x^2 - 12}{x^3 - x^2 - 6x}$

5. Determine the horizontal asymptote(s) of each function.

*(a) $f(x) = \dfrac{5x^3 - 8x + 1}{6x^3 + 7x^2 + 5x - 2}$

(b) $f(x) = \dfrac{1 - 7x^2}{x^2 + 3x + 2}$

*(c) $f(x) = \dfrac{x^3 - 27}{x^2 - 9x + 7}$

(d) $f(x) = \dfrac{1 - x^4}{x^5 + x - 3}$

*(e) $f(x) = \dfrac{(2x - 3)(5x + 1)}{(x + 4)(x - 3)}$

(f) $f(x) = \dfrac{(x - 9)(x + 2)}{(x + 5)(3x - 4)}$

*(g) $y = \dfrac{x^5 + x^3 + x}{x^6 + x^4 + x^2}$

(h) $y = \dfrac{1 + x^7}{x^4}$

*(i) $y = \dfrac{(x - 6)(x + 1)(x - 3)}{(1 - x)(x + 7)}$

(j) $y = \dfrac{(x + 5)(x + 2)}{(x - 4)(x - 1)(x)}$

6. Sketch the graph of each rational function. Make use of domain, range, intercepts, symmetry, asymptotes, and additional points as needed.

*(a) $y = \dfrac{8}{x^2 + 4}$

(b) $y = \dfrac{9}{x^2 + 9}$

*(c) $y = \dfrac{x^2}{x^2 - 1}$

(d) $y = \dfrac{x^2}{x^2 - 4}$

*(e) $y = \dfrac{x}{x - 2}$

(f) $y = \dfrac{2x}{x + 1}$

*(g) $y = \dfrac{1}{(x - 2)(x + 2)}$

(h) $y = \dfrac{1}{x^2 - 9}$

*(i) $y = \dfrac{2x^2}{x^2 + 1}$

(j) $y = \dfrac{x^2}{x^2 + 3}$

*(k) $y = \dfrac{x}{x^2 - x - 6}$

(l) $y = \dfrac{2x}{(x + 3)(x - 2)}$

*(m) $y = \dfrac{x}{x^2 - 4}$

(n) $y = \dfrac{x}{x^2 - 9}$

REVIEW EXERCISES FOR CHAPTER 5

1. Determine all zeros of each polynomial function.

*(a) $f(x) = x^3 - 6x^2 + 5x + 12$ (b) $f(x) = 2x^3 - x^2 - 7x + 6$
*(c) $p(x) = 2x^4 + x^3 - 17x^2 - 9x - 9$
 (d) $p(x) = 3x^3 + 7x^2 - 18x + 8$
*(e) $y = x^3 - x^2 - 5x + 2$ (f) $y = x^4$

2. Sketch the graph of each polynomial function.

*(a) $p(x) = x^3 - 5x + 1$ (b) $f(x) = x^3 - 3x^2 + 4$
*(c) $y = -x^3 + x^2 - 3x$ (d) $g(x) = -x^3 + 3x^2 + x + 1$

3. For each rational function, determine its real zeros, domain, vertical asymptote(s), and horizontal asymptote.

*(a) $f(x) = \dfrac{7(x - 1)}{(x + 4)(x - 3)}$

(b) $f(x) = \dfrac{(x - 9)(x + 2)}{(x + 9)(x - 2)}$

*(c) $y = \dfrac{x^4 - 16}{x^3 + x^2 - 6x}$

(d) $y = \dfrac{x^2 + 1}{2x^2 + 5}$

4. Sketch the graph of each rational function.

*(a) $y = \dfrac{x^2}{x^2 + 4}$

(b) $y = \dfrac{12}{x^2 + 3}$

Exponential and Logarithmic Functions

6.1 INTRODUCTION

Up to this point we have studied only those functions constructed by using a finite number of algebraic operations—addition, subtraction, multiplication, division, and raising to constant powers. Such functions are called **algebraic functions.** All of the polynomial functions, rational functions, and functions involving radicals that we have used are algebraic functions.

On the other hand, functions that are not algebraic are called **transcendental functions.** In this chapter we shall study exponential functions and logarithmic functions. In the next chapter we shall study trigonometric functions and their inverses. All of these functions are transcendental. The difference in appearance of transcendental functions (compared to algebraic functions) will be readily apparent. You may find it interesting to realize that calculus can be applied to represent transcendental functions as sums of an infinite number of algebraic terms. A few such infinite series representations will be given in Chapter 10, although their derivations must wait until you study calculus.

6.2 EXPONENTIAL FUNCTIONS

In Chapter 1 the notation and properties of exponents were presented. In the chapters which followed, that knowledge was applied. We saw many expressions, relations, and functions that involve exponents and radicals. So what will be different about the *exponential functions* suggested by the chapter and section heading? The difference is that up until now the exponent has been a constant and the base a variable. Recall, for example, the quadratic functions ($y = ax^2 + bx + c$), the

223

square root function ($y = \sqrt{x} = x^{1/2}$), and others. What is different about an exponential function is that the exponent is a variable and the base is a constant. Following are two examples of exponential functions, one with a base greater than 1, the other with a base between 0 and 1.

$$f(x) = 2^x \qquad g(x) = (\tfrac{1}{2})^x = 2^{-x}$$

The graphs of these two functions will serve to illustrate the general features of exponential curves. To obtain the graphs, we take some values of x, compute function values, plot the points obtained, and draw a smooth curve through those points.

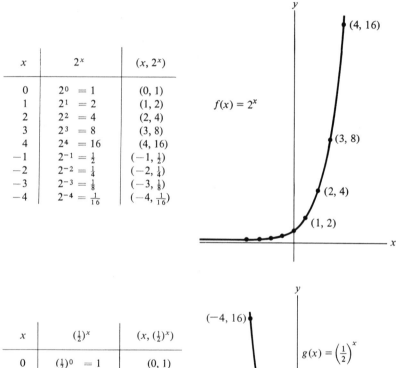

x	2^x	$(x, 2^x)$
0	$2^0 = 1$	$(0, 1)$
1	$2^1 = 2$	$(1, 2)$
2	$2^2 = 4$	$(2, 4)$
3	$2^3 = 8$	$(3, 8)$
4	$2^4 = 16$	$(4, 16)$
-1	$2^{-1} = \tfrac{1}{2}$	$(-1, \tfrac{1}{2})$
-2	$2^{-2} = \tfrac{1}{4}$	$(-2, \tfrac{1}{4})$
-3	$2^{-3} = \tfrac{1}{8}$	$(-3, \tfrac{1}{8})$
-4	$2^{-4} = \tfrac{1}{16}$	$(-4, \tfrac{1}{16})$

x	$(\tfrac{1}{2})^x$	$(x, (\tfrac{1}{2})^x)$
0	$(\tfrac{1}{2})^0 = 1$	$(0, 1)$
1	$(\tfrac{1}{2})^1 = \tfrac{1}{2}$	$(1, \tfrac{1}{2})$
2	$(\tfrac{1}{2})^2 = \tfrac{1}{4}$	$(2, \tfrac{1}{4})$
3	$(\tfrac{1}{2})^3 = \tfrac{1}{8}$	$(3, \tfrac{1}{8})$
4	$(\tfrac{1}{2})^4 = \tfrac{1}{16}$	$(4, \tfrac{1}{16})$
-1	$(\tfrac{1}{2})^{-1} = 2$	$(-1, 2)$
-2	$(\tfrac{1}{2})^{-2} = 4$	$(-2, 4)$
-3	$(\tfrac{1}{2})^{-3} = 8$	$(-3, 8)$
-4	$(\tfrac{1}{2})^{-4} = 16$	$(-4, 16)$

The graph of $f(x) = 2^x$ gradually rises (for negative x and for small positive x) and then suddenly shoots upward (for larger x). Such is the nature of exponential growth. Later in the chapter you will see applications that involve exponential growth. Another observation: The x axis ($y = 0$) is a horizontal asymptote of $f(x) = 2^x$.

The graph of $g(x) = (\frac{1}{2})^x = 2^{-x}$ falls quickly (for negative x and for small positive x) and then falls at a slower rate (for larger x). Such is the nature of exponential decay. Later in the chapter you will see applications that involve exponential decay. Another observation: The x axis ($y = 0$) is a horizontal asymptote of $y = (\frac{1}{2})^x$.

Next, we present the general form of an exponential function.

Exponential function

$$f(x) = b^x$$

$b > 0, \ b \neq 1, \ b$ constant

The domain of $f(x) = b^x$ is the set of all the real numbers, which means that the exponent can be any real number. In Chapter 1 we mentioned only rational exponents. Here we suggest that exponents can be irrational as well as rational. This is done for completeness only; we shall not be using such irrational exponents. The nature of irrational powers is explained in the study of calculus. However, should you encounter an irrational exponent, you can always approximate the irrational number by a rational number and continue, using the rational-exponent approximation.

The range of $f(x) = b^x$ is the set of positive numbers. There is no way to raise a positive base to a power that produces a negative number or zero.

The line $y = 0$ is an asymptote of $f(x) = b^x$. The graph always passes through the point $(0, 1)$.

An important base used for exponential functions is the irrational number e.

$$e \approx 2.718$$

To define the number e properly, you really need calculus. Yet much of the concept can be shown here. The expression

$$\left(1 + \frac{1}{n}\right)^n$$

is the approximate value of e for large values of n. Here is a table that demonstrates this claim. (You can verify the entries in the second column by using a calculator.)

n	$\left(1 + \dfrac{1}{n}\right)^n$
1	2
10	2.593742460
100	2.704813829
1000	2.716923932
10,000	2.718145926
1,000,000	2.718280469
100,000,000	2.718281828

The value of e correct to ten decimal places is 2.7182818284.
Here is the graph of $f(x) = e^x$.

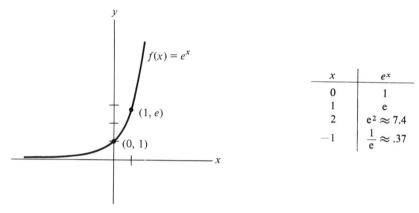

x	e^x
0	1
1	e
2	$e^2 \approx 7.4$
-1	$\dfrac{1}{e} \approx .37$

We can apply the properties of exponents (see Section 1.5) to expressions using e. Here are a few examples.

$$e^x \cdot e^y = e^{x+y}$$

$$(e^x)^y = e^{xy}$$

$$\frac{e^x}{e^y} = e^{x-y}$$

$$e^{-x} = \frac{1}{e^x}$$

$$e^1 = e$$

$$e^0 = 1$$

Example 1 *Simplify the expression* $\dfrac{e^{n+2}}{e^n}$.

Using a basic property of exponents,

$$\frac{e^{n+2}}{e^n} = e^{(n+2)-(n)} = e^2$$

Another approach:

$$\frac{e^{n+2}}{e^n} = \frac{e^n e^2}{e^n} = e^2$$

The section concludes with a sequence of examples that demonstrates some manipulations that can be applied in order to solve certain kinds of equations involving exponential expressions.

Example 2   *Solve for x:* $3^{4x-5} = 81$.
Write 81 as a power of 3: 3^4. Then

$$3^{4x-5} = 3^4$$

It follows from the one-to-one nature of exponential functions that because the bases are equal, the exponents must also be the same. Thus

$$4x - 5 = 4$$

$$x = \tfrac{9}{4}$$

Example 3   *Solve for x:* $(\tfrac{1}{2})^x = 64$.
Both $\tfrac{1}{2}$ and 64 are powers of 2; express them as powers of 2 so that you can equate their exponents.

$$(\tfrac{1}{2})^x = (2^{-1})^x = 2^{-x}$$

and

$$64 = 2^6$$

Thus the equation can be written

$$2^{-x} = 2^6$$

from which we can conclude that

$$-x = 6$$

or

$$x = -6$$

The two equations solved above can be solved by the method shown because both sides can be expressed as powers of the same base. An equation such as $5^x = 9$ cannot be solved this way, but in the next section we shall see just how such an equation can be solved for x.

EXERCISES 6.2

Answers to starred exercises are given in the back of the book.

1. Sketch the graph of each function.
   *(a) $f(x) = 3^x$
   (b) $f(x) = 4^x$
   *(c) $f(t) = (\frac{1}{3})^t$
   (d) $f(t) = 3^{-t}$
   *(e) $f(x) = 3^{x+1}$
   (f) $f(x) = 2^{1-x}$
   *(g) $f(t) = 3 \cdot 2^t$
   (h) $f(t) = 2 \cdot 3^t$
   *(i) $g(x) = \frac{1}{2} \cdot 3^x$
   (j) $f(x) = \frac{1}{5} \cdot 2^x$
   *(k) $f(x) = e^{-x}$
   (l) $f(x) = e^{x+1}$
   *(m) $f(x) = e^{x-1}$
   (n) $f(x) = 1 + e^x$
   *(o) $g(x) = e^x - 1$
   (p) $g(x) = 1 - e^x$
   *(q) $f(x) = |e^x|$
   (r) $f(x) = |e^x - 1|$

*2. Simplify each expression.
   (a) e^0
   (b) e^1
   (c) $\dfrac{3^{2(n+1)}}{3^{2n}}$
   (d) $\dfrac{e^{3(n+1)}}{e^{3n}}$
   (e) $\dfrac{e^{2n+1}}{e^{2n}}$
   (f) $\dfrac{2^n 3^{n+1}}{2^{n+1} 3^{n-1}}$
   (g) $\dfrac{e^n e^5}{e^{n+2}}$
   (h) $\dfrac{2^3 e^n}{2^7 e^{n-1}}$
   (i) $\dfrac{e^{3n}}{e^{2n} e^4}$
   (j) $\dfrac{2 e^{2n}}{e^{-1}}$

3. Solve each of the following exponential equations.
   *(a) $2^x = 16$
   (b) $3^x = 243$
   *(c) $2^m = \dfrac{1}{8}$
   (d) $3^{-y} = 81$
   *(e) $5^{2x} = 25$
   (f) $4^{3x+1} = 256$
   *(g) $2^{7x+2} = 64$
   (h) $2^{5x} = 64^{x+1}$
   *(i) $3^{4-3x} = 27$
   (j) $3^{-1} = 81^n$
   *(k) $7^{2x-1} = 1$
   (l) $6^x = 36^{x+9}$
   *(m) $4^x = 2^{3x-1}$
   (n) $7^{x+2} = 343$
   *(o) $27^x = \left(\dfrac{1}{3}\right)^6$
   (p) $49^{x+2} = 343$
   *(q) $4^{-x} = \dfrac{1}{32}$
   (r) $\left(\dfrac{4}{3}\right)^{2x-3} = \dfrac{16}{9}$
   *(s) $\left(\dfrac{4}{3}\right)^n = \dfrac{9}{16}$
   (t) $\left(\dfrac{2}{3}\right)^{x-5} = \left(\dfrac{9}{4}\right)^3$

$*$(u) $\quad e^{x^2} = e^{2x}$ $\qquad\qquad\qquad$ (v) $\quad e^{x^2} = \dfrac{e^{2x}}{e}$

$*$(w) $\quad e^x = e^{1/x}$ $\qquad\qquad\qquad$ (x) $\quad e^x e^x = e^{7-x}$

4. Exponential functions with bases of 0 and 1 were excluded. Comment on the following functions.

 (a) $\quad f(x) = 0^x$ $\qquad\qquad\qquad$ (b) $\quad f(x) = 1^x$

$*$5. Exponential functions with negative bases were excluded. Recall imaginary numbers such as $\sqrt{-1}, \sqrt{-2}$, and so on. Explain why negative bases were not considered for exponential functions.

6.3 LOGARITHMS

In previous chapters we spent considerable time and effort on manipulation of equations. We found such manipulation useful for determining the domain and range of relations and functions and for solving several kinds of geometric problems and others. In view of this, it seems natural at this point to ask: How can we solve the exponential equation $y = b^x$ for x in terms of y? Actually, we do not yet have the tool that will enable us to manipulate $y = b^x$ as desired. In fact, we must introduce new notation that will solve this problem for us. We define $x = \log_b y$ to mean the same as $y = b^x$.

$$x = \log_b y$$

is the same as

$$y = b^x$$

$$b > 0, b \neq 1.$$

The equation $x = \log_b y$ is read as "x is the **logarithm** of y to the base b" or as "x is the logarithm to the base b of y." As you can see, the logarithm is equal to x and x is the exponent. This means that *a logarithm is an exponent; it is the exponent to which b must be raised to produce y.*

The definition of logarithm may appear strange, but it does serve to give us x in terms of y—it solves the exponential equation for the exponent as desired. Soon we shall see the power of this new notation. But first, let us consider some numerical examples in order for you to become familiar with the new notation.

Exponential Form	Logarithmic Form
$8 = 2^3$	$\log_2 8 = 3$
$10^2 = 100$	$\log_{10} 100 = 2$
$2^{-3} = \frac{1}{8}$	$\log_2 \frac{1}{8} = -3$
$5^0 = 1$	$\log_5 1 = 0$

Example 4 *Solve for x:* $5^x = 9$.

Rewrite the equation in logarithmic form and you will have solved for the exponent x.

$$x = \log_5 9$$

Example 5 *Solve for x:* $2^{3x-1} = 19$.

Since what we are trying to solve for is in the exponent, changing the equation to logarithmic form will help.

$$3x - 1 = \log_2 19$$

Next, add 1 to both sides.

$$3x = 1 + \log_2 19$$

Finally, divide both sides by 3.

$$x = \frac{1 + \log_2 19}{3}$$

Example 6 *Solve for x:* $\log_2 5x = 4$.

In exponential form, the equation is

$$5x = 2^4$$

or

$$5x = 16$$

Thus

$$x = \frac{16}{5}$$

Example 7 *Solve for x:* $\log_x 9 = \frac{1}{2}$.

In exponential form, the equation becomes

$$x^{1/2} = 9$$

from which

$$x = 81$$

Example 8   *Determine the value of* $\log_2 64$.

Since you do not know the value of $\log_2 64$, let it equal x and then solve for x.

$$\log_2 64 = x$$

In exponential notation, the equation becomes

$$2^x = 64$$

Perhaps you can see that x must be 6, since $2^6 = 64$. If not, then consider that 64 can be rewritten as a power of 2. Thus

$$2^x = 64$$

becomes

$$2^x = 2^6$$

from which it follows immediately that $x = 6$.

Now that you are familiar with the notation of logarithms, let us return to our original definition and consider the inverse of an exponential function. Recall that

$$y = b^x \quad \text{is the same as} \quad x = \log_b y$$

Recalling that we interchange x and y in order to obtain an inverse, let us interchange x and y in the form $x = \log_b y$ to obtain the inverse $y = \log_b x$. Using function notation,

$$\boxed{\begin{array}{l} \text{If} \quad f(x) = b^x \\ \text{then} \quad f^{-1}(x) = \log_b x. \end{array}}$$

Note that the graph of an exponential function ($y = b^x$) shows that no two distinct ordered pairs have the same second coordinate. This means that its inverse ($y = \log_b x$) will have no two distinct ordered pairs with the same first coordinate. Indeed, $y = \log_b x$ is a function itself. Hence the f^{-1} notation is appropriate. *The domain of $y = \log_b x$ is the set of positive numbers*; x must be positive. *The range of $y = \log_b x$ is the set of all the real numbers.*

Since $f(x) = \log_2 x$ is the inverse of $f(x) = 2^x$, its graph can be sketched from the graph of $f(x) = 2^x$ by reflecting it across the line $y = x$. This technique was explained in Chapter 3. The following figure shows both graphs.

The Log Function as the Inverse of the Exponential Function

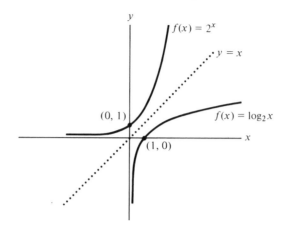

Let us consider the graph of $f(x) = \log_2 x$ from another point of view. To obtain points, select a value for $\log_2 x$ first, and then determine the corresponding x. It is much simpler this way than it would be to pick x first and then determine the corresponding $\log_2 x$. The domain of the function is all real numbers greater than zero; $D = \{x \mid x \text{ real}, x > 0\}$. Keep in mind that this means that logarithms of negative numbers and zero are not defined. The range is all the real numbers; $R = \{y \mid y \in \text{Reals}\}$. The domain of the log function is the same as the range of the exponential function. The range of the log function is the same as the domain of the exponential function. The y axis ($x = 0$) is an asymptote of $f(x) = \log_2 x$. Also, the point $(1, 0)$ is on the graph of any logarithmic function $f(x) = \log_b x$. The graph of $f(x) = \log_2 x$ and some points of the function are shown in the next figure.

A Logarithmic Function

the points

the graph

$\log_2 x$	x	point $(x, \log_2 x)$
0	1	$(1, 0)$
1	2	$(2, 1)$
2	4	$(4, 2)$
3	8	$(8, 3)$
4	16	$(16, 4)$
-1	1/2	$(1/2, -1)$
-2	1/4	$(1/4, -2)$
-3	1/8	$(1/8, -3)$
-4	1/16	$(1/16, -4)$

$f(x) = \log_2 x$

The number e is used frequently as a base for logarithms, especially in science and calculus, where it arises naturally. Such **natural logarithms,** as they are called, are written by using the notation *ln* rather than $\log_e$. In other words, $\log_e x$ is usually written as $\ln x$.

$$\ln x = \log_e x$$

It follows that

$$\ln e = 1$$
$$\ln 1 = 0$$

Just as $y = \log_2 x$ is the inverse of $y = 2^x$, so is $y = \ln x$ the inverse of $y = e^x$. Here is a graph of $y = e^x$ and its inverse $y = \ln x$. These graphs are particularly important in the study of calculus.

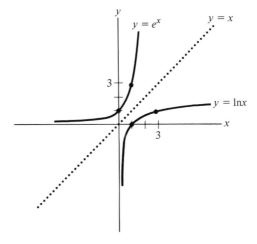

Example 9   *Solve each equation for x.*   (a) $e^{7x} = 2$ (b) $4e^{5x} = 3$

(a)   The equation

$$e^{7x} = 2$$

can be written in logarithmic form as

$$7x = \ln 2$$

Then

$$x = \frac{\ln 2}{7}$$

(b)   The equation

$$4e^{5x} = 3$$

cannot be written in logarithmic form as it stands. However, if you divide both sides by 4, the resulting form *can* be written as a logarithm. The steps:

$$e^{5x} = \frac{3}{4}$$

$$5x = \ln \frac{3}{4}$$

$$x = \frac{1}{5} \ln \frac{3}{4}$$

Example 10 *Solve each equation for x.*   (a) $\ln 2x = 5$ (b) $3 \ln 7x = 8$

(a)   The equation is

$$\log_e 2x = 5$$

In exponential form, this is

$$2x = e^5$$

Thus

$$x = \frac{e^5}{2}$$

(b)   The equation

$$3 \ln 7x = 8$$

cannot be written in exponential form yet. First, you must divide both sides by 3. The result is

$$\ln 7x = \frac{8}{3}$$

This equation can be written in exponential form as

$$7x = e^{8/3}$$

Finally,

$$x = \frac{e^{8/3}}{7}$$

Two important results follow as restatements of the definition of logarithm.

$$\boxed{\begin{array}{l} 1.\ e^{\ln x} = x \\[2mm] 2.\ \ln e^x = x \end{array}}$$

If the exponential equation $e^{\ln x} = x$ is written in logarithmic form, with base e, exponent $\ln x$, and result x, we get $\ln x = \ln x$. Since this is a true statement and since $e^{\ln x} = x$ is an equivalent form of that statement, we see that $e^{\ln x} = x$ is true. Similarly, if we write $\ln e^x = x$ as an exponential equation, it becomes $e^x = e^x$. So it follows that $\ln e^x = x$.

The two boxed results can also be obtained by using composition of functions. Let $f(x) = e^x$. Then $f^{-1}(x) = \ln x$. Since $(f \circ f^{-1})(x) = x$ and here $(f \circ f^{-1})(x) = e^{\ln x}$, it follows that $e^{\ln x} = x$. Similarly, $(f^{-1} \circ f)(x) = \ln e^x = x$.

Example 11   *Simplify.*   (a) $5 \ln e^{x+1}$ (b) $e^{\ln x^2}$

   (a) $5 \ln e^{x+1} = 5(x + 1)$ using Property 2

   (b) $e^{\ln x^2} = x^2$ using Property 1

Logarithms were invented in 1614 by John Napier, a Scottish baron, and were used primarily to simplify calculations. But the widespread use of computers and hand-held calculators has virtually eliminated this application. The use of logarithms to simplify calculations, however, is easiest to accomplish when base 10 is used. Consequently, logarithms using base 10 became known as **common logarithms,** a name still used today. The notation $\log_{10}$ is usually abbreviated simply as *log*. In other words, when no base is specified, base 10 is usually implied.

$$\log x = \log_{10} x$$

It follows that

$$\log 10 = 1$$
$$\log \ 1 = 0$$

EXERCISES 6.3

1. Write each exponential equation as an equivalent logarithmic equation.

   *(a) $3^4 = 81$ (b) $25 = 5^2$

   *(c) $10^3 = 1000$ (d) $128 = 2^7$

   *(e) $9^{1/2} = 3$ (f) $16^{1/4} = 2$

   *(g) $4^{-1} = \dfrac{1}{4}$ (h) $15^0 = 1$

   *(i) $2^a = b$ (j) $x^y = z$

   *(k) $3^y = x + 1$

2. Write each logarithmic equation as an exponential equation.
   *(a) $\log_{10} 100 = 2$ (b) $\log_2 64 = 6$
   *(c) $\log_{25} 5 = \dfrac{1}{2}$ (d) $\log_9 1 = 0$
   *(e) $\log_3 \dfrac{1}{9} = -2$ (f) $\log_g h = f$

3. Determine the value of each logarithm.
   *(a) $\log 10{,}000$ (b) $\log_5 125$
   *(c) $\log_2 1024$ (d) $\log_3 243$
   *(e) $\log_{27} 3$ (f) $\log_{32} 2$
   *(g) $\log_{16} 8$ (h) $\log_{1/2} 4$
   *(i) $\log_2(.125)$ (j) $\log_2(\log_2 256)$
   *(k) $\log(\log 10)$ (l) $\log(\log 10^{100})$

4. Solve each equation for x.
   *(a) $3^x = 7$ (b) $4^x = 11$
   *(c) $10^x = e$ (d) $10^x = 5$
   *(e) $2^{5x} = 17$ (f) $3^{x+4} = 14$
   *(g) $5^{x-1} = 16$ (h) $4^{3x} = 5$

5. Solve each equation for x.
   *(a) $\log_2 x = 4$ (b) $\log_{10} x = 3$
   *(c) $\log_3 4x = 5$ (d) $\log_2 3x = 5$
   *(e) $\log_x 7 = \dfrac{1}{2}$ (f) $\log_x 10 = \dfrac{1}{2}$
   *(g) $\log_x 4 = \dfrac{1}{3}$ (h) $\log_x 6 = \dfrac{1}{3}$
   *(i) $\log_3 81 = x$ (j) $\log_{10}(.01) = x$

6. Simplify each expression.
   *(a) $e^{\ln m}$ (b) $\ln e^t$ *(c) $xe^{\ln x}$
   (d) $x \ln e^x$ *(e) $\ln\sqrt{e}$ (f) $\ln\sqrt[n]{e}$
   *(g) $e \ln e$ (h) $e(4 \ln e^4 + e \ln 1)$ *(i) $e(1 + e^{\ln 3})$

7. Solve each equation for x.
   *(a) $\ln 3x = 2$ (b) $\ln x^3 = 4$
   *(c) $5 \ln 2x = 20$ (d) $\ln \sqrt{x} = 6$
   *(e) $1 + \ln x^2 = 9$ (f) $2 \ln(x - 1) = 16$

8. Solve each equation for x.
   *(a) $e^x = 5$ (b) $e^{x-5} = 6$
   *(c) $ce^{ax} = 1$ (d) $abe^{3x} = 4$

*(e) $7x + e = 13$ (f) $1 - 9ex = 7$

*(g) $a = a_0 e^{xt} + b$ (h) $5e^3 - 4x = 19 + m$

*(i) $a - be^{1-cx} = df + g$ (j) $ve^{mx-b} = 7$

9. Graph each function and its inverse.

*(a) $f(x) = 3^x$ (b) $f(x) = e^x$

*(c) $f(x) = \log_3 x$ (d) $f(x) = \log x$

*(e) $f(x) = \log_{1/2} x$ (f) $f(x) = \log_{3/2} x$

*(g) $h(x) = \log_2 (x + 1)$

10. Sketch a graph of each function. Begin with the graph of $y = \ln x$ and use the concepts from Sections 3.8 and 3.9 as applicable.

*(a) $y = -\ln x$ (b) $y = 2 \ln x$

*(c) $y = 3 + \ln x$ (d) $y = \ln(x - 2)$

*(e) $y = \ln(x + 1)$ (f) $y = -\dfrac{1}{2} \ln x$

11. Sketch a graph of each function. Begin with the graph of $y = 2^x$ and use the concepts from Sections 3.8 and 3.9 as applicable.

*(a) $y = 2^{x+3}$ (b) $y = -2^x + 1$

*(c) $y = 3 \cdot 2^x$ (d) $y = 2^{x-1} - 3$

*12. $\ln e^x = x$, $\ln e = 1$, and $\ln 1 = 0$ are special cases of the following results.

$$\log_b b^x = x$$

$$\log_b b = 1$$

$$\log_b 1 = 0$$

The results follow immediately when the definition of logarithm is used to restate the equations in exponential form. Use these results to evaluate each expression below.

(a) $\log_{10} 10^8$ (b) $\log_2 2^{10}$

(c) $\log_9 9$ (d) $\log_7 7$

(e) $\log_3 1$ (f) $\log_5 1$

(g) $\log_b b^{x+y}$ (h) $\log_b b^{x^2}$

*13. The expression $\ln x^2$ means $\ln(x^2)$, that is, $\ln$ of x^2. To specify the square of $\ln x$, write $(\ln x)^2$ or $\ln^2 x$.

$\ln x^2$ means $\ln(x^2)$
$\ln^2 x$ means $(\ln x)^2$

Evaluate each expression.

(a) $\ln^2 e^3$ (b) $\ln^2 e^4$

(c) $\ln e^2$ (d) $\ln e^3$

(e) $\ln^2 e$ (f) $\ln^2 1$

14. Determine the domain of each function.

*(a) $f(x) = \ln(-x)$ (b) $f(x) = \ln(x + 1)$

*(c) $f(x) = \ln(x - 1)$ (d) $f(x) = \ln|x - 1|$

*(e) $f(x) = \ln(x^2 - 4)$ (f) $f(x) = \ln x^2 - 4$

*(g) $f(x) = \ln(\ln x)$ (h) $f(x) = \ln|\ln x|$

15. If the graph of $y = \log_b x$ contains the given point (x, y), determine the value of base b.

*(a) $(16, 2)$ (b) $(16, 4)$ *(c) $(8, -3)$

(d) $(25, -2)$ *(e) $(1/9, 2)$ (f) $(1/8, -3)$

6.4 PROPERTIES OF LOGARITHMS

Three important properties of logarithms make them useful for algebraic manipulations and for simplifying calculations. The properties are stated now, proved, and applied afterward. They are stated for logarithms using any base $b > 0, \neq 1$. The numbers M and N are positive.

$$\log_b (M \cdot N) = \log_b M + \log_b N$$

$$\log_b \frac{M}{N} = \log_b M - \log_b N$$

$$\log_b M^p = p \cdot \log_b M$$

In all three proofs we will use the fact that if $A = B$, then $\log_b A = \log_b B$.

$\log_b (M \cdot N) = \log_b M + \log_b N$

Let $x = \log_b M$ and $y = \log_b N$. From $x = \log_b M$ we get the exponential form $M = b^x$. Similarly, from $y = \log_b N$ we have $N = b^y$. Thus

$$M \cdot N = b^x \cdot b^y = b^{x+y}$$

So

$\log_b (M \cdot N) = \log_b b^{x+y}$ if $A = B$, then $\log_b A = \log_b B$.

            $= x + y$ by 12 of Exercises 6.3: $\log_b b^x = x$.

            $= \log_b M + \log_b N$ since $x = \log_b M$ and $y = \log_b N$

$$\log_b \frac{M}{N} = \log_b M - \log_b N$$

Let $x = \log_b M$ and $y = \log_b N$. Then $M = b^x$ and $N = b^y$. Therefore

$$\frac{M}{N} = \frac{b^x}{b^y} = b^{x-y}$$

and

$$\log_b \frac{M}{N} = \log_b b^{x-y}$$

$$= x - y$$

$$= \log_b M - \log_b N$$

$$\log_b M^p = p \cdot \log_b M$$

Let $x = \log_b M$. Then $M = b^x$. Therefore

$$M^p = (b^x)^p = b^{px}$$

Thus

$$\log_b M^p = \log_b b^{px}$$

$$= px$$

$$= p \cdot \log_b M$$

Example 12   *If $\log_b 2 \approx 0.3010$, $\log_b 3 \approx 0.4771$, and $\log_b 5 \approx 0.6990$, compute the approximate value of:*   (a) $\log_b 6$ (b) $\log_b 1.5$ (c) $\log_b 25$.

(a) $\log_b 6 = \log_b (2 \cdot 3)$

$\qquad\qquad = \log_b 2 + \log_b 3$ first property of logarithms

$\qquad\qquad \approx 0.3010 + 0.4771$ using the values of the logarithms

$\qquad\qquad \approx 0.7781$

(b) $\log_b 1.5 = \log_b \dfrac{3}{2}$

$\qquad\qquad = \log_b 3 - \log_b 2$ second property of logarithms

$\qquad\qquad \approx 0.4771 - 0.3010$ using the values of the logarithms

$\qquad\qquad \approx 0.1761$

(c) $\log_b 25 = \log_b 5^2$

$$= 2 \cdot \log_b 5 \qquad \text{third property of logarithms}$$

$$\approx 2(0.6990) \qquad \text{using the value of the logarithm}$$

$$\approx 1.3980$$

Example 13 *Compute the approximate value of* $\log_b \sqrt{\dfrac{6}{5}}$, *if* $\log_b 2 \approx 0.3010$, $\log_b 3 \approx 0.4771$, *and* $\log_b 5 \approx 0.6990$.

The properties of logarithms yield, in steps,

$$\log_b \sqrt{\dfrac{6}{5}} = \log_b \left(\dfrac{6}{5}\right)^{1/2} \qquad \text{notation}$$

$$= \tfrac{1}{2} \log_b \dfrac{6}{5} \qquad \text{third property of logarithms}$$

$$= \tfrac{1}{2}(\log_b 6 - \log_b 5) \qquad \text{second property of logarithms}$$

$$= \tfrac{1}{2}(\log_b 3 \cdot 2 - \log_b 5) \qquad \text{since } 6 = 3 \cdot 2$$

$$= \tfrac{1}{2}(\log_b 3 + \log_b 2 - \log_b 5) \qquad \text{first property of logarithms}$$

$$\approx \tfrac{1}{2}(0.4771 + 0.3010 - 0.6990) \qquad \text{using the values of the logarithms}$$

$$\approx \tfrac{1}{2}(0.0791)$$

$$\approx 0.03955$$

Example 14 *Write* $\log_b 5 + 2 \log_b 7$ *as the logarithm of a single number.*

$$\log_b 5 + 2 \log_b 7 = \log_b 5 + \log_b 7^2 \qquad \text{third property of logarithms}$$

$$= \log_b 5 + \log_b 49 \qquad \text{since } 7^2 = 49$$

$$= \log_b (5 \cdot 49) \qquad \text{first property of logarithms}$$

$$= \log_b 245 \qquad \text{since } 5 \cdot 49 = 245$$

Some equations can be solved readily by applying properties of logarithms. Here are a few examples.

Example 15 *Solve for x:* $\quad 2^{x+1} = 7^{4-x}$.
Since

$$2^{x+1} = 7^{4-x}$$

then

$$\log 2^{(x+1)} = \log 7^{(4-x)}$$

Although any base could have been used, e and 10 are the most popular and useful. We chose to use base 10. Continuing,

$$(x + 1) \log 2 = (4 - x) \log 7$$

or

$$x \log 2 + 1 \log 2 = 4 \log 7 - x \log 7$$

After collecting x terms on the left and non-x terms on the right, we have

$$x \log 2 + x \log 7 = 4 \log 7 - \log 2$$

Factor out an x on the left side.

$$x(\log 2 + \log 7) = 4 \log 7 - \log 2$$

Divide both sides by $\log 2 + \log 7$, the coefficient of x.

$$x = \frac{4 \log 7 - \log 2}{\log 2 + \log 7}$$

Thus we have solved for x. In the next section we shall see how to obtain approximate values for $\log 7$, $\log 2$, and other logarithms.

Example 16   *Solve for x:* $\log (x + 1) - \log 2x = 3$.

  If the two logarithms are combined as one, then it will be a simple matter to change that logarithmic equation to an exponential equation and solve it for x. By applying the second property of logarithms to the left side of the given equation, we obtain

$$\log \frac{x + 1}{2x} = 3$$

In exponential form this is the same as

$$10^3 = \frac{x + 1}{2x}$$

or

$$1000 = \frac{x + 1}{2x}$$

which is readily solved by a series of algebraic manipulations.

$$2000x = x + 1$$
$$1999x = 1$$
$$x = \frac{1}{1999}$$

EXERCISES 6.4

1. Let $\log_b 2 \approx 5$, $\log_b 3 \approx 8$, and $\log_b 5 \approx 11.5$. Compute the approximate value of each number.

*(a) $\log_b 6$ (b) $\log_b 10$

*(c) $\log_b 15$ (d) $\log_b 4$

*(e) $\log_b 27$ (f) $\log_b 50$

*(g) $\log_b 30$ (h) $\log_b 1.5$

*(i) $\log_b .6$ (j) $\log_b \dfrac{2}{3}$

*(k) $\log_b \sqrt{3}$ (l) $\log_b \sqrt[4]{10}$

*(m) $\log_b \dfrac{3}{2}$ (n) $\dfrac{\log_b 3}{\log_b 2}$

*2. Write each expression as the logarithm of a single number.
(a) $\log_t 7 + \log_t 5$ (b) $\log_b 6 + 3 \cdot \log_b 5$
(c) $2 \log_b 6 + 2 \log_b 4$ (d) $\log_a 1 + \log_a 7 - \log_a 2$
(e) $\log_r 4 + \log_r 3 + \log_r 10$ (f) $\dfrac{1}{2} \log_b 9 + \dfrac{1}{4} \log_b 16 + \log_b 5$

*3. Simplify each expression by using the properties of logarithms.
(a) $\log_b 7 + \log_b x$ (b) $\log_b x + \log_b x^2$
(c) $\log_b x^3 - \log_b x$ (d) $\log_b(x^2 - 1) - \log_b(x + 1)$

4. Solve each equation for x. You may get extraneous roots; so check all "solutions" in the original equation. Remember, logarithms of negative numbers are not real numbers.
*(a) $\log x + \log(x + 3) = 1$
(b) $\log x^2 - \log 5 = \log 7 + \log 2x$
*(c) $\ln x + \ln(x - 1) = 0$
(d) $\ln(x + 1) - \ln x = 1$
*(e) $\log_4 (x + 6) - \log_4 10 = \log_4 (x - 1) - \log_4 2$

5. Solve each equation for x in terms of the other numbers or letters.

*(a) $3 \cdot 10^x = 8$ (b) $ab^x = c$

*(c) $(ab)^x = c$ (d) $\dfrac{ab^x}{c} = d$

*(e) $ab^{cx} = d$ (f) $\dfrac{ab^{x+1}}{c} = d$

*6. The *Richter scale* measures the relative magnitude of earthquakes. The magnitude M of an earthquake is given by

$$M = \log_{10} \frac{I}{I_0}$$

I_0 is a constant, minimum measurable intensity that is compared with the intensity I of the earthquake being measured.

(a) Show that the intensity I of an earthquake of magnitude 2 on the Richter scale is 100 times the minimum measurable intensity I_0. (*Hint:* Substitute the two numbers given here and then change the logarithmic equation to an exponential equation.)

(b) Compare the intensity of an earthquake of magnitude 3 with I_0.

(c) How much greater is the intensity of an earthquake of magnitude 3 than an earthquake of magnitude 2?

(d) Compare the intensities of earthquakes of magnitude 5 and magnitude 8.

7. Use properties of logarithms and ingenuity to verify each statement.

(a) $\ln \dfrac{1}{x} = -\ln x$

(b) $\dfrac{1}{a} \ln \dfrac{1}{c} = -\dfrac{\ln c}{a}$

(c) $2 + \ln y = \ln e^2 y$

*8. What is wrong with the following "proof" that $-1 = +1$?

$$(-1)^2 = +1$$
$$\log_{10}(-1)^2 = \log_{10}(+1)$$
$$2\log_{10}(-1) = \log_{10}(+1)$$
$$2\log_{10}(-1) = 0$$
$$\log_{10}(-1) = 0$$
$$\log_{10}(-1) = \log_{10}(+1)$$

Thus

$$-1 = +1$$

9. Let $x = 100$ and $y = 10$, and show by example that

$$\frac{\log_{10} x}{\log_{10} y} \neq \log_{10} \frac{x}{y}$$

10. Since $e^{\ln x} = x$, it follows that for $a > 0$

$$a^x = e^{\ln a^x} = e^{x \ln a}$$

Thus

$$\boxed{a^x = e^{x \ln a}}$$

Use this result to express each power given as a power of e.

*(a) 7^t (b) 2^6

*(c) x^2 (d) y^x

11. Is $\ln x^2 = 2 \ln x$ for all values of x? Explain.

6.5 EVALUATING COMMON LOGARITHMS

As shown next, the values of some common logarithms can be determined by thinking in exponential form.

$$\log 10,000 = 4 \quad \text{since } 10^4 = 10,000$$
$$\log 1000 = 3 \quad \text{since } 10^3 = 1000$$
$$\log 100 = 2 \quad \text{since } 10^2 = 100$$
$$\log 10 = 1 \quad \text{since } 10^1 = 10$$
$$\log 1 = 0 \quad \text{since } 10^0 = 1$$
$$\log .1 = -1 \quad \text{since } 10^{-1} = .1$$
$$\log .01 = -2 \quad \text{since } 10^{-2} = .01$$

Most logarithms, however, must be found by using a calculator or looked up in a table. Just how the entries of that table are obtained or how the calculator determines values is explained in Chapter 10. Table III gives *approximate* values of common logarithms; calculators offer better approximations. The table contains logarithms of numbers from 1.00 to 9.99. For example, log 1.74 can be found in the table by going down the n column as far as 1.7 and then over to the column labeled 4. The number there is 0.2405.† Thus, log 1.74 $\approx$ 0.2405. The table can

---

† The table entries do not have zeros before the decimal point, but zeros are used here to be consistent with the development that will occur in the next few pages of this section.

be read in reverse; that is, if log $n = 0.2405$, then $n \approx 1.74$. The number 1.74 is called the **antilogarithm** of 0.2405. Use the table to verify each of the following statements.

$$\log 4.91 \approx 0.6911$$

$$\log 7.67 \approx 0.8848$$

$$\log 2.00 \approx 0.3010$$

antilog $0.9355 \approx 8.62$ *or* $10^{0.9355} \approx 8.62$

antilog $0.0128 \approx 1.03$ *or* $10^{0.0128} \approx 1.03$

antilog $0.8457 \approx 7.01$ *or* $10^{0.8457} \approx 7.01$

With a calculator, log 4.91 is obtained by entering the number 4.91 and then pressing the "log" key. Antilog calculations are done by using exponential notation; that is, antilog 0.9355 is considered as $10^{0.9355}$ and determined using a "y^x" (or the like) key. Use a calculator to verify the three logarithm values and the three antilogarithms listed above.

The logarithm of a positive number N not between 1.00 and 9.99 can also be read from this table. The number N should be written in scientific notation—that is, as a number n between 1.00 and 9.99 times a power of 10. The logarithm of N is then the logarithm of n *plus* the power to which 10 is raised.

$$\begin{aligned}
\log N &= \log (n \cdot 10^c) \\
&= \log n + \log 10^c \\
&= \log n + c \qquad \text{since } \log_{10} 10^c = c \\
&= c + \log n
\end{aligned}$$

The three cases shown next demonstrate the role of the c in locating the decimal point. This is why logarithms with base 10 are useful.

$$\log 17.4 = \log 1.74 \cdot 10^1 \approx 1 + .2405 = 1.2405$$

$$\log 174 = \log 1.74 \cdot 10^2 \approx 2 + .2405 = 2.2405$$

$$\log 1740 = \log 1.74 \cdot 10^3 \approx 3 + .2405 = 3.2405$$

When log N is written in the form log $N = c + \log n$, c is called the **characteristic** and log n is called the **mantissa.** The characteristic is the power of 10. The mantissa is the number obtained from the table. In log $1740 \approx 3.2405$, the characteristic is 3 and the mantissa is approximately .2405.

Logarithms of numbers having fewer than three digits can be found in the table after supplying enough zeros to make a three-digit number.

$$\log 2.6 = \log 2.60 \approx 0.\underline{4150}$$

$$\log 53 = \log 53.0 \approx 1.\underline{7243}$$

$$\log 8 = \log 8.00 \approx 0.\underline{9031}$$

The characteristic of log .0359 is -2, since $\log .0359 = \log 3.59 \cdot 10^{-2} = -2 + \log 3.59 \approx -2 + .5551$. Be careful when using such a negative characteristic, because it cannot simply be attached to the front of the mantissa, as was the effect with positive characteristics. Note

$$\log 529 \approx 2 + .7235 = 2.7235$$

But

$$\log .0359 \approx -2 + .5551 \neq -2.5551$$

Instead

$$\log .0359 \approx -2 + .5551 = -1.4449$$

Only if you are working such problems as those of Section 6.9 without a calculator, should you leave the expression as $-2 + .5551$.† Here are two additional examples.

$$\log .359 \approx -1 + .5551 = -0.4449$$

$$\log .00359 \approx -3 + .5551 = -2.4449$$

If you are using a table, then after the antilogarithm of a mantissa is obtained from the table, it should be multiplied by 10^c, where c is the characteristic of the logarithm. For example,

$$\text{antilog } 2.8267 = (\text{antilog } .8267) \cdot 10^2$$

$$\approx 6.71 \cdot 10^2$$

$$\approx 671$$

If a calculator is used, there is no such concern. Here is the same antilog problem with a calculator approach.

$$\text{antilog } 2.8267 = 10^{2.8267}$$

$$\approx 671$$

———

† Such a form is easier to work with *only* in noncalculator settings. Some people prefer to write $-2 + .5551$ as $8.5551 - 10$. Similarly, $-1 + .5551$ can be written as $9.5551 - 10$ and $-3 + .5551$ as $7.5551 - 10$.

Also,

$$\text{antilog}(-2.4449) = 10^{-2.4449}$$

$$\approx .00359$$

This last antilog is tricky if done without a calculator, since $-2.4449 = -2 - .4449$. To make the mantissa positive, you must add 1 to $-.4449$ and then compensate for this by subtracting 1 from the -2. Thus,

$$\text{antilog}(-2 - .4449) = \text{antilog}(-2 - 1 + 1 - .4449)$$

$$= \text{antilog}(-3 + .5551)$$

$$\approx 3.59 \cdot 10^{-3}$$

$$\approx .00359$$

Next is an example of the concept of linear interpolation. Although the presence of a calculator eliminates any real need for this particular application, the concept of interpolation is used in a variety of situations in mathematics, science, and engineering. Logarithms of numbers with four or more digits can be found by using the table and a method called **linear interpolation.** Consider, for example, determining the logarithm of 14.83. The logarithms of 14.8 and 14.9 are available directly from the table. The logarithm of 14.83 is between them.

$$\log 14.80 \approx 1.1703$$

$$\log 14.83$$

$$\log 14.90 \approx 1.1732$$

Since 14.83 is .3 of the way from 14.80 to 14.90, log 14.83 is approximately .3 of the way from log 14.80 to log 14.90. In other words,

$$\log 14.83 \approx \log 14.80 + .3 (\log 14.90 - \log 14.80)$$

$$\approx 1.1703 + .3 (1.1732 - 1.1703)$$

$$\approx 1.1703 + .3 (.0029)$$

$$\approx 1.1703 + .00087$$

$$\approx 1.17117 \text{ or } 1.1712$$

Here is a brief explanation of what is happening in linear interpolation. The two known logarithms are approximate functional values for $f(x) = \log x$. The curve passing through them is indeed curved, but in small intervals it is approximately a straight line. Linear interpolation techniques approximate the curve between the two points by a straight line between the two points. The number obtained by the interpolation is from the line rather than from the actual logarithm curve. A graphic illustration of this process is shown in the next drawing.

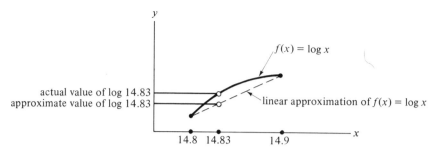

Often the *antilog* cannot be determined directly from the table; interpolation is needed. For example, the antilogarithm of 2.8930 must be found by interpolation, since the mantissa .8930 is not in the table. The mantissa .8930 is located between .8927 and .8932.

$$2.8927 \approx \log 781.0$$

$$2.8930 = \log 781.?$$

$$2.8932 \approx \log 782.0$$

Note that .8930 is $\frac{3}{5}$, or .6, of the way from .8927 to .8932, because there is .0003 unit from .8927 to .8930 and .0005 unit from .8927 to .8932. The fraction .0003/.0005 reduces to $\frac{3}{5}$, or .6. Thus the antilog of 2.8930 is approximately 781.6. The digits of the antilog are 7816. The characteristic of 2 determines the location of the decimal point.

EXERCISES 6.5

1. Determine the approximate value of each logarithm.
   *(a) log 38.6 (b) log 491
   *(c) log 5.4 (d) log 984
   *(e) log 13,000 (f) log .834
   *(g) log 1.5 (h) log 12.9
   *(i) log .0065

2. Determine the approximate value of each antilogarithm.
   *(a) antilog 2.4116 (b) $10^{1.9335}$
   *(c) antilog 3.1523 (d) antilog(-0.2581)
   *(e) $10^{1.7016}$ (f) $10^{4.3997}$
   *(g) antilog(-2.1871) (h) $10^{0.4829}$
   *(i) antilog(-1.7305)

3. Evaluate each expression.
   *(a) $\log(6.23 \times 10^3)$ (b) $\log(8.15 \times 10^6)$
   *(c) $10^{1.7952}$ (d) $10^{2.3284}$

4. Determine the approximate value of each logarithm. Use interpolation.
    *(a) log 489.2   (b) log 3415
    *(c) log 29.63   (d) log 1.599
    *(e) log 2316   (f) log 59.07
    *(g) log .01642   (h) log 5008
    *(i) log .0001491

5. Determine the approximate value of each antilogarithm. Use interpolation.
    *(a) $10^{1.8770}$ (b) $10^{-1+.7431}$
    *(c) antilog 4.0653   (d) antilog 3.2934
    *(e) $10^{2.4410}$ (f) antilog(-1.4714)
    *(g) antilog(-0.8409)   (h) antilog(-2.0945)
    *(i) $10^{0.6397}$

6.6 EVALUATING NATURAL LOGARITHMS

The approach to using the natural logarithm table (Table II) resembles that of common logarithms. We employ scientific notation and the fact that ln 10 ≈ 2.3026.† The value of ln N is determined by first writing N as $n \cdot 10^c$, where n is between 1.00 and 9.99. Then properties of logarithms are used.

$$\ln N = \ln n \cdot 10^c$$
$$= \ln n + \ln 10^c$$
$$= \ln n + c(\ln 10)$$
$$\approx \ln n + c(2.3026)$$

Next, ln n is looked up in Table II. Here is a specific example.

Example 17 *Determine* ln 7580:   *(a) by using Table II*   *(b) by calculator.*

(a)   ln 7580 = $\ln(7.58 \cdot 10^3)$

$\qquad$ = ln 7.58 + ln 10^3

$\qquad$ = ln 7.58 + 3 · ln 10

$\qquad$ ≈ ln 7.58 + 3(2.3026)   We know that ln 10 ≈ 2.3026.

$\qquad$ ≈ 2.0255 + 3(2.3026)   From Table II, ln 7.58 ≈ 2.0255.

$\qquad$ ≈ 2.0255 + 6.9078

$\qquad$ ≈ 8.9333

---

† The numbers 2.3026 and 1/2.3026 occur frequently in chemistry and physics conversions.

(b)   ln 7580 ≈ 8.9333

This was done by entering 7580 and pressing the "ln" key.

For hand calculations, natural logarithms are not as easy to work with as common logarithms. With common logarithms, you are dealing with powers of 10 and the characteristic keeps track of your decimal point. With natural logarithms, you are dealing with powers of e, which means powers of 2.718 (approximately). With common logarithms, there is an integer characteristic and a mantissa. This makes obtaining the antilog very easy. On the other hand, with natural logarithms you have a multiple of 2.3026 instead of the nice integer characteristic; so obtaining the antilog is difficult with a table. However, such an antilog is easy to obtain with a calculator, because it is a power of e. Note this comparison of antilogs shown next.

$$\log_{10} x = 2.5977 \quad\longrightarrow\quad x = 10^{2.5977}$$

$$\log_e x = 2.5977 \quad\longrightarrow\quad x = e^{2.5977}$$

Here is an example in which the antilog can be obtained by using Table I, the table of powers of e, or a calculator.

Example 18   *Solve for x:*   ln x = 1.6.

$$\ln x = 1.6$$

is the same as

$$\log_e x = 1.6$$

In exponential form, we have

$$x = e^{1.6}$$

From Table I or a calculator,

$$x \approx 4.9530$$

EXERCISES 6.6

1.   Determine the approximate value of each logarithm.

*(a) ln 4.59	(b) ln 9.32
*(c) ln 546	(d) ln 76.4
*(e) ln 10,000	(f) ln 6750
*(g) ln 4370	(h) ln 85,000,000
*(i) ln .540	(j) ln .783
*(k) ln .0097	(l) ln .09

2. Solve for x. Use Table I.

*(a) $\ln x = .05$ (b) $\ln x = 4$

*(c) $\ln x = 2.7$ (d) $\ln x = 1.8$

*(e) $\ln x = 4.5$ (f) $\ln x = 7.5$

6.7   EXPONENTIAL GROWTH AND DECAY

Both in business and in science there are many examples of quantities that increase (grow) or decrease (decay) exponentially. When interest is compounded continuously (Example 19), the amount invested grows exponentially. The growth of bacteria in a culture (Example 20) is exponential. The decomposition of radioactive material (Example 21) is an example of exponential decay. One formula, readily derived by calculus, can be used for all of these exponential growth and decay situations.

$$A = Ce^{kt}$$

$t = $ time in years, days, hours, and so on

$A = $ amount after time t

$C = $ amount initially

$k = $ constant: rate of growth $(k > 0)$ or

decay $(k < 0)$

Example 19   *$1000 is invested at 9% annual interest compounded continuously.*
(a) How much has accrued in 5 years?
(b) How long will it take to double the principal?

(a)   The exponential growth formula applies to compound interest problems in which the compounding is continuous. By continuous compounding we mean that the interest is compounded every instant (not merely quarterly or daily). The interest rate, 9%, is the growth constant, but it must be written in decimal form. Thus we use

$$A = Ce^{kt}$$

with

$$C = 1000$$

$$k = .09$$

$$t = 5 \text{ (years)}$$

This means

$$A = 1000e^{(.09)5}$$
$$= 1000e^{.45}$$

From Table I or a calculator, $e^{.45} \approx 1.5683$; so

$$A \approx 1000(1.5683)$$

or

$$A \approx 1568.30$$

The amount accrued in 5 years is approximately $1568.30.

(b)   Again we have

$$A = Ce^{kt}$$

Here

$$C = 1000$$
$$k = .09$$
$$A = 2000 \quad \text{double the original } \$1000$$

We seek the value of t, and we begin with

$$2000 = 1000e^{(.09)t}$$

First, divide both sides by 1000. The result is

$$2 = e^{.09t}$$

Next, to solve this exponential equation with the unknown in the exponent, change it to logarithm form.

$$.09t = \ln 2$$

Then divide by .09 and it will be solved for t.

$$t = \frac{\ln 2}{.09}$$

Now we can use a calculator or Table II to approximate $\ln 2$ and thus obtain a more meaningful result.

$$t \approx \frac{.6931}{.09} \approx 7.7$$

It will take approximately 7.7 years to double the principal.

Example 20 *The number of bacteria in a culture increases from 600 to 1800 in $2\frac{1}{2}$ hours. Assuming the growth of bacteria to be exponential, determine a formula for the number of bacteria present at any time t.*

We have

$$A = Ce^{kt}$$

The formula will be complete when C and k are determined. Then the amount A will be a function of time t alone. We shall assume that the initial number of bacteria is 600, since that is the first observation. Thus $C = 600$ and

$$A = 600e^{kt}$$

Next, note that when $t = 2.5$, $A = 1800$. Substituting these values into the formula yields

$$1800 = 600e^{k(2.5)}$$

or

$$3 = e^{2.5k}$$

Solve for k by changing to logarithm form.

$$2.5k = \ln 3$$

or

$$k = \frac{\ln 3}{2.5} \approx \frac{1.0986}{2.5} \approx .4394$$

Thus $k \approx .4394$ and the formula is

$$A = 600e^{.4394t}$$

Example 21 *As radium emits alpha particles it decomposes (decays) exponentially into the element radon. Radium has a half-life of 1600 years, which means it takes 1600 years for half of a mass of radium to decay to radon. If we begin now with a mass of 100 grams of radium, how much will remain 500 years from now?*

We have

$$A = Ce^{kt}$$

Of course, $C = 100$, since we begin with 100 grams of radium.

$$A = 100e^{kt}$$

Because it takes 1600 years for half of the 100 grams to decay, we know that $A = 50$ when $t = 1600$. Using this information in the formula will enable us to determine k.

$$50 = 100e^{k(1600)}$$

or

$$.5 = e^{1600k}$$

In logarithm form, this is

$$1600k = \ln(.5)$$

Thus

$$k = \frac{\ln(.5)}{1600} \approx \frac{-.6931}{1600} \approx -.0004$$

Therefore the formula is

$$A = 100e^{-.0004t} \qquad \text{The minus indicates decay.}$$

In 500 years,

$$A = 100e^{(-.0004)(500)}$$
$$= 100e^{-.20}$$
$$\approx 100(.8187) \qquad \text{from Table I}$$
$$\approx 81.87$$

Approximately 81.87 grams will remain after 500 years.

EXERCISES 6.7

*1. If $5000 is invested at 8% interest per year compounded continuously, how much will accrue after 5 years?

2. If $6000 is invested at 7% interest per year compounded continuously, how much will accrue after 10 years?

*3. If $4000 is invested at 8% interest per year compounded continuously, how long will it take to double the original investment?

4. If $4000 is invested at 9% interest per year compounded continuously, how long will it take to double the original amount invested?

*5. How much money should you invest now at 10% interest per year compounded continuously so that you will have $6000 in 3 years?

*6. The population of Concord, California, was 36,000 in 1960 and 85,000 in 1970. Determine k for this population. (Assume exponential growth.)

*7. Suppose that a population grows exponentially with $k = .01$. If the present population is 10,000, what will the population be 20 years from now?

*8. The number of bacteria in a culture triples every hour. If we begin with 2000 bacteria, how long will it take before there will be a half million bacteria?

*9. Lead 210 has a half-life of 22 years. How much of a 200-gram mass of lead 210 will remain after 150 years? (*Note:* Use only two decimal places for the k value.)

10. If the half-life of a substance is 13.2 years, how much of a 70-gram mass of the substance will remain after 75 years? (*Note:* Use only two decimal places for the k value.)

*11. At what annual interest rate compounded continuously will money double in 7 years?

12. At what annual interest rate compounded continuously will money triple in 10 years?

*13. How much money should be invested at 8% per year compounded continuously for 5 years in order to have the same amount as you would have if $1000 were invested at 6% per year compounded continuously for 10 years?

*14. Radiocarbon dating is used in archaeology to determine the age of findings. The technique was devised in 1948 by Dr. Willard Libby of the University of Chicago and is based on the fact that all living animals contain the same amount of carbon 14 per unit of weight. They acquire it from the atmosphere through respiration. Once the animal dies, however, it no longer obtains carbon 14. Furthermore, the amount of carbon 14 it contained at the time of death decays (that is, changes into a different form of carbon). It takes 5730 years for the amount of carbon 14 to drop to half its original level.
    (a) Determine the decay constant k.
    (b) A skull found in 1980 contained only 40% of the carbon 14 found in living animals. How old is the skull?

*15. After being given intravenously, a drug is removed from the blood (to organs that will use it or eliminate it) at an exponentially declining rate. Suppose the concentration of the drug when administered is 100 units per volume and the decay constant is $-.03$. Assume that time is measured in minutes.

(a) What will be the concentration after 15 minutes?

(b) How long will it be until 80% of the drug has been *eliminated* from the bloodstream?

16. If a cool body is placed in a warmer environment, it will heat up according to

$$y = S - Ce^{kt} \begin{cases} t &= \text{time the body is in a warmer environment} \\ y &= \text{temperature of the body} \\ C &= \text{constant} \\ k &= \text{warming constant} \\ S &= \text{temperature of surrounding environment} \end{cases}$$

Suppose that a roast at room temperature (70°F) is placed in a 350° oven. After 50 minutes, the temperature of the roast is 110°.

(a) Determine the constant C.

(b) Determine the warming constant k.

(c) To the nearest minute, when will the roast be done (temperature 150°)?

*17. When a warm body is placed in a cooler environment, it cools according to Newton's law of cooling:

$$y = Ce^{kt} + S \begin{cases} t &= \text{time the body is in a cooler environment} \\ y &= \text{temperature of the body} \\ C &= \text{constant} \\ k &= \text{cooling constant} \\ S &= \text{temperature of surrounding environment} \end{cases}$$

Suppose that an ice cube tray filled with tap water of temperature 60°F is placed in a freezer having a temperature of 10°.

(a) Determine the constant C.

(b) After 13 minutes the temperature of the water is down to 40°. Determine the cooling constant k. Round to two decimal places.

(c) To the nearest degree, what will be the temperature of the water and tray after 20 minutes?

(d) To the nearest degree, what will be the temperature of the tray (of ice) after 100 minutes?

6.8 CHANGE OF BASE

Suppose you need to evaluate $\log_7 372$. How can you do it, considering that calculators and tables only provide logarithms for bases 10 and e? We shall now see how the logarithm of any positive number to any base can be expressed in terms of logarithms to the base 10 or e and then evaluated by using either a calculator or a table. First, we'll consider base 10 and then base e.

Consider $\log_b a$ and call it x.

$$x = \log_b a$$

In exponential form this equation is

$$b^x = a$$

The logarithms of both sides of this equation are equal; that is,

$$\log_{10} b^x = \log_{10} a$$

or

$$x \log_{10} b = \log_{10} a$$

Finally,

$$x = \frac{\log_{10} a}{\log_{10} b}$$

And since x is $\log_b a$, we have

$$\boxed{\log_b a = \frac{\log_{10} a}{\log_{10} b}}$$

Example 22 *Compute $\log_7 372$ by first changing to common logarithms.*
Applying the formula just derived, we have

$$\log_7 372 = \frac{\log_{10} 372}{\log_{10} 7}$$

$$\approx \frac{2.5705}{0.8451} \qquad \text{from Table III or a calculator}$$

$$\approx 3.04$$

If the procedure used at the beginning of the section is used with natural logarithms rather than common logarithms, the result will be

$$\boxed{\log_b a = \frac{\ln a}{\ln b}}$$

Example 23 *Compute $\log_5 62$ by first changing to natural logarithms.*

$$\log_5 62 = \frac{\ln 62}{\ln 5}$$

$$= \frac{\ln (10)(6.2)}{\ln 5} \qquad \text{if Table II will be used}$$

$$= \frac{\ln 10 + \ln 6.2}{\ln 5}$$

$$\approx \frac{2.3026 + 1.8245}{1.6094} \qquad \text{from Table II}$$

$$\approx \frac{4.1271}{1.6094} \qquad \left\{ \begin{array}{l} \text{from the line above (if table)} \\ \text{or from first line (if calculator)} \end{array} \right.$$

$$\approx 2.564$$

EXERCISES 6.8

1. Compute the approximate value of each logarithm by using common logarithms. Round the result to two decimal places.

   *(a) $\log_5 73$ (b) $\log_7 112$
   *(c) $\log_6 58.4$ (d) $\log_2 940$
   *(e) $\log_{10} 1800$ (f) $\log_9 6.53$
   *(g) $\log_3 29$ (h) $\log_{2.5} 761$
   *(i) $\log_{6.8} 10$ (j) $\log_{9.01} 100$

2. Compute the approximate value of each logarithm by using natural logarithms. Round the result to two decimal places.

   *(a) $\log_3 17$ (b) $\log_5 67$
   *(c) $\log_6 29.8$ (d) $\log_4 186$
   *(e) $\log_8 9870$ (f) $\log_{10} 7.84$
   *(g) $\log_{2.8} 165$ (h) $\log_{31} 874$

*3. Determine a formula for expressing $\log_b N$ in terms of logarithms of any other base B.

4. Show that

$$\log_a e = \frac{1}{\ln a}$$

6.9 COMPUTATION USING LOGARITHMS (HISTORICAL/OPTIONAL)

Logarithms were once widely used to simplify some kinds of calculations. Such use, however, has nearly disappeared since hand-held calculators have become so available. The examples of this section provide both a historical look at logarithms and a little practice with the properties you have studied and applied earlier in the chapter. We have chosen to use common logarithms.

Example 24 *Use logarithms to approximate* $\sqrt{2}$.

Let

$$x = \sqrt{2} = 2^{1/2}$$

Then

$$\log x = \log 2^{1/2}$$
$$= \tfrac{1}{2} \cdot \log 2$$
$$\approx \tfrac{1}{2}(0.3010) \qquad \text{from Table III}$$

or

$$\log x \approx 0.1505$$
$$x \approx \text{antilog } (0.1505)$$
$$x \approx 1.414 \qquad \text{from Table III}$$

Example 25 *Use logarithms to calculate* $\dfrac{(51)(4.1)^2}{10.6}$.

Let

$$x = \frac{(51)(4.1)^2}{10.6}$$

Then

$$\log x = \log \frac{(51)(4.1)^2}{10.6}$$

$$= \log (51)(4.1)^2 - \log 10.6 \qquad \text{by the second log property}$$
$$= \log 51 + \log (4.1)^2 - \log 10.6 \qquad \text{by the first log property}$$
$$= \log 51 + 2 \cdot \log 4.1 - \log 10.6 \qquad \text{by the third log property}$$
$$\approx 1.7076 + 2(0.6128) - 1.0253 \qquad \text{from Table III}$$
$$\approx 1.7076 + 1.2256 - 1.0253$$

Thus

$$\log x \approx 1.9079$$

$$x \approx \text{antilog } (1.9079)$$

$$x \approx 80.9 \qquad\qquad \text{from Table III}$$

EXERCISES 6.9

1. Evaluate each expression by using logarithms. Answers should consist of four digits each.

 *(a) $\sqrt{3}$ (b) $\sqrt{5}$

 *(c) $\sqrt[3]{119}$ (d) $\sqrt[3]{2351}$

 *(e) $(9.26)(43)$ (f) $(83.2)(1.7)(9.15)$

 *(g) $\dfrac{\sqrt{341}}{3}$ (h) $\dfrac{1580}{\sqrt{312}}$

 *(i) $(6.82)^2(15)$ (j) $\dfrac{(29)(19.6)}{(1.07)(2.3)}$

 *(k) $\sqrt{\dfrac{58.64}{2.65}}$ (l) $6(2.07)^9$

 *(m) $\sqrt[3]{(9.7)^2(12.2)^5}$ (n) $\dfrac{\sqrt{22.9}}{\sqrt[3]{3.016}}$

 *(o) $(17)^{2/3}(15)^{4/5}$ (p) $(10)\sqrt[6]{(92.8)(6.73)}$

 *(q) $7.8^{3.4}$ (r) $15^{.08}$

2. Determine which is larger, e^π or π^e. Use $e \approx 2.72$ and $\pi \approx 3.14$.

REVIEW EXERCISES FOR CHAPTER 6

1. Sketch the graph of each function.

 *(a) $f(x) = (1.5)^x$ (b) $f(x) = \left(\dfrac{1}{4}\right)^x$

 *(c) $f(x) = 2^{x+1}$ (d) $f(x) = \left(\dfrac{1}{2}\right)^{x+1}$

 *(e) $f(x) = 2 + \log_3 x$ (f) $f(x) = \log_2 (x + 3)$

 *(g) $f(x) = -\log_2 x$ (h) $f(x) = -3^x$

2. Simplify each expression. Do not use a table or calculator.

   *(a) $\ln e^{150}$ (b) $e^{\ln u}$

   *(c) $\log_3 \dfrac{1}{9}$ (d) $\log \sqrt{1000}$

   *(e) $\ln e^e$ (f) $e^0(1 + e^{\ln 2})$

   *(g) $\log 10^{18}$ (h) $10^{\log 6}$

3. Evaluate each expression with the aid of the appropriate table or a calculator.

   *(a) $10^{3.6551}$ (b) $e^{3.5}$

   *(c) $\log 1.92$ (d) $\ln 63$

   *(e) $\ln(8.3)^2$ (f) $\log (357)^3$

4. Solve each equation for x.

   *(a) $4^x = 17$ (b) $e^{2x} = 9$

   *(c) $y = we^{ux} + v$ (d) $10^{ax-b} = d$

   *(e) $\log x + \log(x + 2) = 1$ (f) $\ln x^2 = 10$

*5. Use natural logarithms to determine the approximate value of $\log_6 30$.

6. Suppose \$50,000 is invested at 11% per year compounded continuously.

   (a) How much will accrue after 5 years?

   (b) How many years will it take to triple the original investment?

*7. Suppose the population of a city increased from 110,000 in 1970 to 150,000 in 1980. (Assume exponential growth.)

   (a) Determine the growth constant k to two decimal places.

   (b) How long will it take for the population to be twice what it was in 1970?

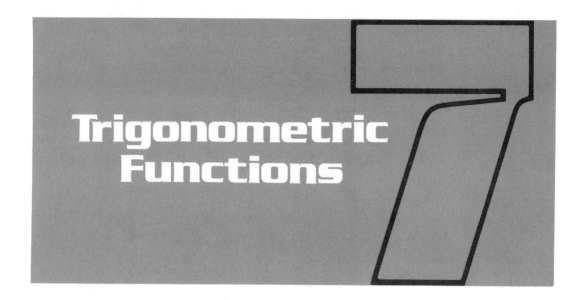

Trigonometric Functions

7.1 INTRODUCTION

The word **trigonometry** is derived from Greek words that mean *triangle measurement*. The early Greeks developed trigonometry to measure triangles, angles, and distances in triangular settings. Their applications included astronomy and surveying; the problem was to determine an unknown distance or angle that could not be measured directly.

Trigonometry as the ancient Greeks knew it is still used today, and we shall study it. But many modern applications require the use of trigonometry in settings that have no triangles or angles. Such applications include analysis of wave phenomena, electronics, study of predator–prey interaction, measure of heartbeat, and others. Our study of trigonometry will include some of the more modern applications. In fact, our first definition of the basic trigonometric functions will be made without the presence of triangles because, for use in calculus, the domains of the trigonometric functions often must be real numbers rather than angles.

When trigonometric functions are considered as functions of real numbers, they are often called **circular functions**. The name "circular functions" was chosen because the functions are defined with respect to a circle rather than a triangle.

7.2 TRIGONOMETRIC POINTS

The circle with radius equal to 1 and center at the origin is called the **unit circle**. A graph of the unit circle is given next.

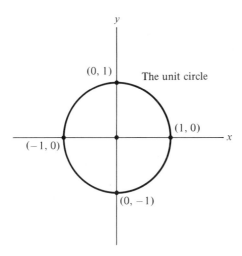

The unit circle

The equation of the unit circle is $x^2 + y^2 = 1$. You might want to verify that the four points shown—(0, 1), (−1, 0), (1, 0), and (0, −1)—do indeed satisfy the equation. Proof that $x^2 + y^2 = 1$ is the equation of the unit circle will wait until the next chapter, however.

We now choose to locate points (x, y) on the unit circle by beginning at the point (1, 0) and then moving a counterclockwise distance t along the circle.

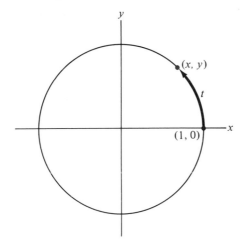

The point associated with $t = 0$ is (1, 0); that is, when $t = 0$, $x = 1$ and $y = 0$. The notation $P(t)$ will be used to indicate the point, called a **trigonometric point**, associated with a particular t value. Thus $P(t) = (x, y)$. Using this notation,

$$P(0) = (1, 0)$$

Notice that the range of P contains ordered pairs of real numbers.

The circumference of a circle is $2\pi r$, where r is the radius. For a unit circle, $r = 1$. So the distance around the unit circle is $2\pi \cdot 1 = 2\pi$. (*Note:* The value of 2π is *approximately* 2(3.14), or 6.28.) Thus $P(2\pi) = (1, 0)$ just as $P(0) = (1, 0)$. Also,

$$P(0) = P(2\pi) = P(4\pi) = P(6\pi) = (1, 0)$$

In fact,

$$P(2n\pi) = (1, 0)$$

for any *whole number n*.

A negative *t* value is associated with a clockwise movement from $(1, 0)$ along the circle.

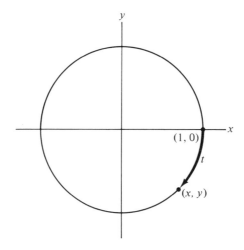

A movement of 2π units in the negative (clockwise) direction means $t = -2\pi$. The movement returns us to $(1, 0)$ just as does a movement of 2π. Thus $P(-2\pi) = (1, 0)$. Furthermore,

$$P(-2\pi) = P(-4\pi) = P(-6\pi) = (1, 0)$$

In fact,

$$P(2n\pi) = (1, 0)$$

for any *integer* (positive, negative, or zero) value of *n*.

How far must we move or measure from $(1, 0)$ to reach $(-1, 0)$? Since $(-1, 0)$ is halfway around the circle, *t* must be half the circumference 2π. This means that $t = \frac{1}{2} \cdot 2\pi = \pi$. Thus

$$\boxed{P(\pi) = (-1, 0)}$$

And once again you might note that moving any multiple of 2π from $P(\pi) = (-1, 0)$ will yield $(-1, 0)$. In general,

$$P(t + 2n\pi) = P(t)$$

For any integer n and any real number t.

To get from $(1, 0)$ to $(0, 1)$, move one-fourth of the distance around the circle. Thus t must be $\frac{1}{4}$ of 2π, or $2\pi/4$, which reduces to $\pi/2$. So we have

$$P\left(\frac{\pi}{2}\right) = (0, 1)$$

Similarly, $(0, -1)$ is three-fourths of the distance around the circle from $(1, 0)$. Since $\frac{3}{4} \cdot 2\pi = \frac{3}{2}\pi$,

$$P\left(\frac{3\pi}{2}\right) = (0, -1)$$

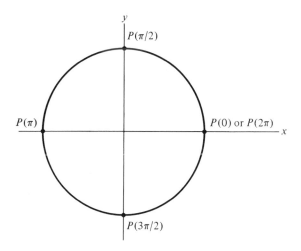

Determining the coordinates of points other than $P(0)$, $P(\pi/2)$, $P(\pi)$, and $P(3\pi/2)$ is complicated. Accordingly, they are available in tables when needed. Because they are used frequently, we compute here $P(\pi/4)$, $P(\pi/3)$, and $P(\pi/6)$.

To compute $P(\pi/4)$, note that $P(\pi/4) = P(\frac{1}{4}\pi)$. This means that it is halfway between $P(0)$ and $P(\pi/2)$; so the central angle of this arc is 45°. (A central angle has its vertex at the center of the circle.)

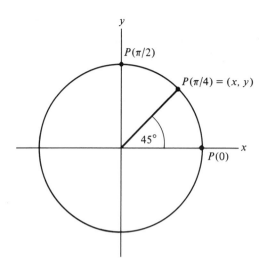

Now construct a perpendicular from $P(\pi/4)$ to the x axis. This produces a $45° - 45°$ right triangle. The sides opposite the 45° angles are equal, since *in any triangle the sides opposite two equal angles are equal.*

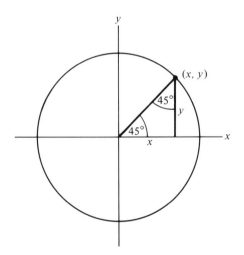

So we know that $x = y$. Thus the coordinates (x, y) can be considered as (x, x) or as (y, y)—both the same. The relationship between x and y for all points on the circle is

$$x^2 + y^2 = 1$$

So if $x = y$, then x can be substituted for y in $x^2 + y^2 = 1$ to get

$$x^2 + x^2 = 1$$

$$2x^2 = 1$$

$$x^2 = \frac{1}{2}$$

$$x = \sqrt{\frac{1}{2}} = \frac{1}{\sqrt{2}} \quad \text{or} \quad \frac{\sqrt{2}}{2}$$

(We ignored the $\pm$ because our point is in the first quadrant and therefore both coordinates are positive.) And since $x = y$, the coordinates of $P(\pi/4)$ are both $\sqrt{2}/2$. This means that

$$\boxed{P\left(\frac{\pi}{4}\right) = \left(\frac{\sqrt{2}}{2}, \frac{\sqrt{2}}{2}\right)}$$

To compute $P(\pi/3)$, note that the arc of length $\pi/3$ is one-sixth of the circumference of the circle; that is, $\pi/3 = \frac{1}{6} \cdot 2\pi$. This means that the central angle of this arc has one-sixth the number of degrees in the circle, $\frac{1}{6}$ of 360° or 60°.

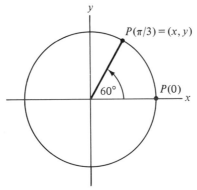

Now construct a perpendicular from $P(\pi/3)$ to the x axis. This produces a 30°–60°–90° triangle with sides x, y, and 1 (the radius).

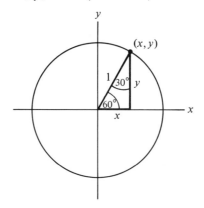

In order to continue, we need to make use of the following theorem.

Theorem

In a 30°–60° right triangle, the side opposite the 30° angle is half the length of the hypotenuse.

To see that this theorem is true, consider an equilateral triangle—one in which all

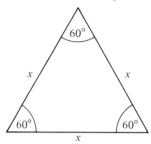

sides are the same length and each of the three angles is 60°. The triangle can be divided into two 30°–60°–90° triangles by drawing a perpendicular line segment from the top vertex

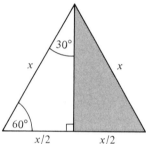

to the base. Now you can see that the base x is divided into two equal parts, each of length $x/2$. The hypotenuse is of length x. Thus the side opposite the 30° angle in a 30°–60°–90° triangle is half the length of the hypotenuse.

Now look back at the triangle with sides x, y, and 1. Since the hypotenuse is 1 and x is opposite the 30° angle, $x = \frac{1}{2}$. To find y, merely substitute $\frac{1}{2}$ for x in $x^2 + y^2 = 1$ to obtain

$$\left(\frac{1}{2}\right)^2 + y^2 = 1$$

$$\frac{1}{4} + y^2 = 1$$

$$y^2 = \frac{3}{4}$$

$$y = \sqrt{\frac{3}{4}} = \frac{\sqrt{3}}{2}$$

Thus

$$P\left(\frac{\pi}{3}\right) = \left(\frac{1}{2}, \frac{\sqrt{3}}{2}\right)$$

The computation of $P(\pi/6)$ is similar to that of $P(\pi/3)$, because the central angle formed by an arc of length $\pi/6$ is 30°. The triangle thus formed has angles of 30°, 60°, and 90°—just as with $\pi/3$. The only difference this time is that y is opposite the 30° angle; so y is $\frac{1}{2}$. The value of x is then easily determined to be $\sqrt{3}/2$.

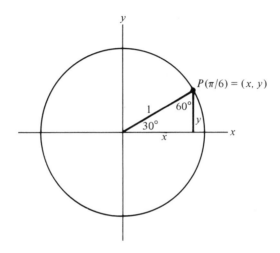

$$P\left(\frac{\pi}{6}\right) = \left(\frac{\sqrt{3}}{2}, \frac{1}{2}\right)$$

EXERCISES 7.2

Answers to starred exercises are given in the back of the book.

1. Use the results of this section and a drawing of the unit circle to determine the (x, y) coordinates of each trigonometric point.

   *(a) $P(3\pi)$

   *(b) $P\left(-\frac{\pi}{2}\right)$

   *(c) $P(-3\pi)$

   *(d) $P\left(\frac{2\pi}{3}\right)$

   *(e) $P(-\pi)$

   *(f) $P(8\pi)$

   *(g) $P\left(\frac{5\pi}{2}\right)$

   (h) $P\left(-\frac{5\pi}{2}\right)$

   (i) $P(10\pi)$

(j) $P\left(-\dfrac{\pi}{3}\right)$ *(k) $P\left(-\dfrac{\pi}{4}\right)$ (l) $P\left(-\dfrac{\pi}{6}\right)$

*(m) $P\left(\dfrac{5\pi}{6}\right)$

2. Prove that each point given is indeed a trigonometric point by showing that each ordered pair satisfies the equation of the unit circle, $x^2 + y^2 = 1$.

(a) $\left(\dfrac{\sqrt{2}}{2}, \dfrac{\sqrt{2}}{2}\right)$

(b) $\left(\dfrac{1}{2}, \dfrac{\sqrt{3}}{2}\right)$

(c) $\left(\dfrac{\sqrt{5}}{3}, \dfrac{2}{3}\right)$

(d) $\left(-\dfrac{3}{4}, \dfrac{\sqrt{7}}{4}\right)$

(e) $\left(\dfrac{1}{\sqrt{5}}, -\dfrac{2}{\sqrt{5}}\right)$

(f) $\left(-\dfrac{2\sqrt{2}}{3}, -\dfrac{1}{3}\right)$

*3. Find the length of the side opposite the 60° angle in a 30°–60°–90° triangle in which the hypotenuse is of length z. Express the answer in terms of z.

4. Find the length of the hypotenuse of a 45°–45°–90° triangle with legs of length x. Express the answer in terms of x.

*5. For the figure shown, determine what is requested.
   (a) Perimeter as a function of x.
   (b) Area as a function of x.

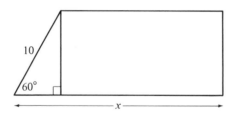

7.3 TRIGONOMETRIC FUNCTIONS

The x coordinate of the trigonometric point $P(t) = (x, y)$ is called the **cosine of t** and it is written **cos t**. The y coordinate is called the **sine of t** and is written **sin t**. Thus

$$x = \cos t$$
$$y = \sin t$$
$$P(t) = (x, y) = (\cos t, \sin t)$$

Since $P(\pi/2) = (0, 1)$ and $P(\pi/2) = (\cos \pi/2, \sin \pi/2)$, then we have $\cos (\pi/2) = 0$ and $\sin (\pi/2) = 1$. Similarly, $P(\pi) = (-1, 0)$ yields $\cos \pi = -1$ and $\sin \pi = 0$. Verify the following table.

t	0	$\dfrac{\pi}{6}$	$\dfrac{\pi}{4}$	$\dfrac{\pi}{3}$	$\dfrac{\pi}{2}$	π	$\dfrac{3\pi}{2}$
$\cos t$	1	$\dfrac{\sqrt{3}}{2}$	$\dfrac{\sqrt{2}}{2}$	$\dfrac{1}{2}$	0	-1	0
$\sin t$	0	$\dfrac{1}{2}$	$\dfrac{\sqrt{2}}{2}$	$\dfrac{\sqrt{3}}{2}$	1	0	-1

$\sqrt{3}/2 \approx .866$ and $\sqrt{2}/2 \approx .707$. Note that all values of $\cos t$ and $\sin t$ are between -1 and 1, which follows from their unit circle origin.

$$-1 \le \cos t \le 1$$
$$-1 \le \sin t \le 1$$

There are other trigonometric functions in addition to sine and cosine. They are defined as

tangent of $t = \tan t = \dfrac{y}{x}$ or $\dfrac{\sin t}{\cos t}$

cotangent of $t = \cot t = \dfrac{x}{y}$ or $\dfrac{\cos t}{\sin t}$ or $\dfrac{1}{\tan t}$

secant of $t = \sec t = \dfrac{1}{x}$ or $\dfrac{1}{\cos t}$

cosecant of $t = \csc t = \dfrac{1}{y}$ or $\dfrac{1}{\sin t}$

Note that these four trigonometric functions are defined in terms of the sine and cosine functions. The tangent and cotangent are reciprocals of each other. Cosine and secant are reciprocals. Sine and cosecant are also reciprocals. Tangent and secant are not defined for cosine (that is, x) equal to zero. Similarly, cotangent and cosecant are not defined for sine equal to zero. In each case, division by zero would result.

Since $P(\pi/2) = (0, 1)$, then

$$\cos \frac{\pi}{2} = 0$$

$$\sin \frac{\pi}{2} = 1$$

$$\tan \frac{\pi}{2} = \text{undefined} \left(\frac{1}{0}\right)$$

$$\cot \frac{\pi}{2} = \frac{0}{1} = 0$$

$$\sec \frac{\pi}{2} = \text{undefined} \left(\frac{1}{0}\right)$$

$$\csc \frac{\pi}{2} = \frac{1}{1} = 1$$

Similarly, since $P(\pi/3) = (\frac{1}{2}, \sqrt{3}/2)$, then

$$\cos \frac{\pi}{3} = \frac{1}{2}$$

$$\sin \frac{\pi}{3} = \frac{\sqrt{3}}{2}$$

$$\tan \frac{\pi}{3} = \frac{\frac{\sqrt{3}}{2}}{\frac{1}{2}} = \sqrt{3}$$

$$\cot \frac{\pi}{3} = \frac{\frac{1}{2}}{\frac{\sqrt{3}}{2}} = \frac{1}{\sqrt{3}} \quad \text{or} \quad \frac{\sqrt{3}}{3}$$

$$\sec \frac{\pi}{3} = \frac{1}{\frac{1}{2}} = 2$$

$$\csc \frac{\pi}{3} = \frac{1}{\frac{\sqrt{3}}{2}} = \frac{2}{\sqrt{3}} \quad \text{or} \quad \frac{2\sqrt{3}}{3}$$

EXERCISES 7.3

*1. Complete the table.

t	0	$\dfrac{\pi}{6}$	$\dfrac{\pi}{4}$	$\dfrac{\pi}{3}$	$\dfrac{\pi}{2}$	π	$\dfrac{3\pi}{2}$
$\cos t$							
$\sin t$							
$\tan t$							
$\cot t$							
$\sec t$							
$\csc t$							

*2. Complete the table.

	$P(t)$ in quadrant:			
	I	II	III	IV
Sign of: $\cos t$	$+$	$-$		
$\sin t$	$+$			
$\tan t$				
$\cot t$				
$\sec t$				
$\csc t$				

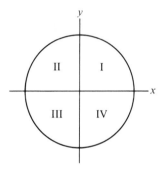

This table will be used in the first two examples of the next section and frequently in later sections.

3. Determine $\cos t$, $\sin t$, $\tan t$, $\cot t$, $\sec t$, and $\csc t$ for each trigonometric point $P(t)$ given below.

*(a) $P(t) = (0, -1)$

(b) $P(t) = \left(-\dfrac{1}{2}, \dfrac{\sqrt{3}}{2}\right)$

*(c) $P(t) = \left(-\dfrac{3}{4}, \dfrac{\sqrt{7}}{4}\right)$

(d) $P(t) = \left(\dfrac{1}{3}, \dfrac{2\sqrt{2}}{3}\right)$

*(e) $P(t) = \left(-\dfrac{1}{\sqrt{5}}, \dfrac{2}{\sqrt{5}}\right)$

(f) $P(t) = \left(-\dfrac{\sqrt{5}}{3}, -\dfrac{2}{3}\right)$

7.4 TRIGONOMETRIC IDENTITIES

If we substitute cos t for x and sin t for y in

$$x^2 + y^2 = 1$$

we get

$$(\cos t)^2 + (\sin t)^2 = 1$$

which is usually written

$$\boxed{\sin^2 t + \cos^2 t = 1}$$

where $\sin^2 t$ means $(\sin t)^2$ and $\cos^2 t$ means $(\cos t)^2$.

The relationship $\sin^2 t + \cos^2 t = 1$, true for all values of t, is an example of an identity. An **identity in t** is an equation that is true for all values of t for which both sides are defined.

If both sides (all terms) of the preceding identity are divided by $\sin^2 t$, the result is

$$\frac{\sin^2 t}{\sin^2 t} + \frac{\cos^2 t}{\sin^2 t} = \frac{1}{\sin^2 t}$$

or

$$\boxed{1 + \cot^2 t = \csc^2 t}$$

which is an identity.

If both sides of the identity $\sin^2 t + \cos^2 t = 1$ are divided by $\cos^2 t$, the result is

$$\frac{\sin^2 t}{\cos^2 t} + \frac{\cos^2 t}{\cos^2 t} = \frac{1}{\cos^2 t}$$

or

$$\boxed{\tan^2 t + 1 = \sec^2 t}$$

which is an identity.

The three identities just derived are often useful in other forms. For example, $\sin^2 t + \cos^2 t = 1$ can be written $\sin^2 t = 1 - \cos^2 t$ or $\cos^2 t = 1 - \sin^2 t$. These forms can be useful for making substitutions. Similarly, $1 + \cot^2 t = \csc^2 t$ can be written $\csc^2 t - \cot^2 t = 1$ or $\cot^2 t = \csc^2 t - 1$. The identity $\tan^2 t + 1 = \sec^2 t$ may be useful as $\sec^2 t - \tan^2 t = 1$ or as $\tan^2 t = \sec^2 t - 1$.

$\sin^2 t = 1 - \cos^2 t$	$\cos^2 t = 1 - \sin^2 t$
$\tan^2 t = \sec^2 t - 1$	$\sec^2 t - \tan^2 t = 1$
$\cot^2 t = \csc^2 t - 1$	$\csc^2 t - \cot^2 t = 1$

The definitions of the six trigonometric functions and the identities given here can be used to make substitutions in order to establish and prove other identities. Such proofs are usually done by changing the more complicated side of the identity step by step until it simplifies to the expression on the other side. Sometimes, however, it is better to change both sides of the identity to a common form. It is often helpful to reduce the tangent, cotangent, secant, and cosecant to sines and cosines. All steps of the proof must be reversible. For example, you cannot multiply both sides by zero in order to obtain $0 = 0$, since you could not reverse the step and go from $0 = 0$ to the given identity. Furthermore, you cannot multiply both sides by the same quantity or cross multiply because doing so would assume that both sides are equal to begin with, and that is what you are trying to prove. Finally, keep in mind that eventually you will be using the methods learned here when you encounter complex expressions that you wish to simplify; then there will be no "other side of the equation."

Example 1 *Prove the identity*

$$\cos t \cdot \csc t \overset{?}{=} \cot t$$

(*Note:* The *question mark* (?) indicates that we have not proved the equality; it is removed only when the two sides have been shown to be equal.)

We will begin by changing $\csc t$ to $1/\sin t$. The result is

$$\cos t \cdot \frac{1}{\sin t} \overset{?}{=} \cot t$$

or

$$\frac{\cos t}{\sin t} \overset{?}{=} \cot t$$

Finally, since $\cos t/\sin t$ is the same as $\cot t$ (by an earlier definition), we can replace $\cos t/\sin t$ by $\cot t$. This yields

$$\cot t = \cot t$$

The identity is proved.

Note: The last step or line of a proof of this type should show two *identical* quantities, such as cot t = cot t in the proof just completed; not just two equal quantities, the *same* quantity.

Example 2 *Prove the identity*

$$\frac{\sin^2 t}{1 - \sin^2 t} \overset{?}{=} \tan^2 t$$

Change $\tan^2 t$ to $(\sin^2 t)/(\cos^2 t)$. The result is

$$\frac{\sin^2 t}{1 - \sin^2 t} \overset{?}{=} \frac{\sin^2 t}{\cos^2 t}$$

Since $\cos^2 t$ is the same as $1 - \sin^2 t$ (by a previous identity), replace $\cos^2 t$ by $1 - \sin^2 t$. This step yields

$$\frac{\sin^2 t}{1 - \sin^2 t} = \frac{\sin^2 t}{1 - \sin^2 t}$$

We might just as well have replaced $1 - \sin^2 t$ by $\cos^2 t$ on the left side. The result would then have been

$$\frac{\sin^2 t}{\cos^2 t} = \frac{\sin^2 t}{\cos^2 t}$$

Either way, the identity is proved.

For the remainder of this section, and elsewhere in the chapter, letters other than t will be used to represent real numbers or angles. Thus you may see cos u or sin x or sin θ. (θ is the Greek letter theta.) Greek letters are often used when the trigonometric function involved is a function of an angle rather than a function of a real number.

Example 3 *Prove the identity*

$$(1 - \sin u)(1 + \sin u) \overset{?}{=} \frac{1}{\sec^2 u}$$

Multiply out $(1 - \sin u)(1 + \sin u)$ to get $1 - \sin^2 u$.

$$1 - \sin^2 u \overset{?}{=} \frac{1}{\sec^2 u}$$

Replace $1 - \sin^2 u$ by $\cos^2 u$. The result is

$$\cos^2 u \overset{?}{=} \frac{1}{\sec^2 u}$$

Since $1/\sec u$ is the same as $\cos u$, replace $1/\sec^2 u$ with $\cos^2 u$. This completes the proof of the identity.

$$\cos^2 u = \cos^2 u$$

Example 4 *Prove the identity*

$$\frac{\csc t}{\cot t + \tan t} \overset{?}{=} \cos t$$

Make the following substitutions on the left side in order to change all those terms to sines and cosines:

$$\csc t = \frac{1}{\sin t}$$

$$\cot t = \frac{\cos t}{\sin t}$$

$$\tan t = \frac{\sin t}{\cos t}$$

The result is

$$\frac{\dfrac{1}{\sin t}}{\dfrac{\cos t}{\sin t} + \dfrac{\sin t}{\cos t}} \overset{?}{=} \cos t$$

Now simplify the complex fraction. This is done by multiplying both numerator and denominator by the least common denominator of all the denominators (sin t, sin t, cos t), which is sin t cos t.

$$\frac{\sin t \cos t \cdot \left(\dfrac{1}{\sin t} \right)}{\sin t \cos t \cdot \left(\dfrac{\cos t}{\sin t} + \dfrac{\sin t}{\cos t} \right)} \overset{?}{=} \cos t$$

This becomes

$$\frac{\cos t}{\cos^2 t + \sin^2 t} \overset{?}{=} \cos t$$

Next, substitute 1 for $\cos^2 t + \sin^2 t$.

$$\frac{\cos t}{1} \overset{?}{=} \cos t$$

$$\cos t = \cos t$$

The identity is proved.

Example 5 *Prove the identity*

$$\tan \theta + \cot \theta \overset{?}{=} \sec^2 \theta \cdot \cot \theta$$

First, change all functions to sine and cosine.

$$\frac{\sin \theta}{\cos \theta} + \frac{\cos \theta}{\sin \theta} \overset{?}{=} \frac{1}{\cos^2 \theta} \cdot \frac{\cos \theta}{\sin \theta}$$

Combine the fractions on the left by using the common denominator $\cos \theta \sin \theta$.

$$\frac{\sin \theta}{\cos \theta} \cdot \frac{\sin \theta}{\sin \theta} + \frac{\cos \theta}{\sin \theta} \cdot \frac{\cos \theta}{\cos \theta} \overset{?}{=} \frac{1}{\cos^2 \theta} \cdot \frac{\cos \theta}{\sin \theta}$$

On the left, $\sin \theta \cdot \sin \theta = \sin^2 \theta$ and $\cos \theta \cdot \cos \theta = \cos^2 \theta$. On the right, $\cos^2 \theta = \cos \theta \cdot \cos \theta$.

$$\frac{\sin^2 \theta + \cos^2 \theta}{\cos \theta \sin \theta} \overset{?}{=} \frac{1}{\cos \theta \cos \theta} \cdot \frac{\cos \theta}{\sin \theta}$$

On the left, replace $\sin^2 \theta + \cos^2 \theta$ by 1. On the right, divide out $\cos \theta / \cos \theta$. The result is

$$\frac{1}{\cos \theta \sin \theta} = \frac{1}{\cos \theta \sin \theta}$$

The identity is proved.

Example 6 *Prove the identity*

$$\frac{1 + \sin x}{\cos x} \overset{?}{=} \frac{\cos x}{1 - \sin x}$$

At first it is difficult to determine just how to begin proving this identity, since all the expressions are already given in terms of sin x and cos x. Note that if $1 + \sin x$ is multiplied by $1 - \sin x$, it becomes $1 - \sin^2 x$, or $\cos^2 x$. This is a simplification and it leads to additional simplification. Of course, if you multiply the numerator of the fraction by $1 - \sin x$, you must also multiply the denominator by $1 - \sin x$.

$$\frac{1 + \sin x}{\cos x} \cdot \frac{1 - \sin x}{1 - \sin x} \overset{?}{=} \frac{\cos x}{1 - \sin x}$$

$$\frac{\cos^2 x}{\cos x (1 - \sin x)} \overset{?}{=} \frac{\cos x}{1 - \sin x}$$

Divide out cos x/cos x on the left side. This completes the proof.

$$\frac{\cos x}{1 - \sin x} = \frac{\cos x}{1 - \sin x}$$

The relationships between tangent and cotangent, between sine and cosecant, and between cosine and secant suggest the following three identities, two of which you are asked to prove in Exercise 1.

$$\tan t \cdot \cot t = 1$$
$$\sin t \cdot \csc t = 1$$
$$\cos t \cdot \sec t = 1$$

Proving identities is useful beyond merely being able to show that two expressions are indeed equivalent. The manipulations involved can also be used to rewrite trigonometric expressions in simpler or more desirable forms. A few such situations are presented in the exercises; many more will occur throughout the chapter. Here is an example.

Example 7 *Use identities to simplify the expression.*

$$\frac{5\sin^2 t + 5\cos^2 t}{5\csc t}$$

$$\frac{5 \sin^2 t + 5 \cos^2 t}{5 \csc t} = \frac{5(\sin^2 t + \cos^2 t)}{5 \csc t} \qquad \text{after factoring}$$

$$= \frac{\sin^2 t + \cos^2 t}{\csc t} \qquad \text{after dividing out the fives}$$

$$= \frac{1}{\csc t} \qquad \text{since } \sin^2 t + \cos^2 t = 1$$

$$= \sin t \qquad \text{since } 1/\csc t = \sin t$$

EXERCISES 7.4

1. Prove each identity.
   (a) $\sin t \csc t = 1$

   (b) $\cos t \sec t = 1$

   (c) $\tan t \cos t = \sin t$

   (d) $\sin t \sec t = \tan t$

   (e) $\tan u = \dfrac{\sec u}{\csc u}$

   (f) $\sec u = \dfrac{\tan u}{\sin u}$

   (g) $(1 + \cos x)(1 - \cos x) = \sin^2 x$

   (h) $\dfrac{\sec^2\theta}{\tan^2\theta + 1} = 1$

   (i) $\dfrac{\cos^2\theta}{1 - \cos^2\theta} = \cot^2\theta$

   (j) $(\tan \theta)(\tan \theta + \cot \theta) = \sec^2\theta$

   (k) $(\cos x)(\tan x + \cot x) = \csc x$

   (l) $\cos^2\theta - \sin^2\theta = 2 \cos^2\theta - 1$

   (m) $\sin^2 u(1 + \cot^2 u) = 1$

   (n) $\dfrac{\sec^2 t - 1}{\sec^2 t} = \sin^2 t$

2. Prove each identity.
   (a) $\cos^2 t - \sin^2 t = 1 - 2 \sin^2 t$

   (b) $2 \cos^2 t - 1 = 1 - 2 \sin^2 t$

   (c) $(\csc^2 u - 1) \tan^2 u = 1$

   (d) $(1 - \cos u)(1 + \cos u) = \tan^2 u \cos^2 u$

   (e) $(1 + \tan^2\theta)(1 - \sin^2\theta) = 1$

   (f) $(\sin \theta)(\csc \theta - \sin \theta) = \cos^2\theta$

   (g) $\tan x \cos x + \dfrac{1}{\csc x} = 2 \sin x$

   (h) $\tan x \sec x = \dfrac{\sin x}{1 - \sin^2 x}$

   (i) $\dfrac{\tan^2 t}{\sec^2 t} = 1 - \cos^2 t$

   (j) $\dfrac{\sin^2\theta + \cos^2\theta}{\csc^2\theta - \cot^2\theta} = 1$

   (k) $\csc u - \sin u = \cos u \cot u$

   (l) $\cos t \cot t + \sin t = \csc t$

   (m) $\sin^2 x(1 + \tan^2 x) = \tan^2 x$

   (n) $\dfrac{\sec x + 2}{\csc x} = 2 \sin x + \tan x$

3. Use identities to simplify each expression as much as possible.
   *(a) $\tan^2 t + 1 - \sec^2 t$

   *(b) $4 \sin^2 t + 4 \cos^2 t$

   *(c) $\csc^2 t - \cot^2 t - \sin^2 t$

   *(d) $(1 - \cos^2 t) \cot^2 t$

   *(e) $\dfrac{\tan t(\tan t + \cot t)}{\cot^2 t + 1}$

   (f) $\dfrac{3 \sin^2\theta + 3 \cos^2\theta}{\sec^2\theta}$

   *(g) $\dfrac{2 \sec^2 u - 2 \tan^2 u}{\cos^2 u + \sin^2 u}$

   (h) $\dfrac{\sin x}{\cos x} + \dfrac{\cos x}{\sin x}$

$*$(i) $\dfrac{1 + \sec x}{\tan x + \sin x}$ (j) $\dfrac{\cot^2 t - \csc^2 t}{5 \sec t}$

4. Prove each identity.

(a) $\tan \theta + \dfrac{1}{\tan \theta} = \dfrac{\csc \theta}{\cos \theta}$ (b) $\sec^2 x \csc^2 x = \sec^2 x + \csc^2 x$

(c) $\tan t + \cot t = \csc t \sec t$ (d) $\tan^2 u \sin^2 u = \tan^2 u - \sin^2 u$

(e) $\dfrac{\sin x}{\csc x} + \dfrac{\cos x}{\sec x} = 1$ (f) $\dfrac{1 - \cos x}{\sin x} = \dfrac{\sin x}{1 + \cos x}$

(g) $\cot^2 \theta = \dfrac{\cos^2 \theta}{1 - \cos^2 \theta}$ (h) $\dfrac{\sin x \cos x}{\tan x + \cot x} = \dfrac{\sin^2 x}{\sec^2 x}$

(i) $\dfrac{1 + \sec t}{\tan t + \sin t} = \dfrac{1}{\sin t}$ (j) $\sec x + \cot x = \dfrac{\tan x + \cos x}{\sin x}$

(k) $\dfrac{\cos x \cot x}{\cot x - \cos x} = \dfrac{\cos x + \cot x}{\cos x \cot x}$

(l) $\dfrac{1}{1 - \sin \theta} - \dfrac{1}{1 + \sin \theta} = 2 \tan \theta \sec \theta$

(m) $\sec x - \tan x = \dfrac{1}{\sec x + \tan x}$

(n) $\dfrac{\sec u + 1}{\sec u - 1} = (\cot u + \csc u)^2$

(o) $\dfrac{\sec t \csc t}{\tan t + \cot t} = 1$

(p) $\dfrac{\csc \theta}{1 + \csc \theta} - \dfrac{\csc \theta}{1 - \csc \theta} = 2 \sec^2 \theta$

5. Show that $-\ln |\csc t + \cot t| = \ln |\csc t - \cot t|$. Although these two expressions do not look equal, they are—and they are alternative ways of expressing a formula that is used in calculus. Sometimes in calculus your answer does not match the one given in the back of the book. So *you* must determine whether yours is an alternative form or a wrong answer.

7.5   ANGLE MEASUREMENT

Measurement of angles in units called *degrees* is not new to you. In fact, angles of 30°, 45°, 90°, and others are familiar to you. A complete revolution is 360° which suggests that a **degree** is $\frac{1}{360}$ of a revolution. This, then, is the system for angular measure that has been passed down from the ancient Babylonians, having survived for over 5000 years. The choice of 360 degrees for a complete revolution was an arbitrary decision by the Babylonians. Consequently, in more advanced mathematics it is not surprising that an alternative system of measurement leads to simpler expressions.

The alternative system measures angles in units called **radians**. The radian concept was first introduced in the 1870s by a mathematician and a physicist, who mutually agreed on the need for a new unit of measure for angles.

It is simplest to introduce radian measure with the unit circle setting we have been using, although a formal definition must wait until the next section. To obtain trigonometric points, we went counterclockwise around the circle, beginning at the point $(1, 0)$. The number of radians in any central angle θ created by moving around the unit circle is the number of units in the length of the corresponding arc. In the drawing shown here the arc length t is the radian measure of angle θ; that is, angle θ is t radians.

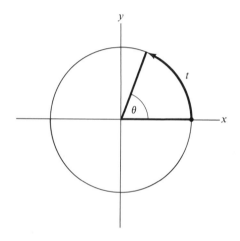

An entire revolution of $360°$ corresponds to an arc length of 2π. It follows that

$$360° = 2\pi \text{ radians}$$
$$180° = \pi \text{ radians}$$

This last equation suggests a convenient way to change units between radians and degrees. Since $180° = \pi$ radians the fractions $\pi/180°$ and $180°/\pi$ are each equal to 1. They can be used as multipliers to change units.

Example 8   *Change* $30°$, $45°$, $60°$, $90°$, *and* $225°$ *to radian measure.*

Multiply each by 1 in the form $\pi/180°$. Their values will remain the same, but the units will change. The degrees will divide out. Notice that no units are written in the end. When no unit is specified, the unit is understood to be radians (rather than degrees).

$$30° = \frac{30°}{1} \cdot \frac{\pi}{180°} = \frac{\pi}{6}$$

$$45° = \frac{45°}{1} \cdot \frac{\pi}{180°} = \frac{\pi}{4}$$

$$60° = \frac{60°}{1} \cdot \frac{\pi}{180°} = \frac{\pi}{3}$$

$$90° = \frac{90°}{1} \cdot \frac{\pi}{180°} = \frac{\pi}{2}$$

$$225° = \frac{225°}{1} \cdot \frac{\pi}{180°} = \frac{5\pi}{4}$$

Example 9   *Change π/4, π/10, and 2π/3 from radians to degrees.*

Multiply each by 1 in the form 180°/π. The π will divide out and degrees will be introduced.

$$\frac{\pi}{4} = \frac{\pi}{4} \cdot \frac{180°}{\pi} = 45°$$

$$\frac{\pi}{10} = \frac{\pi}{10} \cdot \frac{180°}{\pi} = 18°$$

$$\frac{2\pi}{3} = \frac{2\pi}{3} \cdot \frac{180°}{\pi} = 120°$$

The conversion methods shown in Examples 8 and 9 are very neat and they yield exact results, not approximations. But there are times when the numbers involved are not so nice (2.6 radians, for example), in which case you might like to know approximately how many degrees are in a radian and vice versa. If you take the equation

$$180° = \pi \text{ radians}$$

and divide both sides by π, the result is

$$1 \text{ radian} = \frac{180°}{\pi} \approx \frac{180°}{3.14}$$

When this is divided, the result is

$$\boxed{1 \text{ radian} \approx 57.3°}$$

Similarly, if you divide both sides of the equation $180° = \pi$ radians by 180, the result is

$$1° = \frac{\pi}{180} \approx \frac{3.14}{180}$$

When divided, the result is

$$\boxed{1° \approx .01745 \text{ radian}}$$

Example 10   *Change 2.6 radians to degrees and change 13° to radians.*

$$2.6 \text{ radians} \approx 2.6 \text{ radians} \cdot \frac{57.3°}{\text{radian}} \approx 148.98°$$

$$13° \approx 13° \cdot \frac{.01745 \text{ radian}}{\text{degree}} \approx .22685 \text{ radian}$$

Keep in mind that this method of conversion yields *approximations*. The method shown in Examples 8 and 9 always yields exact results. The approximation is introduced when 3.14 is used for π.

You would do well to memorize the following table of some commonly used angles in both degrees and radians. They are used so often in trigonometry that you should know them. Furthermore, most applications of trigonometry in calculus (limits, series, integrals, and polar coordinates) use radian measure.

Degrees	0°	30°	45°	60°	90°	180°	270°	360°
Radians	0	$\frac{\pi}{6}$	$\frac{\pi}{4}$	$\frac{\pi}{3}$	$\frac{\pi}{2}$	π	$\frac{3\pi}{2}$	2π

EXERCISES 7.5

1. Change each measure from degrees to radians. Use the method of Example 8 to obtain an *exact* value.

    *(a)   36°   (b)   270°   *(c)   75°
    (d)   240°   *(e)   135°   (f)   330°
    *(g)   210°   (h)   315°   *(i)   300°
    (j)   900°   *(k)   500°   (l)   400°

2. Change each measure from radians to degrees. Use the method of Example 9 to obtain an *exact* value.

    *(a) $\frac{\pi}{6}$ (b) $\frac{\pi}{3}$ *(c) $\frac{\pi}{5}$

(d) $\dfrac{\pi}{9}$ *(e) $\dfrac{3\pi}{4}$ (f) $\dfrac{7\pi}{6}$

*(g) 3π (h) $\dfrac{3\pi}{2}$ *(i) $\dfrac{8\pi}{3}$

(j) $\dfrac{13\pi}{4}$ *(k) $\dfrac{9\pi}{4}$ (l) $\dfrac{5\pi}{2}$

3. Change from radians to degrees or degrees to radians as appropriate. Use the method of Example 10. If no unit is given, assume it is radians.

    *(a)   4   (b)   9   *(c)   7°

    (d)   17°   *(e)   5.1   (f)   12.3

    *(g)   23°   (h)   15.9°   *(i)   100

    (j)   83   *(k)   81.7°   (l)   1000°

4. The force F that propels a skier parallel to the slope that the skier is descending is computed as

$$F = W \sin \theta$$

where W is the weight of the skier and θ is the angle of the slope being descended. What is the force for a 200-pound skier going down a 30° slope?

*5. The range of a cannon with muzzle velocity v, fired at an angle of elevation θ, is given by

$$r = \dfrac{v^2}{g} \sin 2\theta \qquad g = \text{constant}$$

For what value of θ will the range of the cannon be greatest?

7.6 RADIUS r AND RIGHT TRIANGLES

You may recall the appearance of right triangles within the unit circle in Section 7.2.

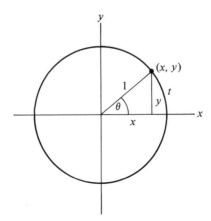

We defined cosine of t and sine of t as $\cos t = x$ and $\sin t = y$. Since the arc length t can be obtained by moving around the unit circle through an angle of θ, it seems reasonable to define cosine of θ and sine of θ in a similar manner: $\cos \theta = x$ and $\sin \theta = y$.

The definitions of the trigonometric functions can be generalized for a circle of any radius r. Consider the point (x', y') on the unit circle and (x, y) on a concentric circle of radius r as shown in the figure.

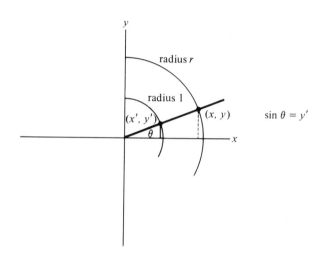

A triangle can be extracted from this setting.

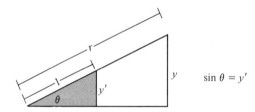

Using the proportionality of corresponding sides of similar triangles,

$$\frac{y'}{1} = \frac{y}{r}$$

or

$$y' = \frac{y}{r}$$

Now since $y' = \sin \theta$,

$$\sin \theta = y' = \frac{y}{r}$$

or

$$\sin \theta = \frac{y}{r}$$

Similarly,

$$\cos \theta = \frac{x}{r}$$

Using the definitions of the other four trigonometric functions in terms of sine and cosine, we can readily obtain

$$\tan \theta = \frac{y}{x} \qquad \cot \theta = \frac{x}{y}$$

$$\sec \theta = \frac{r}{x} \qquad \csc \theta = \frac{r}{y}$$

Radian measure is different when the circle is not the unit circle; it is not simply the arc length. Let us consider a circle of radius r and the unit circle.

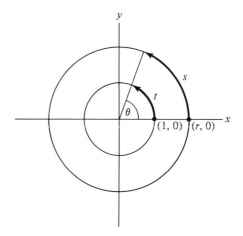

We know that $\theta = t$ radians, since t is the arc of the unit circle that corresponds to central angle θ. But we want to express angle θ in terms of s, from the circle of radius r. *A theorem of geometry says that the ratio of the lengths of the two arcs is the same as the ratio of the lengths of the two radii.* In symbols,

$$\frac{s}{t} = \frac{r}{1}$$

This proportion can be solved for t. The result is

$$t = \frac{s}{r}$$

And since t is the same as θ, we have

$$\theta = \frac{s}{r} \quad \begin{cases} \theta = \text{angle in radians} \\ s = \text{arc length} \\ r = \text{radius of circle} \end{cases} \quad \begin{array}{l} \textbf{radian} \\ \textbf{measure} \end{array}$$

It is worth noting that angle θ contains 1 radian when the length of arc and the radius are equal. This situation occurs, of course, when angle θ is approximately 57.3°.

Example 11 *A central angle has an arc of length 5 centimeters on a circle of radius 4 centimeters. Find the radian measure of the angle.*

$$\theta = \frac{s}{r} = \frac{5 \text{ cm}}{4 \text{ cm}} = 1.25$$

The angle is 1.25 radians. A similar problem would be to determine the arc length s when given angle θ and the radius of the circle.

Next we shall consider the area of a sector of a circle. A sector is the region bounded by a central angle and an arc of the circle.

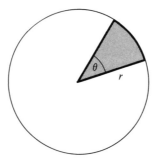

From geometry, the ratio of the area of a sector to the area inside the whole circle is the same as the ratio of the central angle θ to a whole revolution 2π. If A represents the area of a sector, then this statement becomes

$$\frac{A}{\pi r^2} = \frac{\theta}{2\pi}$$

When solved for A, the result is

$$A = \tfrac{1}{2}r^2\theta \quad \begin{cases} A = \text{area of sector} \\ r = \text{radius of circle} \\ \theta = \text{central angle in radians} \end{cases}$$

Example 12 *Determine the area of a sector of a circle if the central angle is $\pi/3$ and the radius is 12 meters.*

$$A = \tfrac{1}{2}r^2\theta$$

$$A = \frac{1}{2}(12)^2\frac{\pi}{3} = 24\pi \quad \text{square meters}$$

Certain trigonometry problems are best solved by using a right-triangle approach, which is what we will do next. The right (90°) angle will often be shown in drawings with a small box marking.

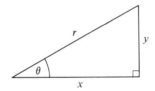

Sine, cosine, and tangent can be defined for nonright angle θ of a right triangle in terms of the hypotenuse of the triangle and the sides opposite and adjacent to angle θ. For any right triangle, the **hypotenuse** is the side opposite the right angle. The **opposite side** is the side opposite angle θ. The **adjacent side** is the side next to (adjacent to) angle θ. These terms are illustrated in the following triangle.

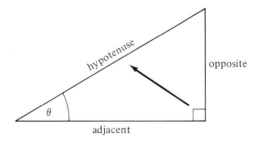

Here, then, are the definitions of sine, cosine, and tangent for a right triangle. They are expressed for the nonright angle θ. Note that these definitions are consistent with previous definitions based on circles of radius r. The positions opposite, adjacent, and hypotenuse are used instead of y, x, and r, respectively.

$$\sin \theta = \frac{\text{opposite}}{\text{hypotenuse}}$$

$$\cos \theta = \frac{\text{adjacent}}{\text{hypotenuse}}$$

$$\tan \theta = \frac{\text{opposite}}{\text{adjacent}}$$

Example 13 *Determine* $\sin \theta$, $\cos \theta$, *and* $\tan \theta$ *for the given triangle.*

$$\sin \theta = \frac{\text{opposite}}{\text{hypotenuse}} = \frac{4}{5}$$

$$\cos \theta = \frac{\text{adjacent}}{\text{hypotenuse}} = \frac{3}{5}$$

$$\tan \theta = \frac{\text{opposite}}{\text{adjacent}} = \frac{4}{3}$$

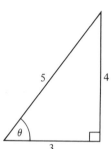

Example 14 *Determine* $\sin \phi$, $\cos \phi$, *and* $\tan \phi$. *(* ϕ *is the Greek letter phi.)*

The length of the hypotenuse is not known but can be determined by using the Pythagorean theorem, $a^2 + b^2 = c^2$, with c being the hypotenuse.

$$1^2 + 2^2 = x^2$$

$$5 = x^2$$

$$x = \sqrt{5} = \text{hypotenuse}$$

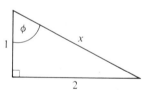

Now

$$\sin \phi = \frac{\text{opposite}}{\text{hypotenuse}} = \frac{2}{\sqrt{5}}$$

$$\cos \phi = \frac{\text{adjacent}}{\text{hypotenuse}} = \frac{1}{\sqrt{5}}$$

$$\tan \phi = \frac{\text{opposite}}{\text{adjacent}} = \frac{2}{1} = 2$$

Right-triangle trigonometry can be used to determine the lengths of sides of a triangle or the measure of angles of a triangle. Here are a few examples.

Example 15   *Find the length of side x in the triangle.*

The side *adjacent* to the angle of 44° is known. The side *opposite* the angle is what we seek. The trigonometric function that is defined in terms of the adjacent and opposite sides is *tangent*. Thus

$$\tan \theta = \frac{\text{opposite}}{\text{adjacent}}$$

becomes

$$\tan 44° = \frac{x}{6}$$

or

$$x = 6 \cdot \tan 44°$$

Values of trigonometric functions of angles in degrees can be obtained from Table V in the appendix or by using a calculator. Such values are almost always approximations rather than exact values. To find the tangent of an angle in Table V, go down the leftmost column until you get to the desired angle (44° in this case). Then move across the table until you are under the appropriate function (tan in this case). You can see that tan 44° ≈ .9657. Thus

$$x \approx 6(.9657)$$

$$\approx 5.7942$$

If using a calculator, enter 44 (which represents 44°) and press the "tan" key. Be sure that the calculator is set for degrees rather than radians.

Example 16   *Determine the number of degrees in the angle n.*

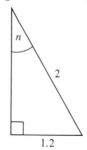

The hypotenuse, 2, and opposite side, 1.2, are given. Because sine is the trigonometric function defined in terms of hypotenuse and opposite, we proceed as follows:

$$\sin n = \frac{\text{opposite}}{\text{hypotenuse}} = \frac{1.2}{2} = .6000$$

An approximate value for angle n can be obtained by using Table V. You must reverse the table lookup procedure used in Example 15. Look down the sine column until you find .6000 or the closest number to it that appears in the table. In this case, the number is .6018. Then look to the left to see which angle is associated with that sine value. Here the angle is 37°. Thus

$$n \approx 37°$$

The reverse table lookup procedure can also be accomplished by using a calculator; however, a complete understanding of what is going on will not be clear until the concept of inverse trigonometric functions is presented in Section 7.11. Depending on your calculator, there will be a key that reads either "inv" or "arc." To find the n such that $\sin n \approx .6000$, enter .6000 and then press the inv key and then the sin key or else the arc key and then the sin key. Be sure that the calculator is set for degrees rather than radians. (Another possibility: some calculators have one key, $\sin^{-1}$, that will accomplish the reverse table lookup.)

The next example illustrates an application of right-triangle trigonometry to indirect measurement. The exercises include several other situations in which trigonometry is used to accomplish the indirect measurement.

Example 17   *Indirect measurement by right-triangle trigonometry.*
Here the distance across a river will be determined indirectly by using right-triangle trigonometry.

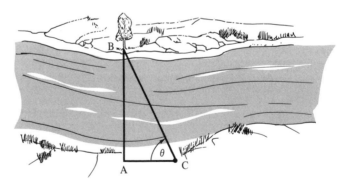

Walk along the shore until you are opposite a tree, bush, large rock, or other reference point on the other shore. Call the point you are standing at A and call the reference on the other shore B. Then walk along the shore in a line perpendicular to AB until you are perhaps 100 or 200 feet from A. Call this new point C. Now approximate the angle θ between AC and the reference point on the opposite shore. Knowing AC (the distance from A to C) and angle θ, you should be able to approximate the length of AB, the distance across the river. Assume in this example that AC is 200 feet and that angle θ is 65°.

The distance across the river can be determined by solving the next triangle for x.

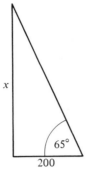

With respect to the 65° angle, the side of length x is opposite and the 200-foot side is adjacent. This means that tangent should be used.

$$\tan 65° = \frac{x}{200}$$

From Table V, $\tan 65° \doteq 2.1445$. So we have

$$2.1445 \approx \frac{x}{200}$$

or

$$x \approx 200(2.1445) \approx 428.90$$

It is approximately 429 feet across the river.

We need to introduce two concepts that will be used in the applied problems of Exercises 7.6. The *angle of elevation* is the angle between the horizontal and the line of sight when the object is above the horizontal. The *angle of depression* is the angle between the horizontal and the line of sight when the object is below the horizontal.

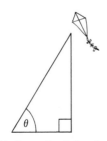

θ is the angle of elevation.

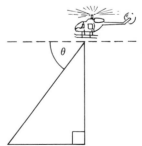

θ is the angle of depression.

Right triangles can be used to obtain rough approximations for the entries in Table V. To obtain sin 40°, for example, construct a right triangle (the larger the better) with a 40° angle in it. Then measure the lengths of the opposite and hypotenuse. Divide the length of the opposite by the length of the hypotenuse. That's it! Keep in mind that this method is not recommended; it is ancient and crude. On the other hand, it demonstrates the ingenuity of ancient people in creating definitions and corresponding tables in order to solve problems of astronomy and navigation by measuring indirectly things they could not measure directly.

A more modern and more accurate method of generating trigonometric tables will be shown in Chapter 10.

Example 18 *Let* $\cos \theta = 5/13$ *and* θ *be in the first quadrant. Use a right triangle to determine the value of* $\sin \theta$ *and* $\tan \theta$. *Also determine the value of* $\csc \theta$, $\sec \theta$, *and* $\cot \theta$.

In a right triangle, $\cos \theta$ = adjacent/hypotenuse. This means the triangle showing $\cos \theta = 5/13$ can be drawn as

By the Pythagorean theorem the third side of this triangle is 12, so we have

Immediately,

$$\sin \theta = \frac{\text{opposite}}{\text{hypotenuse}} = \frac{12}{13}$$

$$\tan \theta = \frac{\text{opposite}}{\text{adjacent}} = \frac{12}{5}$$

Then, using the definitions given in Section 7.3,

$$\csc \theta = \frac{1}{\sin \theta} = \frac{13}{12}$$

$$\sec \theta = \frac{1}{\cos \theta} = \frac{13}{5}$$

$$\cot \theta = \frac{1}{\tan \theta} = \frac{5}{12}$$

Example 19   *If* $\sin \theta = \dfrac{3x}{5}$, *and* θ *is in quadrant I, determine* $\tan \theta$.

Since $\sin \theta = 3x/5 = $ opposite/hypotenuse, we have the right triangle shown next.

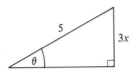

By using the Pythagorean theorem, we find that the third side of the triangle is $\sqrt{(5)^2 - (3x)^2}$, or $\sqrt{25 - 9x^2}$.

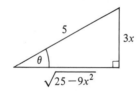

Thus,

$$\tan \theta = \frac{\text{opposite}}{\text{adjacent}} = \frac{3x}{\sqrt{25 - 9x^2}}$$

EXERCISES 7.6

1. Use $\theta = s/r$ and the two given values to determine the third (unknown) value.
    *(a)   Arc length 10 mm, radius 2 mm
    (b)   Arc length 3π in., radius 5 in.
    *(c)   Arc length $\dfrac{7\pi}{9}$ ft, radius $\dfrac{7\pi}{9}$ ft
    (d)   Angle 3 radians, radius 7 cm

*(e)   Angle $\frac{\pi}{5}$ radians, radius 8 in.

(f)   Angle $\frac{\pi}{3}$ radians, radius 7 mm

*(g)   Angle $\frac{\pi}{2}$ radians, arc length 10 ft

(h)   Angle 8 radians, arc length 3 in.

*(i)   Angle $\frac{2\pi}{3}$ radians, arc length $\frac{2\pi}{3}$ mm

(j)   Angle 45°, radius 12 cm (Be careful!)

*(k)   Angle 30°, arc length 9 ft

2.   Determine the area of each sector for the given radius and central angle.

*(a)   Radius 6 cm, central angle $\frac{\pi}{2}$

(b)   Radius 10 cm, central angle $\frac{3\pi}{5}$

*(c)   Radius 7 in., central angle $\frac{\pi}{3}$

(d)   Radius 5 in., central angle $\frac{5\pi}{6}$

*(e)   Radius 9 ft, central angle 60° (Be careful!)

(f)   Radius 20 ft, central angle 36°

*(g)   Radius 3 mm, central angle 50°

*3.   Two concentric (same center) circles have radii of 4 inches and 5 inches. Determine the area of the part of the sector of the larger circle that is outside the smaller circle, when the central angle is 60°.

*4.   A restaurant has two pies, one with a 4-inch radius and one with a 6-inch radius. The smaller pie has already been sliced into six equal pieces. The chef now wants to cut pieces from the larger pie so that they will be the same size (that is, area of top crust the same) as those of the smaller pie. What should be the central angle (in radians) of each slice of the larger pie?

5.   Use Table V (appendix) to determine the approximate value of each expression.

*(a) sin 56°	(b) cos 12°	*(c) tan 87°
(d) tan 34°	*(e) sin 17°	(f) sin 40°
*(g) cos 83°	(h) cot 6°	*(i) sec 17°
(j) csc 48°	*(k) csc 23°	(l) cot 1°
*(m) tan 10°	(n) sec 38°	*(o) cos 89°

6. Use Table V and *reverse the table lookup procedure*. Locate the given value in the body of the table and determine the angle θ in degrees.
    *(a) $\sin \theta = .3584$ (b) $\sin \theta = .9659$
    *(c) $\cos \theta = .9994$ (d) $\cos \theta = .6820$
    *(e) $\tan \theta = 4.0108$ (f) $\tan \theta = .4452$

*7. For the right triangle shown (below, left), find the sine, cosine, and tangent of angles x and y.

   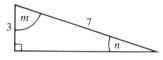

8. For the right triangle shown (above, right), find the sine, cosine, and tangent of angles m and n.

9. For each right triangle that follows, find the approximate length of side x (to the nearest tenth).

*(a)

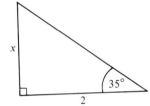

(b)

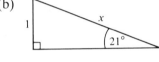

*(c)

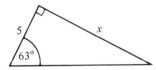

(d)

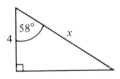

*(e)

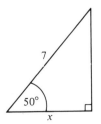

(f)

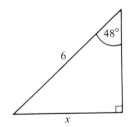

10. For each right triangle that follows, determine the approximate number of degrees in angle θ (to the nearest degree).

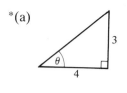

*(a)

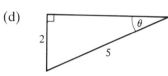

(b)

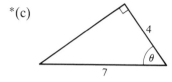

*(c)

(d)

*11. Define cot θ, sec θ, and csc θ in terms of the hypotenuse, opposite, and adjacent sides of a right triangle.

12. Verify each identity for a right triangle with nonright angle θ, adjacent side a, opposite side b, and hypotenuse c. Begin by writing each trigonometric function in terms of a, b, and c.

(a) $\tan \theta \cos \theta = \sin \theta$

(b) $\sin^2\theta + \cos^2\theta = 1$

(c) $(1 + \cos \theta)(1 - \cos \theta) = \tan^2\theta \cos^2\theta$

(d) $\tan \theta + \dfrac{1}{\tan \theta} = \dfrac{\csc \theta}{\cos \theta}$

(e) $\tan^2\theta + 1 = \sec^2\theta$

*13. In forestry, right-triangle trigonometry is sometimes used to determine the height of a tree. The observer measures her distance from the base of the tree and the angle of elevation θ to the top of the tree.

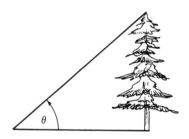

To the nearest foot, what is the height of the tree if the distance of the observer from the tree is 73 feet and the angle of elevation is 39°?

14. The next drawing suggests a way to determine the distance from the planet Venus to the sun. Determine the length of segment VS, the approximate distance from Venus to the sun. (The figure is not drawn to scale.)

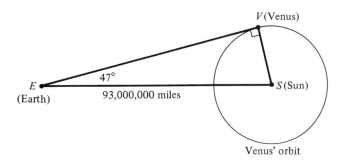

*15. Airports use *ceilometers* to measure the height of a cloud cover in order to determine whether to allow planes to land and take off. A *ceilometer* (shown below) consists of a light beam projector, a detector, and a recorder. The projector directs an intense beam of light vertically up into the clouds. The detector (a photocell) is located on the ground a fixed distance from the projector. Where the light from the projector hits the cloud base, a spot is created. The detector senses the light spot. The angle between the ground and the light spot is then given by the recorder. Finally, the use of right-triangle trigonometry gives the height.

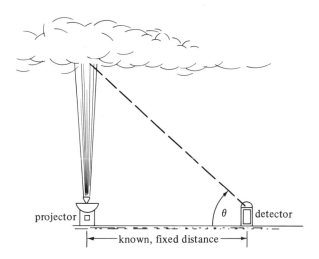

If the known fixed distance along the ground is 200 feet and the angle θ given by the recorder is 42°, how high is the cloud cover?

16. The string of a kite is attached to the ground. The angle formed between the string and the ground is 58°. If the length of the string is 1000 feet (that is, you have let out 1000 feet of string), how high is the kite? (See the drawing on the next page.)

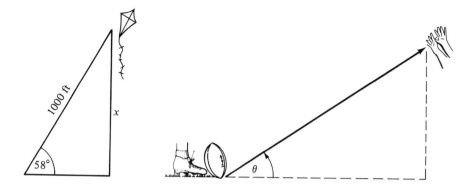

*17. Attempting to block field goals is a common defensive tactic in football.
   (a) How high must the defensive player get his hand to block the ball if it is kicked at an angle of 30° and the defensive player is 18 feet from where the ball is originally kicked?
   (b) How high must the defensive player get his hand to block the ball if it is kicked at an angle of 35° and he is 18 feet from where the ball is originally kicked?
   (c) A good defensive player can get his hand up to a height of 11 feet. If the ball is kicked at an angle of 40°, how close must the player be to the ball in order to block the kick?

*18. A police helicopter is hovering 500 ft above the scene of an accident (A). One of the officers in the copter spots a man walking. The angle of depression (θ) is 40°.
   (a) How far is the man from the scene of the accident?
   (b) How far is the helicopter from the man?

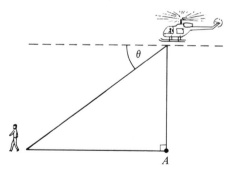

*19. Based on the drawing shown on the next page, how far is the plane from the ship, if it is flying at an altitude of 3000 ft and the angle of depression to the ship is 35°?

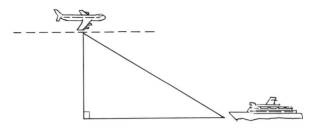

20. For each problem, determine the values of the other five trigonometric functions. Assume the angle given is in Quadrant I.

*(a) $\sin t = \dfrac{1}{3}$

(b) $\cos t = \dfrac{1}{5}$

*(c) $\csc u = 4$

(d) $\tan u = 2$

*(e) $\sin t = \dfrac{2}{3}$

(f) $\cos u = \dfrac{4}{5}$

*(g) $\sec \theta = \sqrt{3}$

(h) $\cot t = \dfrac{3}{2}$

*(i) $\sin t = \dfrac{\sqrt{2}}{7}$

(j) $\sec \theta = \dfrac{5}{3}$

21. For each problem, determine the values of the other five trigonometric functions. Assume the angle is in Quadrant I.

*(a) $\sin t = \dfrac{m}{3}$

(b) $\cos t = \dfrac{2}{m}$

*(c) $\tan u = \dfrac{2m}{7}$

(d) $\cot t = \dfrac{\sqrt{m^2 - 9}}{3}$

*(e) $\sec \theta = \dfrac{m}{\sqrt{m^2 - 16}}$

(f) $\csc \theta = \dfrac{m^2 + 1}{m}$

7.7 TRIGONOMETRIC FUNCTIONS BEYOND QUADRANT I

Based on our earlier work with the unit circle and with radian versus degree measure of angles, we have the following table, which you should memorize.

θ	$\sin \theta$	$\cos \theta$	$\tan \theta$
0 or 0°	0	1	0
$\dfrac{\pi}{6}$ or 30°	$\dfrac{1}{2}$	$\dfrac{\sqrt{3}}{2}$	$\dfrac{\sqrt{3}}{3}$
$\dfrac{\pi}{4}$ or 45°	$\dfrac{\sqrt{2}}{2}$	$\dfrac{\sqrt{2}}{2}$	1
$\dfrac{\pi}{3}$ or 60°	$\dfrac{\sqrt{3}}{2}$	$\dfrac{1}{2}$	$\sqrt{3}$
$\dfrac{\pi}{2}$ or 90°	1	0	—

You have used Table V or a calculator to determine the value of any trigonometric function for an acute angle θ other than $0°$, $30°$, $45°$, $60°$, or $90°$. (An *acute angle* is an angle greater than $0°$ but less than $90°$.)

Values for trigonometric functions of real numbers or angles measured in radians can be determined by using Table IV or a calculator. Here are a few examples. The approximations obtained here come from Table IV.

$$\sin 1.3 \approx .9636$$

$$\cos .2 \approx .9801$$

$$\tan 1 \approx 1.557$$

$$\sin \frac{\pi}{5} \approx .5891$$

In computing $\sin (\pi/5)$, change π to 3.14 and divide it by 5. This simplifies to approximately .63. Then you can readily look up $\sin .63$ in the table.

In your use of Tables IV and V you may have noticed that θ was used for angles in degrees and t was used for angles in radians. Any letters could have been used (x, y, α, ϕ, and so on), θ could have been used for both, or t could have been used for both. In this section, however, we shall use the same convention—θ for angles in degrees, t for angles in radians. This distinction is used here to avoid confusion, because even in the same sentence we shall refer to angles in both radians and degrees.

Tables supply values of trigonometric functions only within the first quadrant. So trigonometric functions of $t > \pi/2$ or $\theta > 90°$ are not directly available from tables. However, functions of $t > \pi/2$ can be expressed in terms of functions of t_1, where $0 < t_1 < \pi/2$. Also, functions of $\theta > 90°$ can be expressed in terms of functions of θ_1, where $0° < \theta_1 < 90°$. Consider a trigonometric point $P(t)$ on the unit circle in the second quadrant.

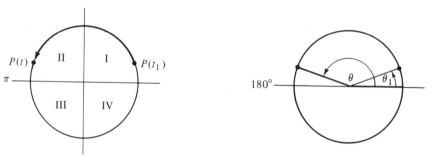

You can see that the magnitudes of the coordinates of $P(t)$ and $P(t_1)$ are the same. Specifically, the y coordinates (sines) are identical and the x coordinates (cosines) are opposite in sign. Thus $\sin t = \sin t_1$ and $\cos t = -\cos t_1$. Similarly, $\sin \theta = \sin \theta_1$ and $\cos \theta = -\cos \theta_1$. Note also that

$$t_1 = \pi - t$$

$$\theta_1 = 180° - \theta$$

Thus

$$
\left.\begin{array}{l}
\sin t = \sin(\pi - t) \\
\cos t = -\cos(\pi - t) \\
\sin \theta = \sin(180° - \theta) \\
\cos \theta = -\cos(180° - \theta)
\end{array}\right\} \quad \text{quadrant II}
$$

Illustrations and studies can also be made for the third and fourth quadrants. The conclusions are:

$$
\left.\begin{array}{l}
\sin t = -\sin(t - \pi) \\
\cos t = -\cos(t - \pi) \\
\sin \theta = -\sin(\theta - 180°) \\
\cos \theta = -\cos(\theta - 180°)
\end{array}\right\} \quad \text{quadrant III}
$$

and

$$
\left.\begin{array}{l}
\sin t = -\sin(2\pi - t) \\
\cos t = \cos(2\pi - t) \\
\sin \theta = -\sin(360° - \theta) \\
\cos \theta = \cos(360° - \theta)
\end{array}\right\} \quad \text{quadrant IV}
$$

In summary,

1. For trigonometric functions of θ (degrees):
   (a) If θ is in quadrant II, $\theta_1 = 180° - \theta$.
   (b) If θ is in quadrant III, $\theta_1 = \theta - 180°$.
   (c) If θ is in quadrant IV, $\theta_1 = 360° - \theta$.

2. For trigonometric functions of t (radians):
   (a) If t is in quadrant II, $t_1 = \pi - t$.
   (b) If t is in quadrant III, $t_1 = t - \pi$.
   (c) If t is in quadrant IV, $t_1 = 2\pi - t$.

Recall that the pattern of signs for sine and cosine in each quadrant is

	I	II	III	IV
sine	+	+	−	−
cosine	+	−	−	+

Signs for any other trigonometric functions are easily derived from these signs and the definition of the function. Here are some examples that demonstrate how to use these rules to obtain values of trigonometric functions in quadrants II, III, and IV. A few additional remarks on examples involving tangent, cotangent, secant, and cosecant follow the examples.

$$\sin 150° = \sin(180° - 150°) = \sin 30° = \frac{1}{2}$$

$$\cos 135° = -\cos(180° - 135°) = -\cos 45° = -\frac{\sqrt{2}}{2}$$

$$\cos 240° = -\cos(240° - 180°) = -\cos 60° = -\frac{1}{2}$$

$$\sin 315° = -\sin(360° - 315°) = -\sin 45° = -\frac{\sqrt{2}}{2}$$

$$\sin \frac{7\pi}{6} = -\sin\left(\frac{7\pi}{6} - \pi\right) = -\sin \frac{\pi}{6} = -\frac{1}{2}$$

$$\cos \frac{5\pi}{4} = -\cos\left(\frac{5\pi}{4} - \pi\right) = -\cos \frac{\pi}{4} = -\frac{\sqrt{2}}{2}$$

Also,

$$\tan 210° = \tan(210° - 180°) = \tan 30° = \frac{\sqrt{3}}{3}$$

$$\cot \frac{2\pi}{3} = -\cot\left(\pi - \frac{2\pi}{3}\right) = -\cot \frac{\pi}{3} = -\frac{\sqrt{3}}{3}$$

$$\csc \frac{11\pi}{6} = -\csc\left(2\pi - \frac{11\pi}{6}\right) = -\csc \frac{\pi}{6} = -2$$

$$\sec \frac{7\pi}{4} = \sec\left(2\pi - \frac{7\pi}{4}\right) = \sec \frac{\pi}{4} = \sqrt{2}$$

The sign for $\tan 210°$ was determined to be $+$, since tangent = sine/cosine and both sine and cosine are negative in the third quadrant. A similar approach can be used for cotangent, secant, and cosecant. However, you may prefer to change tangent, cotangent, secant, and cosecant to sines and cosines and work them out completely that way. Here are $\tan 210°$ and $\sec 7\pi/4$ worked out in this alternative way.

$$\tan 210° = \frac{\sin 210°}{\cos 210°}$$

$$= \frac{-\sin(210° - 180°)}{-\cos(210° - 180°)}$$

$$= \frac{\sin 30°}{\cos 30°}$$

$$= \frac{\frac{1}{2}}{\frac{\sqrt{3}}{2}}$$

$$= \frac{1}{\sqrt{3}} \quad \text{or} \quad \frac{\sqrt{3}}{3}$$

$$\sec \frac{7\pi}{4} = \frac{1}{\cos \frac{7\pi}{4}}$$

$$= \frac{1}{\cos\left(2\pi - \frac{7\pi}{4}\right)}$$

$$= \frac{1}{\cos \frac{\pi}{4}}$$

$$= \frac{1}{\frac{\sqrt{2}}{2}} = \frac{2}{\sqrt{2}} = \sqrt{2}$$

For $\theta > 360°$, subtract as many multiples of $360°$ as necessary to produce a new θ between $0°$ and $360°$. Then apply the rules above as needed. Similarly, for $t > 2\pi$, subtract as many multiples of 2π as necessary to produce a new t between 0 and 2π. Then apply the rules above as needed. This follows from the previously shown property, $P(t + 2n\pi) = P(t)$. Here are two examples

$$\cos 570° = \cos(570° - 360°)$$

$$= \cos 210°$$

$$= -\cos(210° - 180°)$$

$$= -\cos 30°$$

$$= -\frac{\sqrt{3}}{2}$$

$$\sin \frac{19\pi}{4} = \sin 4\frac{3}{4}\pi$$

$$= \sin\left(4\frac{3}{4}\pi - 4\pi\right)$$

$$= \sin \frac{3\pi}{4}$$

$$= \sin\left(\pi - \frac{3\pi}{4}\right)$$

$$= \sin \frac{\pi}{4}$$

$$= \frac{\sqrt{2}}{2}$$

In the preceding examples, you knew the exact values of the trigonometric functions. This will not always be the case. Consider an example that makes use of Table V.

$$\sin 253° = -\sin(253° - 180°)$$

$$= -\sin 73°$$

$$\approx -.9563$$

In order to do a similar problem involving radians, you must know the approximate decimal values of the boundaries between quadrants.

$$\frac{\pi}{2} \approx 1.57$$

$$\pi \approx 3.14$$

$$\frac{3\pi}{2} \approx 4.71$$

$$2\pi \approx 6.28$$

This example uses Table IV.

$$\cos 2.63 \approx -\cos(3.14 - 2.63)$$

$$\approx -\cos(.51)$$

$$\approx -.8727$$

EXERCISES 7.7

*1. Use Table IV or a calculator to determine the approximate value of each expression.

(a) sin 1.2   (b) cos .5   (c) sin .35
(d) cos 1.56   (e) tan .23   (f) csc .73
(g) sec .93   (h) cot 1.46   (i) sin 1.57
(j) tan .01   (k) cos .9   (l) csc .28
(m) tan .47   (n) sec 1.30   (o) sec 1.1

*2. Use Table IV or a calculator to determine the approximate value of each expression. Use 3.14 as an approximate value of π and round the division result to two decimal places.

(a) $\sin \dfrac{\pi}{10}$ (b) $\sin \dfrac{\pi}{9}$ (c) $\cos \dfrac{\pi}{7}$

(d) $\tan \dfrac{\pi}{5}$ (e) $\cot \dfrac{\pi}{8}$ (f) $\sec \dfrac{2\pi}{5}$

(g) $\sec \dfrac{3\pi}{7}$ (h) $\cos \dfrac{2\pi}{9}$ (i) $\sin \dfrac{3\pi}{8}$

*3. Use Table IV and *reverse the table lookup procedure*. Locate the given value in the body of the table and determine the angle t in radians.

(a) sin t = .5564   (b) sin t = .9949
(c) cos t = .9888   (d) cos t = .3993
(e) tan t = 3.467   (f) tan t = .0601

4. Determine the exact value of each expression. *Do not* use the tables in the appendix or a calculator.

*(a) sin 210°   (b) sin 135°   *(c) sin 240°
(d) cos 300°   *(e) cos 120°   (f) cos 210°
*(g) sin 330°   (h) cos 150°   *(i) cos 315°
(j) sin 225°

5. Determine the exact value of each expression. *Do not* use the tables in the appendix or a calculator.

*(a) $\sin \dfrac{3\pi}{4}$ *(b) $\cos \dfrac{7\pi}{6}$ *(c) $\sin \dfrac{11\pi}{6}$

(d) $\cos \dfrac{2\pi}{3}$ *(e) $\sin \dfrac{5\pi}{4}$ (f) $\sin \dfrac{5\pi}{3}$

*(g) $\cos \dfrac{5\pi}{4}$ (h) $\cos \dfrac{5\pi}{3}$ *(i) $\sin \dfrac{7\pi}{4}$

(j) $\cos \dfrac{11\pi}{6}$ *(k) $\cos \dfrac{7\pi}{4}$ (l) $\sin \dfrac{2\pi}{3}$

6. Determine the exact value of each expression. *Do not* use the tables in the appendix or a calculator.

*(a) tan 225°   (b) tan 150°   *(c) cot 210°

(d) cot 300°   *(e) csc 120°   (f) sec 135°

*(g) csc 315°   (h) sec 240°   *(i) cot 120°

(j) tan 330°   *(k) csc 150°

7. Determine the exact value of each expression. *Do not* use the tables in the appendix or a calculator.

*(a) $\tan \dfrac{5\pi}{4}$ (b) $\csc \dfrac{5\pi}{6}$ *(c) $\tan \dfrac{7\pi}{6}$

*(d) $\sec \dfrac{2\pi}{3}$ (e) $\sec \dfrac{5\pi}{4}$ *(f) $\cot \dfrac{2\pi}{3}$

*(g) $\csc \dfrac{5\pi}{3}$ (h) $\cot \dfrac{5\pi}{3}$ *(i) $\csc \dfrac{7\pi}{6}$

8. Determine the exact value of each expression. *Do not* use the tables in the appendix.

*(a) cos 420°   (b) sin 405°   *(c) cos 570°

(d) cos 600°   *(e) sin 510°   (f) sin 480°

*(g) cos 945°   (h) sin 1050°   *(i) cos 630°

9. Determine the exact value of each expression. *Do not* use the tables in the appendix.

*(a) $\sin \dfrac{9\pi}{4}$ (b) $\sin \dfrac{7\pi}{3}$ *(c) $\cos \dfrac{8\pi}{3}$

(d) $\sin \dfrac{11\pi}{3}$ *(e) $\cos \dfrac{15\pi}{4}$ (f) $\sin \dfrac{7\pi}{2}$

*(g) $\sin \dfrac{11\pi}{4}$ (h) $\cos \dfrac{19\pi}{6}$ *(i) $\cos \dfrac{21\pi}{4}$

10. Determine the approximate value of each expression. Use Table V.

*(a) sin 137°   (b) cos 265°   *(c) cos 346°

(d) sin 325°   *(e) sin 214°   (f) cos 162°

*(g) cos 273°   (h) cos 457°   *(i) sin 281°

(j) tan 95°   *(k) sin 509°   (l) cos 195°

*(m) cot 139°   (n) sec 100°   *(o) tan 260°

(p) csc 310°   *(q) sec 190°   (r) csc 220°

11. Determine the approximate value of each expression. Use Table IV.

*(a) sin 1.97   (b) cos 5.88   *(c) cos 2

(d) sin 4   *(e) sin 6.02   (f) cos 3.86

*(g) tan 3   (h) cot 5   *(i) sec 2.5

(j) csc 4.3   *(k) tan 4.70   (l) cot 5.99
*(m) sin 7.31   (n) cos 9.83   *(o) sin 10

7.8 GRAPHS

Let us graph the trigonometric functions. To graph sine, use the function

$$f(t) = \sin t$$

In this way, values can be selected for t in order to get points of the form $(t, f(t))$. Follow the value of sine around the unit circle. Sine increases from 0 to 1 between 0 and $\pi/2$.

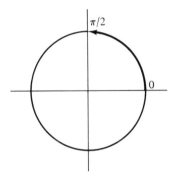

The graph thus far is

t	$\sin t$
0	0
$\dfrac{\pi}{6}$	$\dfrac{1}{2}$
$\dfrac{\pi}{4}$	$\dfrac{\sqrt{2}}{2}$
$\dfrac{\pi}{3}$	$\dfrac{\sqrt{3}}{2}$
$\dfrac{\pi}{2}$	1

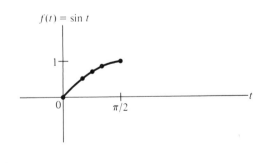

For graphing purposes, you might like to remember two approximations:

$$\sqrt{2} \approx 1.4$$
$$\sqrt{3} \approx 1.7$$

These are not as good approximations as would be needed in other applications, but they are sufficient for our graphing purposes.

Then sine decreases from 1 to 0 between $\pi/2$ and π.

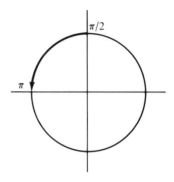

The graph now appears as

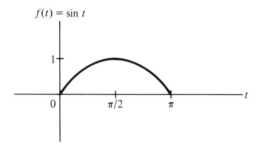

Sine decreases from 0 to -1 between π and $3\pi/2$.

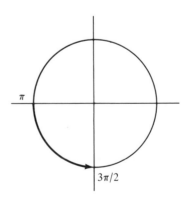

The graph now appears as

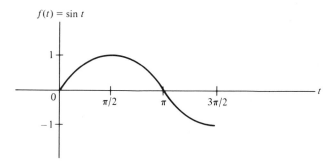

Sine increases from -1 to 0 between $3\pi/2$ and 2π.

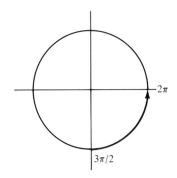

The graph now appears as

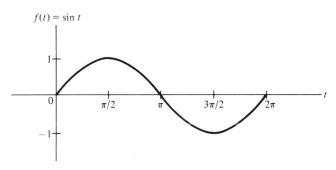

The cycle is complete. If we go around the circle again (that is, use values of t between 2π and 4π), the curve will be repeated. Similarly, if we go around the circle in the negative direction, we get additional cycles of the basic graph.

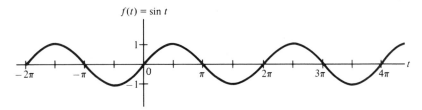

For future convenience in graphing, the function $f(t) = \sin t$ will be written $f(x) = \sin x$ or $y = \sin x$. In this way, elements of the domain are values for x rather than values for t, and graphing can be done in the plane traditionally labeled xy.

If you look at the graph of the sine function, you will see that it repeats its pattern of functional values every 2π. This means that $f(x) = \sin x$ *is periodic with period* 2π. In general,

> A function f is **periodic** with period p if $f(x + p) = f(x)$ for all x in the domain of f, and p is the smallest positive number for which this is true.

In the case of the sine function,

$$\sin(x + 2\pi) = \sin x$$

and 2π is the smallest number p for which $\sin(x + p) = \sin x$.

The period of $y = \sin x$ is 2π, but the period of $y = \sin 2x$ is π. The curve finishes its cycle twice as fast because each angle value x is doubled before the sine is determined. Here are some sample points to show this. The graph follows.

x	$y = \sin x$	$y = \sin 2x$
0	$y = \sin 0 = 0$	$y = \sin 0 = 0$
$\dfrac{\pi}{4}$	$y = \sin \dfrac{\pi}{4} = \dfrac{\sqrt{2}}{2}$	$y = \sin \dfrac{\pi}{2} = 1$
$\dfrac{\pi}{2}$	$y = \sin \dfrac{\pi}{2} = 1$	$y = \sin \pi = 0$
$\dfrac{3\pi}{4}$	$y = \sin \dfrac{3\pi}{4} = \dfrac{\sqrt{2}}{2}$	$y = \sin \dfrac{3\pi}{2} = -1$
π	$y = \sin \pi = 0$	$y = \sin 2\pi = 0$

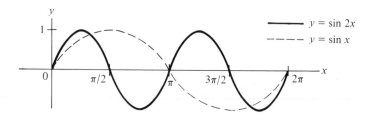

The graph of $y = \sin 4x$ finishes its cycle four times as fast as does $y = \sin x$; so its period is $2\pi/4$, or $\pi/2$. In general,

$$y = \sin bx \text{ has period } \frac{2\pi}{|b|}.$$

With this type of graph, you will always know the beginning point and ending point of the "first" cycle. For example, $y = \sin 3x$ has a period of $2\pi/3$. So one cycle begins at $x = 0$ and ends at $x = 2\pi/3$; that is, the cycle begins at $(0, 0)$ and ends at $(2\pi/3, 0)$. The x coordinate halfway through the cycle is half of $2\pi/3$, or $\pi/3$.

The x coordinate of the point halfway between 0 and $\pi/3$ is half of $\pi/3$, or $\pi/6$. The x coordinate of the point halfway between $\pi/3$ and $2\pi/3$ is the average of $\pi/3$ and $2\pi/3$—namely, $(\pi/3 + 2\pi/3)/2$, or $\pi/2$. The graph:

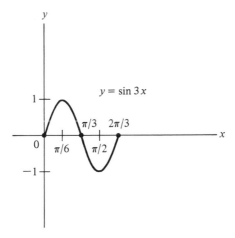

Now consider the graph of $y = 3 \sin x$. The values of $\sin x$ are found and then multiplied by 3 to determine the functional values. For example, when $x = \pi/2$, $y = 3 \cdot \sin(\pi/2) = 3 \cdot 1 = 3$. The graph of $y = 3 \sin x$ between 0 and 2π is shown next.

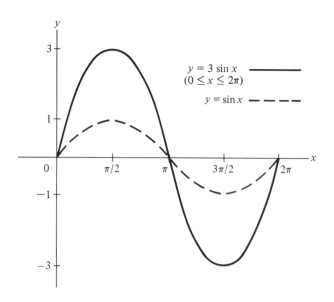

The graph of $y = 3 \sin x$ reaches a maximum height of 3, the graph of $y = \sin x$ (which is $y = 1 \sin x$) reaches a maximum height of 1, and so on. Using a concept of Section 3.9, we can see that the graph of $y = 3 \sin x$ is a stretching of the graph of $y = \sin x$. In general, the graph of $y = a \sin x$ reaches a maximum height of $|a|$. Absolute value is needed because in cases like $y = -2 \sin x$ the maximum height is 2, not -2. Note, too, that as in Section 3.9, multiplication of a function by -1 has the effect of reflecting its graph across the x axis. The graph of $y = -2 \sin x$ is such a reflection of the graph of $y = 2 \sin x$.

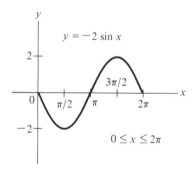

The number $|a|$ is called the **amplitude.** This means

$$y = a \sin x \text{ has } amplitude \, |a|.$$

If we combine the ideas conveyed by $y = \sin bx$ (period $2\pi/|b|$) and

$y = a \sin x$ (amplitude $|a|$), we obtain

$$y = a \sin bx \quad \begin{cases} \text{amplitude: } |a| \\ \text{period: } \dfrac{2\pi}{|b|} \end{cases}$$

Example 20 *Sketch the graph of* $y = \frac{3}{2} \sin \frac{1}{2}x$.

The equation $y = \frac{3}{2} \sin \frac{1}{2}x$ fits the form $y = a \sin bx$, where $a = \frac{3}{2}$ and $b = \frac{1}{2}$. This means that

$$\text{Amplitude} = |a| = \left| \frac{3}{2} \right| = \frac{3}{2}$$

$$\text{Period} = \frac{2\pi}{|b|} = \frac{2\pi}{\frac{1}{2}} = 4\pi$$

The graph is as follows.

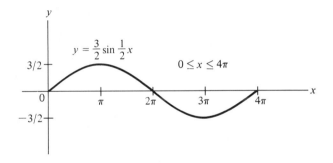

In order to keep the units of the same scale for both the horizontal and the vertical axes, you should consider using very rough approximations for π and $\pi/2$, such as $\pi \approx 3$ and $\pi/2 \approx 1.5$. This was done in the graph just sketched and throughout this section.

Notice the pattern in the graphs of sine functions. They begin at height 0, go to height a one-fourth of the way through the cycle, return to 0 halfway through the cycle, go to height $-a$ three-fourths of the way through the cycle, and return to 0 at the end of the cycle.

The sine graph can be shifted to the left or right by changing its form to $y = a \sin (bx + c)$. If $bx + c = 0$ (that is, $x = -c/b$), then y is zero. The number $-c/b$ is called the **phase shift**. It is the amount the graph of $y = a \sin bx$ must be shifted to become the graph of $y = a \sin(bx + c)$. When $-c/b < 0$ (negative), the shift is leftward. When $-c/b > 0$ (positive), the shift is to the right.

Now let us combine amplitude, period, and phase shift into one form.

$$y = a \sin(bx + c) \quad \left\{ \begin{array}{l} \text{amplitude: } |a| \\ \text{period: } \dfrac{2\pi}{|b|} \\ \text{phase shift: } -\dfrac{c}{b} \end{array} \right.$$

Example 21 *Sketch one cycle of the graph of* $y = \sin(x + \pi)$.

The equation $y = \sin(x + \pi)$ fits the form $y = a \sin(bx + c)$, where $a = 1$, $b = 1$, and $c = \pi$. This means that

$$\text{Amplitude} = |a| = |1| = 1$$

$$\text{Period} = \frac{2\pi}{|b|} = \frac{2\pi}{1} = 2\pi$$

$$\text{Phase shift} = -\frac{c}{b} = -\frac{\pi}{1} = -\pi$$

Begin graphing by plotting the point $(-\pi, 0)$. Because the phase shift is $-\pi$, the cycle will begin at $(-\pi, 0)$ rather than at $(0, 0)$. Next, sketch a sine graph with period 2π and amplitude 1. One complete cycle that begins at $-\pi$ will extend as far as π.

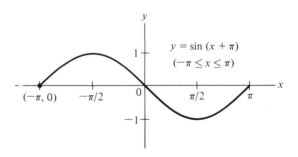

You might find this sort of graphing easier if you consider the sine graph as having four parts to each cycle, as we derived it from the unit circle. Since the period is 2π in this case, each part (or fourth) takes up $2\pi/4$, or $\pi/2$ units along the horizontal. So the graph can be completed in the following five steps.

1. Begin at $(-\pi, 0)$.
2. Go up to maximum of 1, $\pi/2$ units later (at $-\pi/2$).

3. Come down to 0, $\pi/2$ units later (at 0).
4. Continue down to minimum -1, $\pi/2$ units later (at $\pi/2$).
5. Go up to 0, $\pi/2$ units later (at π).

Note: Recalling from Section 3.8 that the graph of $y = f(x + c)$ is c units to the left of the graph of $y = f(x)$ if c is positive, you can see that the graph of $y = \sin(x + \pi)$ is π units to the left of the graph of $y = \sin x$.

Example 22 *Sketch one cycle of the graph of $y = 3 \sin(2x - \pi)$.*
The equation $y = 3 \sin(2x - \pi)$ fits the form $y = a \sin(bx + c)$ with $a = 3$, $b = 2$, and $c = -\pi$. This means that

$$\text{Amplitude} = |a| = 3$$

$$\text{Period} = \frac{2\pi}{|b|} = \frac{2\pi}{2} = \pi$$

$$\text{Phase shift} = -\frac{c}{b} = -\frac{-\pi}{2} = \frac{\pi}{2}$$

Begin graphing by plotting the point $(\pi/2, 0)$, since a phase shift of $\pi/2$ indicates that the cycle will begin at $(\pi/2, 0)$ rather than at $(0, 0)$. Next, sketch a sine graph with period π and amplitude 3. One complete cycle that begins at $\pi/2$ will extend as far as $\pi/2 + \pi$, or $3\pi/2$. If you consider the graph in four parts, then each part takes up $\pi/4$ units along the horizontal. Here are the steps in drawing: Begin at $(\pi/2, 0)$; go up to a maximum value of 3, $\pi/4$ units later (at $3\pi/4$); come down to 0, $\pi/4$ units later (at π); continue down to a minimum value of -3, $\pi/4$ units later (at $5\pi/4$); and then go up to 0, $\pi/4$ units later (at $3\pi/2$).

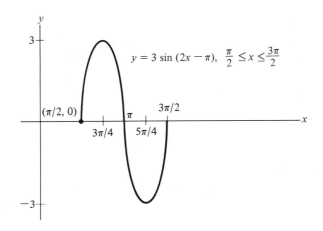

$y = 3 \sin (2x - \pi)$, $\frac{\pi}{2} \le x \le \frac{3\pi}{2}$

Example 23 *Sketch one cycle of the graph of y = −2 sin(3x + 1).*

The equation $y = -2 \sin (3x + 1)$ fits the form $y = a \sin(bx + c)$, where $a = -2$, $b = 3$, and $c = 1$. Thus

$$\text{Amplitude} = |a| = |-2| = 2$$

$$\text{Period} = \frac{2\pi}{|b|} = \frac{2\pi}{3}$$

$$\text{Phase shift} = -\frac{c}{b} = -\frac{1}{3}$$

Begin graphing at $(-\frac{1}{3}, 0)$. Since the period is $2\pi/3$, each quarter of the graph will take one-fourth of $2\pi/3$ units along the horizontal; so each part takes $\pi/6$ units along the horizontal. The cycle ends at $-\frac{1}{3} + 2\pi/3$. Because a is negative, the cycle will begin by going downward rather than upward.

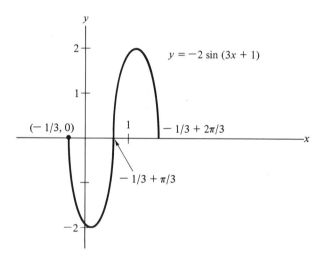

An examination of the unit circle shows that **cosine** varies from 1 to 0 between 0 and $\pi/2$, and 0 to -1 between $\pi/2$ and π, from -1 to 0 between π and $3\pi/2$, and from 0 to 1 between $3\pi/2$ and 2π. The graph of $y = \cos x$ is periodic with period 2π and amplitude 1.

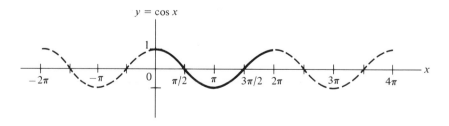

The graph of $y = a \cos(bx + c)$ has amplitude $|a|$, period $2\pi/|b|$, and phase shift $-c/b$.

Example 24 *Sketch one cycle of the graph of $y = \dfrac{3}{2} \cos\left(x + \dfrac{\pi}{2}\right)$.*

The equation $y = \dfrac{3}{2} \cos\left(x + \dfrac{\pi}{2}\right)$ fits the form $y = a \cos(bx + c)$, with $a = 3/2$, $b = 1$, and $c = \pi/2$. This means that

$$\text{Amplitude} = |a| = \frac{3}{2}$$

$$\text{Period} = \frac{2\pi}{|b|} = \frac{2\pi}{1} = 2\pi$$

$$\text{Phase shift} = -\frac{c}{b} = -\frac{\pi/2}{1} = -\frac{\pi}{2}$$

The cycle begins at $x = -\pi/2$. Since this is *cosine* (rather than sine), the y value is a, which is 3/2 in this example. So the cycle begins at $(-\pi/2, 3/2)$. The period is 2π, so the cycle ends at $x = -\dfrac{\pi}{2} + 2\pi$, which is $x = 3\pi/2$. The endpoint of the cycle is $(3\pi/2, 3/2)$. The graph:

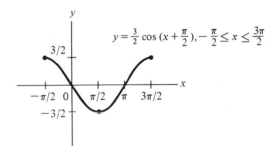

The graph of $y = \tan x$ can be sketched by observing that

$$\tan x = \frac{\sin x}{\cos x}$$

and by using the unit circle. When $x = 0$, $\sin x = 0$ and $\cos x = 1$; thus $\tan 0 = 0/1 = 0$. Between 0 and $\pi/2$, $\sin x$ increases and $\cos x$ decreases. As a result, $\tan x$ increases. And as $\cos x$ gets close to zero near $\pi/2$, $\tan x$ gets very large, tending toward infinity. Moreover, $\tan \pi/2$ is not defined because $\cos \pi/2 = 0$, and division by zero is not defined. The line $x = \pi/2$ is an asymptote.

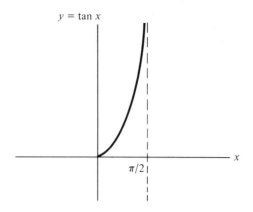

Similarly, tangent varies from $-\infty$ to 0 between $\pi/2$ and π, from 0 to ∞ between π and $3\pi/2$, and so forth. The period of $y = \tan x$ is π.

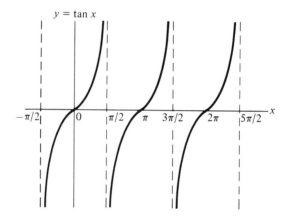

The graph of $y = \cot x$ is somewhat similar and follows from studying $\cot x$ as $\cos x/\sin x$ or as $1/\tan x$. The period of $y = \cot x$ is π.

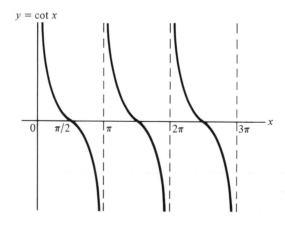

The graph of $y = \csc x$ is easily sketched once $y = \sin x$ has been drawn, since $\csc x = 1/\sin x$. Where sine is 1, cosecant is 1. As sine decreases to zero, cosecant increases toward infinity. As sine increases from zero to 1, cosecant decreases from infinity to 1, and so on.

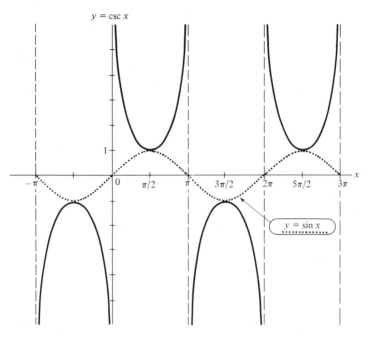

Similarly, the graph of $y = \sec x$ can be sketched by first drawing $y = \cos x$ and then using the fact that $\sec x = 1/\cos x$.

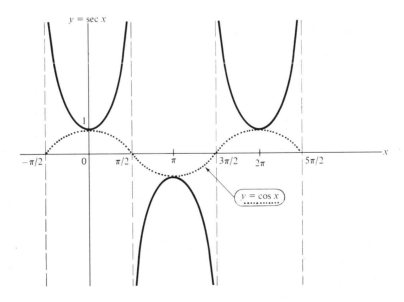

The section ends with a look at some applications that involve sine functions.

Sometimes the interdependence of two animal species will result in a fluctuation in both species. Consider, for example, a territory inhabited by lynxes (the predators) and rabbits (their prey), the rabbits being the main food of the lynxes. The following graph illustrates the interdependence of the two species.

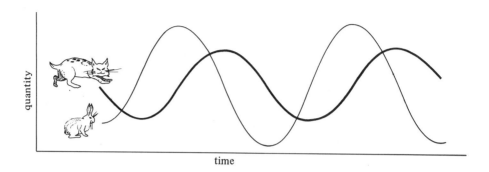

Ecologists refer to the relationship of the lynx and the rabbit as a predator-prey interaction. The interaction leads to a cycle consisting of four distinct types of population growth patterns.

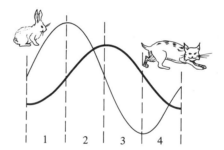

1. The rabbit population has become abundant; so the lynx population is increasing.
2. The lynx population has increased to the extent that the rabbit population is actually decreasing.
3. The rabbit population has decreased to the extent that the lynx population is actually decreasing.
4. The lynx population has decreased to the point that the rabbit population is now increasing.

Michael Faraday discovered the principle of the electric generator in 1831. He found that an electric current can be generated by rotating a coil of wire in a magnetic field. The voltage produced alternates between positive and negative, as shown in the next diagram.

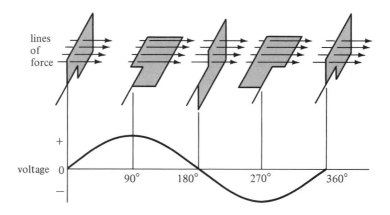

Transmission of electrical signals, such as radio waves, can be described by functions involving sine. The equation $y = A \sin 2\pi ft$, for example, represents the transmission of a single frequency, where A is the amplitude, f is the frequency, and t is the time. Each radio station in your area has a different transmission frequency and that is what you dial or tune in to hear a particular station's transmission. The simple equation $y = A \sin 2\pi ft$ describes the carrier wave only. The carrier must be modified, or modulated, in order to carry music or voices rather than just a single tone. Mathematically, the modulation changes $y = A \sin 2\pi ft$

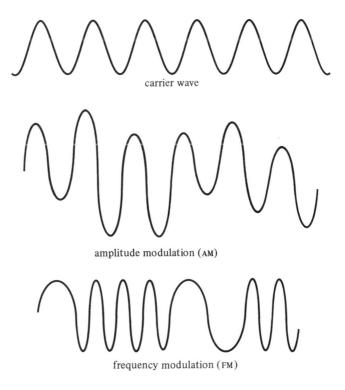

carrier wave

amplitude modulation (AM)

frequency modulation (FM)

into a complicated function composed of several sine functions. For amplitude modification (AM) the amplitude of the carrier wave is varied according to the signal to be sent. Unfortunately, AM transmission is quite susceptible to interference from various sources (voltage-level changes near power lines and lightning, for example). Consequently, frequency modulation (FM) has become popular for high-quality radio transmission. In FM transmission the frequency of the carrier wave is varied according to the signal to be sent.

EXERCISES 7.8

1. Sketch a graph of each function for x values between -2π and 2π.
   *(a) $y = \sin x$ (b) $y = \cos x$
   *(c) $y = \tan x$ (d) $y = \cot x$
   *(e) $y = \sec x$ (f) $y = \csc x$

2. Determine the amplitude and period of each function and then sketch one cycle of the graph.

   *(a) $y = 4 \sin x$ (b) $y = \dfrac{1}{2} \sin x$

   *(c) $y = -3 \sin x$ (d) $y = -\sin x$

   *(e) $y = \sin 4x$ (f) $y = \sin \dfrac{1}{2} x$

   *(g) $y = \sin 3x$ (h) $y = \sin 6x$
   *(i) $y = 3 \sin 2x$ (j) $y = -\sin 2x$

   *(k) $y = 2 \sin 4x$ (l) $y = 2 \sin \dfrac{1}{2} x$

   *(m) $y = -3 \sin \dfrac{1}{2} x$ (n) $y = -\dfrac{1}{2} \sin 3x$

   *(o) $y = 2 \sin \dfrac{3x}{2}$ (p) $y = 5 \sin \dfrac{x}{4}$

3. Determine the period and amplitude, but do not graph.

   *(a) $y = \dfrac{5}{7} \sin \dfrac{2}{3} x$ (b) $y = \dfrac{2}{5} \sin \dfrac{4}{3} x$

   *(c) $y = -\dfrac{5}{3} \sin 7x$ (d) $y = \dfrac{\pi}{2} \sin \dfrac{1}{5} x$

   *(e) $y = \pi \sin \dfrac{x}{\pi}$ (f) $y = \dfrac{\sin 2\pi x}{3}$

4. Determine the amplitude, period, and phase shift of each function. Then sketch one cycle of the graph.

*(a) $y = \sin(x - \pi)$

(b) $y = \sin\left(x - \dfrac{\pi}{2}\right)$

*(c) $y = \sin\left(x + \dfrac{\pi}{2}\right)$

(d) $y = \sin(2x + \pi)$

*(e) $y = \sin(2x - \pi)$

(f) $y = 3\sin(2x - \pi)$

*(g) $y = -\sin(2x + \pi)$

(h) $y = -2\sin(x + \pi)$

*(i) $y = 3\sin\left(2x + \dfrac{\pi}{2}\right)$

(j) $y = -\sin\left(2x - \dfrac{\pi}{2}\right)$

*(k) $y = 5\sin(4x + \pi)$

(l) $y = 3\sin(4x - 2\pi)$

*(m) $y = -2\sin(3x - \pi)$

(n) $y = -\sin\left(x + \dfrac{3\pi}{2}\right)$

*(o) $y = 4\sin\left(x - \dfrac{3\pi}{2}\right)$

(p) $y = 4\sin(3x + \pi)$

*(q) $y = 2\sin(2x - 1)$

(r) $y = 3\sin(5x + 2)$

*(s) $y = -\sin(x + 3)$

(t) $y = \pi\sin(2x - 5)$

*5. Sketch graphs of $y = \cos x$ and $y = \sin(x + \pi/2)$. Compare.

6. Sketch one cycle of the graph of each function.

*(a) $y = \cos(x - \pi)$

(b) $y = 2\cos\left(x + \dfrac{\pi}{2}\right)$

*(c) $y = -\cos(2x - \pi)$

(d) $y = 3\cos(2x + \pi)$

*(e) $y = 2\cos\left(x - \dfrac{\pi}{2}\right)$

(f) $y = -\cos(4x + \pi)$

*(g) $y = 5\cos\left(x + \dfrac{\pi}{3}\right)$

(h) $y = -4\cos\left(x - \dfrac{3\pi}{2}\right)$

7. Write the equations of the asymptotes of each curve.

*(a) $y = \tan x$

(b) $y = \cot x$

*(c) $y = \csc x$

(d) $y = \sec x$

8. Sketch the graph of each function for x values between -2π and 2π.

*(a) $y = |\tan x|$

(b) $y = |\cot x|$

*(c) $y = |\sec x|$

(d) $y = |\csc x|$

9. Sketch the graph of each function.

*(a) $f(x) = \begin{cases} \sin x & 0 \le x \le \pi \\ -\sin x & \pi < x \le 2\pi \\ \sin x & 2\pi < x \le 3\pi \end{cases}$

(b) $\quad y = \begin{cases} 0 & x < 0 \\ \sin x & 0 \le x < \pi \\ \pi - x & \pi \le x \end{cases}$

*(c) $\quad y = \begin{cases} -\sin x & -\pi \le x < 0 \\ \tan x & 0 \le x < \dfrac{\pi}{2} \\ x - \dfrac{\pi}{2} & x \ge \dfrac{\pi}{2} \end{cases}$

(d) $\quad f(x) = \begin{cases} \cos x & -\dfrac{\pi}{2} \le x \le \dfrac{\pi}{2} \\ 0 & \dfrac{\pi}{2} < x < \pi \\ \sin x & \pi \le x \le 2\pi \end{cases}$

*(e) $\quad y = \begin{cases} \csc x & 0 < x < \pi \\ \cot x & \pi < x < 2\pi \end{cases}$

(f) $\quad y = \begin{cases} \sec x & -\dfrac{\pi}{2} < x < \dfrac{\pi}{2} \\ \tan x & \dfrac{\pi}{2} < x < \dfrac{3\pi}{2} \end{cases}$

7.9 SUMS AND DIFFERENCES

In Section 7.4 we derived a few basic identities, which, in turn, were used to prove other identities and to obtain values for trigonometric functions. Those identities involved functions of one angle, such as θ, t, or u. Now we shall obtain formulas for functions of sums and differences of angles, $u + v$ and $u - v$ rather than just u. Such formulas will be important to you in calculus, but they are also important here, for we use them to obtain still other important results and to make simplifications.

We begin with the proof of a very important result:

$$\cos(u - v) = \cos u \cos v + \sin u \sin v$$

where u and v represent numbers of degrees or radians. This result will be used throughout the section. Note that $\cos(u - v) \ne \cos u - \cos v$. To prove the boxed formula, consider the next drawing, which shows the four trigonometric points $(\cos u, \sin u)$, $(\cos v, \sin v)$, $(\cos(u - v), \sin(u - v))$, and $(1, 0)$.

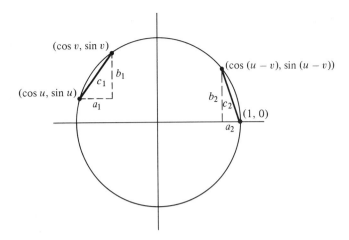

The number c_1 is the distance between (cos u, sin u) and (cos v, sin v), and c_2 is the distance between (cos(u − v), sin(u − v)) and (1, 0). Because the arcs associated with c_1 and c_2 are each of length u − v, it follows that c_1 = c_2.

By the Pythagorean theorem, $c_1{}^2 = a_1{}^2 + b_1{}^2$ and $c_2{}^2 = a_2{}^2 + b_2{}^2$, where

$$|a_1| = |\cos u - \cos v|$$
$$|b_1| = |\sin u - \sin v|$$
$$|a_2| = |\cos(u - v) - 1|$$
$$|b_2| = |\sin(u - v) - 0|$$

Now

$$c_1{}^2 = (\cos u - \cos v)^2 + (\sin u - \sin v)^2$$
$$= \cos^2 u - 2\cos u \cos v + \cos^2 v + \sin^2 u - 2\sin u \sin v + \sin^2 v$$

Replacing $\cos^2 u + \sin^2 u$ by 1 (recall that basic identity) and $\cos^2 v + \sin^2 v$ by 1 simplifies the right side. The simplified form is

$$c_1{}^2 = 2 - 2\cos u \cos v - 2\sin u \sin v$$

The value of $c_2{}^2$ is equal to $c_1{}^2$, but if it is computed directly, the result has a different form. Using the Pythagorean theorem to get that form, we have

$$c_2{}^2 = [\cos(u - v) - 1]^2 + [\sin(u - v) - 0]^2$$
$$= \cos^2(u - v) - 2\cos(u - v) + 1 + \sin^2(u - v)$$

Replacing $\cos^2(u - v) + \sin^2(u - v)$ by 1 yields

$$c_2{}^2 = 2 - 2\cos(u - v)$$

Since $c_1{}^2 = c_2{}^2$, equate the two simplified forms obtained above. The equation $c_1{}^2 = c_2{}^2$ becomes

$$2 - 2\cos u \cos v - 2\sin u \sin v = 2 - 2\cos(u - v)$$

Add -2 to both sides.

$$-2\cos u \cos v - 2\sin u \sin v = -2\cos(u - v)$$

Interchange right and left sides.

$$-2\cos(u - v) = -2\cos u \cos v - 2\sin u \sin v$$

Finally, divide both sides by -2. This step will yield the desired result.

$$\cos(u - v) = \cos u \cos v + \sin u \sin v$$

Example 25 *Use the formula for $\cos(u - v)$ to find the exact value of $\cos(\pi/12)$.*
The number $\pi/12$ can be written as the difference $\pi/3 - \pi/4$, to which the formula can be applied.

$$\cos(u - v) = \cos u \cos v + \sin u \sin v$$

becomes

$$\cos\left(\frac{\pi}{3} - \frac{\pi}{4}\right) = \cos\frac{\pi}{3}\cos\frac{\pi}{4} + \sin\frac{\pi}{3}\sin\frac{\pi}{4}$$

$$= \frac{1}{2}\cdot\frac{\sqrt{2}}{2} + \frac{\sqrt{3}}{2}\cdot\frac{\sqrt{2}}{2}$$

$$= \frac{\sqrt{2}}{4}(1 + \sqrt{3})$$

If $\pi/2$ is substituted for u in the formula for $\cos(u - v)$, an interesting result is obtained.

$$\cos(u - v) = \cos u \cos v + \sin u \sin v$$

becomes

$$\cos\left(\frac{\pi}{2} - v\right) = \cos\frac{\pi}{2}\cos v + \sin\frac{\pi}{2}\sin v$$

$$= 0 \cdot \cos v + 1 \cdot \sin v$$

$$= \sin v$$

Thus

$$\cos\left(\frac{\pi}{2} - v\right) = \sin v$$

If the quantity $(\pi/2 - u)$ is used for v in $\cos(\pi/2 - v) = \sin v$, the result is

$$\cos\left[\frac{\pi}{2} - \left(\frac{\pi}{2} - u\right)\right] = \sin\left(\frac{\pi}{2} - u\right)$$

or

$$\cos u = \sin\left(\frac{\pi}{2} - u\right)$$

Thus we have shown so far that

$$\cos\left(\frac{\pi}{2} - v\right) = \sin v$$

$$\sin\left(\frac{\pi}{2} - v\right) = \cos v$$

Remember that 90° can be used instead of $\pi/2$.

Next we show that $\cos(-v) = \cos v$ by letting $u = 0$ in $\cos(u - v)$.

$$\cos(-v) = \cos(0 - v) = \cos 0 \cos v + \sin 0 \sin v$$

$$= 1 \cdot \cos v + 0 \cdot \sin v$$

$$= \cos v$$

To show that $\sin(-v) = -\sin v$, let $\sin(-v) = \cos(\pi/2 - (-v))$.

$$\sin(-v) = \cos\left(\frac{\pi}{2} - (-v)\right)$$

$$= \cos\left(\frac{\pi}{2} + v\right)$$

$$= \cos\left(v - \left(-\frac{\pi}{2}\right)\right)$$

$$= \cos v \cos\left(-\frac{\pi}{2}\right) + \sin v \sin\left(-\frac{\pi}{2}\right)$$

$$= (\cos v)(0) + (\sin v)(-1)$$

$$= -\sin v$$

Since

$$\tan v = \frac{\sin v}{\cos v}$$

then

$$\tan(-v) = \frac{\sin(-v)}{\cos(-v)} = \frac{-\sin v}{\cos v} = -\tan v$$

We have shown the following:

$$\cos(-v) = \cos v$$
$$\sin(-v) = -\sin v$$
$$\tan(-v) = -\tan v$$

These results can also be seen from graphs of the sine, cosine, and tangent functions or from the unit circle.

Example 26 *Determine the exact values of* $\sin(-315°)$ *and* $\cos\left(-\dfrac{2\pi}{3}\right)$.

$$\sin(-315°) = -\sin 315° \qquad\qquad \text{since } \sin(-v) = -\sin v$$

$$= -[-\sin(360° - 315°)] \qquad \text{since sine is } - \text{ in quadrant IV}$$

$$= \sin 45°$$

$$= \frac{\sqrt{2}}{2}$$

$$\cos\left(-\frac{2\pi}{3}\right) = \cos\left(\frac{2\pi}{3}\right) \qquad\qquad \text{since } \cos(-v) = \cos v$$

$$= -\cos\left(\pi - \frac{2\pi}{3}\right) \qquad \text{since cosine is } - \text{ in quadrant II}$$

$$= -\cos\frac{\pi}{3}$$

$$= -\frac{1}{2}$$

A formula for $\cos(u + v)$ can be obtained from the $\cos(u - v)$ formula by writing $\cos(u + v)$ as $\cos[u - (-v)]$. Thus

$$\cos(u + v) = \cos[u - (-v)]$$
$$= \cos u \cos(-v) + \sin u \sin(-v)$$

And since $\cos(-v) = \cos v$ and $\sin(-v) = -\sin v$,

$$\boxed{\cos(u + v) = \cos u \cos v - \sin u \sin v}$$

A formula for $\sin(u + v)$ can be obtained by using $\sin t = \cos(\pi/2 - t)$, with $t = u + v$.

$$\sin(u + v) = \cos\left[\frac{\pi}{2} - (u + v)\right]$$

$$= \cos\left[\left(\frac{\pi}{2} - u\right) - v\right]$$

$$= \cos\left(\frac{\pi}{2} - u\right)\cos v + \sin\left(\frac{\pi}{2} - u\right)\sin v$$

Using previous results, we can replace $\cos(\pi/2 - u)$ by $\sin u$ and $\sin(\pi/2 - u)$ by $\cos u$. The result is

$$\boxed{\sin(u + v) = \sin u \cos v + \cos u \sin v}$$

Example 27 *Determine the exact value of* sin 75° *by considering* 75° *as* 45° + 30°.

$$\sin 75° = \sin(45° + 30°)$$
$$= \sin 45° \cos 30° + \cos 45° \sin 30°$$
$$= \frac{\sqrt{2}}{2} \cdot \frac{\sqrt{3}}{2} + \frac{\sqrt{2}}{2} \cdot \frac{1}{2}$$
$$= \frac{\sqrt{6} + \sqrt{2}}{4}$$

A formula for $\sin(u - v)$ is easily derived from $\sin(u + v)$.

$$\sin(u - v) = \sin[u + (-v)]$$
$$= \sin u \cos(-v) + \cos u \sin(-v)$$
$$= \sin u \cos v - \cos u \sin v$$

since $\cos(-v) = \cos v$ and $\sin(-v) = -\sin v$. So we have shown that

$$\boxed{\sin(u - v) = \sin u \cos v - \cos u \sin v}$$

Example 28 *If* sin *u* = 1/5 *and* cos *v* = 1/3, *determine the value of* sin(*u* − *v*). *Assume that u and v are in the first quadrant.*

From sin *u* = 1/5, we obtain a right triangle with acute angle *u*, opposite side 1 and hypotenuse 5. By the Pythagorean theorem, the other side is $\sqrt{24}$, or $2\sqrt{6}$.

$$\sin u = \frac{1}{5} \longrightarrow$$

Similarly,

$$\cos v = \frac{1}{3} \longrightarrow$$

Now

$$\sin(u - v) = \sin u \cos v - \cos u \sin v$$

$$= \frac{1}{5} \cdot \frac{1}{3} - \frac{2\sqrt{6}}{5} \cdot \frac{2\sqrt{2}}{3}$$

$$= \frac{1 - 8\sqrt{3}}{15}$$

The following identities are useful in symmetry tests for graphs in polar coordinates and for solution of systems of equations in polar coordinates. They can be proved by using sum and difference formulas or by appealing to the unit circle.

$$\sin(\pi + \theta) = -\sin \theta$$
$$\cos(\pi + \theta) = -\cos \theta$$
$$\sin(\pi - \theta) = \sin \theta$$
$$\cos(\pi - \theta) = -\cos \theta$$

Here is the unit circle approach to showing that $\sin(\pi + \theta) = -\sin \theta$. Observe that the y coordinate (sine) has the same magnitude for both θ and $\pi + \theta$. But the signs are different.

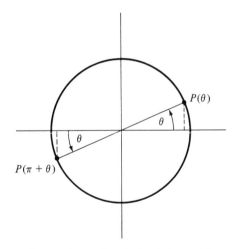

A formula for $\tan(u + v)$ can be derived by writing tangent as sine divided by cosine.

$$\tan(u + v) = \frac{\sin(u + v)}{\cos(u + v)}$$

$$= \frac{\sin u \cos v + \cos u \sin v}{\cos u \cos v - \sin u \sin v}$$

Although this form of $\tan(u + v)$ is used occasionally (see Exercise 21), the generally more useful form is expressed in terms of $\tan u$ and $\tan v$, and it can be obtained by dividing each term in both the numerator and denominator by the product $\cos u \cos v$. As a result, all terms will contain either cosine/cosine, which is one, or sine/cosine, which is tangent.

$$\tan(u + v) = \frac{\dfrac{\sin u \cos v}{\cos u \cos v} + \dfrac{\cos u \sin v}{\cos u \cos v}}{\dfrac{\cos u \cos v}{\cos u \cos v} - \dfrac{\sin u \sin v}{\cos u \cos v}}$$

$$= \frac{\dfrac{\sin u}{\cos u} \cdot \dfrac{\cos v}{\cos v} + \dfrac{\cos u}{\cos u} \cdot \dfrac{\sin v}{\cos v}}{\dfrac{\cos u}{\cos u} \cdot \dfrac{\cos v}{\cos v} - \dfrac{\sin u}{\cos u} \cdot \dfrac{\sin v}{\cos v}}$$

$$= \frac{\tan u \cdot 1 + 1 \cdot \tan v}{1 \cdot 1 - \tan u \cdot \tan v}$$

Thus

$$\boxed{\tan(u + v) = \frac{\tan u + \tan v}{1 - \tan u \tan v}}$$

It can also be shown that

$$\boxed{\tan(u - v) = \frac{\tan u - \tan v}{1 + \tan u \tan v}}$$

Example 29 *Show that* $\tan(t + \pi) = \tan t.$

By the $\tan(u + v)$ formula above, with t for u and π for v, we have

$$\tan(t + \pi) = \frac{\tan t + \tan \pi}{1 - \tan t \tan \pi}$$

$$= \frac{\tan t + 0}{1 - (\tan t) \cdot 0}$$

$$= \frac{\tan t}{1}$$

$$= \tan t$$

Sin $2t$ can be expressed in terms of sin t and cos t, by considering sin $2t$ as $\sin(t + t)$ and using the formula for $\sin(u + v)$ with $u = t$ and $v = t$.

$$\sin 2t = \sin(t + t)$$
$$= \sin t \cos t + \cos t \sin t$$
$$= \sin t \cos t + \sin t \cos t$$

or

> **Double-angle formula**
>
> $$\sin 2t = 2 \sin t \cos t$$

We call $\sin 2t = 2 \sin t \cos t$ a *double-angle formula* because it provides the sine of twice an angle ($2t$) in terms of the sine and cosine of the angle (t).

Example 30 *Given* $\sin t = \frac{3}{5}$ *and t in quadrant* II, *determine* $\sin 2t$.

First of all, $\sin 2t \neq 2 \cdot \sin t$. We have just derived a formula for $\sin 2t$, namely,

$$\sin 2t = 2 \sin t \cos t$$

We know the value of sin t. We can obtain the value of cos t from a right triangle in the second quadrant with sin $t = 3/5$. The opposite side is 3 and the hypotenuse is 5. The Pythagorean theorem suggests that the other side is 4. However, the triangle is in quadrant II, so that side is actually -4, as you can see from the next illustration.

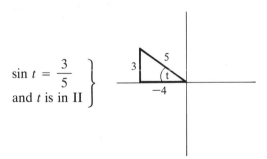

$$\left.\begin{array}{l} \sin t = \dfrac{3}{5} \\[2mm] \text{and } t \text{ is in II} \end{array}\right\}$$

From the triangle, cos $t = -4/5$.

Now

$$\sin 2t = 2 \sin t \cos t$$

becomes

$$\sin 2t = 2(\tfrac{3}{5})(-\tfrac{4}{5}) = -\tfrac{24}{25}$$

Next, consider

$$\cos 2t = \cos(t + t)$$
$$= \cos t \cos t - \sin t \sin t$$

or

$$\cos 2t = \cos^2 t - \sin^2 t$$

One alternative form of cos 2t can be obtained by using $1 - \sin^2 t$ for $\cos^2 t$ in the formula $\cos 2t = \cos^2 t - \sin^2 t$.

$$\cos 2t = \cos^2 t - \sin^2 t$$
$$= 1 - \sin^2 t - \sin^2 t$$
$$= 1 - 2 \sin^2 t$$

Still another form comes from letting $\sin^2 t$ be $1 - \cos^2 t$ in $\cos 2t = \cos^2 t - \sin^2 t$.

$$\cos 2t = \cos^2 t - \sin^2 t$$
$$= \cos^2 t - (1 - \cos^2 t)$$
$$= \cos^2 t - 1 + \cos^2 t$$
$$= 2 \cos^2 t - 1$$

Thus there are three formulas for cos 2t in terms of sin t, cos t, or both.

Double-angle formulas

$$\cos 2t = \cos^2 t - \sin^2 t$$

$$\cos 2t = 1 - 2 \sin^2 t$$

$$\cos 2t = 2 \cos^2 t - 1$$

Example 31   *Use a double-angle formula to write each expression as a single term.*
(a) $\cos^2 4\theta - \sin^2 4\theta$ (b) $1 - 2 \sin^2 7w$ (c) $6 \sin \theta \cos \theta$

(a)   The expression $\cos^2 4\theta - \sin^2 4\theta$ fits the form of the first of the three boxed double-angle formulas for cosine. Here t is 4θ; so $2t$ is 8θ. This means that the expression $\cos^2 4\theta - \sin^2 4\theta$ can be replaced by the single term $\cos 8\theta$.

(b)   The expression $1 - 2 \sin^2 7w$ fits the form of a double-angle formula for cosine; it is the cosine of twice $7w$. Thus

$$1 - 2 \sin^2 7w = \cos 14w$$

(c)   The expression $6 \sin \theta \cos \theta$ is three times $2 \sin \theta \cos \theta$; so it is three times the sine of 2θ. Here is the work:

$$6 \sin \theta \cos \theta = 3 \cdot 2 \sin \theta \cos \theta$$
$$= 3 \cdot \sin 2\theta$$
$$= 3 \sin 2\theta$$

The double-angle formula $\cos 2t = 2 \cos^2 t - 1$ can be solved for $\cos t$ in terms of $\cos 2t$.

$$\cos 2t = 2 \cos^2 t - 1$$
$$1 + \cos 2t = 2 \cos^2 t$$
$$2 \cos^2 t = 1 + \cos 2t$$
$$\cos^2 t = \frac{1 + \cos 2t}{2}$$

Finally,

$$\cos t = \pm \sqrt{\frac{1 + \cos 2t}{2}}$$

This new equation gives the cosine of half an angle in terms of the cosine of the angle: $\cos t$ in terms of $\cos 2t$. This *half-angle formula* is usually written using $u/2$ for t.

Half-angle formula

$$\cos \frac{u}{2} = \pm \sqrt{\frac{1 + \cos u}{2}}$$

Note: If $u/2$ is in quadrant I or IV, $\cos u/2$ is positive. It is negative in II or III. A similar formula for sine can be derived by beginning with double angle formula $\cos 2t = 1 - 2 \sin^2 t$. The formula is

---

Half-angle formula

$$\sin \frac{u}{2} = \pm \sqrt{\frac{1 - \cos u}{2}}$$

Note: If $u/2$ is in quadrant I or II, $\sin u/2$ is positive. It is negative in III or IV.

Example 32 *Given* $\cos 2\theta = \frac{1}{4}$ *and* θ *in quadrant I, determine* $\cos \theta$.
We can use the half-angle formula

$$\cos \frac{u}{2} = \pm \sqrt{\frac{1 + \cos u}{2}}$$

Here $u = 2\theta$ and the sign is $+$, since θ (the half angle) is in the first quadrant. Thus

$$\cos \theta = \sqrt{\frac{1 + \cos 2\theta}{2}} = \sqrt{\frac{1 + \frac{1}{4}}{2}} = \sqrt{\frac{5}{8}} = \frac{\sqrt{5}}{2\sqrt{2}}, \quad \text{or} \quad \frac{\sqrt{10}}{4}$$

Example 33 *Determine the value of* $\sin \pi/8$ *by using a half-angle formula.*
We shall use the formula for $\sin u/2$ and note that $\pi/8$ is in quadrant I so that $\sin u/2$ is positive. Also, since $u/2$ is to be $\pi/8$, it follows that u is $\pi/4$. Thus

$$\sin \frac{\pi}{8} = \sqrt{\frac{1 - \cos \pi/4}{2}}$$

$$= \sqrt{\frac{1 - \sqrt{2}/2}{2}}$$

$$= \sqrt{\frac{2 - \sqrt{2}}{4}}$$

$$= \frac{1}{2} \sqrt{2 - \sqrt{2}}$$

Example 34 *If* $\tan 2\theta = \frac{3}{4}$ *and* 2θ *is in the first quadrant, determine* $\cos \theta$ *and* $\sin \theta$.
Using a right triangle, the fact that tangent = opposite/adjacent, and the Pythagorean theorem, we have

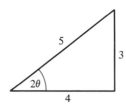

Now

$$\cos 2\theta = \frac{4}{5}$$

By the half-angle formula,

$$\cos \theta = \sqrt{\frac{1 + \cos 2\theta}{2}}$$

$$= \sqrt{\frac{1 + \frac{4}{5}}{2}}$$

$$= \sqrt{\frac{9}{10}} = \frac{3}{\sqrt{10}}$$

Finally, $\sin \theta$ can be determined from another half-angle formula or from the identity $\sin^2 \theta + \cos^2 \theta = 1$, noting that θ is in quadrant I. The result is

$$\sin \theta = \frac{1}{\sqrt{10}}$$

This identical procedure will be needed in Section 8.7, when rotation of axes is presented.

Two of the double-angle cosine formulas, $\cos 2t = 2 \cos^2 t - 1$ and $\cos 2t = 1 - 2 \sin^2 t$, can be manipulated into a form that is particularly useful in calculus. The two results are shown next and are followed by an example that shows how they are used.

$$\cos^2 t = \tfrac{1}{2}(1 + \cos 2t)$$

$$\sin^2 t = \tfrac{1}{2}(1 - \cos 2t)$$

Example 35   *Express* $\sin^4 x$ *in terms of cosines involving only the first power.*

$$\sin^4 x = (\sin^2 x)^2$$

$$= \left[\frac{1}{2}(1 - \cos 2x) \right]^2 \qquad \text{using the second formula above}$$

$$= \frac{1}{4}(1 - 2 \cos 2x + \cos^2 2x) \qquad \text{multiplying out}$$

$$= \frac{1}{4}\left(1 - 2 \cos 2x + \frac{1 + \cos 4x}{2} \right) \qquad \text{using the first formula above}$$

$$= \frac{1}{4}\left(1 - 2 \cos 2x + \frac{1}{2} + \frac{\cos 4x}{2} \right)$$

$$= \frac{1}{4}\left(\frac{3}{2} - 2 \cos 2x + \frac{\cos 4x}{2} \right)$$

$$= \frac{3}{8} - \frac{1}{2} \cos 2x + \frac{1}{8} \cos 4x$$

Note that the procedure changes the *degree*. We do not *seek* double angles etc., although we obtain them in the process.

Using

$$\tan \frac{u}{2} = \frac{\sin \dfrac{u}{2}}{\cos \dfrac{u}{2}}$$

yields

$$\boxed{\tan\frac{u}{2} = \pm\sqrt{\frac{1 - \cos u}{1 + \cos u}}}$$

Note: If $u/2$ is in quadrant I or III, tan $u/2$ is positive. It is negative in II or IV.

An alternate form for tan $u/2$, one used in calculus, can be obtained from the preceding formula, as shown next.

$$\tan \frac{u}{2} = \pm\sqrt{\frac{1 - \cos u}{1 + \cos u}} = \pm\sqrt{\frac{1 - \cos u}{1 + \cos u} \cdot \frac{1 - \cos u}{1 - \cos u}}$$

$$= \pm\sqrt{\frac{(1 - \cos u)^2}{1 - \cos^2 u}} = \pm\sqrt{\frac{(1 - \cos u)^2}{\sin^2 u}}$$

$$= \pm\sqrt{\left(\frac{1 - \cos u}{\sin u}\right)^2} = \frac{1 - \cos u}{\sin u}$$

A slight variation in this procedure produces a different form. The two forms are summarized in the next box.

$$\boxed{\tan\frac{u}{2} = \frac{1 - \cos u}{\sin u} = \frac{\sin u}{1 + \cos u}}$$

A formula for tan $2t$ can be obtained from tan$(u + v)$. Begin with

$$\tan(u + v) = \frac{\tan u + \tan v}{1 - \tan u \tan v}$$

and let u and v both equal t. Then

$$\tan(t + t) = \frac{\tan t + \tan t}{1 - \tan t \tan t}$$

or

$$\tan 2t = \frac{2 \tan t}{1 - \tan^2 t}$$

The section ends with an example showing the use of a double-angle formula to prove an identity.

Example 36   *Prove the identity* $(\sin \theta + \cos \theta)^2 = 1 + \sin 2\theta$.
Begin by multiplying out the left side of the equation. Thus

$$(\sin \theta + \cos \theta)^2 \overset{?}{=} 1 + \sin 2\theta$$

becomes

$$\sin^2\theta + 2 \sin \theta \cos \theta + \cos^2\theta \overset{?}{=} 1 + \sin 2\theta$$

Next, replace $\sin^2\theta + \cos^2\theta$ by 1 and replace $2 \sin \theta \cos \theta$ by $\sin 2\theta$. The identity is proved.

$$1 + \sin 2\theta = 1 + \sin 2\theta$$

EXERCISES 7.9

1.   Use the approach suggested in Examples 25 and 27 to determine the required sine or cosine.

*(a) $\sin 15°$ (*Note*: $15° = 45° - 30°$.)

*(b) $\cos 75°$ (*Note*: $75° = 45° + 30°$.)

(c) $\sin 105°$ (*Note*: $105° = 60° + 45°$.)

*(d) $\cos \dfrac{7\pi}{12}$ $\left(Note: \dfrac{7\pi}{12} = \dfrac{\pi}{3} + \dfrac{\pi}{4}. \right)$

(e) $\sin \dfrac{5\pi}{12}$ $\left(Note: \dfrac{5\pi}{12} = \dfrac{2\pi}{3} - \dfrac{\pi}{4}. \right)$

(f) $\cos \dfrac{11\pi}{12}$ $\left(Note: \dfrac{11\pi}{12} = \dfrac{3\pi}{4} + \dfrac{\pi}{6}. \right)$

2. Determine the exact value of each expression.
   *(a) $\sin(-60°)$ (b) $\cos(-135°)$ *(c) $\tan(-120°)$
   (d) $\sin(-300°)$ *(e) $\cos(-210°)$ (f) $\cos(-225°)$
   *(g) $\sin(-150°)$ (h) $\tan(-315°)$ *(i) $\sec(-330°)$
   (j) $\csc(-240°)$ *(k) $\cot(-135°)$ (l) $\cot(-240°)$
   *(m) $\sin(-480°)$ (n) $\cos(-405°)$ *(o) $\cos(-570°)$

3. Determine the exact value of each expression.

   *(a) $\sin\left(-\dfrac{3\pi}{4}\right)$ (b) $\cos\left(-\dfrac{5\pi}{6}\right)$ *(c) $\sin\left(-\dfrac{2\pi}{3}\right)$

   (d) $\cos\left(-\dfrac{7\pi}{4}\right)$ *(e) $\cos\left(-\dfrac{4\pi}{3}\right)$ (f) $\sin\left(-\dfrac{11\pi}{6}\right)$

   *(g) $\tan\left(-\dfrac{5\pi}{3}\right)$ (h) $\tan\left(-\dfrac{11\pi}{6}\right)$ *(i) $\cot\left(-\dfrac{7\pi}{4}\right)$

   (j) $\sec\left(-\dfrac{7\pi}{6}\right)$ *(k) $\csc\left(-\dfrac{5\pi}{4}\right)$ (l) $\cot\left(-\dfrac{3\pi}{4}\right)$

   *(m) $\sin\left(-\dfrac{13\pi}{6}\right)$ (n) $\cos\left(-\dfrac{10\pi}{3}\right)$ *(o) $\cos\left(-\dfrac{13\pi}{4}\right)$

4. Determine the approximate value of each expression. Some use radians; some use degrees.
   *(a) $\sin(-193°)$ *(b) $\cos(-98°)$ *(c) $\sin(-4.07)$
   (d) $\cos(-1.13)$ *(e) $\tan(-.67)$ (f) $\cot(-234°)$
   *(g) $\sin(-310°)$ (h) $\sin(-6.03)$ *(i) $\cos(-2.51)$

*5. If $\sin u = \frac{4}{5}$ and $\sin v = \frac{5}{13}$, evaluate each expression. Assume that u and v are in the first quadrant.
   (a) $\cos u$ (b) $\cos v$
   (c) $\sin(u + v)$ (d) $\cos(u + v)$
   (e) $\sin(u - v)$ (f) $\cos(u - v)$

6. If $\sin u = \frac{1}{3}$ and $\cos v = \frac{3}{4}$, evaluate each expression. Assume that u and v are in the first quadrant.
   (a) $\cos u$ (b) $\sin v$
   (c) $\cos(u + v)$ (d) $\cos(u - v)$
   (e) $\sin(u - v)$ (f) $\sin(u + v)$

7. Use formulas for $\sin(u + v)$, $\cos(u + v)$, and so on to prove each of the following identities.
   (a) $\sin(x + \pi) = -\sin x$ (b) $\cos(\pi + x) = -\cos x$
   (c) $\tan(\theta + 180°) = \tan \theta$ (d) $\sin(t + 2\pi) = \sin t$
   (e) $\cos(t + 2\pi) = \cos t$ (f) $\cos(t - \pi/2) = \sin t$

(g) $\sin(\theta - 90°) = -\cos\theta$　　　(h) $\sin(\theta + 90°) = \cos\theta$

(i) $\cos(\theta + 90°) = -\sin\theta$　　　(j) $\sin(\theta + 720°) = \sin\theta$

(k) $\sin(\pi - \theta) = \sin\theta$　　　(l) $\cos(\pi - \theta) = -\cos\theta$

*8. In Example 29, we showed that $\tan(t + \pi) = \tan t$. It happens that π is the smallest positive number p for which $\tan(t + p) = \tan t$. What does this mean about the tangent function?

*9. Use a double-angle formula to condense each expression to a single term.

(a) $\cos^2 2\theta - \sin^2 2\theta$　　　(b) $\cos^2 7\theta - \sin^2 7\theta$

(c) $1 - 2\sin^2 3\theta$　　　(d) $2\cos^2 5\theta - 1$

(e) $2\sin 3u \cos 3u$　　　(f) $2\sin\tfrac{1}{2}\theta \cos\tfrac{1}{2}\theta$

(g) $\sin 5x \cos 5x$　　　(h) $4\sin 3w \cos 3w$

(i) $8\sin 7x \cos 7x$　　　(j) $\tfrac{1}{2}\sin 5\theta \cos 5\theta$

(k) $4\cos^2 x - 2$　　　(l) $3 - 6\sin^2 9t$

(m) $\sin^2 3\theta - \cos^2 3\theta$　　　(n) $2\sin^2 8x - 1$

10. Use half-angle formulas to determine the value of each expression. (See Example 33.)

*(a) $\cos\dfrac{\pi}{8}$　　　(b) $\sin\dfrac{3\pi}{8}$　　　*(c) $\sin 15°$

(d) $\tan\dfrac{\pi}{8}$　　　*(e) $\tan 15°$　　　(f) $\cos 75°$

11. If $\cos 2\theta = \tfrac{1}{3}$ and θ is in quadrant I, determine each value.

*(a) $\cos\theta$　　　(b) $\sin\theta$　　　*(c) $\sec\theta$

(d) $\csc\theta$　　　*(e) $\tan\theta$　　　(f) $\cot\theta$

*12. If $\cos 2x = -\tfrac{2}{5}$ and x is in quadrant I, determine each value.

(a) $\cos x$　　　(b) $\sin x$　　　(c) $\sec x$

(d) $\csc x$　　　(e) $\tan x$　　　(f) $\cot x$

*13. If $\sin\theta = -\tfrac{3}{5}$ and $270° < \theta < 360°$, determine the exact value of each expression.

(a) $\sin\dfrac{\theta}{2}$　　　(b) $\cos\dfrac{\theta}{2}$　　　(c) $\tan\dfrac{\theta}{2}$

14. Assume 2θ is in the first quadrant. Determine $\cos\theta$ and $\sin\theta$ for the given value of $\tan 2\theta$.

*(a) $\tan 2\theta = \dfrac{4}{3}$　　　(b) $\tan 2\theta = \dfrac{5}{12}$

*(c) $\tan 2\theta = \dfrac{12}{5}$　　　(d) $\tan 2\theta = \dfrac{7}{24}$

*(e) $\tan 2\theta = \dfrac{24}{7}$　　　(f) $\tan 2\theta = \sqrt{15}$

15. Express in terms of cosines involving only the first power. (See Example 35.)

*(a) $\sin^2 x$ (b) $\cos^2 x$

*(c) $\cos^4 x$ *(d) $\sin^2 x \cos^2 x$

16. If $\sin u = \frac{5}{13}$ and u is in quadrant II, evaluate each expression.

*(a) $\sin 2u$ (b) $\cos 2u$ *(c) $\tan 2u$

17. If $\cos x = \frac{1}{2}$ and x is in the fourth quadrant, evaluate each expression.

*(a) $\cos 2x$ (b) $\sin 2x$ *(c) $\tan 2x$

18. If $\sin t = -\frac{1}{5}$ and $\sec u = \frac{4}{3}$, determine the value of $\sin(t + u)$ and $\tan(t + u)$. Assume that t and u are both in quadrant IV.

*19. (a) Derive a formula for $\sin 3t$ in terms of $\sin t$.
    Hint: Write $\sin 3t$ as $\sin(2t + t)$ and use the formula for $\sin(u + v)$.
    (b) Derive a formula for $\cos 3t$ in terms of $\cos t$.

20. Show that $\tan\left(t + \dfrac{\pi}{4}\right) = \dfrac{1 + \tan t}{1 - \tan t}$.

21. Show that $\tan(\theta + 90°) = -\cot \theta$. Use the $\tan(u + v)$ formula that involves sines and cosines rather than the tangent form (Why?). This result will be used in Exercise 23 to prove the relationship between the slopes of perpendicular lines, after Exercise 22 provides the foundation.

*22. The slope of a line has been defined as $\Delta y / \Delta x$. It is the same as the tangent of the angle of inclination α of the line with respect to the x axis.

$$\tan \alpha = \frac{\text{opposite}}{\text{adjacent}} = \frac{\Delta y}{\Delta x} = m$$

Thus

$$\boxed{m = \tan \alpha}$$

Determine the slope of the line inclined at angle α with respect to the x axis, for each given α.

(a) 45°   (b) 60°   (c) 150°

(d) 135°   (e) 0°   (f) 90°

23. Here is a proof that if two lines are perpendicular, then the slope of one line is the negative of the reciprocal of the slope of the other line. Follow the steps and justify each one.

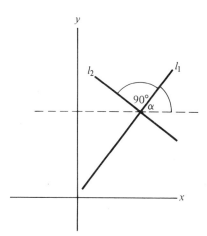

The slope m_1 of line l_1 is $\tan \alpha$. The slope m_2 of line l_2 is $\tan(\alpha + 90°)$. Thus

$$\begin{aligned} m_2 &= \tan(\alpha + 90°) \\ &= -\cot \alpha \qquad \text{by Exercise 21} \\ &= -\frac{1}{\tan \alpha} \\ &= -\frac{1}{m_1} \end{aligned}$$

*24. Derive a formula for $\cot(u + v)$ in terms of $\cot u$ and $\cot v$. Then derive a formula for $\cot 2t$ in terms of $\cot t$.

25. Prove each identity.

(a) $\sin 2\theta = \dfrac{2 \tan \theta}{\sec^2 \theta}$

(b) $\sin^2 t \cot t = \dfrac{\sin 2t}{2}$

(c) $\cos 2u + \sin^2 u = \cos^2 u$

(d) $\dfrac{\sin 2x}{\sin x} - \dfrac{\cos 2x}{\cos x} = \sec x$

(e) $\dfrac{\cos 2u}{\sin u \cos u} = \cot u - \tan u$

(f) $\csc 2\theta = \dfrac{1}{2 \sin \theta \cos \theta}$

(g) $\tan \theta + \cot \theta = 2 \csc 2\theta$

26. Show that for $0 \le x \le \pi/2$, $\sqrt{1 + \sin x} = \sin \tfrac{1}{2}x + \cos \tfrac{1}{2}x$

27. The three formulas shown here are sometimes used in calculus to replace a product (see right side of equations) by a sum (see left side of equations).

$$\begin{aligned} \tfrac{1}{2}[\cos(u + v) + \cos(u - v)] &= \cos u \cos v \\ \tfrac{1}{2}[\cos(u - v) - \cos(u + v)] &= \sin u \sin v \\ \tfrac{1}{2}[\sin(u + v) + \sin(u - v)] &= \sin u \cos v \end{aligned}$$

(a) Use the formulas you know for $\cos(u + v)$ and $\cos(u - v)$ to derive the first formula.

(b) Use the formulas you know for $\sin(u + v)$ and $\sin(u - v)$ to derive the third formula.

(c) Derive the second formula.

*(d) Rewrite $\cos 5x \cos 2x$ by using one of the formulas.

(e) Rewrite $\sin 7x \sin 3x$ by using one of the formulas.

*(f) Rewrite $\sin 5x \cos 3x$ by using one of the formulas.

(g) Rewrite $\sin 2x \cos 9x$ by using one of the formulas.

28. Use the facts that $\sin(-x) = -\sin x$, $\cos(-x) = \cos x$, and $\tan(-x) = -\tan x$ to prove the following identities.

(a) $\csc(-x) = -\csc x$ (b) $\sec(-x) = \sec x$

(c) $\cot(-x) = -\cot x$

29. For each function given, determine the symmetry of its graph with respect to the x axis, y axis, and origin. Use the tests suggested in Section 3.7.

*(a) $y = \sin x$ (b) $y = \cos x$

*(c) $y = \tan x$ (d) $y = \cot x$

*(e) $y = \sec x$ (f) $y = \csc x$

*(g) $y = |\sin x|$ (h) $y = |\cos x|$

7.10 TRIGONOMETRIC EQUATIONS

This section consists of several examples of equations that involve trigonometric expressions. Each equation is solved.

Example 37 *Solve for x:* $\cos x - 1 = 0$

If $\cos x - 1 = 0$, then $\cos x = 1$. So x is any number whose cosine is 1. Thus $x = 0, 2\pi, 4\pi, -2\pi, -4\pi, \ldots$. This can be written compactly as $n \cdot 2\pi$, where n is any integer, or

$$x = 2n\pi \qquad n = \text{any integer } (0, \pm 1, \pm 2, \ldots)$$

Example 38 *Solve for θ:* $\cos \theta = -1/2$

Note that $\cos \theta = 1/2$ when $\theta = \pi/3$. But we want the cosine to be $-1/2$; so place $\pi/3$ in quadrants II and III, where cosine is negative. In quadrant II, $\theta = \pi - \pi/3 = 2\pi/3$. In quadrant III, $\theta = \pi + \pi/3 = 4\pi/3$. Thus

$$\theta = \frac{2\pi}{3} + 2n\pi \qquad n = \text{any integer}$$

$$\theta = \frac{4\pi}{3} + 2n\pi \qquad n = \text{any integer}$$

Example 39   *Solve for t:* $2 \sin t - 1 = 0$

If $2 \sin t - 1 = 0$, then $2 \sin t = 1$, or $\sin t = \frac{1}{2}$. So t is any number whose sine is $\frac{1}{2}$. Thus $t = \pi/6$. Sine is also positive in quadrant II; so place $\pi/6$ in II as $t = \pi - \pi/6 = 5\pi/6$. Thus

$$t = \frac{\pi}{6} + 2n\pi \qquad n = \text{any integer}$$

$$t = \frac{5\pi}{6} + 2n\pi \qquad n = \text{any integer}$$

To place an acute angle θ in another quadrant, use the following guideline:

$$\text{II:} \qquad \pi - \theta$$
$$\text{III:} \qquad \pi + \theta$$
$$\text{IV:} \qquad 2\pi - \theta$$

Example 40   *Solve $\sin^2 x + 4 \sin x + 3 = 0$ for x.*

The equation is quadratic in $\sin x$. To make this more apparent, let us rewrite it as

$$(\sin x)^2 + 4(\sin x) + 3 = 0$$

The expression can be factored as

$$(\sin x + 1)(\sin x + 3) = 0$$

Thus

$$\sin x + 1 = 0 \qquad \bigg| \qquad \sin x + 3 = 0$$

The equation $\sin x + 3 = 0$ leads to $\sin x = -3$, which is impossible because the sine function only has functional values between -1 and 1.†

On the other hand, $\sin x + 1 = 0$ leads to $\sin x = -1$ or

$$x = \frac{3\pi}{2} + 2n\pi \qquad n = \text{any integer}$$

Example 41   *Solve $2 \cos^2 x + \sin^2 x - 2 = 0$ for x.*

The identity $\sin^2 x = 1 - \cos^2 x$ can be used to replace $\sin^2 x$ by $1 - \cos^2 x$. The result is an equation that is quadratic in $\cos x$. Thus

$$2 \cos^2 x + \sin^2 x - 2 = 0$$

---

† Recall that $-1 \leq \sin x \leq 1$ and $-1 \leq \cos x \leq 1$.

becomes

$$2 \cos^2 x + 1 - \cos^2 x - 2 = 0$$

or

$$\cos^2 x - 1 = 0$$

This leads to

$$\cos x = \pm 1$$

We know that $\cos x = 1$ when $x = 2n\pi$, as shown in Example 37. The equation $\cos x = -1$ has for solutions $x = \pi, 3\pi, 5\pi, -\pi, -3\pi, \ldots$. In other words, $x = $ odd multiples of π. Just as $2n\pi$ was used to guarantee *even* multiples of π, $(2n + 1)\pi$ can be used to guarantee *odd* multiples of π. The solutions, then, are

$$x = 2n\pi \qquad \text{even multiples of } \pi$$
$$x = (2n + 1)\pi \qquad \text{odd multiples of } \pi \qquad n = \text{any integer}$$

Since our solution contains all even and all odd multiples of π, it must, of course, contain *all integral multiples of* π. Thus the two solutions shown can be combined as

$$x = n\pi \qquad n = \text{any integer}$$

Example 42 *Solve the equation* $\sin 2\theta = \sqrt{3}/2$ *for* θ.
If $\sin 2\theta = \sqrt{3}/2$, then

$$2\theta = \frac{\pi}{3} + 2n\pi \qquad n = \text{any integer}$$

$$2\theta = \frac{2\pi}{3} + 2n\pi \qquad n = \text{any integer}$$

Divide both sides of each equation by 2 in order to solve for θ.

$$\theta = \frac{\pi}{6} + n\pi \qquad n = \text{any integer}$$

$$\theta = \frac{\pi}{3} + n\pi \qquad n = \text{any integer}$$

EXERCISES 7.10

1. Determine the two angles between 0 and 2π that satisfy each equation.

*(a) $\sin t = \dfrac{\sqrt{3}}{2}$

(b) $\sin u = \dfrac{\sqrt{2}}{2}$

*(c) $\cos \theta = \dfrac{\sqrt{2}}{2}$

(d) $\cos v = \dfrac{1}{2}$

*(e) $\cos t = \dfrac{\sqrt{3}}{2}$

(f) $\sin t = -\dfrac{\sqrt{2}}{2}$

*(g) $\sin \theta = -\dfrac{\sqrt{3}}{2}$

(h) $\cos \theta = -\dfrac{1}{2}$

*(i) $\cos x = -\dfrac{\sqrt{2}}{2}$

(j) $\cos x = -\dfrac{\sqrt{3}}{2}$

2. Solve each equation for all values of the variable.

*(a) $\sin x = 1$

(b) $2 \cos t - 1 = 0$

*(c) $\sin y = 0$

(d) $\cos^2 x = \dfrac{1}{4}$

*(e) $\sin^2 x + 3 \sin x + 2 = 0$

(f) $\sin^2 t = \dfrac{1}{2}$

*(g) $\sin^2 x - \dfrac{3}{4} = 0$

(h) $2 \cos^2 x - 3 \cos x + 1 = 0$

*(i) $2 \sin^2 x + 5 \sin x - 3 = 0$

(j) $\tan^2 u - 1 = 0$

*(k) $\cos^2 x + 7 \cos x + 12 = 0$

(l) $\cos^2 x + \cos x = 0$

*(m) $\sin^2 x + \sin x = 0$

(n) $2 \sin^2 x + \cos^2 x = 0$

*(o) $\cos^2 v - \sin^2 v = 0$

(p) $2 \cos 2\theta + 1 = 0$

*(q) $\sin 2\theta = \dfrac{1}{2}$

(r) $\sin^2 2x - \dfrac{1}{4} = 0$

*(s) $\tan 2\theta = \sqrt{3}$

(t) $2 \cos^2 2x + \cos 2x = 0$

*(u) $\tan 2x = \dfrac{1}{\sqrt{3}}$

7.11 INVERSES

Can you find a value of x such that $\sin x = \frac{1}{2}$? There are many solutions. In radians, $x = \pi/6, 5\pi/6, 13\pi/6, -7\pi/6$, and others. In degrees, $x = 30°, 150°, 390°, -210°$, and others. However, there are some settings in which we seek a únique value of x. In other words, sometimes we choose to restrict the domain of $y = \sin x$ so that the *inverse* we seek is unique, so that there is precisely one x. In this way, an

inverse function is created. In the example $\sin x = \frac{1}{2}$, the notation changes from

$$\sin x = \frac{1}{2}$$

to

$$\sin^{-1} \frac{1}{2} = x$$

or

$$\arcsin \frac{1}{2} = x$$

We say that x is the **arcsine** of $\frac{1}{2}$. The notation $\sin^{-1}$ *does not* denote an exponent of -1; instead it means *inverse*.

In order to establish the inverse function for sine, we define a new sine function by restricting the domain to numbers between $-\pi/2$ and $\pi/2$ inclusive. In this way, all values for sine are included only once and an inverse function will exist.

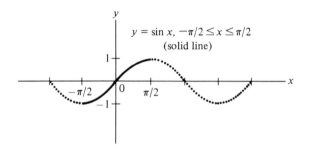

Values for the arcsine will be between $-\pi/2$ and $\pi/2$. For example,

$$\arcsin \frac{\sqrt{3}}{2} = \frac{\pi}{3}$$

$$\sin^{-1} \frac{\sqrt{2}}{2} = \frac{\pi}{4}$$

$$\sin^{-1} 1 = \frac{\pi}{2}$$

$$\arcsin 0 = 0$$

Since $\sin(-x) = -\sin x$ and the domain of the sine function we are using is $-\pi/2 \le x \le \pi/2$, it follows that $\arcsin(-x) = -\arcsin x$. For example,

$$\arcsin\left(-\frac{1}{2}\right) = -\arcsin \frac{1}{2} = -\frac{\pi}{6}$$

$$\arcsin\left(-\frac{\sqrt{3}}{2}\right) = -\arcsin \frac{\sqrt{3}}{2} = -\frac{\pi}{3}$$

$$\sin^{-1}(-1) = -\sin^{-1}1 = -\frac{\pi}{2}$$

Here are two more examples, done with the aid of Table IV.

$$\sin^{-1}(.3709) \approx .38$$

$$\sin^{-1}(-.7643) = -\sin^{-1}(.7643) \approx -.87$$

A calculator can be used, of course. Enter the number (say, .3709). Then press either "$\sin^{-1}$" or "arc" and "sin" or "inv" and "sin"—depending on your calculator. Be sure that the calculator is set for radians rather than degrees.

Thus far we have restricted the domain of $y = \sin x$ to $-\pi/2 \leq x \leq \pi/2$ and in several specific cases we have solved for x. We determined, for instance, that $\sin^{-1}1 = \pi/2$, reasoning that if $1 = \sin x$, then $x = \pi/2$. It follows that if the general equation $y = \sin x$ is solved for x, then the result is $x = \sin^{-1}y$, provided that the domain of $y = \sin x$ is restricted to $-\pi/2 \leq x \leq \pi/2$. This is the formal concept of arcsine.

$x = \sin^{-1} y$ if and only if $y = \sin x$ and $-\pi/2 \leq x \leq \pi/2$.

The inverse sine function is $y = \sin^{-1}x$, which can be obtained from $y = \sin x$ by restating $y = \sin x$ as $x = \sin^{-1}y$ and then interchanging x and y.

The graph of the inverse sine function can be obtained from the graph of $y = \sin x$ $(-\pi/2 \leq x \leq \pi/2)$ by reflecting the restricted sine graph about the line $y = x$. The graph of $y = \sin^{-1}x$ is shown next.

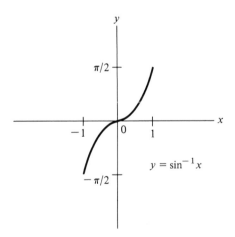

$y = \sin^{-1}x$

In order to establish the inverse function for cosine, or **arccosine**, we define a new cosine function by restricting the domain to numbers between 0 and π inclusive. In this way, all values for cosine are included only once and an inverse function will exist.

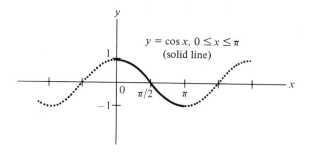

$y = \cos x,\ 0 \leq x \leq \pi$
(solid line)

Values for arccosine will be between 0 and π. For example,

$$\arccos \frac{\sqrt{3}}{2} = \frac{\pi}{6}$$

$$\cos^{-1}\frac{1}{2} = \frac{\pi}{3}$$

$$\cos^{-1}1 = 0$$

$$\arccos\frac{\sqrt{2}}{2} = \frac{\pi}{4}$$

Since the domain of the cosine function we are using is $0 \leq x \leq \pi$, the arccosine of a negative number is computed as π minus the arccosine of the opposite of the number. For example,

$$\arccos\left(-\frac{1}{2}\right) = \pi - \arccos\frac{1}{2} = \pi - \frac{\pi}{3} = \frac{2\pi}{3}$$

$$\arccos\left(-\frac{\sqrt{2}}{2}\right) = \pi - \arccos\frac{\sqrt{2}}{2} = \pi - \frac{\pi}{4} = \frac{3\pi}{4}$$

$$\cos^{-1}(-1) = \pi - \cos^{-1}1 = \pi - 0 = \pi$$

Here are two more examples, done with the aid of Table IV.

$$\cos^{-1}(.9582) \approx .29$$

$$\cos^{-1}(-.5148) = \pi - \cos^{-1}(.5148)$$

$$\approx \pi - 1.03$$

$$\approx 3.14 - 1.03$$

$$\approx 2.11$$

The concept of arccosine can be stated formally as

$$x = \cos^{-1}y \quad \text{if and only if} \quad y = \cos x$$
$$\text{and } 0 \le x \le \pi.$$

The graph of the inverse cosine function can be obtained from the graph of $y = \cos x$ ($0 \le x \le \pi$) by reflecting the restricted cosine graph about the line $y = x$.

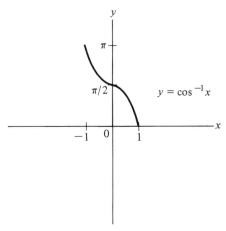

In order to establish the inverse function for tangent, **arctangent,** we define a new tangent function by restricting the domain to numbers between $-\pi/2$ and $\pi/2$, exclusive. In this way, all values for tangent are included only once and an inverse function will exist.

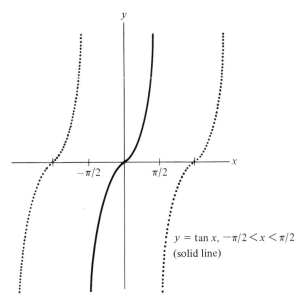

Values for arctangent will be between $-\pi/2$ and $\pi/2$. For example,

$$\arctan \sqrt{3} = \frac{\pi}{3}$$

$$\tan^{-1}1 = \frac{\pi}{4}$$

$$\tan^{-1}(.4111) \approx .39$$

Since $\tan(-x) = -\tan x$ and the domain of the tangent function we are using is $-\pi/2 < x < \pi/2$, it follows that $\arctan(-x) = -\arctan x$. For example,

$$\arctan(-1) = -\arctan 1 = -\frac{\pi}{4}$$

$$\tan^{-1}\left(-\frac{\sqrt{3}}{3}\right) = -\tan^{-1}\left(\frac{\sqrt{3}}{3}\right) = -\frac{\pi}{6}$$

The formal definition of arctangent and the graph of the inverse tangent function are given next.

$$x = \tan^{-1}y \quad \text{if and only if} \quad y = \tan x$$
$$\text{and} \quad -\pi/2 < x < \pi/2.$$

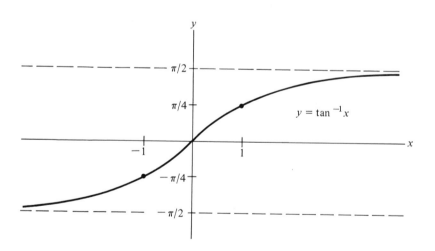

Example 43 *Solve for x:* $ab = c \sin x$

As a first step, we can solve for $\sin x$.

$$\sin x = \frac{ab}{c}$$

Then using our knowledge of inverse trigonometric functions,

$$x = \sin^{-1}\left(\frac{ab}{c}\right)$$

Note that $\sin^{-1}(ab/c)$ is the only solution between $-\pi/2$ and $\pi/2$. We could obtain additional solutions, if desired, but $\sin^{-1}(ab/c)$ is the principal solution.

Example 44   *Determine the value of* $\sin\left(\cos^{-1}\dfrac{1}{2} + \tan\left(\sin^{-1}\dfrac{\sqrt{2}}{2}\right)\right)$.

Since $\cos^{-1}\frac{1}{2} = \pi/3$, the expression $\sin(\cos^{-1}\frac{1}{2})$ simplifies to $\sin \pi/3$, which is equal to $\sqrt{3}/2$. Similarly, $\sin^{-1}\sqrt{2}/2 = \pi/4$; so $\tan(\sin^{-1}\sqrt{2}/2)$ reduces to $\tan(\pi/4)$ or 1. Thus the entire expression

$$\sin\left(\cos^{-1}\frac{1}{2}\right) + \tan\left(\sin^{-1}\frac{\sqrt{2}}{2}\right)$$

simplifies to

$$\frac{\sqrt{3}}{2} + 1$$

You may prefer to write 1 as $\frac{2}{2}$ in order to combine the fractions as

$$\frac{\sqrt{3} + 2}{2} \quad \text{or} \quad \frac{2 + \sqrt{3}}{2}$$

Right triangles are useful in problems such as the last example when the numbers involved are not such familiar ones.

Example 45   *Use a right triangle to help simplify the expression* $\tan(\sin^{-1}\frac{2}{3})$.

Since arcsine is defined only in quadrants I and IV and $\sin\theta$ here is $\frac{2}{3}$ (positive), we conclude that θ is in quadrant I. The triangle:

$$\sin\theta = \frac{2}{3} = \frac{\text{opposite}}{\text{hypotenuse}}$$

The length of the third side was determined to be $\sqrt{5}$ by using the Pythagorean theorem. We now seek the tangent from this environment in which sine is $\frac{2}{3}$. From the right triangle, $\tan \theta = 2/\sqrt{5}$ Thus

$$\tan\left(\sin^{-1}\frac{2}{3}\right) = \frac{2}{\sqrt{5}}, \quad \text{or} \quad \frac{2\sqrt{5}}{5}$$

Example 46 *Use a right triangle to help simplify the expression* $\tan(\cos^{-1}(-\frac{3}{7}))$.

Since arccosine is defined only in quadrants I and II and $\cos \theta$ here is $-\frac{3}{7}$ (negative), we conclude that θ is in quadrant II. The triangle:

$$\cos \theta = -\frac{3}{7} = \frac{\text{adjacent}}{\text{hypotenuse}}$$

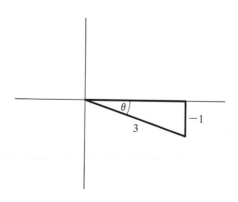

The length of the third side was determined to be $2\sqrt{10}$ by using the Pythagorean theorem. We seek the tangent from this environment in which cosine is $-\frac{3}{7}$. From the right triangle, $\tan \theta = 2\sqrt{10}/(-3) = -2\sqrt{10}/3$. Thus

$$\tan\left(\cos^{-1}\left(-\frac{3}{7}\right)\right) = -\frac{2\sqrt{10}}{3}$$

When needed, as in the case of $\cos(\sin^{-1}(-\frac{1}{3}))$, a right triangle in the fourth quadrant will appear as follows:

Example 47 *Determine the value of* cot(arccos 2x) *and write it as a simple expression in* x. *Assume* $0 < 2x < 1$.

Arccosine is defined only in quadrants I and II. We can see that $\cos \theta$ is $2x$ and $0 < 2x < 1$. This means $2x$ is positive and so θ is in quadrant I. Furthermore,

$$\cos \theta = \frac{\text{adjacent}}{\text{hypotenuse}} = 2x = \frac{2x}{1}$$

The triangle:

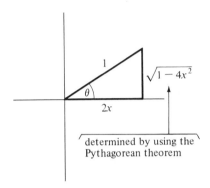

determined by using the
Pythagorean theorem

Finally,

$$\cot \theta = \frac{\text{adjacent}}{\text{opposite}} = \frac{2x}{\sqrt{1 - 4x^2}}$$

The **arcsecant** arises in calculus; so it is important to know something about it. Let $y = \sec x$. Since secant and cosine are reciprocals, it follows that $\cos x = 1/y$. Now

$$y = \sec x \quad \longrightarrow \quad x = \sec^{-1} y$$

$$\frac{1}{y} = \cos x \quad \longrightarrow \quad x = \cos^{-1}\left(\frac{1}{y}\right)$$

Thus

$$x = \sec^{-1} y = \cos^{-1}\left(\frac{1}{y}\right), \quad x \neq \pi/2, \text{ since } \cos \frac{\pi}{2} = 0 \text{ and } \sec \frac{\pi}{2} \text{ undefined.}$$

$$\boxed{\begin{array}{l} x = \sec^{-1} y = \cos^{-1}\left(\frac{1}{y}\right) \\[2mm] \text{if and only if } y = \sec x \text{ and} \\ 0 \leq x \leq \pi, x \neq \pi/2 \end{array}}$$

Example 48 *Determine the value of:* (a) $\sec^{-1} 2$ (b) $\sec^{-1}\left(-\dfrac{2}{\sqrt{3}}\right)$.

(a) $\sec^{-1} 2 = \cos^{-1}\dfrac{1}{2} = \dfrac{\pi}{3}$

(b) $\sec^{-1}\left(-\dfrac{2}{\sqrt{3}}\right) = \cos^{-1}\left(-\dfrac{\sqrt{3}}{2}\right)$

$= \pi - \cos^{-1}\left(\dfrac{\sqrt{3}}{2}\right)$

$= \pi - \dfrac{\pi}{6}$

$= \dfrac{5\pi}{6}$

As a final note, the result from Section 3.6, that $f(f^{-1}(x)) = x$, can be used to simplify an expression such as $\tan(\tan^{-1}u)$.

$$\tan(\tan^{-1}u) = u$$

This type of simplification is valid for any other trigonometric function and its inverse, provided that u is in the range of the trigonometric function (or in the domain of the inverse). See Exercise 9.

EXERCISES 7.11

1.   Evaluate. Use Table IV or a calculator for problems (m) through (t).

*(a) $\sin^{-1}\frac{1}{2}$
  (b) $\arcsin 0$

*(c) $\arccos 0$
  (d) $\cos^{-1}\dfrac{\sqrt{2}}{2}$

*(e) $\tan^{-1} 0$
  (f) $\arctan\dfrac{\sqrt{3}}{3}$

*(g) $\sin^{-1}\left(-\dfrac{\sqrt{3}}{2}\right)$
  (h) $\sin^{-1}(-1)$

*(i) $\cos^{-1}\left(-\dfrac{\sqrt{3}}{2}\right)$
  (j) $\cos^{-1}(-1)$

*(k) $\tan^{-1}(-\sqrt{3})$
  (l) $\tan^{-1}(-1)$

*(m) $\sin^{-1}(.3802)$
  (n) $\sin^{-1}(-.9356)$

*(o) $\cos^{-1}(.7358)$ (p) $\cos^{-1}(-.2288)$

*(q) $\tan^{-1}(.6841)$ (r) $\tan^{-1}(-1.235)$

*(s) $\cos^{-1}(-.9801)$ (t) $\sin^{-1}(-.6210)$

2. Evaluate each expression.

*(a) $\cos\left(\sin^{-1}\dfrac{1}{2}\right)$ (b) $\sin(\cos^{-1}(-1))$

*(c) $\tan\left(\arccos\dfrac{1}{2}\right)$ (d) $\cos(\arctan(-1))$

*(e) $\sin(\arccos 0)$ (f) $\sin(\tan^{-1}1)$

*(g) $\cos\left(\sin^{-1}\left(-\dfrac{1}{2}\right)\right)$ (h) $\tan(\arcsin 0)$

*(i) $\sin\left(\sin^{-1}\dfrac{\sqrt{2}}{2}\right)$ (j) $\cos\left(\cos^{-1}\dfrac{\sqrt{3}}{2}\right)$

*(k) $\tan(\tan^{-1}\sqrt{3})$ (l) $\tan\left(\sin^{-1}\dfrac{\sqrt{2}}{2}\right)$

*(m) $\tan\left(\cos^{-1}\left(-\dfrac{\sqrt{3}}{2}\right)\right)$ (n) $\sin(\tan^{-1}(-\sqrt{3}))$

3. Evaluate each expression. Use Table IV or a calculator.

*(a) $\sin(\tan^{-1}19.670)$ (b) $\cos(\arcsin(.2571))$

*(c) $\tan(\arccos .6216)$ (d) $\sin(\cos^{-1}(-.7776))$

*(e) $\tan(\arccos(-.7776))$ (f) $\tan(\sin^{-1}.8674)$

*(g) $\sin(\arcsin(.9128))$ (h) $\cos(\arccos.9801)$

*(i) $\tan(\arctan.4466)$ (j) $\cos(\tan^{-1}(-.4466))$

4. Use right triangles to simplify each expression.

*(a) $\sin\left(\tan^{-1}\dfrac{3}{4}\right)$ (b) $\cos\left(\sin^{-1}\dfrac{5}{13}\right)$

*(c) $\tan\left(\arccos\dfrac{2}{5}\right)$ (d) $\sin\left(\cos^{-1}\dfrac{\sqrt{3}}{5}\right)$

*(e) $\cos\left(\tan^{-1}\dfrac{1}{10}\right)$ (f) $\tan\left(\sin^{-1}\dfrac{\sqrt{5}}{4}\right)$

*(g) $\sin\left(\tan^{-1}\left(-\dfrac{3}{4}\right)\right)$ (h) $\cos\left(\sin^{-1}\left(-\dfrac{4}{5}\right)\right)$

*(i) $\sin\left(\arccos\left(-\dfrac{2}{5}\right)\right)$ (j) $\tan\left(\cos^{-1}\left(-\dfrac{1}{7}\right)\right)$

5. Solve for x (see Example 43).

*(a) $ab = c \cos x$
*(b) $c = a + b \sin x$
*(c) $y - \tan x = 16$
(d) $2 + \cos x = 3t$
*(e) $5 \cos 3x = bc$
(f) $2 \sin mx = d$
*(g) $a - b \tan(ax + b) = 0$
(h) $1 - \cos(ax - b) = c$

6. Write each trigonometric expression as a simple expression in x. (See Example 47). Assume that the angle is in quadrant I.

*(a) $\tan(\arcsin x)$
(b) $\tan(\arccos 2x)$

*(c) $\sec(\arctan 3x)$
(d) $\sin\left(\operatorname{arcsec}\dfrac{x}{3}\right)$

*(e) $\csc\left(\operatorname{arccot}\dfrac{x}{2}\right)$
(f) $\sec[\arctan(x - 1)]$

*(g) $\sin\left(\arctan\dfrac{x + 1}{5}\right)$
(h) $\tan\left(\arcsin\dfrac{4}{x - 2}\right)$

7. Determine the value of each arcsecant.

*(a) $\operatorname{arcsec}\left(\dfrac{2}{\sqrt{3}}\right)$
(b) $\operatorname{arcsec}(-2)$

*(c) $\sec^{-1}(-1)$
(d) $\sec^{-1}(1)$
*(e) $\sec^{-1}(\sqrt{2})$
(f) $\sec^{-1}(0)$
*(g) $\sec^{-1}(-\sqrt{2})$

8. Graph each inverse function by first sketching the graph of the restricted trigonometric function. Then reflect the restricted graph about the line $y = x$.

*(a) $f^{-1}(x) = \sin^{-1}x$
(b) $f^{-1}(x) = \cos^{-1}x$
*(c) $f^{-1}(x) = \tan^{-1}x$

*9. Simplify each expression.

(a) $\sin(\sin^{-1}x)$
(b) $\cos(\arccos t)$

(c) $\sec(\sec^{-1}3u)$
(d) $\tan\left(\arctan\dfrac{m + 2}{5}\right)$

*10. If $\theta = \tan^{-1}(\tfrac{1}{2})$, determine $\sin 2\theta$.

11. If $\theta = \tan^{-1}(\tfrac{2}{3})$, determine $\cos 2\theta$.

7.12 POLAR COORDINATES

Honeybees use a coordinate system quite different from the rectangular coordinate system. They use **polar coordinates,** a system in which points are located a distance r and an angle θ from the origin. The polar coordinate system was described by Isaac Newton about 1671.

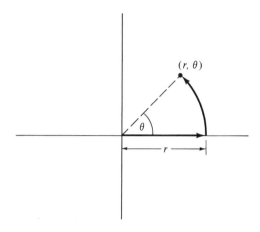

Bees use polar coordinates to tell other bees where a food source is located. The bee returns to the hive with a small quantity of food and makes the smell known to the others. Then it dances in semicircles on the hive. The speed at which it dances specifies the food's distance r from the hive. During the dance the bee duplicates the angular direction of the food with respect to the sun. Thus the bee uses polar coordinates to locate food for other bees. It specifies a distance r and an angle θ.

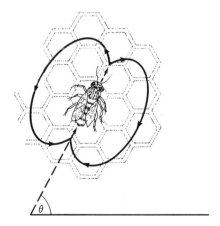

Consider that any point in the plane can be located by using rectangular coordinates (x, y) or polar coordinates (r, θ). This is illustrated in the next drawing.

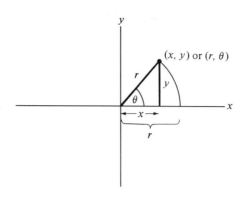

There are several relationships between polar coordinates and rectangular coordinates. A study of the following right triangle reveals them readily.

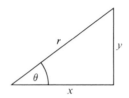

From the Pythagorean theorem

$$x^2 + y^2 = r^2$$

or

$$r = \pm\sqrt{x^2 + y^2}$$

Also,

$$\sin\theta = \frac{y}{r} \quad \text{or} \quad y = r\sin\theta$$

$$\cos\theta = \frac{x}{r} \quad \text{or} \quad x = r\cos\theta$$

$$\tan\theta = \frac{y}{x} \quad \text{or} \quad \theta = \tan^{-1}\left(\frac{y}{x}\right)$$

The next two examples demonstrate conversion of a *point* from polar to rectangular coordinates and vice versa.

Example 49 *Change the point $(r, \theta) = (3, \pi/6)$ to rectangular coordinates.*
Since $x = r \cos \theta$ and $y = r \sin \theta$,

$$(x, y) = (r \cos \theta, r \sin \theta)$$

$$= \left(3 \cos \frac{\pi}{6}, 3 \sin \frac{\pi}{6} \right) \qquad \text{since } r = 3 \text{ and } \theta = \pi/6$$

$$= \left(3 \cdot \frac{\sqrt{3}}{2}, 3 \cdot \frac{1}{2} \right)$$

$$= \left(\frac{3\sqrt{3}}{2}, \frac{3}{2} \right)$$

Example 50 *Change the point $(x, y) = (1, \sqrt{3})$ to polar coordinates.*
Use $r = \sqrt{x^2 + y^2}$ and $\theta = \tan^{-1}(y/x)$.

$$(r, \theta) = \left(\sqrt{x^2 + y^2}, \tan^{-1} \frac{y}{x} \right)$$

$$= (\sqrt{1 + 3}, \tan^{-1}\sqrt{3}) \qquad \text{since } x = 1 \text{ and } y = \sqrt{3}$$

$$= \left(2, \frac{\pi}{3} \right)$$

Note that $r = +\sqrt{x^2 + y^2}$ was used rather than $r = -\sqrt{x^2 + y^2}$. For locating one specific (x, y) point, select the appropriate r, positive or negative, based on where the point is positioned. In this context, r is positive in quadrants I and IV (to the right of the origin) and negative in quadrants II and III (to the left of the origin). Since the point $(1, \sqrt{3})$ is in the first quadrant, we should use $r = +\sqrt{x^2 + y^2}$.

Here are several examples showing the techniques of changing an equation in rectangular coordinates (x and y) to one in polar coordinates (r and θ), and vice versa.

Example 51 *Change $y = 6x + 7$ to an equation in polar coordinates.*
Substitute $r \sin \theta$ for y and $r \cos \theta$ for x. The result is that

$$y = 6x + 7$$

becomes

$$r \sin \theta = 6r \cos \theta + 7$$

or

$$r \sin \theta - 6r \cos \theta = 7$$

or

$$r(\sin \theta - 6 \cos \theta) = 7$$

Finally,

$$r = \frac{7}{\sin \theta - 6 \cos \theta}$$

gives r as a function of θ.

Example 52 *Change $5x^2 + 4y^2 = 15$ to an equation in polar coordinates.*
Using $x = r \cos \theta$ and $y = r \sin \theta$,

$$5x^2 + 4y^2 = 15$$

becomes

$$5(r \cos \theta)^2 + 4(r \sin \theta)^2 = 15$$

or

$$5r^2 \cos^2\theta + 4r^2 \sin^2\theta = 15$$

Note that $5r^2 \cos^2\theta = r^2 \cos^2\theta + 4r^2 \cos^2\theta$. This alternative form can be used to simplify the equation above. The new form is

$$r^2 \cos^2\theta + 4r^2 \cos^2\theta + 4r^2 \sin^2\theta = 15$$

or

$$r^2 \cos^2\theta + 4r^2 (\cos^2\theta + \sin^2\theta) = 15$$

You should now realize that the relation has been manipulated into this form so that substitution of 1 for $\cos^2 \theta + \sin^2 \theta$ can be made. The simplified form is then

$$r^2 \cos^2\theta + 4r^2 = 15$$

or

$$r^2 (\cos^2\theta + 4) = 15$$

If desired, this relation can be solved for r^2, as

$$r^2 = \frac{15}{\cos^2\theta + 4}$$

Example 53 *Change r = 4 to an equation in rectangular coordinates.*

Substitute $\pm\sqrt{x^2 + y^2}$ for r in $r = 4$ to get

$$\pm\sqrt{x^2 + y^2} = 4$$

or, upon squaring both sides,

$$x^2 + y^2 = 16$$

Example 54 *Change* $r = \dfrac{3}{1 - \cos\theta}$ *to an equation in rectangular coordinates.*

Eliminate the fraction by multiplying both sides by $1 - \cos\theta$. The result is

$$r(1 - \cos\theta) = 3$$

Multiply out the left side

$$r - r\cos\theta = 3$$

Now substitute $\pm\sqrt{x^2 + y^2}$ for r and x for $r\cos\theta$. The result is

$$\pm\sqrt{x^2 + y^2} - x = 3$$

or

$$\pm\sqrt{x^2 + y^2} = x + 3$$

After squaring both sides of this equation, we have

$$x^2 + y^2 = x^2 + 6x + 9$$

which can be written as either

$$y^2 = 6x + 9$$

or

$$y^2 - 6x - 9 = 0$$

Now that you have gained some familiarity with polar coordinates we can proceed to graph relations and functions in polar coordinates. For graphing purposes, the polar plane is usually drawn as a series of concentric circles with center at the origin and radii 1, 2, 3, 4, ... Radiating from the center are lines at angles 0°, 15°, 30°, 45°, 60°, . . . , 360° or 0, $\pi/12$, $\pi/6$, $\pi/4$, $\pi/3$, . . . , 2π radians. We shall use radian measure exclusively, for radian measure is used in calculus settings.

In polar coordinates, the *origin* is also called the **pole.** Points (r, θ) are plotted by moving from the pole, as follows.

1. First move a distance r along the polar axis (horizontal). If r is positive, move right; if r is negative, move left.

2. Next swing around through angle θ (from where you are on the horizontal). The point where you stop is (r, θ).

Plotted next are four points of the form (r, θ):

$$\text{point } A \text{ is } \left(4, \frac{\pi}{3}\right): \qquad r \text{ is } 4, \theta \text{ is } \frac{\pi}{3}$$

$$\text{point } B \text{ is } (3, 0): \qquad r \text{ is } 3, \theta \text{ is } 0$$

$$\text{point } C \text{ is } \left(-5, \frac{\pi}{6}\right): \qquad r \text{ is } -5, \theta \text{ is } \frac{\pi}{6}$$

$$\text{point } D \text{ is } \left(5, -\frac{\pi}{4}\right): \qquad r \text{ is } 5, \theta \text{ is } -\frac{\pi}{4}$$

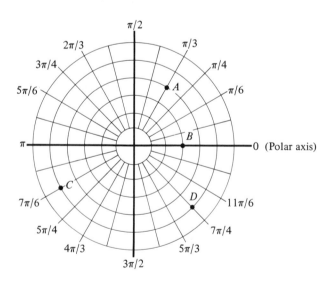

Consider the polar plane above and plot the following three points for practice: $(5, 7\pi/6)$, $(-3, \pi)$, $(-4, 4\pi/3)$. If you have plotted the points correctly, then you realize they are the same as points *C*, *B*, and *A* already plotted in the plane above. You can see that unlike points in rectangular or Cartesian coordinates, two points can be the same even though their coordinates are different. Specifically, you can take any point in polar coordinates and change *r* to $-r$ and θ to $\theta + \pi$. The resulting point, $(-r, \theta + \pi)$, is the same as the original point (r, θ). Changing *r* to $-r$ sends you out the same distance but in the opposite direction (180°, or π, in the "wrong" direction). Adding π to the angle θ compensates for it.

$$\boxed{(r, \theta) = (-r, \theta + \pi)}$$

The coordinates of the pole are $(0, \theta)$—that is, $(0, \pi/6)$, $(0, \pi)$, $(0, \pi/2)$, and so on. As long as *r* is 0, the value of θ does not matter.

The section concludes with the graphs of four equations in polar coordinates.

Example 55   *Sketch the graph of* $r = \dfrac{1}{\cos \theta}$.

Supply values for θ in order to obtain values for *r* and points of the form (r, θ).

θ	$r = \dfrac{1}{\cos \theta}$	(r, θ)
0	$\dfrac{1}{\cos 0} = \dfrac{1}{1} = 1$	$(1, 0)$
$\dfrac{\pi}{6}$	$\dfrac{1}{\cos \pi/6} = \dfrac{1}{\sqrt{3}/2} = \dfrac{2\sqrt{3}}{3} \approx 1.154$	$\left(1.154, \dfrac{\pi}{6}\right)$
$\dfrac{\pi}{4}$	$\dfrac{1}{\cos \pi/4} = \dfrac{1}{\sqrt{2}/2} = \sqrt{2} \approx 1.414$	$\left(1.414, \dfrac{\pi}{4}\right)$
$\dfrac{\pi}{3}$	$\dfrac{1}{\cos \pi/3} = \dfrac{1}{\frac{1}{2}} = 2$	$\left(2, \dfrac{\pi}{3}\right)$
$\dfrac{\pi}{2}$	$\dfrac{1}{\cos \pi/2} = \dfrac{1}{0} =$ undefined	—
$\dfrac{2\pi}{3}$	$\dfrac{1}{\cos 2\pi/3} = \dfrac{1}{(-\cos \pi/3)} = -\dfrac{1}{\cos \pi/3} = -2$	$\left(-2, \dfrac{2\pi}{3}\right)$
$\dfrac{3\pi}{4}$	$\dfrac{1}{\cos 3\pi/4} = \dfrac{1}{(-\cos \pi/4)} = -\dfrac{1}{\cos \pi/4} \approx -1.414$	$\left(-1.414, \dfrac{3\pi}{4}\right)$
$\dfrac{5\pi}{6}$	$\dfrac{1}{\cos 5\pi/6} = \dfrac{1}{(-\cos \pi/6)} = -\dfrac{1}{\cos \pi/6} \approx -1.154$	$\left(-1.154, \dfrac{5\pi}{6}\right)$
π	$\dfrac{1}{\cos \pi} = \dfrac{1}{(-1)} = -1$	$(-1, \pi)$

The graph is as follows.

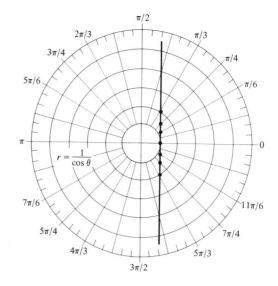

You need only a few points to realize that the graph of $r = 1/\cos \theta$ is a straight line. (It is the line $x = 1$ in rectangular coordinates. This can be shown directly by writing the relation as $r \cos \theta = 1$ and then substituting x for $r \cos \theta$.) Had we used $\theta = 7\pi/6, 5\pi/4, 4\pi/3, 3\pi/2$, and so on, we would not have obtained additional points but rather alternate forms of the same points.

Example 56   *Sketch the graph of $r = 8 \sin \theta$.*

Again, supply θ values in order to obtain values for r. The graph is a circle. As it happens, θ values between 0 and π are sufficient to determine the graph.

θ	$r = 8 \sin \theta$	(r, θ)
0	$r = 8 \cdot 0 = 0$	$(0, 0)$
$\dfrac{\pi}{6}$	$r = 8 \cdot \dfrac{1}{2} = 4$	$\left(4, \dfrac{\pi}{6}\right)$
$\dfrac{\pi}{4}$	$r = 8 \cdot \dfrac{\sqrt{2}}{2} = 4\sqrt{2}$	$\left(4\sqrt{2}, \dfrac{\pi}{4}\right)$
$\dfrac{\pi}{3}$	$r = 8 \cdot \dfrac{\sqrt{3}}{2} = 4\sqrt{3}$	$\left(4\sqrt{3}, \dfrac{\pi}{3}\right)$
$\dfrac{\pi}{2}$	$r = 8 \cdot 1 = 8$	$\left(8, \dfrac{\pi}{2}\right)$
$\dfrac{2\pi}{3}$	$r = 8 \cdot \dfrac{\sqrt{3}}{2} = 4\sqrt{3}$	$\left(4\sqrt{3}, \dfrac{2\pi}{3}\right)$
$\dfrac{3\pi}{4}$	$r = 8 \cdot \dfrac{\sqrt{2}}{2} = 4\sqrt{2}$	$\left(4\sqrt{2}, \dfrac{3\pi}{4}\right)$
$\dfrac{5\pi}{6}$	$r = 8 \cdot \dfrac{1}{2} = 4$	$\left(4, \dfrac{5\pi}{6}\right)$
π	$r = 8 \cdot 0 = 0$	$(0, \pi)$

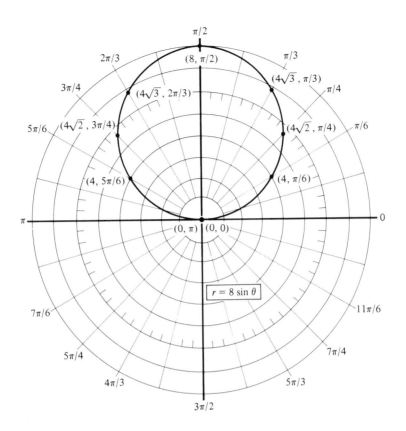

$r = 8 \sin \theta$

Example 57 *Sketch the graph of* $r = 4 + 4 \sin \theta$.

The figure produced is called a **cardioid,** since it is heart shaped. Here are the points and graph.

r	θ
4	0
6	$\dfrac{\pi}{6}$
$4 + 2\sqrt{2}$	$\dfrac{\pi}{4}$
$4 + 2\sqrt{3}$	$\dfrac{\pi}{3}$
8	$\dfrac{\pi}{2}$

r	θ
$4 + 2\sqrt{3}$	$\dfrac{2\pi}{3}$
$4 + 2\sqrt{2}$	$\dfrac{3\pi}{4}$
6	$\dfrac{5\pi}{6}$
4	π
2	$\dfrac{7\pi}{6}$

r	θ
$4 - 2\sqrt{2}$	$\dfrac{5\pi}{4}$
$4 - 2\sqrt{3}$	$\dfrac{4\pi}{3}$
0	$\dfrac{3\pi}{2}$
$4 - 2\sqrt{3}$	$\dfrac{5\pi}{3}$
$4 - 2\sqrt{2}$	$\dfrac{7\pi}{4}$

r	θ
2	$\dfrac{11\pi}{6}$
4	2π

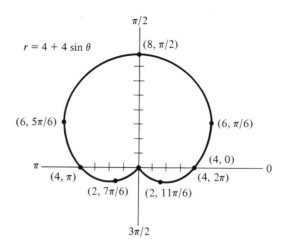

$r = 4 + 4 \sin \theta$

$(8, \pi/2)$

$(6, 5\pi/6)$ $(6, \pi/6)$

$(4, 0)$

$(4, \pi)$ $(4, 2\pi)$

$(2, 7\pi/6)$ $(2, 11\pi/6)$

Example 58 *Sketch the graph of $r^2 = 4 \cos 2\theta$.*

    The figure produced when graphed is called a **lemniscate.** Shown next are a few sample points and their computation. Also given are several other points and the graph of the relation. Note that r is not defined for certain values of θ. Specifically, $r^2 < 0$ whenever $\cos 2\theta < 0$; so there is no real r for $\cos 2\theta < 0$.

    If $\theta = 0$, then $r^2 = 4 \cdot \cos(2 \cdot 0) = 4 \cdot \cos 0 = 4 \cdot 1 = 4$; $r^2 = 4$ yields $r = \pm 2$. Thus we have the points $(2, 0)$ and $(-2, 0)$.

    If $\theta = \pi/6$, then $r^2 = 4 \cdot \cos(2 \cdot \pi/6) = 4 \cdot \cos \pi/3 = 4 \cdot \frac{1}{2} = 2$; $r^2 = 2$ yields $r = \pm\sqrt{2}$. So we have two more points: $(\sqrt{2}, \pi/6)$ and $(-\sqrt{2}, \pi/6)$.

    Here are some other points: $(0, \pi/4)$, $(0, 3\pi/4)$, $(\sqrt{2}, 5\pi/6)$, $(-\sqrt{2}, 5\pi/6)$, $(2, \pi)$, $(-2, \pi)$, $(\sqrt{2}, 7\pi/6)$, $(-\sqrt{2}, 7\pi/6)$, $(0, 5\pi/4)$, $(0, 7\pi/4)$, $(\sqrt{2}, 11\pi/6)$, $(-\sqrt{2}, 11\pi/6)$, $(2, 2\pi)$, $(-2, 2\pi)$. Using $\theta = \pi/12$, $11\pi/12$, $13\pi/12$, and $23\pi/12$ will yield four other useful points. The graph is as follows.

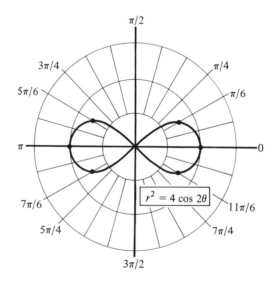

$r^2 = 4 \cos 2\theta$

In working with polar coordinates, you are also likely to see **limaçons** and **rose curves.** Shown next are examples of these curves.

Limaçon (with loop)

Four–leafed rose

EXERCISES 7.12

1. Change each point from polar coordinates to rectangular coordinates.

*(a) $\left(1, \dfrac{\pi}{6}\right)$

(b) $\left(4, \dfrac{\pi}{4}\right)$

*(c) $(3, 2\pi)$

(d) $(-3, 2\pi)$

*(e) $\left(2, \dfrac{\pi}{2}\right)$

(f) $(0, 0)$

*(g) $(1, \pi)$

(h) $\left(-7, \dfrac{\pi}{3}\right)$

*(i) $(0, \pi)$

(j) $\left(-2, \dfrac{5\pi}{6}\right)$

*(k) $\left(\dfrac{3}{2}, \dfrac{5\pi}{4}\right)$

(l) $\left(5, \dfrac{2\pi}{3}\right)$

*(m) $\left(\dfrac{1}{2}, \dfrac{7\pi}{6}\right)$

(n) $\left(3, \dfrac{3\pi}{4}\right)$

*(o) $\left(-5, \dfrac{7\pi}{4}\right)$

(p) $\left(4, \dfrac{5\pi}{3}\right)$

*(q) $\left(2, \dfrac{11\pi}{6}\right)$

(r) $\left(3, \dfrac{4\pi}{3}\right)$

*(s) $(-1, 1)$

(t) $(1, 2\pi)$

*(u) $\left(2, -\dfrac{\pi}{6}\right)$

(v) $\left(6, -\dfrac{\pi}{3}\right)$

*(w) $\left(-4, -\dfrac{\pi}{4}\right)$

(x) $\left(-8, -\dfrac{\pi}{2}\right)$

2. Change each point from rectangular coordinates to polar coordinates.
    *(a) (2, 2)   (b) (5, 0)
    *(c) $(\sqrt{3}, 1)$ (d) $(1, -\sqrt{3})$
    *(e) (-5, 0)   (f) (0, 0)
    *(g) (-1, 1)   (h) (-2, -2)
    *(i) $(-\sqrt{3}, 1)$ (j) $(3, 3\sqrt{3})$
    *(k) (0, 6)   (l) (0, -3)

3. Plot the following points and determine the nature of the curve that passes
    through them.

    *(a) (0, 0) $\left(\dfrac{1}{2}, \dfrac{\pi}{6}\right)$ $\left(\dfrac{\sqrt{2}}{2}, \dfrac{\pi}{4}\right)$ $\left(\dfrac{\sqrt{3}}{2}, \dfrac{\pi}{3}\right)$ $\left(1, \dfrac{\pi}{2}\right)$

    $\left(\dfrac{\sqrt{3}}{2}, \dfrac{2\pi}{3}\right)$ $\left(\dfrac{\sqrt{2}}{2}, \dfrac{3\pi}{4}\right)$ $\left(\dfrac{1}{2}, \dfrac{5\pi}{6}\right)$ $(0, \pi)$

    (b) $\left(-\dfrac{1}{2}, \dfrac{7\pi}{6}\right)$ $\left(-\dfrac{\sqrt{2}}{2}, \dfrac{5\pi}{4}\right)$ $\left(-\dfrac{\sqrt{3}}{2}, \dfrac{4\pi}{3}\right)$ $\left(-1, \dfrac{3\pi}{2}\right)$

    $\left(-\dfrac{\sqrt{3}}{2}, \dfrac{5\pi}{3}\right)$ $\left(-\dfrac{\sqrt{2}}{2}, \dfrac{7\pi}{4}\right)$ $\left(-\dfrac{1}{2}, \dfrac{11\pi}{6}\right)$ $(0, 2\pi)$

    *(c) (2, 0) $\left(1, \dfrac{\pi}{6}\right)$ $\left(0, \dfrac{\pi}{2}\right)$ $\left(1, \dfrac{5\pi}{6}\right)$ $(2, \pi)$

    $\left(3, \dfrac{7\pi}{6}\right)$ $\left(4, \dfrac{3\pi}{2}\right)$ $\left(3, \dfrac{11\pi}{6}\right)$ $(2, 2\pi)$

4. Change each equation to an equation in polar coordinates. Then solve for
    r or r^2 as appropriate. See Examples 51 and 52.
    *(a) $y = 2x - 3$ (b) $x = 5y + 6$
    *(c) $x - y = 0$ (d) $3x + y - 4 = 0$
    *(e) $x^2 + y^2 = 25$ (f) $x^2 + y^2 = 100$
    *(g) $x^2 - y^2 = 16$ (h) $4x^2 + 9y^2 = 36$
    *(i) $x^2 + 7y^2 = 9$ (j) $y = x^2$
    *(k) $y = 5x^2$

5. Change each equation to an equation in rectangular coordinates.
   *(a) $r = 6 \sin \theta$ (b) $r = 4 \sin \theta$
   *(c) $r = 2 \cos \theta$ (d) $r = 9 \cos \theta$
   *(e) $r = 5$ (f) $r = 7$
   *(g) $r = \dfrac{3}{\cos \theta}$ (h) $r = 1 - \cos \theta$
   *(i) $\theta = \dfrac{\pi}{6}$ (j) $r = \theta$
   *(k) $r = \dfrac{1}{\sin \theta}$ (l) $r = 1 + \sin \theta$

6. Use the fact that $(r, \theta) = (-r, \theta + \pi)$ to change each point to an alternate form.
   *(a) $\left(2, \dfrac{\pi}{6}\right)$ (b) $\left(1, \dfrac{\pi}{4}\right)$
   *(c) $\left(3, \dfrac{2\pi}{3}\right)$ (d) $\left(4, \dfrac{5\pi}{6}\right)$
   *(e) $\left(-4, \dfrac{\pi}{2}\right)$ (f) $\left(-1, \dfrac{3\pi}{4}\right)$

7. Obtain points and sketch the graph of each equation in polar coordinates.
   *(a) $r = 3$ (circle)   (b) $r = 6 \sin \theta$ (circle)
   *(c) $r = 6 \cos \theta$ (circle)   (d) $r = -4 \sin \theta$ (circle)
   *(e) $r = -4 \cos \theta$ (circle)   (f) $r = 2 - 2 \cos \theta$ (cardioid)
   *(g) $r = 6 + 6 \cos \theta$ (cardioid)   (h) $r = 2 - 2 \sin \theta$ (cardioid)
   *(i) $r = 4 + 2 \sin \theta$ (limaçon)   (j) $r = 3 + \cos \theta$ (limaçon)
   *(k) $\theta = \dfrac{\pi}{6}$ (line)   (l) $r = \theta$ (spiral)

8. Obtain points and sketch the graph of each equation in polar coordinates.
   *(a) $r^2 = 9 \cos 2\theta$ (lemniscate)
   (b) $r^2 = 4 \sin 2\theta$ (lemniscate)
   *(c) $r = 1 - 2 \cos \theta$ (limaçon with loop)
   (d) $r = 3 + 4 \cos \theta$ (limaçon with loop)
   *(e) $r = \dfrac{2}{1 - \cos \theta}$ (parabola)
   (f) $r = 2 \sin 2\theta$ (four-leafed rose)
   *(g) $r = 4 \cos 2\theta$ (four-leafed rose)
   (h) $r = 2 \cos 3\theta$ (three-leafed rose)
   *(i) $r = 6 \sin 3\theta$ (three-leafed rose)

*9. Examine the chart of points of Example 55 and determine one value of θ that is not in the domain of $r = 1/\cos \theta$.

10. Give three values of θ not in the domain of $r^2 = 4\cos 2\theta$ (from Example 58.)

7.13 POLAR COORDINATES AND COMPLEX NUMBERS

A complex number z can be written in the form $x + iy$ and represented graphically in the **complex plane.** In the complex plane the horizontal (x) axis is called the **real axis** and the vertical (y) axis is called the **imaginary axis.** Here is the geometric representation of a few complex numbers—points in the complex plane.

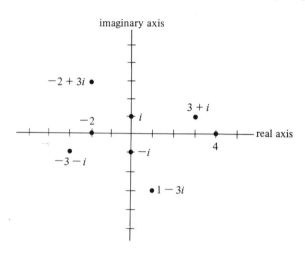

In polar coordinate form, $x = r\cos\theta$ and $y = r\sin\theta$. If $r\cos\theta$ is substituted for x and $r\sin\theta$ for y in

$$z = x + iy$$

the result is

$$z = r\cos\theta + ir\sin\theta$$

or

$$z = r(\cos\theta + i\sin\theta)$$

This is the **polar form** or trigonometric form of a complex number. Since for any integer k, $\cos(\theta + 2k\pi) = \cos\theta$ and $\sin(\theta + 2k\pi) = \sin\theta$,

$$z = r(\cos\theta + i\sin\theta)$$

can be considered as

$$z = r[\cos(\theta + 2k\pi) + i\sin(\theta + 2k\pi)] \qquad k = \text{any integer}$$

Example 59   *Change* $1 + i$ *to polar form.*
We have

$$z = x + iy = 1 + i \cdot 1$$

and we want

$$z = r(\cos \theta + i \sin \theta)$$

Here

$$r = \sqrt{x^2 + y^2} = \sqrt{1^2 + 1^2} = \sqrt{2}$$

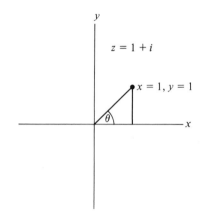

and θ satisfies $\tan \theta = y/x = 1/1$ in quadrant I, meaning $\theta = 45°$, or $\pi/4$. Thus

$$z = \sqrt{2}(\cos 45° + i \sin 45°)$$

or, equivalently,

$$z = \sqrt{2}\left(\cos \frac{\pi}{4} + i \sin \frac{\pi}{4}\right)$$

Example 60   *Change* $4(\cos 30° + i \sin 30°)$ *to rectangular form.*

$$z = 4(\cos 30° + i \sin 30°)$$

$$= 4\left(\frac{\sqrt{3}}{2} + i \cdot \frac{1}{2}\right)$$

$$= 2\sqrt{3} + 2i$$

Now consider the *product* of two complex numbers z_1 and z_2 given in polar form.

$$z_1 = r_1(\cos \theta_1 + i \sin \theta_1)$$

$$z_2 = r_2(\cos \theta_2 + i \sin \theta_2)$$

$$z_1 z_2 = [r_1(\cos \theta_1 + i \sin \theta_1)][r_2(\cos \theta_2 + i \sin \theta_2)]$$

$$= r_1 r_2(\cos \theta_1 + i \sin \theta_1)(\cos \theta_2 + i \sin \theta_2)$$

$$= r_1 r_2[(\cos \theta_1 \cos \theta_2 - \sin \theta_1 \sin \theta_2) + i(\sin \theta_1 \cos \theta_2 + \cos \theta_1 \sin \theta_2)]$$

$\cos \theta_1 \cos \theta_2 - \sin \theta_1 \sin \theta_2$ is $\cos(\theta_1 + \theta_2)$ and $\sin \theta_1 \cos \theta_2 + \cos \theta_1 \sin \theta_2$ is $\sin(\theta_1 + \theta_2)$. The following result is obtained upon substitution.

$$z_1 z_2 = r_1 r_2[\cos(\theta_1 + \theta_2) + i \sin(\theta_1 + \theta_2)]$$

Example 61 *Determine the value of $z_1 \cdot z_2$, if $z_1 = 5(\cos 20° + i \sin 20°)$ and $z_2 = 8(\cos 40° + i \sin 40°)$. Write the product in polar form and in rectangular form.*

Using the formula just obtained,

$$z_1 z_2 = 5 \cdot 8[\cos (20° + 40°) + i \sin (20° + 40°)]$$

$$= 40(\cos 60° + i \sin 60°) \qquad \text{polar form}$$

$$= 40\left(\frac{1}{2} + i \cdot \frac{\sqrt{3}}{2}\right)$$

$$= 20 + 20i\sqrt{3} \qquad \text{rectangular form}$$

The **quotient** of two complex numbers z_1 and z_2 given in polar form is

$$\frac{z_1}{z_2} = \frac{r_1}{r_2}[\cos(\theta_1 - \theta_2) + i \sin(\theta_1 - \theta_2)] \qquad (z_2 \neq 0)$$

Example 62 *Determine the value of $\dfrac{z_1}{z_2}$ for z_1 and z_2 of the previous example.*

Using the formula with

$$z_1 = 5(\cos 20° + i \sin 20°)$$

and

$$z_2 = 8(\cos 40° + i \sin 40°)$$

we obtain

$$\frac{z_1}{z_2} = \frac{5}{8}[\cos(20° - 40°) + i \sin(20° - 40°)]$$

$$= \frac{5}{8}[\cos(-20°) + i \sin(-20°)]$$

$$= \frac{5}{8}(\cos 20° - i \sin 20°) \qquad \text{polar form}$$

Rectangular form can be obtained by using the approximations for cos 20° and sin 20° available in Table V or from a calculator.

$$\frac{z_1}{z_2} = \frac{5}{8}(\cos 20° - i \sin 20°)$$

$$\approx \frac{5}{8}(.9397 - i \cdot .3420)$$

$$\approx .5873 - .2138i \qquad \text{rectangular form}$$

Positive integral *powers* of a complex number

$$z = r(\cos \theta + i \sin \theta)$$

are given by **De Moivre's theorem:**

$$\boxed{z^n = r^n(\cos n\theta + i \sin n\theta)}$$

Mathematical induction, explained in Chapter 10, can be used to prove that this theorem is true for all positive integers n. Here we shall just show that it is true for $n = 2$ and $n = 3$. The extension to higher powers should be apparent.

$$z^2 = z \cdot z = [r(\cos \theta + i \sin \theta)][r(\cos \theta + i \sin \theta)]$$
$$= r \cdot r[\cos(\theta + \theta) + i \sin(\theta + \theta)]$$
$$= r^2(\cos 2\theta + i \sin 2\theta)$$
$$z^3 = z^2z = [r^2(\cos 2\theta + i \sin 2\theta)][r(\cos \theta + i \sin \theta)]$$
$$= r^2r[\cos(2\theta + \theta) + i \sin(2\theta + \theta)]$$
$$= r^3(\cos 3\theta + i \sin 3\theta)$$

Example 63 *Use De Moivre's theorem to determine the value of $(1 + i)^{12}$.*
First, change $(1 + i)^{12}$ to polar form.

$$1 + i = r(\cos \theta + i \sin \theta)$$

$$= \sqrt{2}\left(\cos \frac{\pi}{4} + i \sin \frac{\pi}{4}\right) \qquad \text{This is the result of Example 59.}$$

So

$$(1 + i)^{12} = \left[\sqrt{2}\left(\cos \frac{\pi}{4} + i \sin \frac{\pi}{4}\right)\right]^{12}$$

$$= (\sqrt{2})^{12}\left[\cos\left(12 \cdot \frac{\pi}{4}\right) + i \sin\left(12 \cdot \frac{\pi}{4}\right)\right]$$

$$= 2^6(\cos 3\pi + i \sin 3\pi)$$

$$= 64(\cos 3\pi + i \sin 3\pi) \qquad \text{polar form}$$

$$= 64(-1 + i \cdot 0)$$

$$= -64 \qquad\qquad\qquad \text{rectangular form}$$

De Moivre's theorem can be used to prove the following result, which is used to find the nth roots of a complex number. If z is a complex number, then

$$\sqrt[n]{z} = z^{1/n} = r^{1/n}\left(\cos \frac{\theta + k \cdot 360°}{n} + i \sin \frac{\theta + k \cdot 360°}{n}\right)$$

where $k = 0, 1, 2, \ldots , n - 1$ and $r^{1/n}$ is the principal nth root of r.

The numbers

$$r^{1/n}\left(\cos \frac{\theta + k \cdot 360°}{n} + i \sin \frac{\theta + k \cdot 360°}{n}\right)$$

are indeed nth roots of z if they yield z when raised to the nth power. The following steps verify this fact. By De Moivre's theorem,

$$\left[r^{1/n}\left(\cos \frac{\theta + k \cdot 360°}{n} + i \sin \frac{\theta + k \cdot 360°}{n}\right)\right]^n$$

is the same as

$$(r^{1/n})^n\left(\cos n \frac{\theta + k \cdot 360°}{n} + i \sin n \frac{\theta + k \cdot 360°}{n}\right)$$

which simplifies to z, as

$$r[\cos(\theta + k \cdot 360°) + i \sin(\theta + k \cdot 360°)]$$

and then

$$r(\cos \theta + i \sin \theta)$$

which is z in polar form.

Example 64 *Find the five fifth roots of* 1. *Leave them in polar form.*

$$z = 1 = 1 + 0i \quad \begin{cases} r = \sqrt{1^2 + 0^2} = 1 \\ \theta = 0° \quad \text{from } \tan \theta = \dfrac{y}{x} = \dfrac{0}{1} = 0 \end{cases}$$

Here $n = 5$, since there are five fifth roots of z. We shall call the roots z_0, z_1, z_2, z_3, and z_4 to correspond to the k values 0 through 4. Also, the principal fifth root of 1 is 1.

$$z_k = 1^{1/5}\left(\cos \frac{\theta + k \cdot 360°}{5} + i \sin \frac{\theta + k \cdot 360°}{5}\right) \quad k = 0, 1, 2, 3, 4$$

So

$$z_0 = 1\left(\cos \frac{0° + 0 \cdot 360°}{5} + i \sin \frac{0° + 0 \cdot 360°}{5}\right) = 1(\cos 0° + i \sin 0°)$$

$$z_1 = 1\left(\cos \frac{0° + 1 \cdot 360°}{5} + i \sin \frac{0° + 1 \cdot 360°}{5}\right) = 1(\cos 72° + i \sin 72°)$$

$$z_2 = 1\left(\cos \frac{0° + 2 \cdot 360°}{5} + i \sin \frac{0° + 2 \cdot 360°}{5}\right) = 1(\cos 144° + i \sin 144°)$$

$$z_3 = 1\left(\cos \frac{0° + 3 \cdot 360°}{5} + i \sin \frac{0° + 3 \cdot 360°}{5}\right) = 1(\cos 216° + i \sin 216°)$$

$$z_4 = 1\left(\cos \frac{0° + 4 \cdot 360°}{5} + i \sin \frac{0° + 4 \cdot 360°}{5}\right) = 1(\cos 288° + i \sin 288°)$$

EXERCISES 7.13

1. Change each number to polar form. Use Table V in the appendix or a calculator for approximations only when needed.

*(a) $\sqrt{3} + i$ (b) 1

*(c) i (d) -1
*(e) $-i$ (f) $1 - i$
*(g) $1 + i\sqrt{3}$ (h) $2 + 2i$
*(i) $3 + 4i$ (j) $3 - 2i$

2. Change each number from polar to rectangular form.
    *(a) $3(\cos 90° + i \sin 90°)$ (b) $10(\cos 60° + i \sin 60°)$

    *(c) $2\left(\cos \dfrac{\pi}{4} + i \sin \dfrac{\pi}{4}\right)$ (d) $6\left(\cos \dfrac{3\pi}{4} + i \sin \dfrac{3\pi}{4}\right)$

    *(e) $1\left(\cos \dfrac{7\pi}{4} + i \sin \dfrac{7\pi}{4}\right)$ (f) $3(\cos 180° + i \sin 180°)$

    *(g) $7(\cos 270° + i \sin 270°)$ (h) $2(\cos 225° + i \sin 225°)$
    *(i) $4(\cos 150° + i \sin 150°)$ (j) $7(\cos 570° + i \sin 570°)$

3. Compute each product $z_1 z_2$ and leave it in polar form.
    *(a) $z_1 = 3(\cos 45° + i \sin 45°)$, $z_2 = 1(\cos 15° + i \sin 15°)$
    (b) $z_1 = 6(\cos 60° + i \sin 60°)$, $z_2 = 3(\cos 2° + i \sin 2°)$

    *(c) $z_1 = 5\left(\cos \dfrac{\pi}{2} + i \sin \dfrac{\pi}{2}\right)$, $z_2 = 7\left(\cos \dfrac{\pi}{4} + i \sin \dfrac{\pi}{4}\right)$

    (d) $z_1 = 9\left(\cos \dfrac{7\pi}{4} + i \sin \dfrac{7\pi}{4}\right)$, $z_2 = 4\left(\cos \dfrac{\pi}{4} + i \sin \dfrac{\pi}{4}\right)$

    *(e) $z_1 = 1\left(\cos \dfrac{2\pi}{3} + i \sin \dfrac{2\pi}{3}\right)$, $z_2 = 2\left(\cos \dfrac{3\pi}{4} + i \sin \dfrac{3\pi}{4}\right)$

*4. Compute each quotient $\dfrac{z_1}{z_2}$ using the numbers z_1 and z_2 from Exercise 3.
     Leave the quotient in polar form.

5. Use De Moivre's theorem to compute each power.
    *(a) $[3(\cos 30° + i \sin 30°)]^4$ (b) $[2(\cos 60° + i \sin 60°)]^5$
    *(c) $[7(\cos 45° + i \sin 45°)]^4$ (d) $(1 + i\sqrt{3})^5$
    *(e) $(\sqrt{3} + i)^4$ (f) $(i - 1)^8$
    *(g) $(1 + i)^{20}$

6. Find all n nth roots for each part. Write parts (a) to (f) in $a + bi$ form.
    *(a) three cube roots of 1   (b) four fourth roots of 1
    *(c) three cube roots of 8   (d) three cubes roots of $-i$
    *(e) four fourth roots of -1 (f) four fourth roots of $-16i$
    *(g) four fourth roots of $1 + i$ (h) five fifth roots of $1 - i$

7.14 LAWS OF SINES AND COSINES

In Section 7.6 we determined an unknown side or angle of a right triangle. Now
we want to extend that capability to triangles that need not be right triangles. The

law of sines and the **law of cosines** are the two relationships among the sides and angles of a triangle that will provide us with the capability we seek.

First we shall develop the law of sines. Consider this triangle.

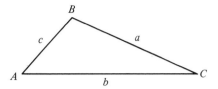

We shall use capital letters A, B, and C for the angles and lowercase letters a, b, and c for the sides opposite those angles; that is, a represents the length of the side opposite angle A. Now construct a perpendicular from B to side b. Call this altitude h.

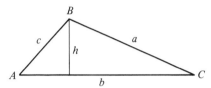

By right-triangle trigonometry applied to the two right triangles created,

$$\sin A = \frac{h}{c} \quad \text{or} \quad h = c \sin A$$

and

$$\sin C = \frac{h}{a} \quad \text{or} \quad h = a \sin C$$

Since $h = c \sin A$ and $h = a \sin C$, we conclude that

$$c \sin A = a \sin C$$

If both sides of this equation are divided by $\sin A \sin C$, the result is

$$\frac{c}{\sin C} = \frac{a}{\sin A}$$

Furthermore, if the altitude h were constructed to a side other than b, then b and $\sin B$ would enter the proportion in the same way as c and $\sin C$ and a and $\sin A$ above. The result is three different-looking proportions, each of which conveys the same idea. The three proportions can be combined into the following compact form.

Law of sines

$$\frac{a}{\sin A} = \frac{b}{\sin B} = \frac{c}{\sin C}$$

The law of sines is intended for use with triangles in which the concern is with two angles and the sides opposite those angles. You will know the values of three of them and seek the value of the fourth.

If desired, you can use the form that has the sines in the numerators—namely,

$$\frac{\sin A}{a} = \frac{\sin B}{b} = \frac{\sin C}{c}$$

Example 65 *Find the length of side x opposite the 23° angle.*
From the law of sines,

$$\frac{x}{\sin 23°} = \frac{15}{\sin 118°}$$

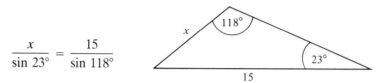

or

$$x = \frac{15(\sin 23°)}{\sin 118°}$$

$$\approx \frac{15(.3907)}{(.8829)} \qquad \sin 118° = \sin(180° - 118°) = \sin 62° \approx .8829$$

$$\approx 6.6$$

Example 66 *Determine the size of the angle opposite the side of length 11.*

$$\frac{\sin x}{11} = \frac{\sin 30°}{7}$$

$$\sin x = \frac{11(\sin 30°)}{7} = \frac{11(.5000)}{7} \approx .7857$$

which means

$$x \approx 52°$$

And a glance at the triangle drawn confirms that 52° looks about right. But what if no triangle had been drawn and it came down to sin x ≈ .7857? While it is possible that x ≈ 52°, is it not also possible that x ≈ 180° − 52°, or 128°? After all, sin 128° = sin(180° − 128°) = sin 52° ≈ .7857. If, in fact, no triangle had been drawn for you, then you would have to consider both angles to be solutions unless you have some justification for rejecting one of the angles.

We have been discussing the *ambiguous case* that occurs when the law of sines is used to determine an unknown angle. Two other outcomes are also possible. Here are all three possibilities.

1. $0 < \sin \theta < 1$, which suggests two possible angles as solutions. You can eliminate one angle *only if* you can justify eliminating it; otherwise, there are two solutions.
2. $\sin \theta = 1$, which means $\theta = 90°$.
3. $\sin \theta > 1$, which means there is no angle; the triangle cannot be constructed. (There is no angle whose sine is greater than 1.)

The *law of cosines* offers another relationship among angles and sides of a triangle. Specifically, it gives a relationship among the three sides and one angle. Consider the next triangle, with angle A at the origin and side b along the horizontal axis.

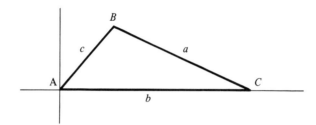

Construct a perpendicular from B to side b. Call this altitude y. The altitude divides side b into two parts; call the length of the left part x; so the right part is of length $b - x$.

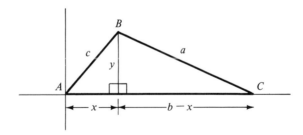

If we apply right-triangle trigonometry to the left triangle, we obtain

$$\sin A = \frac{y}{c} \quad \text{or} \quad y = c \sin A$$

and

$$\cos A = \frac{x}{c} \quad \text{or} \quad x = c \cos A$$

Next, let us focus on the other right triangle. By the Pythagorean theorem,

$$a^2 = (b - x)^2 + y^2$$

Now we can take the two preceding results, $y = c \sin A$ and $x = c \cos A$, and substitute them into $a^2 = (b - x)^2 + y^2$. The result is

$$a^2 = (b - c \cos A)^2 + (c \sin A)^2$$

which we can multiply out and simplify.

$$a^2 = b^2 - 2bc \cos A + c^2\cos^2 A + c^2 \sin^2 A$$
$$a^2 = b^2 - 2bc \cos A + c^2(\cos^2 A + \sin^2 A)$$
$$a^2 = b^2 - 2bc \cos A + c^2$$

Finally,

> **Law of cosines**
>
> $$a^2 = b^2 + c^2 - 2bc \cos A$$

Note that A is the angle between sides b and c—that is, opposite side a.

The law is a generalization of the Pythagorean theorem. Notice that if A is a right angle, then $\cos A = 0$, and $a^2 = b^2 + c^2$, with a being the hypotenuse.

The law of cosines is intended to be used in settings where (1) you know the lengths of all three sides and seek an angle *or* (2) you know the lengths of two sides and the measure of the angle included between them and seek the length of the third side.

Example 67 *Determine the length of the unknown side.*

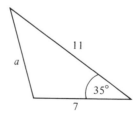

Call the length of the unknown side a. Then by the law of cosines,

$$a^2 = b^2 + c^2 - 2bc \cos A$$

or

$$a^2 = 11^2 + 7^2 - 2 \cdot 11 \cdot 7 \cdot \cos 35°$$

$\begin{cases} \text{We are letting } b = 11 \text{ and} \\ c = 7, \text{ but those two could} \\ \text{have been interchanged.} \end{cases}$

$$\approx 121 + 49 - 154(.8192)$$

$$\approx 44$$

If $a^2 \approx 44$, then $a \approx \sqrt{44}$, or about 6.63 (from Table VI or a calculator).

Example 68 *Find the value of θ in the triangle.*
    Call angle θ by the name A so that it fits the formula of the law of cosines. Then a is 4 and the formula can be used as

$$a^2 = b^2 + c^2 - 2bc \cos A$$

or

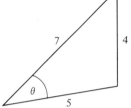

$$4^2 = 7^2 + 5^2 - 2 \cdot 7 \cdot 5 \cdot \cos A$$

$$16 = 49 + 25 - 70 \cdot \cos A$$

which yields

$$\cos A = \frac{-58}{-70} = .8285$$

and then

$$A \approx 34°$$

The angle θ is approximately 34°.

Note: If the cosine of the angle being sought is *negative*, then the angle will be between 90° and 180° (second quadrant). For example, if $\cos A = -.8285$, then $A \approx 34°$ placed in the second quadrant, or $180° - 34°$, which is 146°.

EXERCISES 7.14

*1.   Use the law of sines to determine the size of the unknown angle or side x. Determine angles to the nearest degree and sides to the nearest tenth.

(a)   (b)

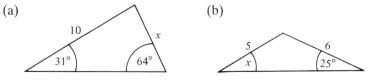

(c)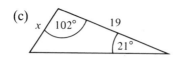

(d)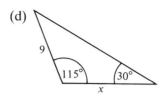

2. Use the law of sines to find the requested side or angle. Each triangle has angles *A*, *B*, and *C* and sides *a*, *b*, and *c*. Side *a* is opposite angle *A*, and so on. Determine angles to the nearest degree and sides to the nearest tenth.

*(a) Find *a* if $A = 42°$, $B = 80°$, and $b = 12$.

(b) Find *c* if $A = 100°$, $C = 29°$, and $a = 17$.

*(c) Find *b* if $B = 50°$, $C = 73°$, and $c = 19$.

(d) Find *A* if $a = 21$, $b = 15$, and $B = 23°$.

*(e) Find *B* if $b = 32$, $c = 6$, and $C = 15°$.

(f) Find *C* if $a = 20$, $c = 8$ and $A = 125°$.

*(g) Find *A*, if $b = 17$, $c = 25$, and $B = 26°$.

(h) Find *B*, if $a = 4$, $c = 30$, and $C = 110°$.

3. Use the law of cosines to determine angle *x* or the unknown side *x*. Determine angles to the nearest degree and sides to the nearest tenth. Use Table VI or a calculator for square roots.

*(a)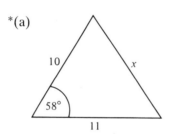

*(b)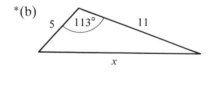

*(c)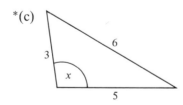

(d)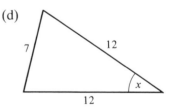

*(e)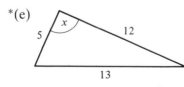

*(f)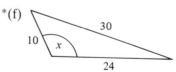

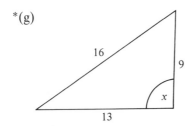

*(g)

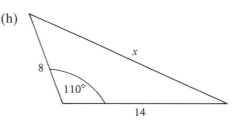

(h)

4. Use the law of cosines to find the requested side or angle. Each triangle has angles A, B, and C and sides a, b, and c. Side a is opposite angle A, and so on. Determine angles to the nearest degree and sides to the nearest whole number. Use Table VI or a calculator for square roots when needed.

*(a) Find a if $b = 6$, $c = 9$, and $A = 34°$.

(b) Find b if $a = 3$, $c = 7$, and $B = 115°$.

*(c) Find c if $a = 20$, $b = 15$, and $C = 73°$.

(d) Find b if $a = 14$, $c = 9$, and $B = 7°$.

*(e) Find a if $c = 10$, $b = 13$, and $A = 106°$.

(f) Find A if $a = 4$, $b = 2$, and $c = 3$.

*(g) Find B if $a = 15$, $b = 11$, and $c = 8$.

(h) Find C if $a = 3$, $b = 4$, and $c = 5$.

5. Express y as a function of x.

*(a)

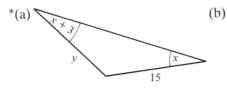

(b)

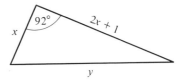

*(c)

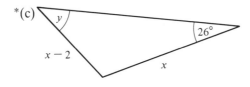

6. Two points (A and B) are 350 feet apart. Across the river is a point C. When a triangle is formed, angle A is 70° and angle B is 35°. How far is it from point A to point C to the nearest foot?

*7. A tree is tilted so that the angle (ϕ) it makes with the ground is 110°. A forest ranger walks to a point 75 feet from the base of the tree and estimates that the angle of inclination (θ) to the top of the tree is 43°.

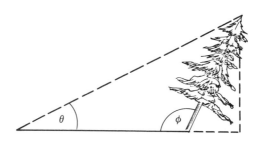

(a) How large is the third angle of the triangle?

(b) How long is the tree (to the nearest foot)?

(c) How high is the top of the tree from the ground?

8. Two boats leave a dock at the same time. Each travels in a straight line. The angle between their paths is 118°. One boat travels at 20 miles per hour, the other at 35 miles per hour.

(a) How far does each boat travel in 4 hours?

(b) How far apart are the boats in 4 hours? (Use a calculator.)

*9. A highway is to be constructed through a region consisting of a hill of rocks and stone. From a point off to the side of the road, the distance to one side of the hill is 230 feet and the distance to the other side is 195 feet. The angle α between the two sightings is 34°. How long a portion of roadway will be constructed once the hill has been eliminated? (Use a calculator.)

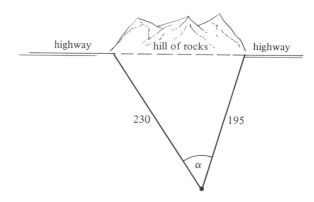

10. A baseball diamond is a square with sides of length 90 feet. The pitcher stands 60.5 feet from home plate and is on the straight line between second base and home. How far is the pitcher's throw to first base in an effort to pick off a runner? (Use a calculator.)

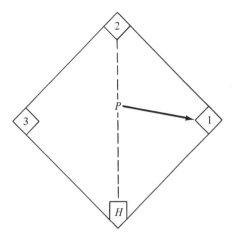

*11. From a distant point the angle of elevation of a kite is 25°. From 200 feet closer in, the angle of elevation is 32°. How high is the kite?

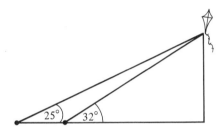

7.15   VECTORS

Vectors are frequently used in science and engineering. A vector quantity is one with both magnitude and direction. We have studied velocity, which is a directed speed, and it is a vector quantity. Recall that + indicated speed in an upward direction and − indicated speed in a downward direction. Of course, the direction can be any angle, not necessarily just up or down.

A **vector** is a directed line segment. Here are two vectors. The point P is the *initial point* of vector $\mathbf{v}_1$; it is the point where $\mathbf{v}_1$ begins. Point Q is the *terminal point* of vector $\mathbf{v}_1$; it is the point where $\mathbf{v}_1$ ends.

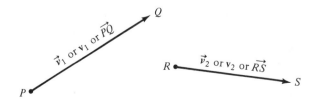

Observe the notation used for vectors. A vector can be named by using the end letters of the line segment and drawing an arrow above them, as $\overrightarrow{PQ}$ or $\overrightarrow{RS}$ above. We can also just pick any letter, such as v, with or without a subscript. On paper you will have to write an arrow above the v: $\vec{v}$. But in books boldface letters, such as **v**, are often used instead. Note that the vector $\overrightarrow{PQ}$ begins at P and ends at Q and $\overrightarrow{RS}$ begins at R and ends at S.

The two vectors drawn below are equal because they have the same **magnitude**, or length, and the same direction. If either vector had an angular position different from the other vector *or* if one of them was longer, then the two vectors would not be equal. The magnitude of a vector **v** is denoted by $|\mathbf{v}|$.

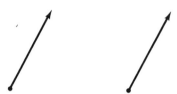

The **sum** of two vectors **u** and **v**, also called the **resultant**, can be obtained as follows. Without changing the angular orientation of **v**, move it so that its initial point is at the terminal point of **u**. Then the vector drawn from the initial point of **u** to the terminal point of **v** will be the sum **u** + **v**. This situation is illustrated next.

Here is another way to determine the sum of two vectors **u** and **v**. Place the two vectors so that their initial points are at the same point. Then complete a parallelogram, as shown below. The diagonal drawn (**w**) with the same initial point as **u** and **v** is the sum **u** + **v**.

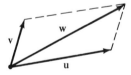

A **scalar** is a real number, a quantity that has magnitude only. When a vector is multiplied by a scalar, the result is a vector called a **scalar multiple** of the original vector. If the scalar is positive, then the scalar multiple will be directed exactly as the original vector; its length will be greater if the scalar is greater than 1 or shorter if the scalar is less than 1. If the scalar is negative, then the scalar multiple will be oriented in the direction opposite that of the original vector. Here are a few examples.

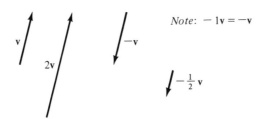

Note: $-1\mathbf{v} = -\mathbf{v}$

Example 69   *Two forces are exerted at the same point. The forces are 3 kilograms and 8 kilograms. The angular positioning of the forces is shown in the diagram below. Determine the magnitude of the resultant force* **F**.

The resultant force can be obtained by constructing the diagonal of a parallelogram that has the two given vectors (representations of the forces) as sides. We begin with this diagram.

Next, complete the parallelogram and note that adjacent interior angles of a parallelogram are supplementary (that is, add up to 180°).

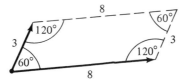

Next, draw the resultant vector **F** and focus on the lower (shaded) triangle. Apply the law of cosines to obtain the magnitude of **F**.

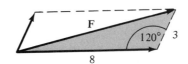

$$|\mathbf{F}|^2 = 8^2 + 3^2 - 2(8)(3)\cos 120°$$

$$= 64 + 9 - 48\left(-\frac{1}{2}\right)$$

$$= 64 + 9 + 24$$

$$= 97$$

Thus

$$|\mathbf{F}| = \sqrt{97}$$

The magnitude of the resultant force $\mathbf{F}$ is $\sqrt{97}$.

A vector $\mathbf{v}$ is not changed if it is moved around the plane, unless its magnitude or angular orientation is changed. So we can place the initial point of the vector $\mathbf{v}$ at the origin $(0, 0)$ of our ordinary xy plane. The terminal point is then at some point (a, b).

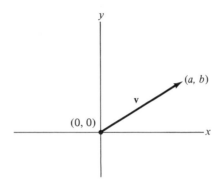

Now, we choose to represent $\mathbf{v}$ by a notation that tells us that its terminal point is (a, b). We write

$$\mathbf{v} = \langle a, b \rangle$$

The symbol $\langle a, b \rangle$ is the ordered pair (a, b) that represents the vector $\mathbf{v}$. We say that a is the **x component** and b is the **y component**. The magnitude of $\mathbf{v}$ is determined by the Pythagorean theorem.

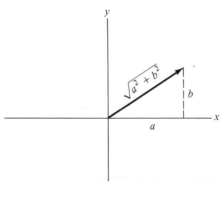

$$|\mathbf{v}| = \sqrt{a^2 + b^2}$$

Example 70   *Determine the magnitude of the vector* $\mathbf{v} = \langle -3, 7 \rangle$.

$$| \mathbf{v} | = \sqrt{(-3)^2 + (7)^2}$$
$$= \sqrt{9 + 49}$$
$$= \sqrt{58}$$

The magnitude of $\mathbf{v}$ is $\sqrt{58}$.

Example 71   *Determine the vector* $\mathbf{v} = \langle x, y \rangle$ *if* $| \mathbf{v} | = 6$ *and the direction angle of* $\mathbf{v}$ *with respect to the x axis is* $60°$.

    The vector is

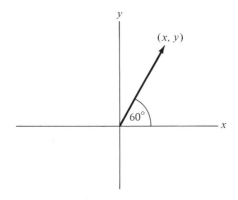

Now recall two relationships from our work with polar coordinates.†

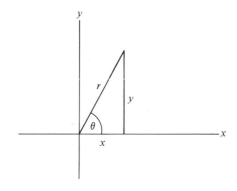

$$x = r \cos \theta$$
$$y = r \sin \theta$$

---

† If you have forgotten these relationships or if you did not study polar coordinates, refer back to page 362.

Here $r = |\mathbf{v}| = 6$ and $\theta = 60°$. Thus

$$x = 6 \cdot \cos 60° = 6 \cdot \frac{1}{2} = 3$$

$$y = 6 \cdot \sin 60° = 6 \cdot \frac{\sqrt{3}}{2} = 3\sqrt{3}$$

So

$$\mathbf{v} = \langle 3, 3\sqrt{3} \rangle$$

A drawing can be made to show that if $\mathbf{u} = \langle a, b \rangle$ and $\mathbf{v} = \langle c, d \rangle$, then the resultant vector is $\langle a + c, b + d \rangle$. This suggests the following rule for addition of vectors.

$$\langle a, b \rangle + \langle c, d \rangle = \langle a + c, b + d \rangle$$

Subtraction of vectors is defined in terms of addition, as in basic algebra.

$$\mathbf{u} - \mathbf{v} = \mathbf{u} + (-\mathbf{v})$$

The rule for scalar multiples is

$$k\langle a, b \rangle = \langle ka, kb \rangle$$

where k is a scalar.

Example 72   *Let* $\mathbf{u} = \langle 9, 3 \rangle$ *and* $\mathbf{v} = \langle 5, -6 \rangle$. Determine
      (a) $\mathbf{u} + \mathbf{v}$ (b) $\mathbf{u} - \mathbf{v}$ (c) $7\mathbf{u}$ (d) $-4\mathbf{u} + 8\mathbf{v}$.

(a) $\begin{aligned}\mathbf{u} + \mathbf{v} &= \langle 9, 3 \rangle + \langle 5, -6 \rangle \\ &= \langle 9 + 5, 3 - 6 \rangle \\ &= \langle 14, -3 \rangle \end{aligned}$

(b) $\begin{aligned}\mathbf{u} - \mathbf{v} &= \mathbf{u} + (-\mathbf{v}) \\ &= \langle 9, 3 \rangle + \langle -5, 6 \rangle \\ &= \langle 9 - 5, 3 + 6 \rangle \\ &= \langle 4, 9 \rangle \end{aligned}$

(c) $\begin{aligned}7\mathbf{u} &= 7\langle 9, 3 \rangle \\ &= \langle 7 \cdot 9, 7 \cdot 3 \rangle \\ &= \langle 63, 21 \rangle \end{aligned}$

(d) $-4\mathbf{u} + 8\mathbf{v} = -4\langle 9, 3\rangle + 8\langle 5, -6\rangle$
$$= \langle -4 \cdot 9, -4 \cdot 3\rangle + \langle 8 \cdot 5, 8(-6)\rangle$$
$$= \langle -36, -12\rangle + \langle 40, -48\rangle$$
$$= \langle -36 + 40, -12 - 48\rangle$$
$$= \langle 4, -60\rangle$$

EXERCISES 7.15

1. In each exercise two forces measured in kilograms (kg) are exerted at the same point. Given are the two forces and the angle θ between them. Determine the magnitude of the resultant force to the nearest kg.

   *(a) 10 kg, 8 kg, $\theta = 30°$ (b) 3 kg, 5 kg, $\theta = 45°$
   *(c) 15 kg, 6 kg, $\theta = 150°$ (d) 20 kg, 8 kg, $\theta = 120°$
   *(e) 7 kg, 6 kg, $\theta = 34°$ (f) 10 kg, 2 kg, $\theta = 98°$

2. Determine the magnitude of each vector.

   *(a) $\langle 3, 4\rangle$ (b) $\langle 5, 12\rangle$
   *(c) $\langle -3, 0\rangle$ (d) $\langle 0, 4\rangle$
   *(e) $\langle -9, -9\rangle$ (f) $\langle 10, -3\rangle$
   *(g) $\left\langle -\dfrac{1}{5}, \dfrac{2\sqrt{6}}{5}\right\rangle$ (h) $\left\langle \dfrac{\sqrt{5}}{3}, \dfrac{2}{3}\right\rangle$
   *(i) $\langle 1, 0\rangle$ (j) $\langle 0, 1\rangle$

*3. Any vector whose magnitude is 1 is called a **unit vector**.

   (a) Which of the vectors in Exercise 2 are unit vectors?
   (b) Recall the unit circle and trigonometric points. List six unit vectors other than those noted in part (a).

4. Determine the vector $\mathbf{v}$ that has the given magnitude $|\mathbf{v}|$ and direction angle θ.

   *(a) $|\mathbf{v}| = 8, \theta = 30°$ (b) $|\mathbf{v}| = 10, \theta = 45°$
   *(c) $|\mathbf{v}| = 3, \theta = 90°$ (d) $|\mathbf{v}| = 2, \theta = 120°$
   *(e) $|\mathbf{v}| = \frac{1}{2}, \theta = 210°$ (f) $|\mathbf{v}| = 7, \theta = 315°$
   *(g) $|\mathbf{v}| = 1, \theta = 135°$ (h) $|\mathbf{v}| = 9, \theta = 240°$

5. Given vector $\mathbf{v}$, determine its direction angle θ by using

   $$\theta = \tan^{-1}\frac{y}{x}$$

   Be sure to draw the vector in order to get θ in the proper quadrant. After all, arctangent is only defined for $-90° < \theta < 90°$; yet vectors can be in any quadrant. Express the direction as an angle between $0°$ and $360°$.

   *(a) $\langle 4, 4\rangle$ (b) $\langle 1, \sqrt{3}\rangle$
   *(c) $\langle 2, -2\rangle$ (d) $\langle 1, -\sqrt{3}\rangle$

*(e) $\langle 5, 0 \rangle$ (f) $\langle 3, \sqrt{3} \rangle$

*(g) $\langle -1, \sqrt{3} \rangle$ (h) $\langle -6, 6 \rangle$

*(i) $\langle -3, -\sqrt{3} \rangle$ (j) $\langle -7, -7 \rangle$

6. Let $\mathbf{u} = \langle 7, -2 \rangle$ and $\mathbf{v} = \langle 1, 6 \rangle$. Determine each of the following vectors.

    *(a) $\mathbf{u} + \mathbf{v}$ (b) $\mathbf{u} - \mathbf{v}$

    *(c) $6\mathbf{u}$ (d) $-8\mathbf{v}$

    *(e) $3\mathbf{u} + 2\mathbf{v}$ (f) $\mathbf{v} - \mathbf{u}$

    *(g) $3\mathbf{v} - 8\mathbf{u}$ (h) $-14\mathbf{u} - 9\mathbf{v}$

    *(i) $0\mathbf{u}$ (j) $0\mathbf{v}$

7. The vector obtained in Parts (i) and (j) of Exercise 6 is called the **zero vector**; $\mathbf{0} = \langle 0, 0 \rangle$. Verify each of these properties involving the zero vector.

    (a) $k\mathbf{0} = \mathbf{0}$ (b) $\mathbf{v} + \mathbf{0} = \mathbf{v}$

    (c) $\mathbf{v} + (-\mathbf{v}) = \mathbf{0}$ (d) $0\mathbf{v} = \mathbf{0}$

REVIEW EXERCISES FOR CHAPTER 7

1. Determine the exact value of each expression.

    *(a) $\sin 135°$ (b) $\cos(-315°)$

    *(c) $\cos 510°$ (d) $\sin 960°$

    *(e) $\csc\left(-\dfrac{2\pi}{3}\right)$ (f) $\tan \dfrac{29\pi}{6}$

    *(g) $\sec(-585°)$ (h) $\csc 1050°$

    *(i) $\cot \dfrac{11\pi}{6}$ (j) $\sin(-50\pi)$

2. If $\sin u = \frac{2}{3}$ and $\cos v = \frac{1}{5}$, determine the value of each expression given next. Assume u and v are in the first quadrant.

    *(a) $\cos u$ (b) $\sin v$

    *(c) $\sin(u - v)$ (d) $\cos(u - v)$

    *(e) $\sin 2u$ (f) $\cos 2v$

    *(g) $\sin(-v)$ (h) $\tan \dfrac{u}{2}$

    *(i) $\cos \dfrac{1}{2} v$ (j) $\sin \dfrac{1}{2} u$

3. Solve each equation for all values of the variable.

    *(a) $2 \sin^2 x + 9 \sin x - 5 = 0$

    (b) $2 \cos^3 u - \cos u = 0$

    *(c) $2 \sin 2\theta + 1 = 0$

4. Sketch one cycle of the graph of each function.

*(a) $y = \sin\left(x + \dfrac{\pi}{2}\right)$ (b) $y = 3 \cos x$

*(c) $y = -2 \sin 4x$ (d) $y = 2 \sin (x - \pi)$

5. Change from radians to degrees.

*(a) $\dfrac{11\pi}{6}$ (b) $\dfrac{\pi}{36}$

6. Change from degrees to radians.
   *(a) $150°$ (b) $80°$

7. If $\csc \theta = -5$ and θ is in the fourth quadrant, determine each value.
   *(a) $\cos \theta$ (b) $\tan \theta$

*8. A central angle determines an arc of length 12 inches on a circle of *diameter* 8 inches. How many radians are in the angle?

9. Evaluate each expression.

*(a) $\cos\left(\sin^{-1}\dfrac{\sqrt{3}}{2}\right)$ (b) $\tan\left(\cos^{-1}\dfrac{\sqrt{2}}{2}\right)$

*(c) $\sin\left[\cos^{-1}\left(-\dfrac{2}{7}\right)\right]$ (d) $\cos^{-1}\left(-\dfrac{1}{2}\right)$

*(e) $\sec^{-1}\left(-\dfrac{2}{\sqrt{3}}\right)$ (f) $\sec\left(\tan^{-1}\dfrac{3}{2}\right)$

*10. If $\tan 2\theta = 2\sqrt{2}$ and 2θ is in the first quadrant, determine $\cos \theta$ and $\sin \theta$.

11. Prove each identity.
    (a) $\cos u(\sec u - \cos u) = \sin^2 u$
    (b) $\sin t \tan t + \cos t = \sec t$
    (c) $\dfrac{\cos^2\theta}{\cot \theta} = \dfrac{1}{2} \sin 2\theta$
    (d) $\sin\left(x + \dfrac{3\pi}{2}\right) = -\cos x$

*12. Change $r = 5 + 5 \sin \theta$ to an equation in rectangular coordinates.

13. Change $x^2 + y^2 - 8y + 8 = 0$ to an equation in polar coordinates.

14. Obtain points and sketch the graph.
    *(a) $r = 4 - 4 \sin \theta$ (cardioid)
    (b) $r^2 = 16 \sin 2\theta$ (lemniscate)

15. Use the law of sines or law of cosines to determine the requested side (to the nearest tenth) or angle (to the nearest degree). Each triangle has angles A, B, and C and sides a, b, and c. Side a is opposite angle A and so on.

*(a) Find c if $a = 10$, $b = 12$, and $C = 23°$.

(b) Find b if $A = 35°$, $B = 105°$, and $a = 60$.

*(c) Find C if $b = 20$, $c = 15$, and $B = 50°$.

(d) Find A if $a = 7$, $b = 9$, and $c = 10$.

*16. Determine the magnitude of the vector $\langle 4, -7 \rangle$.

17. Two forces, 30 kg and 10 kg, are exerted at the same point. The angle between them is 60°. Determine the magnitude of the resultant force.

*18. Determine the vector **v** that has magnitude 12 and direction angle 45°.

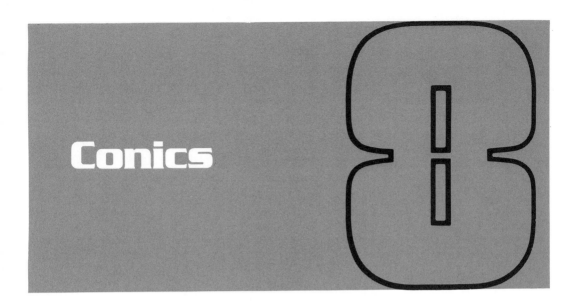

Conics

8.1 INTRODUCTION

We now begin a study of curves described by second-degree equations. Four kinds of curves will be studied: circles, parabolas, ellipses, and hyperbolas. Each of these curves is an example of a **conic section** or, less formally, a **conic**. Each type of curve can be obtained by the intersection of a plane with a right circular cone (hence the word *conic*). The nature of the intersecting plane determines which curve results.

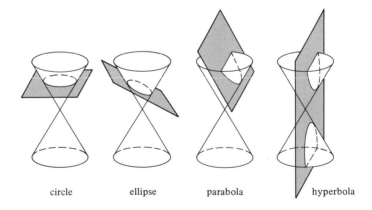

circle   ellipse   parabola   hyperbola

Conics were originally studied by the early Greeks. They were named by Apollonius about 225 B.C.

Each of the four conics will be defined as a set of points that satisfies a distance criterion. As a result, the distance formula (from Chapter 2) will be used to derive formulas for all four conics.

8.2 CIRCLES

A **circle** is a set of points whose distance from a fixed point is constant. The fixed point is called the **center**. The constant distance is called the **radius**. Consider a circle with radius r, center (h, k), and points of the form (x, y).

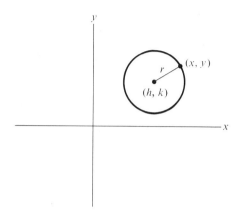

If the distance formula, $d = \sqrt{(x_2 - x_1)^2 + (y_2 - y_1)^2}$, is applied to say that the distance between the points (x, y) and (h, k) is r, the resulting equation is

$$\sqrt{(x - h)^2 + (y - k)^2} = r$$

On squaring both sides, we obtain the standard form for the equation of a circle.

Circle

$$(x - h)^2 + (y - k)^2 = r^2$$

center: (h, k)

radius: r

Example 1   *Write an equation of the circle with center at $(5, -3)$ and radius 9.*
The circle is

$$(x - 5)^2 + (y + 3)^2 = 81$$

Example 2   *Determine the center and radius of the circle $(x + 4)^2 + (y - 1)^2 = 7$ and sketch its graph.*
The equation $(x + 4)^2 + (y - 1)^2 = 7$ is already in the standard form $(x - h)^2 + (y - k)^2 = r^2$. Here $h = -4$, $k = 1$, and $r^2 = 7$. So the center is at $(-4, 1)$ and the radius is $\sqrt{7}$. The graph:

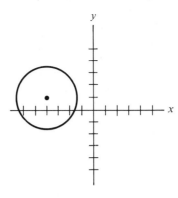

Note: Throughout this chapter it will be necessary for graphing purposes to approximate the values of the square root of a number that is not a perfect square. This can be done several ways.

1. Using Table VI.
2. Using a calculator.
3. Estimation based on knowing (from memorization) a few square root approximations, such as

$$\sqrt{2} \approx 1.4$$

$$\sqrt{3} \approx 1.7$$

$$\sqrt{5} \approx 2.2$$

$$\sqrt{7} \approx 2.6$$

4. Estimation based on known square roots of perfect squares. For example, $\sqrt{13}$ is between 3 and 4 because $\sqrt{13}$ is between $\sqrt{9}$ and $\sqrt{16}$.

Example 3 *Determine the center and radius of the circle $x^2 + y^2 + 8x - 10y - 8 = 0$.*
To find the center of the circle and radius, change the equation to the standard form,

$$(x - h)^2 + (y - k)^2 = r^2$$

This can be done by grouping the x terms together and the y terms together and then completing the two squares. Begin with

$$x^2 + y^2 + 8x - 10y - 8 = 0$$

First, group the terms as suggested.

$$(x^2 + 8x) + (y^2 - 10y) = 8$$

Completing the square for $x^2 + 8x$ yields $(x + 4)^2$ or $x^2 + 8x + 16$. So 16 must be added to the right side of the equation to compensate for the additional 16 on the left side.

$$(x + 4)^2 + (y^2 - 10y) = 8 + 16$$

Similarly, completing the square for $y^2 - 10y$ yields $(y - 5)^2$, or $y^2 - 10y + 25$. So 25 must be added to the right side of the equation. The result is

$$(x + 4)^2 + (y - 5)^2 = 8 + 16 + 25$$

or

$$(x + 4)^2 + (y - 5)^2 = 49$$

The center is at $(-4, 5)$ and the radius is 7.

Example 4 *Write the equation of the circle with center at the origin and radius 5.*
With center at $(0, 0)$ and radius 5, we have

$$(x - 0)^2 + (y - 0)^2 = 5^2$$

or

$$x^2 + y^2 = 25$$

In general, a circle with center at the origin and radius r has the form shown in the next box.

Circle

$$x^2 + y^2 = r^2$$

center: $(0, 0)$

radius: r

The fact that all points on a circle are the same distance from the center leads to many applications. A roll of tape is made circular so that the tape can be taken off smoothly and evenly. Your car rides well because the tires are round. If a telephone dial were not circular, it would be very awkward to use.

The following photo is an 8-hour exposure of the region surrounding the north celestial pole. It shows how the stars move in concentric circular paths, with the pole as center of each circular path.

(Lick Observatory Photograph)

Center-pivot irrigation is an automatic irrigation system that is based on the properties of a circle. Water is pumped through a radius pipe that runs from the center of the field out to the edge of the circle. Along the radius pipe are dozens of sprinkler outlets through which water can be released and applied to the land. The long radial pipe is mounted on wheels and driven by electric power. The pipe sweeps around the entire field in much the same way that a clock hand sweeps around the face of the clock. The next photo shows the use of center-pivot irrigation on a midwestern farm.

(U.S. Department of Agriculture, Soil Conservation Service)

EXERCISES 8.2

Answers to starred exercises are given in the back of the book.

1. Write the equation of the circle with the given center and radius.
   *(a)   center: (0, 0); radius: 6
   (b)   center: (0, 0); radius: 3

*(c)   center: $(0, 0)$; radius: $\sqrt{7}$

(d)   center: $(0, 0)$; radius: $\sqrt{13}$

*(e)   center: $(3, 12)$; radius: 4

(f)   center: $(1, 0)$; radius: 2

*(g)   center: $(-2, -7)$; radius: 10

(h)   center: $(0, -9)$; radius: 1

*(i)   center: $(5, -4)$; radius: $\sqrt{14}$

(j)   center: $(-3, 8)$; radius: $\sqrt{73}$

2.   Determine the center and radius of each circle and sketch its graph.

*(a) $x^2 + y^2 = 49$ (b) $x^2 + y^2 = 144$

*(c) $x^2 + y^2 = 15$ (d) $x^2 + y^2 = 51$

*(e) $x^2 + (y - 3)^2 = 81$ (f) $(x - 7)^2 + y^2 = 16$

*(g) $(x - 4)^2 + (y - 5)^2 = 64$ (h) $(x - 9)^2 + (y + 8)^2 = 1$

*(i) $(x + 2)^2 + (y - 9)^2 = 100$ (j) $(x + 4)^2 + (y + 15)^2 = 25$

*(k) $(x - 6)^2 + (y + 1)^2 = 19$ (l) $(x + 7)^2 + (y - 3)^2 = 5$

3.   Determine the center and radius of each circle and sketch its graph.

*(a) $x^2 + y^2 + 4x + 6y + 12 = 0$

(b) $x^2 + y^2 + 12x - 10y + 25 = 0$

*(c) $x^2 + y^2 - 6x - 2y = 54$

(d) $x^2 + y^2 + 4x - 6y + 8 = 0$

*(e) $x^2 + y^2 - 14x - 51 = 0$

(f) $x^2 + y^2 + 10x = 9$

*(g) $x^2 + y^2 - 3y - 1 = 0$

(h) $x^2 + y^2 + 7y + 8 = 0$

*(i) $x^2 + y^2 - 3x + y = 1$

(j) $x^2 + y^2 + 5x - 3y - 6 = 0$

4.   The *unit circle* is the circle with center at the origin and radius 1. Write the equation of the unit circle.

5.   Determine the equation of the circle that has the specified center and passes through the specified point.

*(a)   center: $(0, 0)$; through $(4, -3)$

(b)   center: $(0, 2)$; through $(3, 6)$

*(c)   center: $(1, -4)$; through $(6, 8)$

(d)   center: $(9, 0)$; through $(1, -6)$

*(e)   center: $(4, -3)$; through $(2, 0)$

(f)   center: $(3, 5)$; through $(4, -2)$

*(g)   center: $(-5, 3)$; through $(-1, 6)$

8.3 PARABOLAS

A **parabola** is the set of points whose distances from a fixed point (called the **focus**) and a fixed line (called the **directrix**) are equal. The point of the parabola that lies on the perpendicular from the focus to the directrix is called the **vertex**. The vertex is halfway between the focus and the directrix. Consider the focus to be the point $(p, 0)$ and the directrix to be the line $x = -p$.

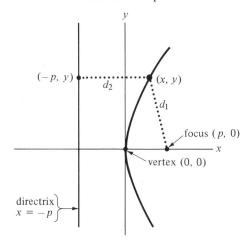

Here distances d_1 and d_2 are equal, where d_1 is the distance from any point (x, y) of the parabola to the focus $(p, 0)$ and d_2 is the distance from the point (x, y) to the directrix. The distance d_2 from a point to a line is measured on the perpendicular from (x, y) to the line $x = -p$; so the y coordinate of the point on $x = -p$ is the same as that of the point (x, y). Thus d_2 is the distance between (x, y) and $(-p, y)$. The relationship $d_1 = d_2$ can be written

$$\sqrt{(x - p)^2 + (y - 0)^2} = |x + p|$$

Squaring both sides yields

$$(x - p)^2 + y^2 = x^2 + 2px + p^2$$

or

$$x^2 - 2px + p^2 + y^2 = x^2 + 2px + p^2$$

which can be simplified to the form shown in the next box.

Parabola

$$y^2 = 4px$$

vertex: $(0, 0)$

focus: $(p, 0)$

directrix: $x = -p$

> Parabolas of the form $y^2 = 4px$
>
> 1. Open to the right if $p > 0$.
> 2. Open to the left if $p < 0$.

Example 5 *Determine the vertex, focus, and directrix of $y^2 = 4x$.*

The equation $y^2 = 4x$ is of the form $y^2 = 4px$. Here $4p = 4$; so $p = 1$. This means that the focus $(p, 0)$ is at $(1, 0)$, the directrix $x = -p$ is $x = -1$, and the vertex, of course, is at the origin $(0, 0)$.

Example 6 *Write the equation of the parabola with vertex at the origin, focus $(3, 0)$, and directrix $x = -3$.*

The equation is of the form $y^2 = 4px$. The focus $(p, 0)$ is $(3, 0)$ in this example; so $p = 3$. This means that the equation of the parabola is $y^2 = 4(3)x$, or $y^2 = 12x$.

Example 7 *Determine the focus, directrix, and vertex of $y^2 = -2x$. Then sketch the graph of the parabola.*

The standard form is $y^2 = 4px$ and the given curve is $y^2 = -2x$. This means that $4p = -2$ or $p = -\frac{1}{2}$. So the focus is $(-\frac{1}{2}, 0)$ and the directrix is $x = \frac{1}{2}$. The vertex is $(0, 0)$.

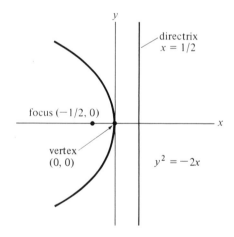

As you sketch the curve, keep in mind that all points of a parabola are the same distance from the focus as they are from the directrix. You might also consider obtaining a few points to guide the curve through. For example, if $x = -2$, then $y^2 = 4$ or $y = \pm 2$. This means that the parabola passes through $(-2, -2)$ and $(-2, 2)$.

If the focus is at $(0, p)$ and the directrix is $y = -p$, then the parabola will appear as follows.

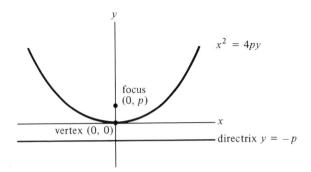

The equation is

Parabola

$$x^2 = 4py$$

vertex: $(0, 0)$

focus: $(0, p)$

directrix: $y = -p$

Parabolas of the form $x^2 = 4py$

1. Open upward if $p > 0$.
2. Open downward if $p < 0$.

Example 8 *Write the equation of the parabola with focus* $(0, -2)$, *directrix* $y = 2$, *and vertex* $(0, 0)$.

The focus $(0, p)$ is $(0, -2)$; so $p = -2$. Thus $x^2 = 4py$ becomes $x^2 = 4(-2)y$ or $x^2 = -8y$.

Example 9 *Determine the focus, directrix, and vertex of* $x^2 = 6y$. *Then sketch the graph of the parabola.*

The standard form is $x^2 = 4py$ and the given curve is $x^2 = 6y$. This means that $4p = 6$, or $p = \frac{3}{2}$. So the focus is $(0, \frac{3}{2})$ and the directrix is $y = -\frac{3}{2}$. The vertex is $(0, 0)$.

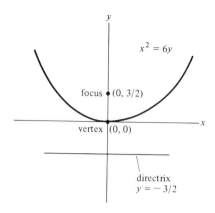

There are many uses for parabola-shaped objects: automobile headlights and flashlights have parabolic mirrors. The bulb of a flashlight is placed at the focus of the parabola so that all light rays leaving the bulb strike the parabolic mirror and are reflected as a powerful concentrated beam of parallel rays.

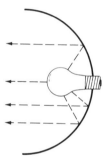

Reflecting telescopes use parabolic mirrors to concentrate (at the focus) the light received from faint objects. Radio, television, and radar waves are beamed efficiently when emitted from the focus of a parabolic transmitter.

The French have built a huge oven that uses a 140-foot high parabolic mirror. The sun's rays are reflected and then concentrated at the focus of the parabola, where the oven is placed. Temperatures of more than 6000° are produced.

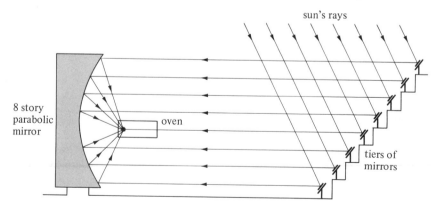

EXERCISES 8.3

1. Determine the vertex, focus, and directrix of each parabola. Then sketch its graph.

   *(a) $y^2 = 8x$ (b) $y^2 = -8x$

   *(c) $x^2 = 12y$ (d) $x^2 = -12y$

   *(e) $y^2 = 10x$ (f) $y^2 = x$

   *(g) $y^2 = -x$ (h) $x^2 = -3y$

   *(i) $x^2 = -y$ (j) $x^2 = y$

   *(k) $y^2 - 4x = 0$ (l) $y^2 + 4x = 0$

   *(m) $x^2 - 2y = 0$ (n) $3x^2 - 4y = 0$

   *(o) $22x + 3y^2 = 0$ (p) $y = \pm 2\sqrt{x}$

   *(q) $x = \pm\sqrt{3y}$

2. Write the equation of the parabola with given focus and directrix.

   *(a) focus $(5, 0)$, directrix $x = -5$

   (b) focus $(-5, 0)$, directrix $x = 5$

   *(c) focus $(0, \frac{1}{2})$, directrix $y = -\frac{1}{2}$

   (d) focus $(0, -2)$, directrix $y = 2$

   *(e) focus $(1, 0)$, directrix $x + 1 = 0$

   (f) focus $(0, -3)$, directrix $y - 3 = 0$

3. Use the given information to determine the equation of each parabola. All have vertex $(0, 0)$.

   *(a) focus $(0, 4)$, opens upward

   (b) focus $(0, -4)$, opens downward

   *(c) focus $(-4, 0)$, opens to the left

   (d) focus $(4, 0)$, opens to the right

   *(e) directrix $x = 6$, opens to the left

   (f) directrix $x = 10$, opens to the left

   *(g) directrix $x = -10$, opens to the right

   (h) directrix $y = -2$, opens upward

   *(i) directrix $y = 2$, opens downward

   (j) directrix $y = 1$, opens downward

8.4 ELLIPSES

An **ellipse** is the set of points the sum of whose distances from two fixed points is constant. The two fixed points are called **foci**. The constant that represents the sum of the two distances will be called $2a$ for reasons that will become apparent later. If the foci are at $(c, 0)$ and $(-c, 0)$, then the ellipse appears as

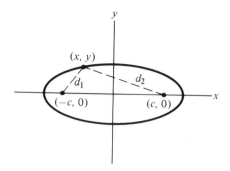

The sum of the distances, $d_1 + d_2$, of any point (x, y) of the ellipse from $(-c, 0)$ and from $(c, 0)$ is equal to the constant $2a$.

$$d_1 + d_2 = 2a$$

Applying the distance formula to obtain values for d_1 and d_2 produces

$$\sqrt{(x + c)^2 + (y - 0)^2} + \sqrt{(x - c)^2 + (y - 0)^2} = 2a$$

Separate the radicals and then square both sides. This process yields, in steps,

$$\sqrt{(x + c)^2 + y^2} = 2a - \sqrt{(x - c)^2 + y^2}$$
$$(x + c)^2 + y^2 = (2a)^2 + (x - c)^2 + y^2 - 4a\sqrt{(x - c)^2 + y^2}$$
$$x^2 + 2cx + c^2 + y^2 = 4a^2 + x^2 - 2cx + c^2 + y^2 - 4a\sqrt{(x - c)^2 + y^2}$$
$$4cx - 4a^2 = -4a\sqrt{(x - c)^2 + y^2}$$
$$cx - a^2 = -a\sqrt{(x - c)^2 + y^2}$$
$$a^2 - cx = a\sqrt{(x - c)^2 + y^2}$$

Now square both sides again.

$$(a^2 - cx)^2 = a^2[(x - c)^2 + y^2]$$
$$a^4 - 2a^2cx + c^2x^2 = a^2(x^2 - 2cx + c^2 + y^2)$$
$$a^4 - 2a^2cx + c^2x^2 = a^2x^2 - 2a^2cx + a^2c^2 + a^2y^2$$
$$a^4 + c^2x^2 = a^2x^2 + a^2c^2 + a^2y^2$$

This last equation can be rewritten

$$a^2x^2 - c^2x^2 + a^2y^2 = a^4 - a^2c^2$$

and factored as

$$(a^2 - c^2)x^2 + a^2y^2 = a^2(a^2 - c^2)$$

From the ellipse sketched earlier you can see that $2a$ (that is, $d_1 + d_2$) is greater than $2c$. Thus $a^2 - c^2$ is a positive number. Let $b^2 = a^2 - c^2$. After making this substitution, the equation above simplifies to

$$b^2x^2 + a^2y^2 = a^2b^2$$

When both sides of this equation are divided by the nonzero number a^2b^2, the final result is

$$\frac{x^2}{a^2} + \frac{y^2}{b^2} = 1$$

The intercepts are useful in graphing an ellipse. If $y = 0$, $x = \pm a$. So $(\pm a, 0)$ are points of the ellipse. Also, if $x = 0$, $y = \pm b$. So $(0, \pm b)$ are points of the ellipse. The line segment that runs from $(-a, 0)$ to $(a, 0)$ is called the **major axis.** The line segment that runs from $(0, -b)$ to $(0, b)$ is called the **minor axis.** The major axis (length $2a$) is longer than the minor axis (length $2b$), since $a > b$. The endpoints of the major axis are called the **vertices** (plural of *vertex*).

Ellipse

$$\frac{x^2}{a^2} + \frac{y^2}{b^2} = 1$$

vertices: $(\pm a, 0)$

foci: $(\pm c, 0)$

useful points: $(0, \pm b)$

$c^2 = a^2 - b^2; a > b$

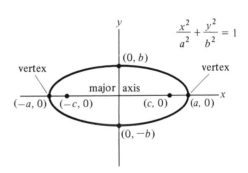

Example 10 *Sketch the ellipse*

$$\frac{x^2}{16} + \frac{y^2}{3} = 1$$

This equation fits the form of the ellipse we have studied. Here $a = 4$ and $b = \sqrt{3}$. The vertices are $(\pm 4, 0)$. The other two intercepts are $(0, \pm\sqrt{3})$. The graph is

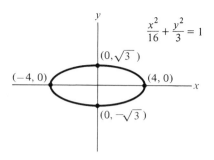

Although not needed here, the foci can be determined from $c^2 = a^2 - b^2$. Here $b^2 = 3$ and $a^2 = 16$; so $c^2 = 13$ or $c = \pm\sqrt{13}$. The foci are $(\pm\sqrt{13}, 0)$. The length of the major axis is 8. The minor axis is $2\sqrt{3}$ units long.

If the foci are at $(0, c)$ and $(0, -c)$, then the equation of the ellipse will be different and its orientation will be different, as shown next.

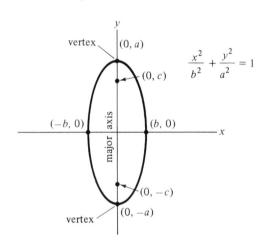

Ellipse

$$\frac{x^2}{b^2} + \frac{y^2}{a^2} = 1$$

vertices: $(0, \pm a)$
foci: $(0, \pm c)$
useful points: $(\pm b, 0)$
$c^2 = a^2 - b^2;\ a > b$

Example 11 *Write the given equation of an ellipse in standard form. Then sketch its graph.*

$$9x^2 + 4y^2 = 36.$$

Divide $9x^2 + 4y^2 = 36$ by 36. Doing so will yield the . . . $= 1$ form that is desired:

$$\frac{9x^2}{36} + \frac{4y^2}{36} = \frac{36}{36}$$

or

$$\frac{x^2}{4} + \frac{y^2}{9} = 1$$

This ellipse is of the second form, with $a = 3$ and $b = 2$. The vertices are at $(0, \pm 3)$ and the other intercepts are $(\pm 2, 0)$. The graph is

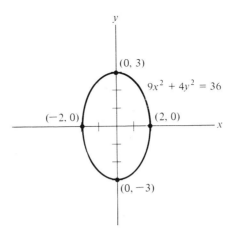

Example 12 *Determine the equation of the ellipse with vertices* $(0, \pm 5)$ *and foci* $(0, \pm 2)$.
Then sketch the graph.

We have $(0, \pm a) = (0, \pm 5)$ and $(0, \pm c) = (0, \pm 2)$. The standard form of the ellipse is

$$\frac{x^2}{b^2} + \frac{y^2}{a^2} = 1$$

The value of b can be computed by using $c^2 = a^2 - b^2$.

$$b^2 = 25 - 4 = 21$$

The desired equation, then, is

$$\frac{x^2}{21} + \frac{y^2}{25} = 1$$

The graph is

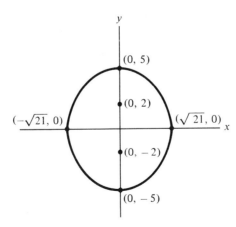

The point $(0, 0)$ is considered to be the *center* of all the ellipses studied in this section. We say that such ellipses are centered about the origin.

The *eccentricity e* is a measure of how flat or round the ellipse is. Eccentricity can be determined from

$$e = \frac{c}{a} = \frac{\sqrt{a^2 - b^2}}{a}$$

If $a = b$, then $a^2 - b^2 = 0$ and $e = 0$. And $a = b$ if the "ellipse" is a circle. The smaller b is relative to a, the closer the value of $\sqrt{a^2 - b^2}$ is to a and thus the closer c/a is to 1. And the smaller b is relative to a, the flatter is the ellipse. Thus for an ellipse, $0 \le e < 1$; and the larger the eccentricity, the flatter the ellipse.

The paths of planets and some comets are ellipses. Satellites launched by NASA and others orbit the earth in paths that are ellipses.

Recall that an ellipse is the set of points the sum of whose distances from two fixed points is constant. Using this concept, you can draw an ellipse with a piece of string, two tacks, and a pencil. Tack down the ends of the string, keeping it loose. Then place a pencil against the string, making the string taut.

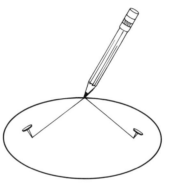

Finally, move the pencil while keeping the string taut.

The inside of the Mormon Tabernacle in Salt Lake City is elliptical. The reading desk (*D* in the next illustration) is near one of the foci. Listeners at the other end of this large building and near the other focus can hear the sound made by dropping a pin on the reading desk. The curved surfaces act as elliptical sound mirrors, thus directing and concentrating the sound toward the other focus.

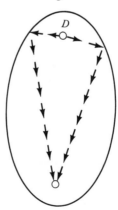

EXERCISES 8.4

1. Obtain the vertices, the other two intercepts, and the foci. Then sketch the graph.

*(a) $\dfrac{x^2}{9} + \dfrac{y^2}{4} = 1$ (b) $\dfrac{x^2}{16} + \dfrac{y^2}{9} = 1$

*(c) $\dfrac{x^2}{9} + \dfrac{y^2}{16} = 1$ (d) $\dfrac{x^2}{16} + \dfrac{y^2}{25} = 1$

*(e) $\dfrac{x^2}{81} + \dfrac{y^2}{49} = 1$ (f) $\dfrac{x^2}{64} + \dfrac{y^2}{144} = 1$

*(g) $\dfrac{x^2}{7} + \dfrac{y^2}{10} = 1$ (h) $\dfrac{x^2}{15} + \dfrac{y^2}{6} = 1$

*(i) $\dfrac{x^2}{\frac{1}{4}} + \dfrac{y^2}{3} = 1$ (j) $\dfrac{x^2}{5} + \dfrac{y^2}{\frac{4}{9}} = 1$

2. Write the given equation in standard form. Then sketch the graph of each ellipse.

*(a) $4x^2 + 9y^2 = 36$ (b) $4x^2 + y^2 = 4$
*(c) $25x^2 + 4y^2 = 100$ (d) $36x^2 + 9y^2 = 324$
*(e) $5x^2 + 9y^2 = 45$ (f) $16x^2 + 3y^2 = 48$
*(g) $x^2 + 16y^2 = 4$ (h) $4x^2 + 25y^2 = 9$
*(i) $9x^2 + y^2 = 25$ (j) $9x^2 + y^2 = 4$

3. Determine the length of the major axis and minor axis of each ellipse.

*(a) $\dfrac{x^2}{49} + \dfrac{y^2}{36} = 1$ (b) $\dfrac{x^2}{25} + \dfrac{y^2}{81} = 1$

*(c) $\dfrac{x^2}{1} + \dfrac{y^2}{3} = 1$ (d) $\dfrac{x^2}{5} + \dfrac{y^2}{4} = 1$

4. Determine the equation of each ellipse.
   *(a) vertices $(0, \pm 4)$, foci $(0, \pm 3)$
   (b) vertices $(\pm 6, 0)$, foci $(\pm 4, 0)$
   *(c) vertices $(\pm 3, 0)$, minor axis length 4
   (d) intercepts $(\pm \sqrt{7}, 0)$ and $(0, \pm 6)$
   *(e) foci $(\pm 5, 0)$, minor axis length 6, centered about origin
   (f) major axis length 20, minor axis length 12, centered about origin

8.5   HYPERBOLAS

A **hyperbola** is the set of points the difference of whose distances from two fixed points is constant. The two fixed points are called **foci**. The constant representing the difference of the two distances will have absolute value $2a$. The distance $d_1 - d_2$ can be positive or negative, so $d_1 - d_2 = \pm 2a$. The foci are at $(\pm c, 0)$.

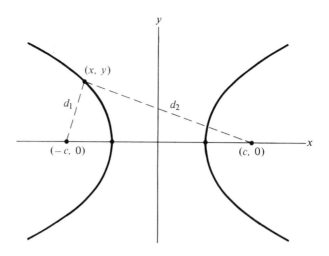

The relationship $d_1 - d_2 = \pm 2a$ leads to

$$\sqrt{(x + c)^2 + (y - 0)^2} - \sqrt{(x - c)^2 + (y - 0)^2} = \pm 2a$$

After a series of squarings and simplifications (as done with the ellipse relationship), a simpler, more useful form is derived. The form is

$$\frac{x^2}{a^2} - \frac{y^2}{b^2} = 1$$

Here $b^2 = c^2 - a^2$, which means that $c^2 > a^2$, unlike the ellipse. The vertices are $(\pm a, 0)$. The points $(0, \pm b)$ are not even on the hyperbola, for if $x = 0$, then $y = \pm bi$. Yet the points $(0, \pm b)$ are useful in graphing. To see why they are, we manipulate the equation

$$\frac{x^2}{a^2} - \frac{y^2}{b^2} = 1$$

into

$$y = \pm \frac{b}{a} x \sqrt{1 - \frac{a^2}{x^2}}$$

As the magnitude of x gets very large, a^2/x^2 gets very small (tends toward zero) and so $1 - a^2/x^2$ tends toward 1. Thus for x large in magnitude, $y = \pm (b/a)x$. This means that the graph tends toward the lines $y = (b/a)x$ and $y = -(b/a)x$. Thus $y = \pm (b/a)x$ are the asymptotes of the hyperbola. The asymptotes are very helpful in sketching the graph of a hyperbola. Observe how a rectangle is drawn and how the asymptotes pass through the corners.

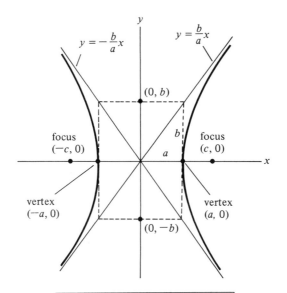

Hyperbola

$$\frac{x^2}{a^2} - \frac{y^2}{b^2} = 1$$

vertices: $(\pm a, 0)$

foci: $(\pm c, 0)$

not on graph: $(0, \pm b)$

asymptotes: $y = \pm\dfrac{b}{a}\,x$

$c^2 = a^2 + b^2$

Incidentally, the line segment from $(-a, 0)$ to $(a, 0)$ is called the **transverse axis.** The line segment from $(0, -b)$ to $(0, b)$ is known as the **conjugate axis.** The point $(0, 0)$ is the **center** of the hyperbola.

Example 13 *Write the given equation of a hyperbola in standard form.*

$$9x^2 - 4y^2 = 36$$

Divide the equation by 36. This step will produce the . . . = 1 form that is desired.

$$\frac{9x^2}{36} - \frac{4y^2}{36} = \frac{36}{36}$$

or

$$\frac{x^2}{4} - \frac{y^2}{9} = 1$$

Example 14 *Sketch the graph of*

$$\frac{x^2}{16} - \frac{y^2}{9} = 1$$

Here $a = 4$ and $b = 3$. The vertices are at $(\pm4, 0)$. The points $(0, \pm3)$ are useful in obtaining the asymptotes. The graph is

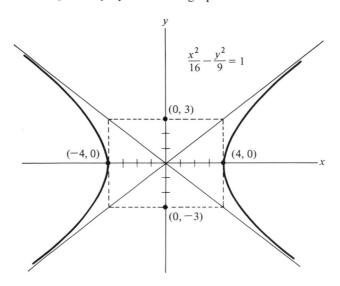

The foci, although not needed here, are $(\pm5, 0)$ because $c = 5$ (from $c^2 = a^2 + b^2 = 16 + 9 = 25$). The equations of the asymptotes are $y = \pm\frac{3}{4}x$.

If the foci are at $(0, c)$ and $(0, -c)$, then the equation of the hyperbola will be different and its orientation will be different, as shown next.

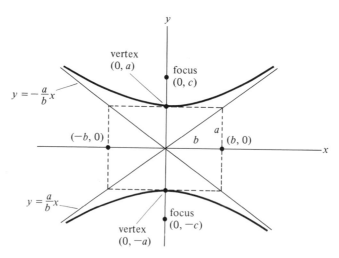

Hyperbola

$$\frac{y^2}{a^2} - \frac{x^2}{b^2} = 1$$

vertices: $(0, \pm a)$

foci: $(0, \pm c)$

not on graph: $(\pm b, 0)$

asymptotes: $y = \pm\dfrac{a}{b} x$

$c^2 = a^2 + b^2$

Example 15   *Sketch the graph of*

$$\frac{y^2}{25} - \frac{x^2}{7} = 1$$

Here $a = 5$ and $b = \sqrt{7}$. The vertices are $(0, \pm 5)$. The points $(\pm\sqrt{7}, 0)$ are useful in obtaining the asymptotes. The graph is

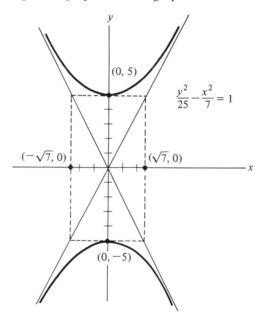

The foci, although not needed here, are $(0, \pm 4\sqrt{2})$ because $c = \sqrt{32}$ (from $c^2 = a^2 + b^2 = 25 + 7 = 32$). The equations of the asymptotes are $y = \pm(5/\sqrt{7})\, x$.

The *Loran* navigation system uses hyperbolas. A ship can obtain signals from two stations (two fixed points) and determine the difference in its distances from the two points. Thus the ship lies on the hyperbola with those stations as foci and has the determined difference in distances from them. A third station can be used together with one of the first two stations to obtain another hyperbola on which the ship lies. The ship then is at the intersection of the two hyperbolas.

The shock wave associated with the sonic boom created by jet aircraft flying faster than the speed of sound has the shape of a cone. So if the plane flies parallel to the ground, the shape of the shock wave on the ground is a hyperbola.

EXERCISES 8.5

1. Obtain the vertices, foci, and asymptotes. Then sketch the graph of each hyperbola.

*(a) $\dfrac{x^2}{9} - \dfrac{y^2}{16} = 1$ (b) $\dfrac{x^2}{25} - \dfrac{y^2}{36} = 1$

*(c) $\dfrac{y^2}{9} - \dfrac{x^2}{16} = 1$ (d) $\dfrac{y^2}{49} - \dfrac{x^2}{4} = 1$

*(e) $\dfrac{x^2}{144} - \dfrac{y^2}{100} = 1$ (f) $\dfrac{y^2}{64} - \dfrac{x^2}{81} = 1$

*(g) $\dfrac{y^2}{5} - \dfrac{x^2}{11} = 1$ (h) $\dfrac{x^2}{14} - \dfrac{y^2}{6} = 1$

*(i) $\dfrac{x^2}{\frac{1}{9}} - \dfrac{y^2}{2} = 1$ (j) $\dfrac{y^2}{\frac{9}{4}} - \dfrac{x^2}{3} = 1$

2. Write the given equation in standard form. Then sketch the graph of each hyperbola.

*(a) $4x^2 - 9y^2 = 36$ (b) $4x^2 - y^2 = 4$
*(c) $16y^2 - 9x^2 = 144$ (d) $25y^2 - 4x^2 = 100$
*(e) $6x^2 - 9y^2 = 54$ (f) $4y^2 - 15x^2 = 60$
*(g) $y^2 - 64x^2 = 64$ (h) $9x^2 - 25y^2 = 4$
*(i) $y^2 - 9x^2 = -25$ (j) $x^2 - 16y^2 = -4$

3. Determine the equation of each hyperbola.
*(a) vertices $(\pm 4, 0)$, foci $(\pm 5, 0)$
(b) vertices $(0, \pm 5)$, foci $(0, \pm 13)$

*(c) vertices $(\pm 3, 0)$, one asymptote $y = \dfrac{7}{3} x$

(d) vertices $(0, \pm 2)$, one asymptote $y = \dfrac{2}{5} x$

*(e) vertices $(0, \pm 4)$, one asymptote $y = \dfrac{12}{5} x$

(f) vertices $(\pm 7, 0)$, one asymptote $y = \dfrac{9}{14} x$

8.6 TRANSLATION OF AXES

The equations of parabolas, ellipses, and hyperbolas that we have already developed are for conics centered about the origin. On the other hand, circles other than those centered at the origin were included. The equation of the circle was considered for all centers (h, k). Specifically, circles centered at the origin can be written in the form

$$x^2 + y^2 = r^2$$

Circles centered at (h, k) can be written

$$(x - h)^2 + (y - k)^2 = r^2$$

Such circles can be thought of as translated from center at $(0, 0)$ to center at (h, k).

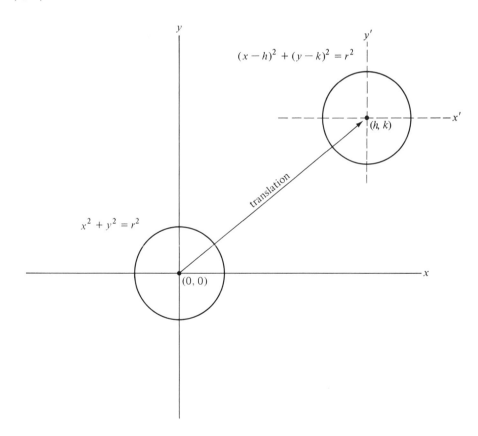

This **translation** can also be viewed as the creation of new coordinate axes x' and y' and a new coordinate system of points (x', y'), in which (h, k) is the origin.

That is,

$$x' = x - h \quad or \quad x = x' + h$$

$$y' = y - k \quad or \quad y = y' + k$$

so that

$$(x - h)^2 + (y - k)^2 = r^2$$

becomes

$$(x')^2 + (y')^2 = r^2$$

When similar translations are applied to the other conics (parabolas, ellipses, and hyperbolas), the resulting conics are as follows:

1. *Parabola* having vertex at (h, k), focus at $(p + h, k)$, and directrix $x = -p + h$.

$$(y - k)^2 = 4p(x - h)$$

2. *Parabola* having vertex at (h, k), focus at $(h, p + k)$, and directrix $y = -p + k$.

$$(x - h)^2 = 4p(y - k)$$

3. *Ellipse* with vertices at $(h \pm a, k)$ and foci at $(h \pm c, k)$, $c^2 = a^2 - b^2$, $a > b$.

$$\frac{(x - h)^2}{a^2} + \frac{(y - k)^2}{b^2} = 1$$

4. *Ellipse* with vertices at $(h, k \pm a)$ and foci at $(h, k \pm c)$, $c^2 = a^2 - b^2$, $a > b$.

$$\frac{(x - h)^2}{b^2} + \frac{(y - k)^2}{a^2} = 1$$

5. *Hyperbola* with foci at $(h \pm c, k)$ and having vertices $(h \pm a, k)$, $c^2 = a^2 + b^2$.

$$\frac{(x - h)^2}{a^2} - \frac{(y - k)^2}{b^2} = 1$$

6. *Hyperbola* with foci at $(h, k \pm c)$ and having vertices at $(h, k \pm a)$, $c^2 = a^2 + b^2$.

$$\frac{(y - k)^2}{a^2} - \frac{(x - h)^2}{b^2} = 1$$

Note: The easiest way to *graph* conics with center (h, k) is to visualize (or draw) new axes x' and y' that make (h, k) the new origin. Then you can apply the principles exactly as studied in the preceding section. An example of each conic follows.

Example 16   *Sketch the graph of the conic*

$$\frac{(x - 3)^2}{25} + \frac{(y + 1)^2}{4} = 1$$

This is an ellipse centered about $(3, -1)$ rather than $(0, 0)$. Since a is 5, the vertices are at $(3 \pm 5, -1)$. Since b is 2, the points $(3, -1 \pm 2)$ are useful; they are the y intercepts in the $x'y'$ plane. These four points, when simplified, are $(8, -1)$, $(-2, -1)$, $(3, 1)$, and $(3, -3)$.

The graph is easily drawn by first locating the center $(3, -1)$. Then move 5 units left and right for the vertices (since $a = 5$) and 2 units up and down from the center for two more useful points (since $b = 2$).

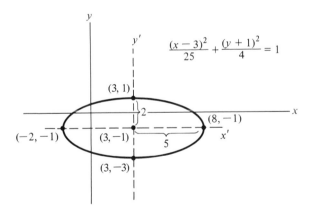

Since $c^2 = a^2 - b^2$, $c^2 = 25 - 4 = 21$. So $c = \pm\sqrt{21}$. This means that the foci are at $(3 \pm \sqrt{21}, -1)$.

Example 17   *Identify and sketch the conic*

$$4x^2 - 9y^2 + 8x + 90y - 257 = 0.$$

The $4x^2 - 9y^2$ portion suggests that this curve is a hyperbola. Accordingly, we should be able to get it into the standard form,

$$\frac{(x - h)^2}{a^2} - \frac{(y - k)^2}{b^2} = 1$$

from which graphing will be straightforward. The standard form contains the completed squares $(x - h)^2$ and $(y - k)^2$. In view of this, terms should be grouped for completing the squares.

$$4x^2 + 8x - 9y^2 + 90y = 257$$

Factor 4 out of $4x^2$ and $8x$. Factor -9 out of $-9y^2$ and $90y$.

$$4(x^2 + 2x) - 9(y^2 - 10y) = 257$$

The desired square for $x^2 + 2x$ is $(x + 1)^2$, which is 1 more than $x^2 + 2x$. Also, this quantity is multiplied by 4. Thus $4(x + 1)^2$ is 4 more than $4(x^2 + 2x)$. So add 4 to the right side of the equation to complete that square.

$$4(x + 1)^2 - 9(y^2 - 10y) = 257 + 4$$

The desired square for $y^2 - 10y$ is $(y - 5)^2$, which is 25 more than $y^2 - 10y$. Also, this quantity is multiplied by -9. Thus $-9(y - 5)^2$ is -225 more than $-9(y^2 - 10y)$. So add -225 to the right side of the equation to complete the square. The result is

$$4(x + 1)^2 - 9(y - 5)^2 = 257 + 4 - 225$$

or

$$4(x + 1)^2 - 9(y - 5)^2 = 36$$

Divide both sides of the equation by 36 to get the standard form.

$$\frac{(x + 1)^2}{9} - \frac{(y - 5)^2}{4} = 1 \qquad a \text{ is 3, } b \text{ is 2}$$

The hyperbola is centered about $(-1, 5)$. The vertices are $(-1 \pm 3, 5)$—that is, $(2, 5)$ and $(-4, 5)$.

The graph is easily drawn by first locating the center $(-1, 5)$. Then move 3 units left and right for the vertices (since $a = 3$) and 2 units up and down from the center (since $b = 2$) for two points not on the graph but useful for drawing the asymptotes.

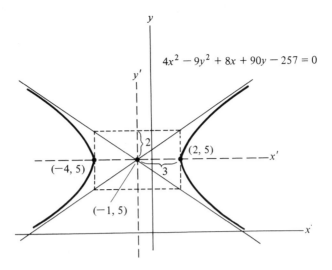

$4x^2 - 9y^2 + 8x + 90y - 257 = 0$

(2, 5)

(−4, 5)

(−1, 5)

Note: For any hyperbola, you can obtain the *equation* of either asymptote by using the center (h, k) through which the line passes and its slope (which is either b/a, $-b/a$, a/b, or $-a/b$, depending on which type of hyperbola and which asymptote you seek).

Example 18   *Sketch $x^2 + 6x - 8y + 17 = 0$.*
   This is a parabola. It can be put into the form $(x - h)^2 = 4p(y - k)$. First, collect the x^2 and x terms on the left side and complete the square.

$$x^2 + 6x = 8y - 17$$

or

$$(x + 3)^2 = 8y - 17 + 9$$

$$(x + 3)^2 = 8y - 8$$

Now factor 8, the coefficient of y, from $8y - 8$. The result is the desired form.

$$(x + 3)^2 = 8(y - 1) \qquad 4p = 8, \text{ so } p = 2$$

The vertex is at $(-3, 1)$. The focus is at $(h, k + p) = (-3, 1 + 2) = (-3, 3)$. The directrix is $y = -p + k$ or $y = -1$.
   The graph is easily drawn by first locating the vertex $(-3, 1)$ at the origin of the $x'y'$ plane. Then move 2 units up (since $p = 2$) for the focus. The directrix is the horizontal line 2 units below the x' axis (since $p = 2$).

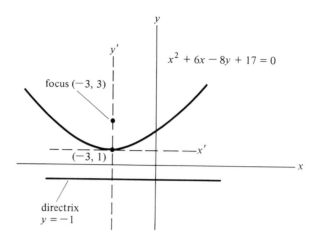

$x^2 + 6x - 8y + 17 = 0$

focus $(-3, 3)$

$(-3, 1)$

directrix $y = -1$

Determining where the graphs of two conics meet is done in Section 9.7.

EXERCISES 8.6

1. Sketch the graph of each equation.

*(a) $\dfrac{(x - 5)^2}{16} + \dfrac{(y - 1)^2}{9} = 1$ (b) $\dfrac{(x + 3)^2}{4} + \dfrac{(y + 1)^2}{25} = 1$

*(c) $(x - 2)^2 = 12(y + 6)$ (d) $(y + 1)^2 = 6(x + 5)$

*(e) $\dfrac{(x - 3)^2}{64} - \dfrac{(y - 5)^2}{9} = 1$ (f) $\dfrac{(y - 4)^2}{49} - \dfrac{(x - 2)^2}{16} = 1$

2. Write each equation in standard form and then sketch its graph.

*(a) $4(x - 2)^2 + 9(y + 1)^2 = 36$

(b) $(x + 5)^2 + 16(y + 3)^2 = 16$

*(c) $25(x - 3)^2 - 4y^2 = 100$

(d) $(x - 5)^2 - 3(y + 2) = 0$

*(e) $y^2 - 7x = 21$

(f) $4x^2 + y^2 + 16x - 2y + 13 = 0$

*(g) $9x^2 - 16y^2 - 160y - 544 = 0$

(h) $y^2 + 6y - 9x - 9 = 0$

*(i) $5x^2 + 3y^2 - 70x + 12y + 242 = 0$

(j) $9y^2 - 2x^2 - 18y - 36x - 157 = 0$

*(k) $2(x - 7)^2 = 28 - 7(y + 4)^2$

(l) $3x^2 - 6x - 6y + 1 = 0$

*(m) $9x^2 - 2y^2 - 36x - 12y = 0$

(n) $16x^2 - y^2 + 160x + 2y + 383 = 0$

*(o) $9x^2 - 4y^2 - 6x - 4y + 36 = 0$

(p) $5x^2 + 4y^2 + 10x - 48y + 129 = 0$

*(q) $2x^2 + 8x - 6y + 11 = 0$

(r) $y^2 - 6y - 4x + 5 = 0$

*(s) $y^2 - 2y - 2x + 7 = 0$

8.7 ROTATION OF AXES

In the preceding section we considered translation of axes and saw how such translation led to simplification of the equations and the graphing process. Now we shall consider **rotation** of axes and its role in simplification of equations and graphs of conics.

Suppose that the origin of the xy plane remains fixed while the x and y axes are rotated through the angle θ. A point (x, y) with respect to the x and y axes becomes the point $(\bar{x}, \bar{y})$ with respect to the new axes $\bar{x}$ and $\bar{y}$.

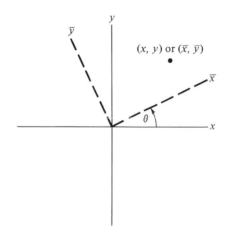

In the next illustration a line segment (of length r) is drawn from the origin to the point (x, y). The angle between the $\bar{x}$ axis and this line segment is called ϕ. The perpendicular from (x, y) to the x axis is of length y. The perpendicular from $(\bar{x}, \bar{y})$ to the $\bar{x}$ axis is of length $\bar{y}$.

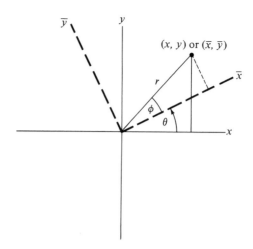

It follows that $\sin(\phi + \theta) = y/r$ and $\cos(\phi + \theta) = x/r$. Also, $\sin \phi = \bar{y}/r$ and $\cos \phi = \bar{x}/r$. These four results can be written in another form.

$$\bar{y} = r \sin \phi$$
$$\bar{x} = r \cos \phi$$

and

$$y = r \sin(\phi + \theta)$$
$$x = r \cos (\phi + \theta)$$

By sum formulas for sine and cosine, $\sin (\phi + \theta) = \sin \phi \cos \theta + \cos \phi \sin \theta$ and $\cos(\phi + \theta) = \cos \phi \cos \theta - \sin \phi \sin \theta$. When these expressions are substituted into the formulas above, the result is

$$y = r \sin \phi \cos \theta + r \cos \phi \sin \theta$$
$$x = r \cos \phi \cos \theta - r \sin \phi \sin \theta$$

Recall that $\bar{y} = r \sin \phi$ and $\bar{x} = r \cos \phi$. Substitute $\bar{y}$ for $r \sin \phi$ and $\bar{x}$ for $r \cos \phi$ in the formula given. The result is

$$\boxed{\begin{array}{l} x = \bar{x} \cos \theta - \bar{y} \sin \theta \\ y = \bar{x} \sin \theta + \bar{y} \cos \theta \end{array}}$$

The general second-degree equation in x and y is

$$Ax^2 + Bxy + Cy^2 + Dx + Ey + F = 0$$

where A, B, and C are not all zero. If $B = 0$, the equation is

$$Ax^2 + Cy^2 + Dx + Ey + F = 0$$

which will yield a circle (when $A = C$ and $AC > 0$), an ellipse (when $A \neq C$ and $AC > 0$), a parabola (when $AC = 0$ and $A \neq C$), and a hyperbola (when $AC < 0$).

But the method of completing the square cannot be applied when $B \neq 0$, that is, when an xy term is present. So in such cases the xy term is removed, and that is accomplished by rotating the axes through an appropriate angle θ. Now let us find out how θ is determined. First, we use the boxed equations above to make substitutions in $Ax^2 + Bxy + Cy^2 + Dx + Ey + F = 0$. The result is a new equation,

$$\overline{A}\overline{x}^2 + \overline{B}\overline{x}\,\overline{y} + \overline{C}\overline{y}^2 + \overline{D}\overline{x} + \overline{E}\overline{y} + \overline{F} = 0$$

The coefficient of the $\overline{x}\,\overline{y}$ term, $\overline{B}$, can be shown to be

$$\overline{B} = A(-2 \sin \theta \cos \theta) + B(\cos^2 \theta - \sin^2\theta) + C(2 \sin \theta \cos \theta)$$

Using identities, $2 \sin \theta \cos \theta$ can be replaced by $\sin 2\theta$ and $\cos^2\theta - \sin^2\theta$ can be replaced by $\cos 2\theta$. The result is

$$\overline{B} = -A(\sin 2\theta) + B(\cos 2\theta) + C(\sin 2\theta)$$

or

$$\overline{B} = (C - A) \sin 2\theta + B \cos 2\theta$$

Clearly $\overline{B} = 0$ when

$$(C - A) \sin 2\theta + B \cos 2\theta = 0$$

or

$$(C - A) \sin 2\theta = -B \cos 2\theta$$

or

$$\frac{\sin 2\theta}{\cos 2\theta} = \frac{-B}{C - A}$$

In other words, the xy term will be removed if θ is chosen such that

$$\tan 2\theta = \frac{B}{A - C}$$

If $A = C$, then $2\theta = 90°$.

Note that if $A = C$, then $A - C = 0$ and $\tan 2\theta$ is not defined. However, if you return to the *derivation* of the boxed formula (three equations above it), you can see that if $A = C$, then $B \cos 2\theta = 0$. It follows that $\cos 2\theta = 0$, which means that $2\theta = 90°$.

Example 19 *Simplify the equation by a rotation of axes.*

$$9x^2 + 24xy + 16y^2 + 90x - 130y = 0$$

To eliminate the xy term by a rotation of axes, select θ such that

$$\tan 2\theta = \frac{B}{A - C}$$

Here $A = 9$, $B = 24$, and $C = 16$ so that

$$\tan 2\theta = \frac{24}{9 - 16} = -\frac{24}{7}$$

In order to make the desired substitutions,

$$\begin{cases} x = \bar{x} \cos \theta - \bar{y} \sin \theta \\ y = \bar{x} \sin \theta + \bar{y} \cos \theta \end{cases}$$

we need to determine $\cos \theta$ and $\sin \theta$ from the fact that $\tan 2\theta = -\frac{24}{7}$. The value of $\cos 2\theta$ can be readily obtained from a right triangle and then used in the half-angle formulas to yield $\cos \theta$ and $\sin \theta$. The triangle corresponding to $\tan 2\theta = -\frac{24}{7}$ is shown next.

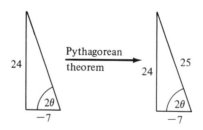

Clearly $\cos 2\theta = -\frac{7}{25}$. Now

$$\cos \theta = \sqrt{\frac{1 + \cos 2\theta}{2}} = \sqrt{\frac{1 - \frac{7}{25}}{2}} = \frac{3}{5}$$

$$\sin \theta = \sqrt{\frac{1 - \cos 2\theta}{2}} = \sqrt{\frac{1 + \frac{7}{25}}{2}} = \frac{4}{5}$$

Thus

$$x = \bar{x} \cos \theta - \bar{y} \sin \theta$$

becomes

$$x = \bar{x} \cdot \tfrac{3}{5} - \bar{y} \cdot \tfrac{4}{5}, \quad \text{or} \quad \tfrac{1}{5}(3\bar{x} - 4\bar{y})$$

and

$$y = \bar{x} \sin \theta + \bar{y} \cos \theta$$

becomes

$$y = \bar{x} \cdot \tfrac{4}{5} + \bar{y} \cdot \tfrac{3}{5}, \quad \text{or} \quad \tfrac{1}{5}(4\bar{x} + 3\bar{y})$$

Now substitute these x and y values into the original equation,

$$9x^2 + 24xy + 16y^2 + 90x - 130y = 0$$

The result is

$$9[\tfrac{1}{5}(3\bar{x} - 4\bar{y})]^2 + 24[\tfrac{1}{5}(3\bar{x} - 4\bar{y})]\,[\tfrac{1}{5}(4\bar{x} + 3\bar{y})] + 16[\tfrac{1}{5}(4\bar{x} + 3\bar{y})]^2$$
$$+ 90[\tfrac{1}{5}(3\bar{x} - 4\bar{y})] - 130[\tfrac{1}{5}(4\bar{x} + 3\bar{y})] = 0$$

which simplifies to

$$\bar{x}^2 - 2\bar{x} - 6\bar{y} = 0$$

or

$$(\bar{x} - 1)^2 = 6(\bar{y} + \tfrac{1}{6})$$

The graph is a parabola with vertex at $(1, -\tfrac{1}{6})$ in the $\bar{x}\bar{y}$ plane. In order to sketch the parabola, the angle θ must be determined. Since $\sin \theta = \tfrac{4}{5} = .8000$, $\theta \approx 53°$. The graph is

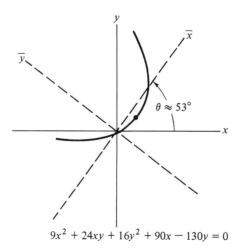

$$9x^2 + 24xy + 16y^2 + 90x - 130y = 0$$

EXERCISES 8.7

1. Given $\tan 2\theta$, determine $\cos \theta$ and $\sin \theta$. Note that if $\tan 2\theta < 0$, then 2θ is in quadrant II; if $\tan 2\theta > 0$, then 2θ is in quadrant I.

   *(a) $\tan 2\theta = \dfrac{7}{24}$
   (b) $\tan 2\theta = \dfrac{5}{12}$

   *(c) $\tan 2\theta = -\dfrac{4}{3}$
   (d) $\tan 2\theta = -\dfrac{3}{4}$

   *(e) $\tan 2\theta = \dfrac{\sqrt{65}}{4}$
   (f) $\tan 2\theta = -\sqrt{15}$

2. Read off A, B, and C and then obtain θ so that you can determine the expressions for x and y that must be substituted to remove the xy term. But *only determine x and y*. Do not actually substitute the expressions into the original equation.

   *(a) $10x^2 + 24xy + 17y^2 - 15 = 0$
   (b) $9x^2 - 24xy + 16y^2 - 160x - 150 = 0$
   *(c) $x^2 + \sqrt{3}\,xy + 2y^2 + x - 10y = 180$
   (d) $2x^2 + 8xy - 4y^2 + x - 19y - 93 = 0$
   *(e) $4x^2 - 4xy + y^2 - 30x = 102$

3. Remove the xy term from each equation by a rotation of axes.

   *(a) $x^2 + 3xy - 3y^2 = \dfrac{21}{2}$
   (b) $xy = 1$

   *(c) $x^2 - 3xy + y^2 = 5$
   (d) $6x^2 - 6xy + 14y^2 - 45 = 0$
   *(e) $2x^2 - 4xy - y^2 = 30$
   (f) $17x^2 + 32xy - 7y^2 - 75 = 0$

4. Remove the xy term from each equation by a rotation of axes.

   *(a) $16x^2 - 24xy + 9y^2 + 100x - 200y + 100 = 0$
   (b) $16x^2 + 24xy + 9y^2 - 50x + 100y = 0$
   *(c) $41x^2 - 24xy + 34y^2 - 90x + 5y + 25 = 0$

   (d) $x^2 + xy + y^2 - 3y + \dfrac{3}{2} = 0$

   *(e) $x^2 - 4xy + 4y^2 + 5\sqrt{5}y + 1 = 0$

5. Suppose that the axes have been rotated through angle θ. For the given point $(\bar{x}, \bar{y})$, determine its coordinates *before* the rotation.

   *(a) $\theta = 60°$, $(\bar{x}, \bar{y}) = (2, 7)$
   (b) $\theta = 60°$, $(\bar{x}, \bar{y}) = \left(\dfrac{1}{2}, -6\right)$

   *(c) $\theta = 30°$, $(\bar{x}, \bar{y}) = (-4, 0)$
   (d) $\theta = 30°$, $(\bar{x}, \bar{y}) = (0, 8)$
   *(e) $\theta = 45°$, $(\bar{x}, \bar{y}) = (7, 7)$
   (f) $\theta = 45°$, $(\bar{x}, \bar{y}) = (-10, 10)$

6. Use the formulas

$$\begin{cases} \bar{x} = x \cos \theta + y \sin \theta \\ \bar{y} = y \cos \theta - x \sin \theta \end{cases}$$

to determine the coordinates of the given point *after* the axes have been rotated through the given angle θ.

*(a) $\theta = 60°$, $(x, y) = (2, 7)$ (b) $\theta = 60°$, $(x, y) = \left(\dfrac{1}{2}, -6\right)$

*(c) $\theta = 30°$, $(x, y) = (-4, 0)$ (d) $\theta = 30°$, $(x, y) = (0, 8)$

*(e) $\theta = 45°$, $(x, y) = (7, 7)$ (f) $\theta = 45°$, $(x, y) = (-10, 10)$

REVIEW EXERCISES FOR CHAPTER 8

1. Write the equation of each conic in standard form. Then sketch its graph.
   *(a) $x^2 + y^2 - 1 = 0$ (b) $x^2 + y^2 - 7 = 0$
   *(c) $9x^2 + y^2 = 9$ (d) $9x^2 - y^2 = 9$
   *(e) $x^2 - y^2 = 10$ (f) $y^2 - x^2 = 10$
   *(g) $x^2 - 10y = 0$ (h) $y^2 - 10x = 0$
   *(i) $4x^2 + 9y^2 = 4$ (j) $4x^2 + 9y^2 = 1$

2. Write the equation of each conic in standard form. Then sketch its graph.
   *(a) $(x - 3)^2 + 4(y + 2)^2 = 4$
   (b) $9(y - 1)^2 - 4(x + 2)^2 = 36$
   *(c) $16(x + 1)^2 - 9(y - 3)^2 = 144$
   (d) $x^2 + y^2 - 10x - 2y - 23 = 0$
   *(e) $x^2 - 4x - 8y + 4 = 0$
   (f) $4x^2 + 4y^2 - 4x - 16y - 47 = 0$
   *(g) $25x^2 - 9y^2 - 100x + 72y - 269 = 0$
   (h) $y^2 - 6y - 6x + 3 = 0$
   *(i) $5x^2 + 9y^2 - 50x + 72y + 224 = 0$
   (j) $64x^2 + 9y^2 - 18y - 135 = 0$

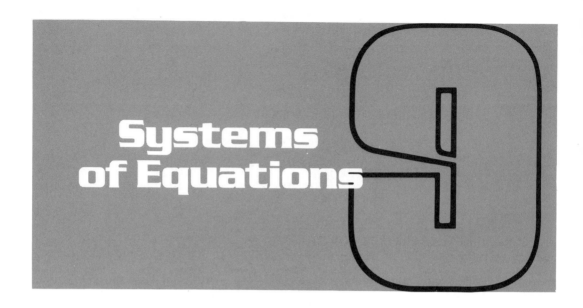

Systems of Equations

9.1 INTRODUCTION AND FUNDAMENTALS

Many problems in mathematics involve finding numbers that satisfy simultaneously a number of linear equations. In this chapter we explain techniques for solving such systems and others.

The graph of any linear function is a straight line. When two such functions are graphed together on the same axes, one of three things must occur. The lines might meet in one point, the lines might be parallel, or the "two" lines might indeed be the same line. This interpretation is based on graphs. Two linear equations in x and y can be manipulated algebraically to find the values of x and y of the point (x, y) where the two lines meet. In other words, you can determine the value of x and the value of y that together satisfy both equations. And once again, one of three things will occur when you attempt to solve the system algebraically. If a solution is obtained, the equations are called **consistent.** If no solution is obtained, and instead such results as $4 = 0$ or $5 = 8$ are produced, the equations are called **inconsistent.** If no solution is obtained, but results such as $0 = 0$ or $7 = 7$ are produced, then the equations are called **dependent.** Such dependent equations have an infinite number of solutions, since both equations represent the same line.

An approximation to the solution of the system

$$\begin{cases} y = 3x + 1 \\ 2x + 3y = 12 \end{cases}$$

can be obtained by graphing.

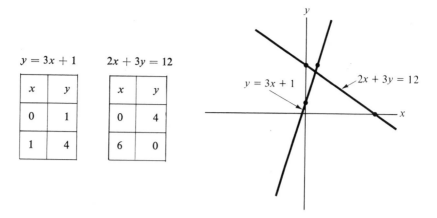

$$y = 3x + 1 \qquad 2x + 3y = 12$$

x	y
0	1
1	4

x	y
0	4
6	0

The system of linear equations is consistent because the lines intersect; they appear to meet at about $(1, 3\frac{1}{2})$. The exact point of intersection can be determined by algebraic techniques to be $(\frac{9}{11}, \frac{38}{11})$. This is done in Example 1 by a method called **substitution.**

Example 1 *Solve the system by substitution.*

$$\begin{cases} y = 3x + 1 \\ 2x + 3y = 12 \end{cases}$$

The first equation is $y = 3x + 1$, which states that y is the same as $3x + 1$. If the expression $3x + 1$ is substituted for y in the other equation, then that equation will contain only one variable, x. Thus

$$2x + 3(y) = 12$$

becomes

$$2x + 3(3x + 1) = 12$$

when $3x + 1$ is substituted for y. The result is an equation in x alone that is easily solved.

$$2x + 3(3x + 1) = 12$$
$$2x + 9x + 3 = 12$$
$$11x + 3 = 12$$
$$11x = 9$$
$$x = \tfrac{9}{11}$$

The value of y can now be found by using the substitution equation $y = 3x + 1$.

Since $x = \frac{9}{11}$,

$$
\begin{aligned}
y &= 3(\tfrac{9}{11}) + 1 \\
&= \tfrac{27}{11} + 1 \\
&= \tfrac{27}{11} + \tfrac{11}{11} \\
&= \tfrac{38}{11}
\end{aligned}
$$

The solution is $x = \frac{9}{11}$, $y = \frac{38}{11}$. This process of substitution is natural to use when one of the two linear equations is written as y in terms of x or as x in terms of y. Otherwise this technique is often a bad choice.

The system

$$
\begin{cases}
3x + 2y = 13 \\
5x - 4y = 7
\end{cases}
$$

can be solved by substitution if you write one equation as y in terms of x or as x in terms of y for substitution into the other equation. Such a process lacks appeal in this case. Instead we shall use a method called **addition,** or **elimination.**

Example 2 *Solve the system by the elimination method.*

$$
\begin{cases}
3x + 2y = 13 \\
5x - 4y = 7
\end{cases}
$$

Begin by multiplying both sides of the top equation by 2. The modified system is

$$
\begin{cases}
6x + 4y = 26 \\
5x - 4y = 7
\end{cases}
$$

Now add the two equations; that is, add $5x - 4y$ to $6x + 4y$ and add 7 to 26. This is an example of adding equal quantities to equal quantities to produce two equal quantities. The resulting new equation is

$$
11x + 0y = 33
$$

or simply

$$
11x = 33
$$

from which

$$
x = 3
$$

Return to either of the original equations to determine y. Let us use the first one,

$3x + 2y = 13$. Since x is 3, the equation

$$3(x) + 2y = 13$$

becomes

$$3(3) + 2y = 13$$
$$9 + 2y = 13$$
$$2y = 4$$
$$y = 2$$

The solution is $x = 3$, $y = 2$.

Return to the original equations and note that the top equation was multiplied by 2 in order to make the coefficients of y equal in magnitude (4) but opposite in sign (one $+$, one $-$). In this way, they add to zero, thus eliminating one of the variables (y).

The technique used in this example is called addition or elimination because one variable is eliminated by adding. In the next example, we consider a system in which the elimination process is a little more complicated.

Example 3 *Solve the system by elimination.*

$$\begin{cases} 3x + 7y = -5 \\ 2x + 9y = 1 \end{cases}$$

If the top equation is multiplied by -2 and the bottom equation is multiplied by 3, then the coefficients of x will "agree" at -6 and 6 and thus add to zero.

$$\begin{cases} 3x + 7y = -5 \xrightarrow{-2} & -6x - 14y = 10 \\ 2x + 9y = 1 \xrightarrow{3} & \underline{6x + 27y = 3} \\ & 13y = 13 \\ & y = 1 \end{cases}$$

The value of x can now be determined by using one of the original equations, say $2x + 9y = 1$, with $y = 1$.

$$2x + 9(y) = 1$$
$$2x + 9(1) = 1$$
$$2x + 9 = 1$$
$$2x = -8$$
$$x = -4$$

The solution is $x = -4$, $y = 1$.

Let us check the solution to be sure that it does indeed satisfy both equations. If it does not, then we had better look for the error or redo the work.

First equation:
$$3x + 7y = -5$$

Let $x = -4$, $y = 1$.
$$3(-4) + 7(1) \overset{?}{=} -5$$
$$-12 + 7 \overset{?}{=} -5$$
$$-5 = -5 \qquad \text{It checks.}$$

Second equation:
$$2x + 9y = 1$$

Let $x = -4$, $y = 1$.
$$2(-4) + 9(1) \overset{?}{=} 1$$
$$-8 + 9 \overset{?}{=} 1$$
$$1 = 1 \qquad \text{It checks.}$$

A system of three equations in three unknowns can be solved by reducing the system to two equations in two unknowns—the *same two unknowns* in both equations, that is.

Example 4 *Solve the following system.*

$$\begin{cases} 5x + 2y + z = 5 \\ 2x + 3y - z = -6 \\ 7x + 4y + 2z = 4 \end{cases}$$

If the first and second equations are added, z will be eliminated.

$$\begin{array}{r} 5x + 2y + z = 5 \\ 2x + 3y - z = -6 \\ \hline 7x + 5y \quad\;\; = -1 \end{array}$$

Now we must use another pair of original equations and eliminate z once again. Returning to the original equations, note that if twice the second equation is added to the third equation, z will be eliminated.

$$\begin{array}{rcl} 2x + 3y - z = -6 & \xrightarrow{\;2\;} & 4x + 6y - 2z = -12 \\ 7x + 4y + 2z = 4 & \longrightarrow & 7x + 4y + 2z = 4 \\ & & \overline{11x + 10y \qquad\;\; = -8} \end{array}$$

We now have two equations in the *same two unknowns*, x and y: $7x + 5y = -1$ and $11x + 10y = -8$. They can be combined as one system and easily solved for x and y. Specifically, multiply $7x + 5y = -1$ by -2 in order to eliminate y.

$$\begin{cases} 7x + 5y = -1 \xrightarrow{-2} & -14x - 10y = 2 \\ 11x + 10y = -8 & \underline{ 11x + 10y = -8} \end{cases}$$

$$\begin{array}{rcr} -3x & = & -6 \\ x & = & 2 \end{array}$$

Now y can be determined by using 2 for x in the equation $7x + 5y = -1$.

$$7(2) + 5y = -1$$
$$14 + 5y = -1$$
$$5y = -15$$
$$y = -3$$

Finally, return to the original system, select any equation, and determine z by substituting 2 for x and -3 for y. The first equation, $5x + 2y + z = 5$, appears to be the easiest to use because the coefficient of the unknown z is simply one.

$$5x + 2y + z = 5$$
$$5(2) + 2(-3) + z = 5$$
$$10 - 6 + z = 5$$
$$4 + z = 5$$
$$z = 1$$

Thus

$$\begin{array}{rcr} x & = & 2 \\ y & = & -3 \\ z & = & 1 \end{array}$$

Each linear equation in three variables represents a plane in three dimensions. The solution to the system, then, can be visualized as the point where the three planes meet. This is an (x, y, z) point in three dimensions. For this example, the planes meet at $(2, -3, 1)$. Three planes could also meet in a straight line, in which case there are an infinite number of solutions. Three planes might have no points in common, in which case there is no solution.

EXERCISES 9.1

Answers to starred exercises are given in the back of the book.

1. Solve each pair of simultaneous linear equations by graphing the lines and approximating the point of intersection if any.

*(a) $\begin{cases} y = 2x + 1 \\ y = -x + 3 \end{cases}$

(b) $\begin{cases} y = 3x - 2 \\ y = x \end{cases}$

*(c) $\begin{cases} y = 4x - 1 \\ y = -4x + 3 \end{cases}$

(d) $\begin{cases} y = 3 - x \\ y = 2x + 2 \end{cases}$

*(e) $\begin{cases} x + y - 5 = 0 \\ x - y = 0 \end{cases}$

(f) $\begin{cases} 2x - y = 3 \\ x + 3y = 6 \end{cases}$

*(g) $\begin{cases} y = 3x - 7 \\ 3x - y = 6 \end{cases}$

(h) $\begin{cases} 3y - 4x = 6 \\ 2y + 5x = 10 \end{cases}$

*(i) $\begin{cases} y = x + 5 \\ x = -3 \end{cases}$

(j) $\begin{cases} x = 3 \\ y = -5 \end{cases}$

*(k) $\begin{cases} 2x - 5y = 10 \\ y = \frac{2}{5}x - 2 \end{cases}$

(l) $\begin{cases} 3x + 2y = 6 \\ 3y - 2x = 12 \end{cases}$

2. Solve each pair of simultaneous linear equations by using substitution. Then check the solution in both equations. (*Note*: Some systems may be dependent or inconsistent.)

*(a) $\begin{cases} 2x + y = 11 \\ y = x + 2 \end{cases}$

(b) $\begin{cases} x + 4y = 8 \\ x = 3y + 1 \end{cases}$

*(c) $\begin{cases} 2x + 3y = 15 \\ y = x \end{cases}$

(d) $\begin{cases} 5x - 8y = 9 \\ x = 2y + 1 \end{cases}$

*(e) $\begin{cases} 5x - 7y = 16 \\ x = 6 \end{cases}$

(f) $\begin{cases} 5x - 2y = 39 \\ x = 1 - 3y \end{cases}$

*(g) $\begin{cases} y = 5x + 1 \\ 4x + 3y = 10 \end{cases}$

(h) $\begin{cases} 4x - 3y = 9 \\ y = 7 - 2x \end{cases}$

*(i) $\begin{cases} y = 3x - 2 \\ 6x - 2y = 34 \end{cases}$

(j) $\begin{cases} x + 5y = 3 \\ x = 3 - 5y \end{cases}$

*(k) $\begin{cases} 2x - y + 6 = 0 \\ 3x - 5y = 5 \end{cases}$

(l) $\begin{cases} x + 2y = 1 \\ 5x - 3y = 13 \end{cases}$

3. Solve each pair of simultaneous linear equations by using elimination. Then check the solution in both equations. (*Note*: Some systems may be dependent or inconsistent.)

*(a) $\begin{cases} x + y = 6 \\ x - y = 4 \end{cases}$

(b) $\begin{cases} x - 3y = 1 \\ 2x + 3y = 20 \end{cases}$

*(c) $\begin{cases} 2x + y = 7 \\ 5x - 3y = 23 \end{cases}$

(d) $\begin{cases} 3x + 7y = 7 \\ x + 5y = -3 \end{cases}$

*(e) $\begin{cases} 3x + y = -5 \\ -6x - 2y = 10 \end{cases}$

(f) $\begin{cases} x - 5y = 4 \\ 2x - 10y = 3 \end{cases}$

*(g) $\begin{cases} 2x + 5y = -1 \\ 6x + 7y = 5 \end{cases}$

(h) $\begin{cases} 3x + 2y = 6 \\ -2x - 5y = 7 \end{cases}$

*(i) $\begin{cases} 5x + 2y = 7 \\ 7x + 3y = 9 \end{cases}$

(j) $\begin{cases} 3x + 5y = 11 \\ 4x + 2y = -4 \end{cases}$

*(k) $\begin{cases} 7x + 3y = 1 \\ 5x + 7y = 8 \end{cases}$

(l) $\begin{cases} 8x - 4y = 7 \\ 5x - 9y = 6 \end{cases}$

4. Solve each system of equations and check your solution.

*(a) $\begin{cases} x + y + z = 6 \\ 2x + 3y - z = 5 \\ 3x + 2y + z = 10 \end{cases}$

(b) $\begin{cases} 5x - y + 2z = 8 \\ 2x + y + 5z = 6 \\ 3x - y + 3z = 7 \end{cases}$

*(c) $\begin{cases} 5x + 3y + z = 7 \\ x + 4y - 2z = 8 \\ 3x + 7y - 4z = 18 \end{cases}$

(d) $\begin{cases} x - 4y + 3z = 1 \\ -2x + 3y + 2z = -7 \\ 3x + 2y + 5z = 17 \end{cases}$

*(e) $\begin{cases} 7x + 3y + 2z = 9 \\ 3x - y + 3z = 17 \\ 5x + 4y + 4z = 13 \end{cases}$

(f) $\begin{cases} 2x - 3y + 4z = -3 \\ 4x + 5y - 5z = 31 \\ 6x + 2y + 3z = 20 \end{cases}$

*(g) $\begin{cases} 2r + 3s + 2t = 3 \\ 3r + 5s + 7t = 19 \\ 6r + 4s + 3t = 12 \end{cases}$

(h) $\begin{cases} 5m + 2n - 3p = -8 \\ 3m - 3n + 5p = 13 \\ -4m + 2n - 2p = -6 \end{cases}$

*(i) $\begin{cases} 5x + 2y + 3z = 1 \\ 7x - 3y + 7z = 16 \\ x + 5y - 5z = -8 \end{cases}$

(j) $\begin{cases} w + 3x + 2y + z = 5 \\ 3w - 5x - y + 3z = 8 \\ 2w + 7x - 3y - 2z = -12 \\ 5w - 4x - 3y - 5z = 5 \end{cases}$

*(k) $\begin{cases} 3w + x + 4y + 3z = 0 \\ w + 5x - y + 2z = 10 \\ 4w - 2x - 5y + 3z = 4 \\ 5w + 7x + 2y + 4z = 7 \end{cases}$

*5. The area of a triangle with base b units and height h units is $A = \frac{1}{2}bh$. Determine the area of the shaded triangle shown on the next page.

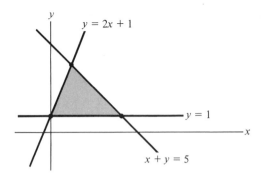

9.2 MATRICES AND GAUSS–JORDAN ELIMINATION

A **matrix** is a rectangular array of numbers. Here are examples of matrices.

$$\begin{pmatrix} 2 & -1 \\ 3 & 4 \end{pmatrix} \qquad \begin{pmatrix} 1 & 6 & 9 \\ 2 & 5 & 0 \end{pmatrix} \qquad \begin{pmatrix} 5 \\ -4 \\ 17 \end{pmatrix}$$

Some matrices have a square shape—that is, the same number of rows as columns. On the other hand, matrices need not be square. The second matrix shown has two rows and three columns; the third matrix has three rows and only one column. A matrix does not have a *single* value. It is an array of values.

In this section matrices will be used to solve systems of n linear equations in n unknowns by a method called **Gauss–Jordan elimination.** It is named for the German mathematician Karl Friedrich Gauss (1777–1855) and French mathematician Camille Jordan (1838–1922), who modified Gauss's original method. The method is also referred to less formally as the *sweepout* method.

We begin by placing the coefficients of the variables and the separate constants into a matrix. The variables are omitted, but the elements of the matrix are kept in order corresponding to their positions in the original equations. And it is assumed at the beginning that the system of equations is set up for the addition method so that x terms align under x terms, y terms under y terms, and the constants are on the other side of the equals sign. Here is an example of how a small system of linear equations is set up in a matrix for solution by Gauss–Jordan elimination.

$$\begin{cases} x + 2y = 1 \\ 2x + 7y = -4 \end{cases} \longrightarrow \begin{pmatrix} 1 & 2 & 1 \\ 2 & 7 & -4 \end{pmatrix}$$

Next, a series of **elementary row operations** (see box below) is performed on the matrix in order to produce a simpler matrix: specifically, one in which enough coefficients have been changed to zero that the values of the variables can be read from the matrix. The preceding matrix, for instance, can be reduced by elementary row operations to the matrix

$$\begin{pmatrix} 1 & 0 & 5 \\ 0 & 1 & -2 \end{pmatrix}$$

which is the same as the system

$$\begin{cases} 1x + 0y = 5 \\ 0x + 1y = -2 \end{cases}$$

or simply

$$\begin{cases} x = 5 \\ y = -2 \end{cases}$$

The process requires four steps. First, a coefficient of one must be obtained for x in the first equation (first row). Then a coefficient of zero is obtained for x in the second equation (second row). Then we proceed to the right to get a coefficient of one for y in the second equation (second row) and finally a coefficient of zero for y in the first equation (first row).

> The elementary row operations are:
> 1. Interchange two rows.
> 2. Replace any row by a multiple of itself.
> 3. Multiply any row by a number and add it (element by element) to another row in order to replace the latter row.

Keep in mind that the elementary row operations are being performed on the skeleton of an equation or system so that, in effect, they are elementary equation (or system) operations. Interchanging two equations in a system preserves the system. To multiply all members of an equation (both sides) by a constant does not change the solution of the system. Nor does multiplying an equation by a constant and adding it to another equation (thus replacing it) change the system.

If we let an asterisk (*) represent any constant, then at first the matrix representation of the system appears as

$$\begin{pmatrix} * & * & * \\ * & * & * \end{pmatrix}$$

and we would like to change it to a matrix of the form

$$\begin{pmatrix} 1 & 0 & * \\ 0 & 1 & * \end{pmatrix}$$

To avoid problems, it is suggested that you follow the steps as outlined, so that your approach to all these problems will be consistent.

$$\begin{pmatrix} * & * & * \\ * & * & * \end{pmatrix}$$

$\downarrow$

$$\begin{pmatrix} 1 & * & * \\ * & * & * \end{pmatrix} \qquad \begin{cases} \text{First, get a 1 in the top} \\ \text{left corner of the matrix.} \end{cases}$$

$\downarrow$

$$\begin{pmatrix} 1 & * & * \\ 0 & * & * \end{pmatrix} \qquad \begin{cases} \text{Next, get a 0 in the position} \\ \text{below it.} \end{cases}$$

$\downarrow$

$$\begin{pmatrix} 1 & * & * \\ 0 & 1 & * \end{pmatrix} \qquad \begin{cases} \text{Third, get a 1 next to the 0} \\ \text{in row 2.} \end{cases}$$

$\downarrow$

$$\begin{pmatrix} 1 & 0 & * \\ 0 & 1 & * \end{pmatrix} \qquad \begin{cases} \text{Finally, get a 0 above the} \\ \text{newly obtained 1.} \end{cases}$$

Example 5   *Use Gauss–Jordan elimination to solve the system*

$$\begin{cases} x + 2y = 1 \\ 2x + 7y = -4 \end{cases}$$

The system can be written as the matrix

$$\begin{pmatrix} 1 & 2 & 1 \\ 2 & 7 & -4 \end{pmatrix}$$

First get a 1 in the top left position. Because there is a 1 there already, proceed to the next step. Get a 0 below the 1. This can be done by multiplying row 1 (each element) by -2 and adding it to row 2 to produce a new row 2. Multiplying row 1 by -2 produces

$$-2 \quad -4 \quad -2$$

When these numbers are added to

$$2 \quad 7 \quad -4$$

the new row 2 produced is

$$0 \quad 3 \quad -6$$

Thus the matrix is now

$$\begin{pmatrix} 1 & 2 & 1 \\ 0 & 3 & -6 \end{pmatrix}$$

Next, get a 1 in the position next to the zero. Perform an operation on row 2 to change the 3 to a 1. Multiply the row by $\frac{1}{3}$. The result is

$$\begin{pmatrix} 1 & 2 & 1 \\ 0 & 1 & -2 \end{pmatrix}$$

The last step is to get a 0 above the new 1. This can be accomplished by multiplying row 2 by -2 and adding it to row 1 in order to produce a new row 1. When row 2 is multiplied by -2, the result is

$$0 \quad -2 \quad 4$$

When added to

$$1 \quad 2 \quad 1$$

the new row 1 produced is

$$1 \quad 0 \quad 5$$

and the matrix becomes

$$\begin{pmatrix} 1 & 0 & 5 \\ 0 & 1 & -2 \end{pmatrix}$$

Now you can see from the matrix that x is 5 and y is -2.

If the matrix of Example 5 was instead

$$\begin{pmatrix} 4 & -3 & 7 \\ 1 & 5 & -8 \end{pmatrix}$$

then row operation 1, interchange of rows, will produce a matrix having 1 in the top left position. After interchanging rows 1 and 2, the matrix appears as

$$\begin{pmatrix} 1 & 5 & -8 \\ 4 & -3 & 7 \end{pmatrix}$$

If the original matrix was

$$\begin{pmatrix} 2 & 7 & 6 \\ 5 & 9 & 4 \end{pmatrix}$$

then you can multiply row 1 by $\frac{1}{2}$ to get a 1 in the top left position. The result is

$$\begin{pmatrix} 1 & \frac{7}{2} & 3 \\ 5 & 9 & 4 \end{pmatrix}$$

A system of three linear equations in three unknowns can be solved by matrices in a similar fashion. The system

$$\begin{cases} 7x + 9y - 4z = 19 \\ x + 3y + 2z = 7 \\ 3x + 7y + 11z = 8 \end{cases}$$

can be written in matrix form as

$$\begin{pmatrix} 7 & 9 & -4 & 19 \\ 1 & 3 & 2 & 7 \\ 3 & 7 & 11 & 8 \end{pmatrix}$$

Application of elementary row operations will eventually produce

$$\begin{pmatrix} 1 & 0 & 0 & -3 \\ 0 & 1 & 0 & 4 \\ 0 & 0 & 1 & -1 \end{pmatrix}$$

or $x = -3$, $y = 4$, $z = -1$. In general, the matrix

$$\begin{pmatrix} * & * & * & * \\ * & * & * & * \\ * & * & * & * \end{pmatrix}$$

is reduced to

$$\begin{pmatrix} 1 & 0 & 0 & * \\ 0 & 1 & 0 & * \\ 0 & 0 & 1 & * \end{pmatrix}$$

There are more steps because there is more to eliminate. But the pattern followed and the nature of the steps are essentially the same as before. Here, then, are the steps in sequence for the general case suggested above.

$$\begin{pmatrix} * & * & * & * \\ * & * & * & * \\ * & * & * & * \end{pmatrix}$$

$\downarrow$

$$\begin{pmatrix} 1 & * & * & * \\ * & * & * & * \\ * & * & * & * \end{pmatrix}$$ First, get a 1 in the top left corner.

$\downarrow$

$$\begin{pmatrix} 1 & * & * & * \\ 0 & * & * & * \\ 0 & * & * & * \end{pmatrix}$$ Then get a 0 below it and another 0 below that zero. This is really two separate steps.

$\downarrow$

$$\begin{pmatrix} 1 & * & * & * \\ 0 & 1 & * & * \\ 0 & * & * & * \end{pmatrix}$$ Next, get a 1 in row 2, column 2.

$\downarrow$

$$\begin{pmatrix} 1 & 0 & * & * \\ 0 & 1 & * & * \\ 0 & 0 & * & * \end{pmatrix}$$ Now, get a 0 above this new 1 and a 0 below it. This is two steps.

$\downarrow$

$$\begin{pmatrix} 1 & 0 & * & * \\ 0 & 1 & * & * \\ 0 & 0 & 1 & * \end{pmatrix}$$ Next, get a 1 in row 3, column 3.

$\downarrow$

$$\begin{pmatrix} 1 & 0 & 0 & * \\ 0 & 1 & 0 & * \\ 0 & 0 & 1 & * \end{pmatrix}$$ Finally, get 0's in both positions above this new 1. This is two more steps.

Example 6 *Use Gauss–Jordan elimination to solve the system*

$$\begin{cases} 7x + 9y - 4z = 19 \\ x + 3y + 2z = 7 \\ 3x + 7y + 11z = 8 \end{cases}$$

The system can be written as the matrix

$$\begin{pmatrix} 7 & 9 & -4 & 19 \\ 1 & 3 & 2 & 7 \\ 3 & 7 & 11 & 8 \end{pmatrix}$$

First, interchange rows 1 and 2 in order to place a 1 in the top left corner.

$$\begin{pmatrix} 1 & 3 & 2 & 7 \\ 7 & 9 & -4 & 19 \\ 3 & 7 & 11 & 8 \end{pmatrix}$$

Next, use this 1 to obtain 0's in the two positions below it. The zero in row 2, column 1, is obtained by multiplying row 1 by -7 and adding that to row 2. When row 1 is multiplied by -7, the result is

$$-7 \quad -21 \quad -14 \quad -49$$

And when these elements are added to corresponding elements of row 2, that row becomes

$$0 \quad -12 \quad -18 \quad -30$$

Similarly, multiply row 1 by -3 and add that to row 3 to produce a 0 in row 3, column 1. If the elements of row 1 are multiplied by -3, they become

$$-3 \quad -9 \quad -6 \quad -21$$

And when they are added to the elements of row 3, the result is

$$0 \quad -2 \quad 5 \quad -13$$

Shown next is the matrix with the new row 2 and new row 3 computed above.

$$\begin{pmatrix} 1 & 3 & 2 & 7 \\ 0 & -12 & -18 & -30 \\ 0 & -2 & 5 & -13 \end{pmatrix}$$

Next, obtain a 1 in row 2, column 2, by multiplying each element of that row by $-\frac{1}{12}$, the reciprocal of -12.

$$\begin{pmatrix} 1 & 3 & 2 & 7 \\ 0 & 1 & \frac{3}{2} & \frac{5}{2} \\ 0 & -2 & 5 & -13 \end{pmatrix}$$

Now get 0's above and below the new 1. A zero below it can be obtained by multiplying row 2 by 2 and adding it to row 3. When row 2 is multiplied by 2, the result is

$$\begin{array}{cccc} 0 & 2 & 3 & 5 \end{array}$$

Add this to

$$\begin{array}{cccc} 0 & -2 & 5 & -13 \end{array}$$

and the new row 3 obtained is

$$\begin{array}{cccc} 0 & 0 & 8 & -8 \end{array}$$

Now multiply row 2 by -3 and add that result to row 1. That is, add

$$\begin{array}{ccccc} 0 & -3 & -\frac{9}{2} & -\frac{15}{2} & -3 \text{ times row 2} \end{array}$$

to

$$\begin{array}{cccc} 1 & 3 & 2 & 7 \end{array}$$

to get the new row 1:

$$\begin{array}{cccc} 1 & 0 & -\frac{5}{2} & -\frac{1}{2} \end{array}$$

The matrix is now

$$\begin{pmatrix} 1 & 0 & -\frac{5}{2} & -\frac{1}{2} \\ 0 & 1 & \frac{3}{2} & \frac{5}{2} \\ 0 & 0 & 8 & -8 \end{pmatrix}$$

Next, get a 1 in row 3, column 3. This is done by multiplying row 3 by $\frac{1}{8}$, the reciprocal of 8. The new matrix is

$$\begin{pmatrix} 1 & 0 & -\frac{5}{2} & -\frac{1}{2} \\ 0 & 1 & \frac{3}{2} & \frac{5}{2} \\ 0 & 0 & 1 & -1 \end{pmatrix}$$

Finally, get 0's above this new 1. A zero in row 1, column 3, can be obtained by multiplying row 3 by $\frac{5}{2}$ (the opposite of $-\frac{5}{2}$) and adding that result to row 1. That is, add

$$0 \qquad 0 \qquad \frac{5}{2} \qquad -\frac{5}{2}$$

to

$$1 \qquad 0 \qquad -\frac{5}{2} \qquad -\frac{1}{2}$$

to get the new row 1:

$$1 \qquad 0 \qquad 0 \qquad -3$$

A zero for row 2, column 3, is obtained by multiplying row 3 by $-\frac{3}{2}$ (the opposite of $\frac{3}{2}$) and adding that result to row 2. That is, add

$$0 \qquad 0 \qquad -\frac{3}{2} \qquad \frac{3}{2}$$

to

$$0 \qquad 1 \qquad \frac{3}{2} \qquad \frac{5}{2}$$

to get the new row 2:

$$0 \qquad 1 \qquad 0 \qquad 4$$

The final matrix is

$$\begin{pmatrix} 1 & 0 & 0 & -3 \\ 0 & 1 & 0 & 4 \\ 0 & 0 & 1 & -1 \end{pmatrix}$$

Thus the system has been reduced to

$$\begin{cases} 1x + 0y + 0z = -3 \\ 0x + 1y + 0z = 4 \\ 0x + 0y + 1z = -1 \end{cases}$$

or simply

$$\begin{cases} x = -3 \\ y = 4 \\ z = -1 \end{cases}$$

As a final note, using this method on a system with an infinite number of solutions (that is, a dependent system) will result in at least one row in which all elements are zero. A system with no solution (that is, an inconsistent system) will yield a row in which all elements except the last one are zero. See Exercise 3 for problems of this type.

EXERCISES 9.2

1. Solve each system of linear equations by Gauss–Jordan elimination (sweep-out).

*(a) $\begin{cases} x + 3y = 10 \\ -3x + 2y = 3 \end{cases}$

(b) $\begin{cases} x - 2y = 3 \\ 4x + 5y = 51 \end{cases}$

*(c) $\begin{cases} m - 5n = 23 \\ 2m - 3n = 11 \end{cases}$

(d) $\begin{cases} 2x + 2y = 12 \\ x + 3y = 14 \end{cases}$

*(e) $\begin{cases} 5x + 12y = 23 \\ x + 2y = 3 \end{cases}$

(f) $\begin{cases} 2u + 3v = 5 \\ 5u - 4v = -22 \end{cases}$

*(g) $\begin{cases} 5x + 4y = 3 \\ 4x + 6y = 1 \end{cases}$

(h) $\begin{cases} 9x - 8y = 0 \\ 3x + 4y = 5 \end{cases}$

*(i) $\begin{cases} 5a - 5b = 10 \\ -4a + 3b = 6 \end{cases}$

(j) $\begin{cases} -3w + 8x = 1 \\ 7w + 4x = 9 \end{cases}$

2. Solve each system of linear equations by Gauss–Jordan elimination.

*(a) $\begin{cases} x + 3y + 3z = 6 \\ 3x + 7y + 11z = 8 \\ 7x + 8y - 5z = 16 \end{cases}$

(b) $\begin{cases} x + y + 2z = 9 \\ 2x + 4y - 3z = 1 \\ 3x + 6y - 5z = 0 \end{cases}$

*(c) $\begin{cases} x - 3y + z = 4 \\ 3x - 8y + 3z = 13 \\ -2x + y + 2z = -5 \end{cases}$ (d) $\begin{cases} x - y - 4z = 12 \\ 2x + y + 3z = -6 \\ 5x + 2y + 2z = 1 \end{cases}$

*(e) $\begin{cases} x + 2y + 3z = 7 \\ 2x - 3y + 8z = -3 \\ -5x - 8y + 5z = 11 \end{cases}$ (f) $\begin{cases} 5x + 3y + 14z = 13 \\ x + y + 4z = 3 \\ -4x - 3y + 3z = 21 \end{cases}$

*(g) $\begin{cases} 3t - 4u + 3v = 9 \\ 4t - 6u + 10v = 28 \\ t - 2u + 5v = 15 \end{cases}$ (h) $\begin{cases} x + 3y + 2z = 7 \\ 3x + 7y + 11z = 8 \\ 7x + 9y - 4z = 19 \end{cases}$

*(i) $\begin{cases} 2p - 4q + 10r = -6 \\ 6p - 10q + 12r = -32 \\ -5p - 9q + 3r = 5 \end{cases}$

3. Attempt to solve each system of linear equations by Gauss–Jordan elimination. Determine whether the system has no solution or an infinite number of solutions.

*(a) $\begin{cases} x - 3y = 10 \\ -2x + 6y = 7 \end{cases}$ (b) $\begin{cases} x + y = -5 \\ 3x + 3y = 14 \end{cases}$

*(c) $\begin{cases} x + 2y = 5 \\ 3x + 6y = 15 \end{cases}$ (d) $\begin{cases} 2x + 8y = -12 \\ -x - 4y = 6 \end{cases}$

9.3 DETERMINANTS

In Section 9.1 the elimination and substitution methods were used to solve systems of linear equations. Now we will apply the elimination method to solve the general system of two equations in two unknowns:

$$\begin{cases} ax + by = k_1 \\ cx + dy = k_2 \end{cases}$$

where a, b, c, d, k_1 and k_2 are constants.

Multiply the first equation by $-c$ and the second equation by a. Doing so will make the coefficients of x equal to $-ac$ and ac. They will add to zero, thus eliminating x.

$$\begin{cases} ax + by = k_1 \quad \xrightarrow{-c} \quad -acx - cby = -ck_1 \\ cx + dy = k_2 \quad \xrightarrow{a} \quad acx + ady = ak_2 \end{cases}$$
$$\overline{\qquad 0 + ady - cby = ak_2 - ck_1}$$

Thus far

$$ady - cby = ak_2 - ck_1$$

Factor out y on the left side.

$$(ad - cb)y = ak_2 - ck_1$$

Next, divide both sides of the equation by the coefficient of y—namely, $ad - cb$. The result is

$$y = \frac{ak_2 - ck_1}{ad - cb}$$

On close examination this formula for y reveals that the denominator, $ad - cb$, is obtained from a times d minus c times b.

$$ax + by = k_1$$
$$cx + dy = k_2$$

To aid in visualizing and remembering this pattern, we define a **determinant** called

$$\begin{vmatrix} a & b \\ c & d \end{vmatrix}$$

as

$$\begin{vmatrix} a & b \\ c & d \end{vmatrix} = a \cdot d - c \cdot b$$

The numerator, $ak_2 - ck_1$, can now be written as a determinant.

$$\begin{vmatrix} a & k_1 \\ c & k_2 \end{vmatrix} = ak_2 - ck_1$$

Putting these two determinants together gives

$$y = \frac{\begin{vmatrix} a & k_1 \\ c & k_2 \end{vmatrix}}{\begin{vmatrix} a & b \\ c & d \end{vmatrix}}$$

if the value of the denominator is not zero.

Observe the following:

1. The denominator determinant contains the coefficients of x and y from the original equations.
2. The numerator determinant contains the coefficients of x. The constants k_1 and k_2 are used instead of the coefficients of y.

If the original equations are solved for x, the result is

$$x = \frac{k_1 d - k_2 b}{ad - cb}$$

or

$$x = \frac{\begin{vmatrix} k_1 & b \\ k_2 & d \end{vmatrix}}{\begin{vmatrix} a & b \\ c & d \end{vmatrix}}$$

The denominator is the same determinant that was used for the denominator of y. The numerator determinant contains the y coefficients, but the constants k_1 and k_2 are used in place of the x coefficients. In summary, if

$$\begin{cases} ax + by = k_1 \\ cx + dy = k_2 \end{cases}$$

then

$$x = \frac{\begin{vmatrix} k_1 & b \\ k_2 & d \end{vmatrix}}{\begin{vmatrix} a & b \\ c & d \end{vmatrix}} \qquad y = \frac{\begin{vmatrix} a & k_1 \\ c & k_2 \end{vmatrix}}{\begin{vmatrix} a & b \\ c & d \end{vmatrix}}$$

This method of using determinants to solve systems of n linear equations in n unknowns is called **Cramer's rule**. It was published about 1750 by the Swiss mathematician Gabriel Cramer.

Example 7 *Solve the system of linear equations by using Cramer's rule.*
The system

$$\begin{cases} 3x - 2y = 7 \\ 4x + 5y = 1 \end{cases}$$

is solved as follows:

$$x = \frac{\begin{vmatrix} 7 & -2 \\ 1 & 5 \end{vmatrix}}{\begin{vmatrix} 3 & -2 \\ 4 & 5 \end{vmatrix}} = \frac{(7)(5) - (1)(-2)}{(3)(5) - (4)(-2)} = \frac{37}{23}$$

$$y = \frac{\begin{vmatrix} 3 & 7 \\ 4 & 1 \end{vmatrix}}{\begin{vmatrix} 3 & -2 \\ 4 & 5 \end{vmatrix}} = \frac{(3)(1) - (4)(7)}{23} = \frac{-25}{23} = -\frac{25}{23}$$

The general system of three linear equations in three unknowns, such as

$$\begin{cases} ax + by + cz = k_1 \\ dx + ey + fz = k_2 \\ gx + hy + jz = k_3 \end{cases}$$

can be solved by the addition method (elimination) to produce

$$x = \frac{(k_1ej + bfk_3 + ck_2h) - (k_3ec + hfk_1 + jk_2b)}{(aej + bfg + cdh) - (gec + hfa + jdb)}$$

$$y = \frac{(ak_2j + k_1fg + ck_3d) - (gk_2c + k_3fa + jk_1d)}{(aej + bfg + cdh) - (gec + hfa + jdb)}$$

$$z = \frac{(aek_3 + bk_2g + k_1hd) - (gek_1 + hk_2a + k_3bd)}{(aej + bfg + cdh) - (gec + hfa + jdb)}$$

Note that the denominator is the same for all three variables x, y, and z. Only the coefficients of x, y, and z are used (that is, only a, b, c, d, e, f, g, h, and j). We can write the denominator as the determinant

$$\begin{vmatrix} a & b & c \\ d & e & f \\ g & h & j \end{vmatrix}$$

to compare with the determinant used for two equations involving two variables. We now seek a mechanical way of computing

$$\begin{vmatrix} a & b & c \\ d & e & f \\ g & h & j \end{vmatrix} = (aej + bfg + cdh) - (gec + hfa + jdb)$$

Copy over the first two columns of the determinant, placing the two columns to the right of the determinant, as

$$\begin{vmatrix} a & b & c \\ d & e & f \\ g & h & j \end{vmatrix}\begin{matrix} a & b \\ d & e \\ g & h \end{matrix}$$

Now observe

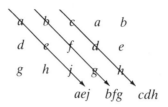

and

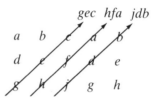

Add the first three products ($aej + bfg + cdh$) and *subtract* from that sum the sum of the other three products ($gec + hfa + jdb$).

Example 8 *Compute the value of the determinant*

$$\begin{vmatrix} 1 & 2 & 4 \\ 3 & 7 & 5 \\ 9 & 6 & 8 \end{vmatrix}$$

Rewrite the determinant as

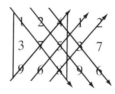

Its value is then

$$(1 \cdot 7 \cdot 8 + 2 \cdot 5 \cdot 9 + 4 \cdot 3 \cdot 6) - (9 \cdot 7 \cdot 4 + 6 \cdot 5 \cdot 1 + 8 \cdot 3 \cdot 2)$$

or

$$(56 + 90 + 72) - (252 + 30 + 48) = -112$$

The value of the determinant is -112.

Let us return now to the expressions for x, y, and z. It has already been shown that the denominator for each of them is

$$\begin{vmatrix} a & b & c \\ d & e & f \\ g & h & j \end{vmatrix}$$

Without too much trouble, the numerators can be written as determinants. They are shown next along with the previously determined denominator determinant.

$$x = \dfrac{\begin{vmatrix} k_1 & b & c \\ k_2 & e & f \\ k_3 & h & j \end{vmatrix}}{\begin{vmatrix} a & b & c \\ d & e & f \\ g & h & j \end{vmatrix}}$$
$\left\{ \begin{array}{l} \text{The column of } x \text{ coefficients has} \\ \text{been replaced by the column of} \\ \text{constants } k_1, k_2, k_3. \end{array} \right.$

$$y = \dfrac{\begin{vmatrix} a & k_1 & c \\ d & k_2 & f \\ g & k_3 & j \end{vmatrix}}{\begin{vmatrix} a & b & c \\ d & e & f \\ g & h & j \end{vmatrix}}$$
$\left\{ \begin{array}{l} \text{The column of } y \text{ coefficients has} \\ \text{been replaced by the column of} \\ \text{constants } k_1, k_2, k_3. \end{array} \right.$

$$z = \dfrac{\begin{vmatrix} a & b & k_1 \\ d & e & k_2 \\ g & h & k_3 \end{vmatrix}}{\begin{vmatrix} a & b & c \\ d & e & f \\ g & h & j \end{vmatrix}}$$
$\left\{ \begin{array}{l} \text{The column of } z \text{ coefficients has} \\ \text{been replaced by the column of} \\ \text{constants } k_1, k_2, k_3. \end{array} \right.$

Example 9   *Solve the following system of linear equations by using determinants (Cramer's rule).*

$$\begin{cases} 2x + y - 5z = 7 \\ 8x - 3y + z = 4 \\ 7x + 9y + 6z = 0 \end{cases}$$

The solution is as follows:

$$x = \frac{\begin{vmatrix} 7 & 1 & -5 \\ 4 & -3 & 1 \\ 0 & 9 & 6 \end{vmatrix}}{\begin{vmatrix} 2 & 1 & -5 \\ 8 & -3 & 1 \\ 7 & 9 & 6 \end{vmatrix}} = \frac{(-306)-(87)}{(-389)-(171)} = \frac{-393}{-560} = \frac{393}{560}$$

$$y = \frac{\begin{vmatrix} 2 & 7 & -5 \\ 8 & 4 & 1 \\ 7 & 0 & 6 \end{vmatrix}}{\begin{vmatrix} 2 & 1 & -5 \\ 8 & -3 & 1 \\ 7 & 9 & 6 \end{vmatrix}} = \frac{(97)-(196)}{-560} = \frac{-99}{-560} = \frac{99}{560}$$

$$z = \frac{\begin{vmatrix} 2 & 1 & 7 \\ 8 & -3 & 4 \\ 7 & 9 & 0 \end{vmatrix}}{\begin{vmatrix} 2 & 1 & -5 \\ 8 & -3 & 1 \\ 7 & 9 & 6 \end{vmatrix}} = \frac{(532)-(-75)}{-560} = \frac{607}{-560} = -\frac{607}{560}$$

If you think this was a lot of work, imagine doing it by the addition method with such large fractions! One nice feature of Cramer's rule is that fractions are essentially eliminated from the computation.

As a final note, Cramer's rule cannot be used to solve systems with an infinite number of solutions or no solution. In such cases, the denominator determinant will be zero.

EXERCISES 9.3

1. Compute the value of each determinant.

*(a) $\begin{vmatrix} 4 & 1 \\ 2 & 3 \end{vmatrix}$

(b) $\begin{vmatrix} 5 & 8 \\ 0 & 0 \end{vmatrix}$

*(c) $\begin{vmatrix} 4 & 7 \\ 0 & 3 \end{vmatrix}$

(d) $\begin{vmatrix} 0 & 9 \\ 0 & 8 \end{vmatrix}$

*(e) $\begin{vmatrix} 5 & 1 \\ 4 & -3 \end{vmatrix}$

(f) $\begin{vmatrix} 15 & 6 \\ -2 & 4 \end{vmatrix}$

*(g) $\begin{vmatrix} 5 & 5 \\ 5 & 5 \end{vmatrix}$

(h) $\begin{vmatrix} 2 & 4 \\ 6 & 12 \end{vmatrix}$

*(i) $\begin{vmatrix} 1 & 2 \\ -2 & -4 \end{vmatrix}$

(j) $\begin{vmatrix} \sin x & -\cos x \\ \cos x & \sin x \end{vmatrix}$

2. Solve each system of linear equations by using Cramer's rule.

*(a) $\begin{cases} x + y = 7 \\ -2x + 5y = 14 \end{cases}$

(b) $\begin{cases} x + 2y = 0 \\ 3x - y = 0 \end{cases}$

*(c) $\begin{cases} 2x - 3y = 11 \\ x - y = 3 \end{cases}$

(d) $\begin{cases} 2x + 2y = 12 \\ x + 3y = 14 \end{cases}$

*(e) $\begin{cases} 4p + q = 1 \\ 4p - 2q = 6 \end{cases}$

(f) $\begin{cases} 5x + 12y = 23 \\ x + 2y = 3 \end{cases}$

*(g) $\begin{cases} 7u + 2v = 9 \\ 3u - 4v = 5 \end{cases}$

(h) $\begin{cases} 12m + 5n = 13 \\ 5m + 6n = -13 \end{cases}$

3. Compute the value of each determinant.

*(a) $\begin{vmatrix} 5 & 2 & 1 \\ 1 & 4 & 0 \\ 3 & 9 & 7 \end{vmatrix}$

(b) $\begin{vmatrix} 5 & 3 & -8 \\ -1 & 0 & 2 \\ 4 & 7 & 6 \end{vmatrix}$

*(c) $\begin{vmatrix} 1 & 2 & 3 \\ 4 & 5 & 6 \\ 7 & 8 & 9 \end{vmatrix}$

(d) $\begin{vmatrix} 5 & 8 & 1 \\ 2 & 0 & 6 \\ 1 & 4 & 0 \end{vmatrix}$

*(e) $\begin{vmatrix} 4 & 0 & 6 \\ 2 & -5 & 1 \\ 7 & 3 & 0 \end{vmatrix}$

(f) $\begin{vmatrix} 1 & 2 & 5 \\ 3 & 0 & 4 \\ 0 & -7 & 6 \end{vmatrix}$

*(g) $\begin{vmatrix} 9 & 8 & 5 \\ 4 & 3 & 7 \\ 1 & 6 & 2 \end{vmatrix}$

(h) $\begin{vmatrix} 7 & -4 & 5 \\ 8 & 3 & 0 \\ 2 & 6 & -9 \end{vmatrix}$

4. Solve each system of equations by using Cramer's rule.

*(a) $\begin{cases} x + 3y = 5 \\ x + z = 4 \\ 3x + 2y - z = 2 \end{cases}$

(b) $\begin{cases} x + 2y + z = 0 \\ y = 6 \\ 2x + 4y + 5z = 9 \end{cases}$

*(c) $\begin{cases} x + y + z = 6 \\ 2x + 3y - z = 0 \\ 5x - 3y - 7z = -4 \end{cases}$

(d) $\begin{cases} x + 2y + 3z = 7 \\ 2x - 3y + 8z = -3 \\ -5x - 8y + 5z = 11 \end{cases}$

*(e) $\begin{cases} 5x + 2y - 3z = 10 \\ 2x + 7y + 5z = 9 \\ 3x - 3y + 2z = 8 \end{cases}$

(f) $\begin{cases} 4r - 3s + 2t = 9 \\ 5r + s - 5t = -3 \\ 2r - 8s + t = 5 \end{cases}$

*(g) $\begin{cases} 6x + 2y + z = 4 \\ 5x - 3y + 4z = 0 \\ x - 2y + 8z = 3 \end{cases}$

(h) $\begin{cases} 3x + 5y + 2z = 15 \\ 2x - 3y = 9 \\ 4x + 2y - 9z = 6 \end{cases}$

9.4 HIGHER-ORDER DETERMINANTS

We have already studied the evaluation and use of determinants of order 2—that is, determinants with 2 rows and 2 columns.

$$\begin{array}{cc} & \text{col. 1} \quad \text{col. 2} \\ & \downarrow \qquad \downarrow \\ \text{row 1} \rightarrow & \begin{vmatrix} a & b \\ \\ c & d \end{vmatrix} \\ \text{row 2} \rightarrow & \end{array}$$

Notation is sometimes used to specify the position of each number by its row and column, as

$$\begin{vmatrix} a_{11} & a_{12} \\ a_{21} & a_{22} \end{vmatrix} \begin{cases} a_{11} = \text{number in row 1, column 1} \\ a_{12} = \text{number in row 1, column 2} \\ a_{21} = \text{number in row 2, column 1} \\ a_{22} = \text{number in row 2, column 2} \end{cases}$$

We have also studied determinants of order 3—that is, determinants with 3 rows and 3 columns. Determinants of order 4 have four rows and four columns. Unfortunately, such determinants (and still-higher-order determinants) cannot be evaluated by the mechanical techniques used with determinants of orders 2 and 3. Solution of the general system of 4 linear equations in four unknowns by the addition or elimination method suggests there are 24 products in the definition of a determinant of order 4. (Recall that there are 2 products in a determinant of order 2 and 6 products in a determinant of order 3.) If our earlier mechanical techniques were applied to a determinant of order 4, only 8 of the 24 products would be produced: 4 from one direction and 4 from the opposite direction. The other 16 products are not readily available without a new definition of determinant.

First, let us redefine a determinant of order 3 and show that this definition leads to the same value as did the earlier definition.

$$\begin{vmatrix} a_{11} & a_{12} & a_{13} \\ a_{21} & a_{22} & a_{23} \\ a_{31} & a_{32} & a_{33} \end{vmatrix} = +a_{11} \begin{vmatrix} a_{22} & a_{23} \\ a_{32} & a_{33} \end{vmatrix} - a_{12} \begin{vmatrix} a_{21} & a_{23} \\ a_{31} & a_{33} \end{vmatrix} + a_{13} \begin{vmatrix} a_{21} & a_{22} \\ a_{31} & a_{32} \end{vmatrix}$$

The numbers a_{11}, a_{12}, and a_{13} are all from row 1. Each is multiplied by the determinant that remains when its row and column are deleted.

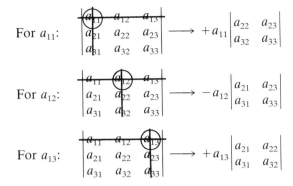

If the sum of the two subscripts is even, then the sign is $+$. This situation occurs for a_{11}, a_{13}, a_{22}, a_{31}, and a_{33}. If the sum is odd, then the sign is $-$. This situation occurs for a_{12}, a_{21}, a_{23}, and a_{32}. The signs alternate in going across any row or down any column. This statement can be illustrated symbolically as

$$
\begin{array}{ccc}
+ & - & + \\
- & + & - \\
+ & - & +
\end{array}
\qquad
\left\{
\begin{array}{l}
\text{The pattern extends indefinitely} \\
\text{both across and down.}
\end{array}
\right.
$$

Although the definition suggests using row 1 to obtain the smaller-order determinants, any row or column can be used. As an example, let us use column 2.

$$
\begin{vmatrix} a_{11} & a_{12} & a_{13} \\ a_{21} & a_{22} & a_{23} \\ a_{31} & a_{32} & a_{33} \end{vmatrix} = -a_{12} \begin{vmatrix} a_{21} & a_{23} \\ a_{31} & a_{33} \end{vmatrix} + a_{22} \begin{vmatrix} a_{11} & a_{13} \\ a_{31} & a_{33} \end{vmatrix} - a_{32} \begin{vmatrix} a_{11} & a_{13} \\ a_{21} & a_{23} \end{vmatrix}
$$

Which row or column you select should depend on the numbers in the determinant. For example, if a row or column contains some zeros, selecting it will simplify computations.

The smaller determinants obtained in this process are called **minors**. Above, the minor of a_{12} is the determinant

$$
\begin{vmatrix} a_{21} & a_{23} \\ a_{31} & a_{33} \end{vmatrix}
$$

A signed minor ($+$ or $-$ according to its position) is called a **cofactor**. Thus the cofactor of a_{12} is

$$
-\begin{vmatrix} a_{21} & a_{23} \\ a_{31} & a_{33} \end{vmatrix}
$$

Now let us use the new definition of determinant to evaluate the determinant

$$\begin{vmatrix} 1 & 2 & 4 \\ 3 & 7 & 5 \\ 9 & 6 & 8 \end{vmatrix}$$

The value of this determinant was shown to be -112, by earlier techniques. We shall use row 1 because no other row or column seems to offer any advantage.

$$\begin{vmatrix} 1 & 2 & 4 \\ 3 & 7 & 5 \\ 9 & 6 & 8 \end{vmatrix} = 1\begin{vmatrix} 7 & 5 \\ 6 & 8 \end{vmatrix} - 2\begin{vmatrix} 3 & 5 \\ 9 & 8 \end{vmatrix} + 4\begin{vmatrix} 3 & 7 \\ 9 & 6 \end{vmatrix}$$

$$= 1(7 \cdot 8 - 6 \cdot 5) - 2(3 \cdot 8 - 9 \cdot 5) + 4(3 \cdot 6 - 9 \cdot 7)$$

$$= 1(56 - 30) - 2(24 - 45) + 4(18 - 63)$$

$$= 1(26) - 2(-21) + 4(-45)$$

$$= 26 + 42 - 180 = -112$$

The new definition of determinants was given for determinants of order 3. The extension of this definition to higher-order determinants should be apparent. Here, for example, is the definition of a determinant of order 4.

$$\begin{vmatrix} a_{11} & a_{12} & a_{13} & a_{14} \\ a_{21} & a_{22} & a_{23} & a_{24} \\ a_{31} & a_{32} & a_{33} & a_{34} \\ a_{41} & a_{42} & a_{43} & a_{44} \end{vmatrix} = a_{11}\begin{vmatrix} a_{22} & a_{23} & a_{24} \\ a_{32} & a_{33} & a_{34} \\ a_{42} & a_{43} & a_{44} \end{vmatrix} - a_{12}\begin{vmatrix} a_{21} & a_{23} & a_{24} \\ a_{31} & a_{33} & a_{34} \\ a_{41} & a_{43} & a_{44} \end{vmatrix}$$

$$+ a_{13}\begin{vmatrix} a_{21} & a_{22} & a_{24} \\ a_{31} & a_{32} & a_{34} \\ a_{41} & a_{42} & a_{44} \end{vmatrix} - a_{14}\begin{vmatrix} a_{21} & a_{22} & a_{23} \\ a_{31} & a_{32} & a_{33} \\ a_{41} & a_{42} & a_{43} \end{vmatrix}$$

The definition is used next to evaluate a determinant of order 4. Column 1 has been selected rather than row 1, however. (Row 4 would also be a good choice.) Notice that each element of column 1 is multiplied by the determinant that remains when its row and column are deleted.

$$\begin{vmatrix} 1 & 5 & 9 & 3 \\ 2 & 4 & 1 & 8 \\ 0 & 3 & 7 & 1 \\ -3 & 5 & 0 & 6 \end{vmatrix} = 1\begin{vmatrix} 4 & 1 & 8 \\ 3 & 7 & 1 \\ 5 & 0 & 6 \end{vmatrix} - 2\begin{vmatrix} 5 & 9 & 3 \\ 3 & 7 & 1 \\ 5 & 0 & 6 \end{vmatrix} + 0 - (-3)\begin{vmatrix} 5 & 9 & 3 \\ 4 & 1 & 8 \\ 3 & 7 & 1 \end{vmatrix}$$

$$= 1(-125) - 2(-12) + 3(-20)$$

$$= -161$$

EXERCISES 9.4

1. Evaluate each determinant by use of cofactors.

*(a)
$$\begin{vmatrix} 1 & 0 & 2 \\ 4 & 1 & 6 \\ 9 & 7 & 8 \end{vmatrix}$$

(b)
$$\begin{vmatrix} 6 & 7 & 8 \\ 0 & -1 & 1 \\ 9 & 4 & 3 \end{vmatrix}$$

*(c)
$$\begin{vmatrix} 0 & 1 & -2 \\ -4 & 0 & 3 \\ -5 & 6 & 0 \end{vmatrix}$$

(d)
$$\begin{vmatrix} 5 & 0 & 9 \\ 6 & 0 & -2 \\ -3 & 0 & 8 \end{vmatrix}$$

*(e)
$$\begin{vmatrix} 7 & 15 & -9 \\ 6 & -8 & 0 \\ 4 & 1 & 20 \end{vmatrix}$$

(f)
$$\begin{vmatrix} 6 & -19 & -8 \\ -4 & 9 & 2 \\ 0 & -3 & 0 \end{vmatrix}$$

*(g)
$$\begin{vmatrix} 5 & 2 & 1 & 0 \\ 9 & 8 & 7 & 6 \\ 4 & -3 & 7 & 4 \\ 8 & 1 & -1 & 6 \end{vmatrix}$$

(h)
$$\begin{vmatrix} 1 & 7 & 3 & -9 \\ 6 & 0 & 1 & 9 \\ 4 & 0 & -8 & 6 \\ 5 & -1 & 7 & 10 \end{vmatrix}$$

*(i)
$$\begin{vmatrix} 5 & 5 & 5 & 5 \\ -1 & 0 & 1 & 0 \\ 3 & -9 & 1 & 6 \\ 4 & 5 & 8 & -7 \end{vmatrix}$$

(j)
$$\begin{vmatrix} 9 & 8 & 7 & 6 \\ 5 & 4 & 3 & 2 \\ 0 & 0 & 0 & 1 \\ -8 & -7 & -6 & -5 \end{vmatrix}$$

2. Solve each system by using Cramer's rule.

*(a)
$$\begin{cases} w + 3x + 5y + 2z = 11 \\ 2w - 5x + 3y - 3z = 5 \\ 4w + 7x + 2y - 5z = -3 \\ 3w + x + y + z = 21 \end{cases}$$

(b)
$$\begin{cases} w + x + y + z = 3 \\ 2w + 3y - 7z = 20 \\ 5w - 2x + y - 5z = -8 \\ -3w + 2y + z = 5 \end{cases}$$

*(c)
$$\begin{cases} 8A + 5B + 6D + F = 3 \\ 9A - 7B - 2D - F = 10 \\ -4A - B + 5D + 7F = -2 \\ A + 4B + D = 0 \end{cases}$$

(d)
$$\begin{cases} 2a + 9b + 5c + 8d = 1 \\ 10a + b + 2c - 5d = 18 \\ -8a - 5b - 3c + d = -6 \\ 3b + 3c - 8d = 12 \end{cases}$$

*(e)
$$\begin{cases} r + 2s + t + u = 10 \\ 5r - 9s + 4t + 8u = 0 \\ -3r + 5s + t - 2u = 1 \\ 10r - 7s - 9t + 5u = 4 \end{cases}$$

(f)
$$\begin{cases} 8r + 5s - 3t - 4w = 4 \\ 5r + 6t + w = 0 \\ 7r + 3s + 5t + 8w = 14 \\ -9r - 8s + 2t - 5w = -16 \end{cases}$$

9.5 APPLICATION: PARTIAL FRACTIONS

It is sometimes necessary in calculus to write a fraction as the sum of two or more fractions called **partial fractions**. A fraction such as

$$\frac{6x^2 - 55x - 21}{x(x + 1)(x - 7)}$$

can be written as the sum of three fractions. Each partial fraction has as its denominator one of the factors from the denominator of the original fraction.

$$\frac{6x^2 - 55x - 21}{x(x + 1)(x - 7)} = \frac{A}{x} + \frac{B}{x + 1} + \frac{C}{x - 7}$$

The numbers A, B, and C are constants. The values of A, B, and C can be determined as follows. First, combine the fractions that are on the right side. Then since the denominators of the two equal fractions (the original and the new one produced on the right side) are the same, their numerators must be equal. So equate the numerators. This leads to three equations in A, B, and C, which can be solved by any method studied earlier in the chapter. Here are the steps. First, combine the fractions that are on the right side.

$$\frac{6x^2 - 55x - 21}{x(x + 1)(x - 7)} = \frac{A(x + 1)(x - 7) + B(x)(x - 7) + C(x)(x + 1)}{x(x + 1)(x - 7)}$$

$$= \frac{Ax^2 - 6Ax - 7A + Bx^2 - 7Bx + Cx^2 + Cx}{x(x + 1)(x - 7)}$$

$$= \frac{(A + B + C)x^2 + (-6A - 7B + C)x - 7A}{x(x + 1)(x - 7)}$$

Because the denominators of the fractions are equal, the numerators of these two equal fractions must be equal. That is,

$$6x^2 - 55x - 21 = (A + B + C)x^2 + (-6A - 7B + C)x - 7A$$

This means that

$$6x^2 = (A + B + C)x^2$$

$$-55x = (-6A - 7B + C)x$$

$$-21 = -7A$$

Equating the coefficients of x^2 and doing the same for x and the constants yields a system of three equations in three unknowns.

$$\begin{cases} A + B + C = 6 \\ -6A - 7B + C = -55 \\ -7A = -21 \end{cases}$$

The solution is

$$A = 3$$
$$B = 5$$
$$C = -2$$

Thus

$$\frac{6x^2 - 55x - 21}{x(x + 1)(x - 7)} = \frac{3}{x} + \frac{5}{x + 1} - \frac{2}{x - 7}$$

Obtaining partial fractions for more complicated denominators is a little more involved. The denominator must be factored as much as possible. (Any polynomial with real coefficients can be written as a product of linear and quadratic factors.) The partial fraction corresponding to a quadratic factor in the denominator has a linear numerator of the form $Ax + B$. The partial fraction corresponding to a linear factor in the denominator has a constant numerator, as demonstrated in the preceding example. If the nth power of any factor appears in the denominator of the original fraction, it must be written n times (using n separate fractions) in the partial fraction representation. Furthermore, in that representation it is written to the nth power in the first denominator, to the $(n - 1)$st power in the second denominator, and so on until it is written as the first power in the last fraction. Consider this example that shows the partial fraction setup for a very complicated case. Then go through Example 10, which follows.

$$\frac{7x^5 + 5x^4 - x^2 + 12}{(x + 3)^3(x^2 - 3x + 7)^2(x - 2)(x^2 + 5x + 1)}$$

$$= \frac{A}{(x + 3)^3} + \frac{B}{(x + 3)^2} + \frac{C}{x + 3} + \frac{Dx + E}{(x^2 - 3x + 7)^2}$$

$$+ \frac{Fx + G}{x^2 - 3x + 7} + \frac{H}{x - 2} + \frac{Ix + J}{x^2 + 5x + 1}$$

Note: The rules for partial fractions apply only to *proper* fractions. Given an improper fraction (that is, the degree of the numerator is greater than or equal to the degree of the denominator), first simplify it (see Chapter 5, Example 13) and then write the resulting proper fraction in terms of partial fractions.

Example 10 *Write the fraction as the sum of partial fractions.*

$$\frac{6x^3 + 36x^2 + 25x + 3}{(x^2)(x^2 + 7x + 1)}$$

First note that x^2 is not a quadratic factor for partial fraction purposes. It can be factored as $(x)(x)$ and thus is a repeated linear factor. On the other hand, the quadratic expression $x^2 + 7x + 1$ cannot be factored; so it is a quadratic factor for partial fraction purposes. Now let us set up the partial fraction form.

$$\frac{6x^3 + 36x^2 + 25x + 3}{(x^2)(x^2 + 7x + 1)} = \frac{A}{(x)^2} + \frac{B}{x} + \frac{Cx + D}{x^2 + 7x + 1}$$

Now, combine the three fractions on the right side of the equation.

$$\frac{6x^3 + 36x^2 + 25x + 3}{(x^2)(x^2 + 7x + 1)} = \frac{A(x^2 + 7x + 1) + B(x)(x^2 + 7x + 1) + (Cx + D)x^2}{(x^2)(x^2 + 7x + 1)}$$

At this point we have two equal fractions and each has the same denominator. Therefore the numerators must also be equal. Equating the numerators yields the equation

$$6x^3 + 36x^2 + 25x + 3 = A(x^2 + 7x + 1) + B(x)(x^2 + 7x + 1) + (Cx + D)x^2$$

As a first step in solving this equation, multiply out the right side.

$$6x^3 + 36x^2 + 25x + 3 = Ax^2 + 7Ax + A + Bx^3 + 7Bx^2 + Bx + Cx^3 + Dx^2$$

Next, group the terms on the right according to powers of x.

$$6x^3 + 36x^2 + 25x + 3 = (B + C)x^3 + (A + 7B + D)x^2 + (7A + B)x + A$$

Next, we equate corresponding coefficients. That is, the coefficient of x^3 on the left side (6) must be equal to the coefficient of x^3 on the right side ($B + C$). The resulting equation is $B + C = 6$. Three other equations are obtained by equating the other coefficients. Here is the resulting system of four equations in four unknowns.

$$\begin{cases} B + C = 6 \\ A + 7B + D = 36 \\ 7A + B = 25 \\ A = 3 \end{cases}$$

Immediately we see that $A = 3$. So we can replace A by 3 in the third equation to get

$$21 + B = 25$$

from which $B = 4$ follows readily. Next, replace B by 4 in the first equation to obtain

$$4 + C = 6$$

which means $C = 2$. Finally, in the second equation, replace A by 3 and B by 4 to obtain

$$3 + 28 + D = 36$$

which means that $D = 5$. In summary, $A = 3$, $B = 4$, $C = 2$, and $D = 5$. Thus

$$\frac{A}{x^2} + \frac{B}{x} + \frac{Cx + D}{x^2 + 7x + 1}$$

becomes

$$\frac{3}{x^2} + \frac{4}{x} + \frac{2x + 5}{x^2 + 7x + 1}$$

which is the desired partial fraction representation of the original fraction.

EXERCISES 9.5

1. Write each proper fraction as the sum of two or more partial fractions. Factor denominator expressions whenever possible.

    *(a) $\dfrac{9x + 10}{x(x + 5)}$

    (b) $\dfrac{-2x + 34}{(x + 3)(x - 2)}$

    *(c) $\dfrac{7x^2 - 82x + 279}{(x + 5)(x - 3)(x - 7)}$

    (d) $\dfrac{8x^2 + 14x + 12}{x(x^2 + 5x + 4)}$

    *(e) $\dfrac{3x^2 + 3x - 16}{x^3 + 3x^2 - 4x}$

    (f) $\dfrac{11x^2 + 33x + 2}{(x + 2)(x^2 + 5x + 1)}$

    *(g) $\dfrac{6x^2 - 3x - 54}{(x - 3)(x^2 - 4x - 12)}$

    (h) $\dfrac{9x^2 + 5x - 3}{x^2(x + 3)}$

    *(i) $\dfrac{7x^2 + 75x + 150}{x(x + 5)^2}$

    (j) $\dfrac{-x^2 + 22x - 9}{x^3 + 3x^2 - 9x + 5}$

    *(k) $\dfrac{5x^3 + x^2 + 5x + 5}{(x^2 + 1)^2}$

2. Simplify each improper fraction (see Chapter 5, Example 13). Then write the resulting proper fraction in terms of partial fractions.

*(a) $\dfrac{x^2 + 15}{x^2 - 9}$

(b) $\dfrac{2x^2 + 9x - 7}{x^2 + 2x - 3}$

*(c) $\dfrac{x^3 + 6x^2 + 17x + 17}{x^2 + 3x + 2}$

(d) $\dfrac{5x^3 + 10x^2 + 4x + 14}{x^2 + 2x}$

9.6 APPLICATION: CIRCLES

The equation of the circle that passes through three given points can be obtained by establishing and solving a system of three linear equations in three unknowns. Any circle can be written in the form

$$x^2 + y^2 + ax + by + c = 0$$

If the x and y coordinates of a point are substituted into this equation, there will be three unknowns: a, b, and c. If this is done for three different points, then three equations in three unknowns will be obtained.

Suppose that a circle passes through the points $(-2, 6)$, $(3, 1)$, and $(1, -3)$. To begin, we use the point $(-2, 6)$ and substitute -2 for x for 6 for y into

$$x^2 + y^2 + ax + by + c = 0$$

The result is

$$4 + 36 + a(-2) + b(6) + c = 0$$

or

$$-2a + 6b + c = -40$$

Similarly, the point $(3, 1)$ yields

$$3a + b + c = -10$$

and $(1, -3)$ yields

$$a - 3b + c = -10$$

The system is

$$\begin{cases} -2a + 6b + c = -40 \\ 3a + b + c = -10 \\ a - 3b + c = -10 \end{cases}$$

The solution to this system, by any of the techniques studied earlier in this chapter, is

$$a = 4$$
$$b = -2$$
$$c = -20$$

so

$$x^2 + y^2 + ax + by + c = 0$$

becomes

$$x^2 + y^2 + 4x - 2y - 20 = 0$$

This is the equation of the circle through the points $(-2, 6)$, $(3, 1)$, and $(1, -3)$.

EXERCISES 9.6

In each problem, determine the equation of the circle that passes through the three given points.

*1. $(3, 3)$, $(8, -2)$, $(7, 1)$

2. $(2, 2)$, $(9, -5)$, $(2, -12)$

*3. $(2, 1)$, $(-2, 3)$, $(3, -2)$

9.7   NONLINEAR SYSTEMS

A system of equations in which at least one equation is not a linear equation is called a *nonlinear system*. The methods of substitution and elimination can be applied to solve such systems. Whenever convenient, sketches should be made of the equations in the system. Solutions obtained must be checked in all equations of the system, because extraneous roots may appear.

Example 11   *Solve the system*

$$\begin{cases} x^2 + y^2 = 16 \\ x + y = 3 \end{cases}$$

Whenever one equation is linear and one is quadratic, use the linear equation to make a substitution into the quadratic equation. Here the second equation can be written $y = 3 - x$, after which $3 - x$ can be substituted for y in the first equation. When this is done, the first equation becomes

$$x^2 + (3 - x)^2 = 16$$

$$x^2 + 9 - 6x + x^2 = 16$$

or

$$2x^2 - 6x - 7 = 0$$

By using the quadratic formula, we get

$$x = \frac{6 \pm \sqrt{92}}{4} = \frac{2(3 \pm \sqrt{23})}{2 \cdot 2} = \frac{3 \pm \sqrt{23}}{2}$$

Now, in order to find corresponding y values, substitute these values of x into the linear equation. The linear equation will yield one y for each x and hence the two points of intersection (anticipated from the graph).

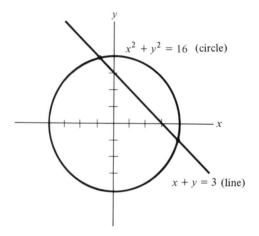

(On the other hand, if these values of x are substituted into the quadratic equation, the result will be two y values for each x value. In other words, using the first equation will suggest that the line crosses the circle in four points. However, when these points are checked in the second equation, only two will check correctly.) So continue by substituting

$$x = \frac{3 + \sqrt{23}}{2}$$

into the linear equation $y = 3 - x$. The result is

$$y = 3 - \frac{3 + \sqrt{23}}{2} = \frac{6}{2} - \frac{3 + \sqrt{23}}{2} = \frac{3 - \sqrt{23}}{2}$$

So one point of intersection is

$$\left(\frac{3 + \sqrt{23}}{2}, \frac{3 - \sqrt{23}}{2} \right)$$

Next, using

$$x = \frac{3 - \sqrt{23}}{2}$$

in $y = 3 - x$ yields

$$y = 3 - \frac{3 - \sqrt{23}}{2} = \frac{6}{2} - \frac{3 - \sqrt{23}}{2} = \frac{3 + \sqrt{23}}{2}$$

The other point of intersection is

$$\left(\frac{3 - \sqrt{23}}{2}, \frac{3 + \sqrt{23}}{2} \right)$$

Example 12 *Solve the system*

$$\begin{cases} x^2 + y^2 = 2 \\ y^2 - x^2 = 4 \end{cases}$$

If the second equation is rewritten as $-x^2 + y^2 = 4$ and added to the first equation, the result is $2y^2 = 6$ or $y = \pm\sqrt{3}$. When $\sqrt{3}$ or $-\sqrt{3}$ is substituted for y into either $x^2 + y^2 = 2$ or $y^2 - x^2 = 4$, the result is $x = \pm i$. This means that there is no real solution. Graphically, there is no point in the xy plane (the real plane) where this circle and hyperbola meet. The graph verifies this.

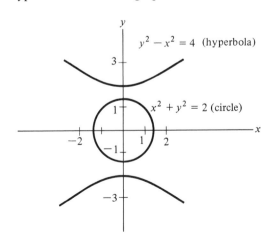

Example 13   *Solve the system*

$$\begin{cases} y = x^2 + 1 \\ x^2 + 4y^2 = 4 \end{cases}$$

Substitute $x^2 + 1$ for y into the second equation. The result is

$$x^2 + 4(x^2 + 1)^2 = 4$$
$$x^2 + 4x^4 + 8x^2 + 4 = 4$$
$$4x^4 + 9x^2 = 0$$
$$x^2(4x^2 + 9) = 0$$

Finally,

$$x = 0 \qquad x = \pm\sqrt{-\frac{9}{4}} = \pm\frac{3}{2}i$$

from which we conclude that $x = 0$, since x must be real. Then

$$y = x^2 + 1 = 0 + 1 = 1$$

The curves meet at $(0, 1)$ only, as shown in the next graph.

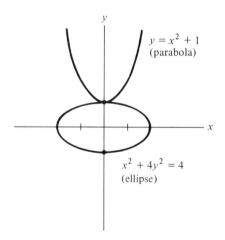

EXERCISES 9.7

1.   Solve each system if possible.

*(a) $\begin{cases} x^2 + y^2 = 25 \\ y - x = 1 \end{cases}$

(b) $\begin{cases} x^2 + 4y^2 = 4 \\ x - y = -4 \end{cases}$

*(c) $\begin{cases} 2x - y = 1 \\ x^2 + y^2 = 12 \end{cases}$ (d) $\begin{cases} y = x^2 + 2 \\ 4x^2 + 9y^2 = 36 \end{cases}$

*(e) $\begin{cases} y = -x^2 + 2 \\ 4x^2 + 9y^2 = 36 \end{cases}$ (f) $\begin{cases} x^2 + y^2 = 16 \\ x^2 - y^2 = 16 \end{cases}$

*(g) $\begin{cases} x^2 + y^2 = 16 \\ x^2 - y^2 = 1 \end{cases}$ (h) $\begin{cases} x^2 + y^2 = 9 \\ x^2 + 4y^2 = 16 \end{cases}$

*(i) $\begin{cases} y = x^2 - 2x - 3 \\ y = -x^2 - x + 6 \end{cases}$ (j) $\begin{cases} x - y^2 = 0 \\ y^2 - x^2 = 16 \end{cases}$

*(k) $\begin{cases} x^2 + y^2 = 9 \\ x = 4 \end{cases}$ (l) $\begin{cases} y^2 - x^2 = 16 \\ y = -3 \end{cases}$

*(m) $\begin{cases} y = x^3 \\ y = 7x \end{cases}$ (n) $\begin{cases} xy = 3 \\ y = x + 2 \end{cases}$

*(o) $\begin{cases} y = -\dfrac{10}{x^2} \\ y = x^2 - 7 \end{cases}$ (p) $\begin{cases} y = \dfrac{12}{x^2} \\ y = x^2 - 4 \end{cases}$

2. A common calculus problem is to find the area between two curves—that is, the area bounded by the curves. In order to set up the calculus, it is necessary to determine the points of intersection of the two curves involved. Also useful is a sketch that shows the desired area shaded. For each pair of equations, use algebra to determine the points of intersection. Then sketch the curves and shade the area enclosed between the curves.

*(a) $y = x^2 - 1$ and $y = x + 1$

(b) $y = x - 7$ and $x = y^2 + 1$

*(c) $x^2 = 4 + y$ and $x^2 + y = 6$

(d) $y = x^4$ and $y = x^2$

*(e) $y = x^3 - 6x^2 + 5x$ and $y = 0$

(f) $y = x^3$ and $y = 9x$

*3. Where does the line with slope 1 and y intercept -3 intersect the circle $x^2 + y^2 - 6x + 2y + 3 = 0$?

4. Solve each problem by letting x and y represent the unknown numbers, establishing two equations in two unknowns, and then solving the system of equations.

*(a) The difference between two numbers is 2. The sum of the squares of the numbers is 52. Determine the numbers.

(b) The perimeter of a rectangle is 60 centimeters and its area is 216 square centimeters. Determine the length and width of the rectangle.

*(c) The area of a rectangle is 200 square centimeters. One side is four times as long as the other. Determine the length and width of the rectangle.

5. Solve each problem by first establishing two equations in the two unknowns x and y.

*(a) The radius of the circle is $\sqrt{15}$. The height of the triangle is twice the length of the base. Determine the lengths of the sides x and y of the triangle.

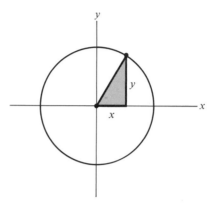

(b) In the right triangle shown here, the base (y) is 3 units longer than the height (x). Determine the size of the base and height of the triangle.

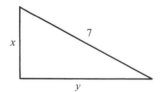

*(c) The area of the trapezoid shown is 57 square inches. The lower base is 5 inches longer than the upper base. Determine the size of each base.

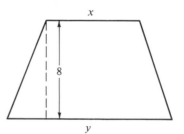

REVIEW EXERCISES FOR CHAPTER 9

1. Solve by substitution or elimination, whichever seems simpler.

*(a) $\begin{cases} 4x - 3y = 36 \\ 5x + 4y = 14 \end{cases}$ (b) $\begin{cases} 5x - 3y = 11 \\ 6x - 5y = 16 \end{cases}$

*(c) $\begin{cases} x = 2y - 3 \\ 5x - 7y = 0 \end{cases}$

(d) $\begin{cases} 3x + 5y + 4z = 5 \\ 2x - 4y - 9z = -7 \\ 5x + 2y - 7z = 3 \end{cases}$

2. Solve by using Gauss–Jordan elimination with matrices.

*(a) $\begin{cases} 2x - 2y = -13 \\ 8x + y = 11 \end{cases}$

(b) $\begin{cases} x + y + 2z = 7 \\ 3x + 2y + 3z = 7 \\ -5x + y - 4z = 1 \end{cases}$

3. Solve by using Cramer's rule.

*(a) $\begin{cases} 3x - 5y = 2 \\ 4x - 9y = -9 \end{cases}$

(b) $\begin{cases} x - y - 4z = 12 \\ 2x + y + 3z = -6 \\ 5x + 2y + 2z = 1 \end{cases}$

4. Write each fraction as the sum of partial fractions.

*(a) $\dfrac{7x^2 - 17x + 14}{(x^2 + 1)(x - 5)}$

(b) $\dfrac{2x^2 - 19x + 54}{(x - 4)^2(x + 1)}$

5. Solve each system if possible.

*(a) $\begin{cases} y = x^2 - 8x + 12 \\ x + y = 6 \end{cases}$

(b) $\begin{cases} x^2 - y^2 = 9 \\ x^2 + 4y^2 = 4 \end{cases}$

10.1 SEQUENCES

To begin, here is an example of an *infinite sequence*.

$$2, 4, 6, 8, 10, \ldots$$

The three dots specify that the sequence continues infinitely in the same manner. Assuming the obvious, the next numbers are 12, 14, 16, and so on. This is a sequence of even numbers. The sequence above is a function. The numbers 2, 4, 6, 8, 10, and so on of the sequence constitute the range of the function. The domain is the set of positive integers. They specify position. The rule of correspondence can be illustrated as follows.

Domain		*Range*	
1	$\longrightarrow$	2	The 1st number is 2.
2	$\longrightarrow$	4	The 2nd number is 4.
3	$\longrightarrow$	6	The 3rd number is 6.
4	$\longrightarrow$	8	The 4th number is 8.
5	$\longrightarrow$	10	The 5th number is 10.
.			
.			
.			
n	$\longrightarrow$	$2n$	The nth number is $2n$.

We shall denote the first term of a sequence by a_1, the second term by a_2, and so on. Thus for the specific sequence above, $a_1 = 2$, $a_2 = 4$, $a_3 = 6, \ldots$, $a_n = 2n$. Since each term of this sequence is simply twice its position number, this sequence is described by writing $a_n = 2n$. The sequence 5, 7, 9, 11, 13, . . . is described by the formula $a_n = 2n + 3$. The sequence 0, 1, 2, 3, 4, . . . is the function $a_n = n - 1$. The sequence $\frac{1}{4}$, $\frac{1}{9}$, $\frac{1}{16}$, $\frac{1}{25}$, . . . is the function $a_n = 1/(n + 1)^2$.

Infinite sequences are functions, but they are unlike any functions that we have studied so far. If you were to obtain points and graph a sequence function, you would find that there are no curves connecting the points. The graph is simply a lot of points with gaps between them all. Another strange feature: regardless of the sequence, the domain is always the same and that domain is the set of positive integers. This suggests the following definition of infinite sequence.

> An **infinite sequence** is a function whose domain is the set of positive integers.

An **arithmetic sequence** is a sequence in which the difference, called d, between any two consecutive terms is constant. The sequence 5, 7, 9, 11, . . . is an arithmetic sequence with $d = 2$. The fifth (next) term in the sequence is 2 more (d more) than the fourth term: $a_5 = a_4 + d = 11 + 2 = 13$. Also, $a_5 = a_1 + 4d$, since each difference moves you one position to the right in the sequence. In general,

> **Arithmetic sequence**
>
> $$a_n = a_1 + (n - 1)d$$

Example 1 *If in an arithmetic sequence $a_1 = 5$ and $d = 3$, determine a_{19}.*

$$a_{19} = a_1 + 18d \qquad n = 19; \text{ so } n - 1 \text{ is } 18.$$

$$= 5 + 18(3)$$

$$= 59$$

The sum S_n of the first n terms of an arithmetic sequence will now be shown to be

> **Arithmetic sequence**
>
> $$S_n = \frac{n}{2}(a_1 + a_n)$$

By S_n is meant $a_1 + a_2 + a_3 + \cdots + a_n$. That is,

$$S_n = a_1 + a_2 + a_3 + \cdots + a_n$$

If all terms on the right side are written by using a_1 and d only, then S_n becomes

$$S_n = a_1 + (a_1 + d) + (a_1 + 2d) + \cdots + (a_1 + (n - 1)d) \qquad (1)$$

Now reverse the order of the terms in the original S_n form, to get

$$S_n = a_n + a_{n-1} + a_{n-2} + \cdots + a_1$$

Next, write each term on the right side of this expression, using a_n and d only. This result is

$$S_n = a_n + (a_n - d) + (a_n - 2d) + \cdots + (a_n - (n - 1)d) \qquad (2)$$

Now add the two forms of S_n labeled (1) and (2).

$$\begin{aligned} S_n &= a_1 + a_1 + d + a_1 + 2d + \cdots + a_1 + (n - 1)d \\ + \ S_n &= a_n + a_n - d + a_n - 2d + \cdots + a_n - (n - 1)d \\ \hline 2S_n &= na_1 + na_n \end{aligned}$$

Note that all the d terms here add to zero and that all that remains on the right side are n a_1's and n a_n's. If n is factored from each term on the right side, the result is

$$2S_n = n(a_1 + a_n)$$

Finally, divide both sides by 2 to produce the desired result.

$$S_n = \frac{n}{2}(a_1 + a_n)$$

Example 2 *Find the sum of the first* 20 *terms of the sequence* 3, 7, 11, 15, ...
The sequence is arithmetic with $d = 4$ and $a_1 = 3$. Thus

$$S_{20} = \frac{20}{2}(a_1 + a_{20})$$

or

$$S_{20} = 10(3 + a_{20})$$

Once a_{20} is determined, the computation can be completed.

$$a_{20} = a_1 + 19d$$
$$= 3 + 19(4)$$
$$= 79$$

Now

$$S_{20} = 10(3 + 79) = 820$$

A formula for a_n for a specific arithmetic sequence can be determined by using the general formula $a_n = a_1 + (n - 1)d$. You merely supply a_1 and d.

Example 3 *Determine a formula for the arithmetic sequence with first term 7 and difference 2.*

Substitute 7 for a_1 and 2 for d in

$$a_n = a_1 + (n - 1)d$$

The result is

$$a_n = 7 + (n - 1)2$$

or

$$a_n = 2n + 5$$

Example 4 *In an arithmetic sequence, $a_5 = 12$ and $d = -4$. Find a_{30}.*

Beginning at a_5, add 25 differences in order to reach a_{30}.

$$a_{30} = a_5 + 25d$$
$$= 12 + 25(-4)$$
$$= -88$$

In an arithmetic sequence, a constant is *added* to a term to get the next term in the sequence. In a **geometric sequence**, each term is *multiplied* by a constant in order to obtain the next term in the sequence. The constant is called r for *ratio*. In the sequence 2, 6, 18, 54, . . . , each term is multiplied by 3 to get the next term to the right of it. So $r = 3$ for this geometric sequence. The next term in the sequence is $a_5 = a_4 \cdot r = 54 \cdot 3 = 162$. The term after that is $a_6 = 486$. The number r is called the *ratio* because it is the quotient (or ratio) of any term divided by the term preceding it in the sequence.

Suppose that a geometric sequence has $a_1 = 3$ and $r = 2$. Then $a_2 = a_1 \cdot r = 3 \cdot 2 = 6$; $a_3 = a_2 \cdot r = 6 \cdot 2 = 12$; and so on. The term a_3 can also be computed as $a_3 = a_1 \cdot r^2$, since $a_3 = a_2 \cdot r = a_1 r \cdot r = a_1 r^2$. Similarly, $a_4 = a_1 r^3$ and, in general,

---

Geometric sequence

$$a_n = a_1 r^{n-1}$$

Example 5 *Find a_8 for a geometric sequence in which a_1 is 9 and $r = -2$.*

$$a_8 = a_1 r^7$$
$$= 9(-2)^7$$
$$= 9(-128)$$
$$= -1152$$

The formula for computing a_n from a_1 and r can be used to obtain the formula for the terms of a geometric sequence.

Example 6 *Determine a formula for a_n for the geometric sequence 7, 21, 63, 189, ...*
Here $a_1 = 7$ and $r = \frac{21}{7} = 3$. When these two numbers are substituted into

$$a_n = a_1 \cdot r^{n-1}$$

the result is

$$a_n = 7 \cdot 3^{n-1}$$

which is a formula that can be used to obtain any term of the sequence.

The sum S_n of the first n terms of a geometric sequence will now be shown to be

---

Geometric sequence

$$S_n = \frac{a_1(1 - r^n)}{1 - r} \qquad r \neq 1$$

The sum of the first n terms of a geometric sequence is

$$S_n = a_1 + a_2 + a_3 + \cdots + a_n$$

or

$$S_n = a_1 + a_1 r + a_1 r^2 + \cdots + a_1 r^{n-1} \qquad (3)$$

if each term is written in terms of a_1 and r only. Now multiply both sides of this equation by r. The result is

$$rS_n = a_1 r + a_1 r^2 + a_1 r^3 + \cdots + a_1 r^n \qquad (4)$$

Next, align corresponding terms of (3) and (4) and subtract (4) from (3); that is,

$$
\begin{aligned}
S_n &= a_1 + a_1 r + a_1 r^2 + \cdots + a_1 r^{n-1} \\
-rS_n &= - a_1 r - a_1 r^2 - \cdots - a_1 r^{n-1} - a_1 r^n \\
\hline
S_n - rS_n &= a_1 - a_1 r^n
\end{aligned}
$$

or after factoring out S_n on the left and a_1 on the right,

$$(1 - r)S_n = a_1(1 - r^n)$$

Finally, divide both sides by $(1 - r)$ to get

$$S_n = \frac{a_1(1 - r^n)}{1 - r} \qquad r \neq 1$$

Example 7 *Find the sum of the first eight terms of the sequence*

$$5, 10, 20, \ldots$$

This is a geometric sequence with a_1 given as 5 and $r = \frac{10}{5} = 2$. Thus

$$S_8 = \frac{a_1(1 - r^8)}{1 - r} = \frac{5(1 - 2^8)}{1 - 2} = \frac{5(-255)}{-1} = 1275$$

EXERCISES 10.1

Answers to starred exercises are given in the back of the book.

1. Generate the first four terms of each sequence: a_1, a_2, a_3, and a_4.

   *(a) $a_n = 3n + 1$
   *(c) $a_n = 3(n - 2)$
   *(e) $a_n = \dfrac{n^2 + 2}{3}$

   (b) $a_n = 2n - 5$
   (d) $a_n = 3n^2 - 4$
   (f) $a_n = \dfrac{2n + 1}{3}$

*(g) $a_n = \dfrac{2n(n-1)}{3}$ (h) $a_n = \dfrac{n^2}{n+1}$

*(i) $a_n = \dfrac{n^2}{2} - n$ (j) $a_n = \dfrac{n}{3} - \dfrac{n^2}{5}$

2. Find a formula for a_n for each sequence.

    *(a) 2, 3, 4, 5, 6, . . .   (b) 3, 6, 9, 12, . . .

    *(c) $1, \dfrac{1}{2}, \dfrac{1}{3}, \dfrac{1}{4}, \ldots$ (d) $-2, -4, -6, -8, \ldots$

    *(e) $\dfrac{1}{2}, \dfrac{2}{3}, \dfrac{3}{4}, \ldots$ (f) $1, \dfrac{1}{4}, \dfrac{1}{9}, \dfrac{1}{16}, \ldots$

    *(g) 9, 16, 25, 36, . . .   (h) $\sqrt{3}, \sqrt{4}, \sqrt{5}, \ldots$

    *(i) $\dfrac{5}{1}, \dfrac{5}{4}, \dfrac{5}{9}, \dfrac{5}{16}, \ldots$ (j) 0, 1, 8, 27, 64, . . .

3. For each arithmetic sequence, find whatever is requested.

    *(a) 3, 5, 7, 9, . . .; find a_{23}.

    (b) 3, 5, 7, 9, . . .; find S_{23}.

    *(c) 7, 10, 13, 16, . . .; find a_{71}.

    (d) 17, 15, 13, 11, 9, . . .; find a_{41}.

    *(e) 2, 6, 10, 14, 18, . . .; find S_{60}.

    (f) $a_{12} = 64$, $d = 8$; find a_1.

    *(g) $a_1 = 50$, $a_2 = 100$; find a_8.

    (h) 5, 8, 11, 14, . . .; find a_{32} and S_{32}.

    *(i) $a_5 = 130$, $a_9 = 102$; find a_1.

    (j) $a_5 = 10$, $a_8 = 46$; find a_1 and a_2.

4. For each geometric sequence, find whatever is requested.

    *(a) $a_1 = 5$, $r = 2$; find a_8.

    (b) 4, 12, 36, . . .; find a_7.

    *(c) $6, 3, \dfrac{3}{2}, \ldots$; find a_{10}.

    (d) $a_1 = 1$, $a_2 = 10$; find a_9.

    *(e) $1, \dfrac{1}{3}, \dfrac{1}{9}, \dfrac{1}{27}, \ldots$; find S_7.

    (f) $\dfrac{3}{7}, \dfrac{3}{14}, \dfrac{3}{28}, \ldots$; find the sum of the first 10 terms.

    *(g) 1, -3, 9, . . .; find a_7.

    (h) 384, -192, . . .; find the sum of the first 5 terms.

    *(i) 320, 160, 80, . . .; find S_8.

(j) $a_6 = 5$, $a_{11} = 1215$; find r.

*(k) $a_2 = 40$, $a_5 = 2560$; find a_3.

(l) $a_5 = 40$, $a_9 = 640$; find a_1.

*(m) $a_2 = 12$, $a_6 = 972$; find two different formulas for a_n.
(*Hint:* Two different r values.)

(n) $a_4 = 8$, $a_7 = 1$; find a formula for a_n.

5. For each sequence, determine whether it is arithmetic, geometric, or neither.

*(a) 4, 7, 10, 13, . . .   (b) 4, 12, 36, 108, . . .

*(c) 1, 8, 16, 24, . . .   (d) 1, 4, 9, 16, . . .

*(e) -3, 1, 5, 9, . . .   (f) 5, 7, 9, 13, . . .

*(g) 3, -6, 12, -24, . . .   (h) 8, 5, 2, -1, . . .

6. Determine a formula for the sum of the integers from 1 through n by using your knowledge of sequences. Proceed by writing out the sequence and determining which kind it is.

* 7. The frequencies of musical notes form a geometric sequence. Middle C has a frequency of 256 vibrations per second. A note one octave higher has a frequency of 512.

(a) Determine the frequency of a note that is two octaves higher than middle C.

(b) What is the frequency of a note two octaves lower than middle C?

8. The sounds of two different instruments playing the same note can be distinguished because of the difference in tone color. Our ears identify the basic note, called the *fundamental frequency*, and several additional frequencies, called *overtones*. Each instrument has its own pattern of strengths and weaknesses among its overtones and this pattern accounts for its distinctive tone color. If an instrument is playing a fundamental of 1500 cycles per second, its overtones (multiples of the fundamental) are 3000, 4500, 6000, 7500, . . . cycles per second.

(a) What kind of sequence is this, and what is the next overtone in the sequence?

(b) Many people cannot hear frequencies above 10,000 cycles per second. Assuming, as before, that overtones are multiples of the fundamental, how many overtones of a fundamental with 1200 cycles per second would such people hear?

* 9. Two people are playing 18 holes of golf. The winner of the first hole wins $1, the winner of the second hole wins $2, the winner of the third hole wins $4, and so on. What is the most either player can win in playing the 18 holes?

10. Carlos, a wealthy pro-football fan, bets on each of his team's 16 games. He bets $100 on the first game, $200 on the second game, $300 on the third game, and so on for the entire season.

    (a) How much will Carlos win if his team wins all its games?

    (b) How much will Carlos win if his team wins its first 13 games and loses the others?

    (c) How much will Carlos win if his team loses its first three games and wins all the others?

*11. Sue studied hard and had a great grade report. Her parents wanted to reward her for her effort and achievement. Sue, who had been studying sequences, asked only that they give her some pennies. She brought out a checkerboard and asked that they put one penny on the first square, two on the second square, four on the third square, eight on the fourth square, and so on until all 64 squares are filled. How much money is the 64 squares of pennies? Once you set this up, a calculator will be helpful. If a calculator is not available, you might want to use logarithms or the rough approximation $2^{10} \approx 1000$.

10.2 PREPARATION FOR INFINITE SERIES

When the terms of an infinite sequence $a_1, a_2, a_3, a_4, \ldots$ are added as $a_1 + a_2 + a_3 + a_4 + \cdots$, the resulting sum is called an *infinite series*. The next section is devoted to the study of infinite series. Because that presentation will include the use of new notation, the purpose of this section is to introduce that notation. Basically we shall be concerned with summation notation and factorial notation.

We begin with summation notation. A capital sigma, $\sum$, is used frequently in mathematics to denote a sum. Here is an example of such use.

$$1 + 2 + 3 + 4 + 5 + 6 = \sum_{k=1}^{6} k$$

Note the compact summation form on the right side. It indicates the sum of numbers of the form k. Below the sigma, $k = 1$ specifies that k begins at 1. The 6 on top of the sigma indicates that 6 is the last value that k takes on. So k begins at 1 and *counts* 1, 2, 3, 4, 5, 6. Here is another example.

$$\sum_{k=2}^{5} k^2 = 2^2 + 3^2 + 4^2 + 5^2$$

$$= 4 + 9 + 16 + 25$$

$$= 54$$

The count is always by ones—that is, by consecutive integers. The counter or index letter need not be k. Often i, j, and n are used. Any letter can be used.

$$\sum_{i=1}^{5} (i + 1) = (1 + 1) + (2 + 1) + (3 + 1) + (4 + 1) + (5 + 1)$$

$$= 2 \quad\quad + 3 \quad\quad + 4 \quad\quad + 5 \quad\quad + 6$$

$$= 20$$

$$\sum_{j=0}^{3} \frac{1}{j + 1} = \frac{1}{0 + 1} + \frac{1}{1 + 1} + \frac{1}{2 + 1} + \frac{1}{3 + 1}$$

$$= 1 \quad\quad + \frac{1}{2} \quad\quad + \frac{1}{3} \quad\quad + \frac{1}{4}$$

$$= \frac{25}{12}$$

$$\sum_{n=-1}^{4} 2n = 2(-1) + 2(0) + 2(1) + 2(2) + 2(3) + 2(4)$$

$$= -2 \quad + 0 \quad + 2 \quad + 4 \quad + 6 \quad + 8$$

$$= 18$$

Consider this example. The *arithmetic mean* (or *mean*) is one type of average. The mean of 10 numbers is computed by adding the numbers and then dividing by 10. If the numbers are denoted by x_1, x_2, x_3, x_4, x_5, x_6, x_7, x_8, x_9, and x_{10}, then the mean (call it $\bar{x}$) is

$$\bar{x} = \frac{x_1 + x_2 + x_3 + x_4 + x_5 + x_6 + x_7 + x_8 + x_9 + x_{10}}{10}$$

Using summation, the mean is written in a more condensed form as

$$\bar{x} = \frac{\sum_{i=1}^{10} x_i}{10} \quad \text{or} \quad \frac{1}{10} \sum_{i=1}^{10} x_i$$

Similarly, the mean of n numbers x_1 through x_n is

$$\bar{x} = \frac{\sum_{i=1}^{n} x_i}{n} \quad \text{or} \quad \frac{1}{n} \sum_{i=1}^{n} x_i$$

As another example, suppose that we want to use rectangles to approximate the area between the graph of $y = f(x)$ and the x axis, shaded in the drawing.

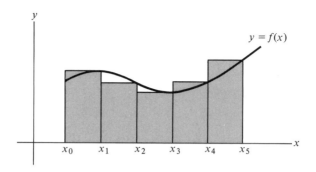

The width of the first rectangle is $x_1 - x_0$ and its length (height) is $f(x_1)$, which is the y coordinate that corresponds to x_1. So the area of the first rectangle is $(x_1 - x_0)f(x_1)$. Similarly, the area of the second rectangle is $(x_2 - x_1)f(x_2)$. The area of all five rectangles combined is

$$A_\square = (x_1 - x_0)f(x_1) + (x_2 - x_1)f(x_2) + (x_3 - x_2)f(x_3)$$
$$+ (x_4 - x_3)f(x_4) + (x_5 - x_4)f(x_5)$$

This unwieldy expression can be simplified by using summation notation. Let i be the subscript used with x within each of the f's. Then the area of the rectangles can be written

$$A_\square = \sum_{i=1}^{5} (x_i - x_{i-1})f(x_i)$$

which is a truly abbreviated form.

Now let us consider factorial notation. Products such as $7 \cdot 6 \cdot 5 \cdot 4 \cdot 3 \cdot 2 \cdot 1$ and $1 \cdot 2 \cdot 3 \cdot 4 \cdot 5$ occur often in infinite series and elsewhere. Consequently, they are named and given a special notation. They are examples of **factorials**. The product $7 \cdot 6 \cdot 5 \cdot 4 \cdot 3 \cdot 2 \cdot 1$ is denoted by 7! and read as 7 *factorial*. Similarly, $1 \cdot 2 \cdot 3 \cdot 4 \cdot 5$ is 5 factorial, written 5!. Here is a table of some factorials.

Product	Name	Notation	Value
$7 \cdot 6 \cdot 5 \cdot 4 \cdot 3 \cdot 2 \cdot 1$	7 factorial	7!	5040
$6 \cdot 5 \cdot 4 \cdot 3 \cdot 2 \cdot 1$	6 factorial	6!	720
$5 \cdot 4 \cdot 3 \cdot 2 \cdot 1$	5 factorial	5!	120
$4 \cdot 3 \cdot 2 \cdot 1$	4 factorial	4!	24
$3 \cdot 2 \cdot 1$	3 factorial	3!	6
$2 \cdot 1$	2 factorial	2!	2
1	1 factorial	1!	1

The number 0! is defined to be 1; $0! = 1$. Such a definition is consistent with factorial notation, as suggested by Exercise 4.

The example that follows demonstrates some simplifications involving factorials.

Example 8 *Simplify.* (a) $\dfrac{10!}{8!}$ (b) $\dfrac{(n+2)!}{n!}$

(a) $\dfrac{10!}{8!} = \dfrac{10 \cdot 9(8!)}{8!} = 10 \cdot 9 = 90$

(b) $\dfrac{(n+2)!}{n!} = \dfrac{(n+2)(n+1)n!}{n!} = (n+2)(n+1) = n^2 + 3n + 2$

A special notation is sometimes used in certain settings in which factorials arise. Here are some examples of the notation and its meaning.

$$\binom{5}{2} = \dfrac{5!}{2!3!}, \text{ which simplifies as } \dfrac{5 \cdot 4 \cdot 3!}{2 \cdot 3!} = 10$$

$$\binom{8}{3} = \dfrac{8!}{3!5!}, \text{ which simplifies as } \dfrac{8 \cdot 7 \cdot 6 \cdot 5!}{3 \cdot 2 \cdot 5!} = 56$$

$$\binom{48}{2} = \dfrac{48!}{2!46!}, \text{ which simplifies as } \dfrac{48 \cdot 47 \cdot 46!}{2 \cdot 46!} = 1128$$

In general,

$$\boxed{\binom{n}{r} = \dfrac{n!}{r!(n-r)!}}$$

The symbol $\binom{n}{r}$ expresses the number of combinations of n things taken r at a time; so the notation $\binom{n}{r}$ is sometimes called combination notation. Our interest in the notation, however, is based on the fact that the coefficients of the terms in the expansion of a binomial (see Section 1.3) can be expressed using this notation. Consequently, the notation $\binom{n}{r}$ is also called a **binomial coefficient**. Here are two examples of binomial expansions. Compare the numbers in each binomial coefficient with the powers of a and b in each term. Also, note that the results of the expansions are the same as those done in Section 1.3 using Pascal's triangle.

$$(a+b)^3 = \binom{3}{0}a^3b^0 + \binom{3}{1}a^2b^1 + \binom{3}{2}a^1b^2 + \binom{3}{3}a^0b^3$$

$$= 1a^3b^0 + 3a^2b^1 + 3a^1b^2 + 1a^0b^3$$

$$= a^3 + 3a^2b + 3ab^2 + b^3$$

$$(a+b)^4 = \binom{4}{0}a^4b^0 + \binom{4}{1}a^3b^1 + \binom{4}{2}a^2b^2 + \binom{4}{3}a^1b^3 + \binom{4}{4}a^0b^4$$

$$= 1a^4b^0 + 4a^3b^1 + 6a^2b^2 + 4a^1b^3 + 1a^0b^4$$

$$= a^4 + 4a^3b + 6a^2b^2 + 4ab^3 + b^4$$

The top number in each binomial coefficient is the power to which the binomial is raised. The lower number in the coefficient is the same as the power of b. The sum of the powers of a and b in any term equals the power to which the binomial is raised.

The **binomial theorem** can now be stated for $(a + b)^n$.

$$(a + b)^n = \binom{n}{0}a^nb^0 + \binom{n}{1}a^{n-1}b^1 + \binom{n}{2}a^{n-2}b^2 + \cdots + \binom{n}{n-1}a^1b^{n-1} + \binom{n}{n}a^0b^n$$

Summation notation can be used to condense this form to

Binomial theorem

$$(a + b)^n = \sum_{i=0}^{n} \binom{n}{i}a^{n-i}b^i$$

The binomial theorem can be proved by mathematical induction, a method of proof introduced in Section 10.4.

EXERCISES 10.2

1. Compute the value of each expression and simplify completely.

*(a) $\displaystyle\sum_{i=0}^{9} i^2$

(b) $\displaystyle\sum_{j=2}^{16} (j - 1)$

*(c) $\displaystyle\sum_{n=1}^{7} (2n + 1)$

(d) $\displaystyle\sum_{n=0}^{5} \frac{n}{n + 1}$

*(e) $\displaystyle\sum_{k=0}^{6} 2^k$

(f) $\displaystyle\sum_{j=-2}^{5} j(j + 2)$

*(g) $\displaystyle\sum_{j=1}^{5} (-1)^j(2j - 1)$

(h) $\displaystyle\sum_{j=1}^{4} (-1)^{j+1} j^2$

*(i) $\displaystyle\sum_{n=1}^{20} \cos n\pi$

(j) $\displaystyle\sum_{n=1}^{20} |\cos n\pi|$

*(k) $\displaystyle\sum_{n=1}^{20} \sin n\pi$

(l) $\displaystyle\sum_{n=1}^{20} |\sin n\pi|$

*(m) $\displaystyle\sum_{n=1}^{10} (-1)^n \cos n\pi$

(n) $\displaystyle\sum_{n=1}^{10} (-1)^{n+1} \cos n\pi$

*(o) $\displaystyle\sum_{n=0}^{10} (-1)^n \sin \frac{(2n + 1)\pi}{2}$

(p) $\displaystyle\sum_{n=0}^{10} (-1)^{n+1} \sin \frac{(2n + 1)\pi}{2}$

2. Write each expression in a condensed form by using summation notation.

*(a) $x_1 + x_2 + x_3 + x_4 + x_5 + x_6 + x_7$

(b) $m_1 x_1 + m_2 x_2 + m_3 x_3 + \cdots + m_{50} x_{50}$

*(c) $a_0 x^0 + a_1 x^1 + a_2 x^2 + a_3 x^3 + \cdots + a_n x^n$

(d) $f(x_1)h + f(x_2)h + f(x_3)h + \cdots + f(x_{100})h$

*(e) $1 + \dfrac{1}{2} + \dfrac{1}{4} + \dfrac{1}{8} + \cdots + \dfrac{1}{1024}$

(f) $.3 + .03 + .003 + .0003 + .00003 + .000003$

*(g) $x_0 f(x_0) + x_1 f(x_1) + x_2 f(x_2) + \cdots + x_{43} f(x_{43})$

3. Simplify.

*(a) $\dfrac{7!}{6!}$

(b) $\dfrac{5!}{2!}$

*(c) $\dfrac{5!}{3!2!}$

(d) $\dfrac{10!}{6!3!1!}$

*(e) $\dfrac{(n+3)!}{n!}$

(f) $\dfrac{(n+1)!}{(n-1)!}$

*(g) $\dfrac{n}{n!}$

(h) $\dfrac{(n+1)!}{n+1}$

*(i) $\dfrac{(x+1)!(x-2)!}{x!(x+2)!}$

(j) $\dfrac{(2n)!}{[2(n+1)]!}$

*(k) $\dfrac{2^n(n+1)!}{n!2^{n+1}}$

(l) $\dfrac{\dfrac{e^{n+1}}{n+1}}{\dfrac{e^n}{n}}$

*(m) $\dfrac{\dfrac{e^{n+1}}{(n+1)!}}{\dfrac{e^n}{n!}}$

(n) $\dfrac{\dfrac{x^{n+1}}{(n+1)!}}{\dfrac{x^n}{n!}}$

*(o) $\dfrac{\dfrac{x^{2(n+1)}}{[2(n+1)]!}}{\dfrac{x^{2n}}{(2n)!}}$

(p) $\dfrac{\dfrac{(n+1)^{n+1}}{(n+1)!}}{\dfrac{n^n}{n!}}$

4. Show why 0! is defined to be 1. (*Hint:* Note that $7! = 7 \cdot 6!$ and, in general, $n! = n(n-1)!$ for n any positive integer. Select an appropriate positive integer.)

*5. Write the definition of a polynomial (page 188) by using summation notation. You may want to consider a_0 as $a_0 x^0$.

6. Determine the value of each binomial coefficient.

*(a) $\dbinom{5}{3}$ (b) $\dbinom{10}{1}$ *(c) $\dbinom{20}{2}$

(d) $\dbinom{5}{5}$ *(e) $\dbinom{5}{0}$ (f) $\dbinom{10}{9}$

7. Use the definition of binomial coefficient to show that

*(a) $\dbinom{n}{n} = 1$ (b) $\dbinom{n}{0} = 1$

*(c) $\dbinom{n}{1} = n$ (d) $\dbinom{n}{x} = \dbinom{n}{n-x}$

8. Use the binomial theorem to expand each binomial.

   *(a) $(a + b)^5$ (b) $(x + y)^6$

   *(c) $(x - y)^4$ (d) $(2x + y)^5$

   *(e) $(x - 2y)^5$ (f) $(3x + 2y)^5$

   *(g) $(a - b)^7$ (h) $(2m + n)^8$

   *(i) $(2x - y)^8$ (j) $(a - 2b)^7$

9. Use the meaning of $\dbinom{n}{r}$ to prove that

$$\dbinom{n}{r-1} + \dbinom{n}{r} = \dbinom{n+1}{r}$$

10.3 INFINITE SERIES

As noted in Section 10.2, when the terms of an infinite sequence $a_1, a_2, a_3, a_4, \ldots$ are added as $a_1 + a_2 + a_3 + a_4 + \cdots$, the resulting infinite sum is called an **infinite series**.

$$Sequence: \quad a_1, a_2, a_3, a_4, \ldots$$

$$Series: \quad a_1 + a_2 + a_3 + a_4 + \cdots$$

We can use summation notation to represent an infinite series. In the series above, the first term is a_1; so our counter will begin at 1. But there is no last term; this is a sum of an infinite number of terms. In view of this, we shall use the symbol ∞ to indicate this idea of an infinite series. Thus

$$a_1 + a_2 + a_3 + a_4 + \cdots = \sum_{n=1}^{\infty} a_n$$

It is often desirable to call the first term a_0 rather than a_1; in which case the series appears as

$$a_0 + a_1 + a_2 + a_3 + \cdots = \sum_{n=0}^{\infty} a_n$$

In Section 10.1 we obtained a formula for the sum of the first n terms of a geometric sequence,

$$S_n = \frac{a(1 - r^n)}{1 - r} \qquad a = \text{first term}, \quad r \neq 1$$

Let us consider what happens to S_n if r is less than 1 in magnitude and n is very large. Focusing on r^n, we see that for $|r| < 1$, $r^2 < r$, $r^3 < r^2$, $r^4 < r^3$, and so on. The term r^n becomes negligibly small if $|r| < 1$ and n is very large. For example,

$$\left(\frac{1}{2}\right)^{20} = \frac{1}{1{,}048{,}576}$$

More specifically, as n increases without bound ($n \to \infty$), the value of r^n gets very close to zero ($r^n \to 0$) for $|r| < 1$. Since $r^n \to 0$ as $n \to \infty$, the r^n in

$$\frac{a(1 - r^n)}{1 - r}$$

can be ignored. Thus as $n \to \infty$ for $|r| < 1$,

$$\frac{a(1 - r^n)}{1 - r} \longrightarrow \frac{a(1 - 0)}{1 - r} \longrightarrow \frac{a}{1 - r}$$

Since the sum S_n for $n \to \infty$ is the same as the series $\sum_{n=0}^{\infty} a_n$, we have

For geometric series only

$$\sum_{n=0}^{\infty} a_n = \frac{a}{1 - r} \qquad \begin{cases} a = \text{first term} \\ r = \text{ratio} \\ |r| < 1 \end{cases}$$

We say that the geometric series **converges** to the number $a/(1 - r)$. If r is not less than 1 in magnitude, then no finite sum exists and the series is said to **diverge** instead.

Example 9 *Determine the number to which the geometric series converges.*

$$\sum_{n=0}^{\infty} 5\left(\frac{1}{2}\right)^n$$

This is a geometric series with $r = \frac{1}{2}$, which is less than 1 in magnitude; so the series will converge. The first term a is the value of $5(\frac{1}{2})^n$ for the first n specified. Since the counter n begins at 0,

$$a = 5\left(\frac{1}{2}\right)^0 = 5 \cdot 1 = 5$$

Thus

$$\sum_{n=0}^{\infty} 5\left(\frac{1}{2}\right)^n = \frac{a}{1-r} = \frac{5}{1-\frac{1}{2}} = \frac{5}{\frac{1}{2}} = 10$$

The series converges to 10.

In this example it was very easy to see that the series was geometric and that r was $\frac{1}{2}$. The key was $(\frac{1}{2})^n$. But many times it is not so obvious that a series is or is not geometric. Let us examine a few series.

Example 10 *Determine whether these series are geometric.*

(a) $\displaystyle\sum_{n=0}^{\infty} \frac{7}{3^n}$ (b) $\displaystyle\sum_{n=0}^{\infty} \frac{4^n}{3^{n+1}}$ (c) $\displaystyle\sum_{n=0}^{\infty} (n+1)\left(\frac{1}{2}\right)^n$ (d) $\displaystyle\sum_{n=1}^{\infty} \frac{2}{3n}$

(a) $\displaystyle\sum_{n=0}^{\infty} \frac{7}{3^n} = \sum_{n=0}^{\infty} 7\left(\frac{1}{3}\right)^n$

In this form you can now see that the series is geometric with $r = \frac{1}{3}$, which is less than 1 in magnitude. So the series converges. The first term is $7(\frac{1}{3})^0 = 7$ and

$$\sum_{n=0}^{\infty} \frac{7}{3^n} = \frac{a}{1-r} = \frac{7}{1-\frac{1}{3}} = \frac{7}{\frac{2}{3}} = \frac{21}{2}$$

The series converges to $\frac{21}{2}$.

(b) $\displaystyle\sum_{n=0}^{\infty} \frac{4^n}{3^{n+1}}$

You can display $\frac{4}{3}$ to a power by writing 3^{n+1} as $3 \cdot 3^n$. Then rewrite $\dfrac{4^n}{3^n}$ as $(\frac{4}{3})^n$.

$$\sum_{n=0}^{\infty} \frac{4^n}{3^{n+1}} = \sum_{n=0}^{\infty} \frac{4^n}{3 \cdot 3^n} = \sum_{n=0}^{\infty} \frac{1}{3}\left(\frac{4}{3}\right)^n$$

So the series is geometric, but $r = \frac{4}{3}$, which is greater than 1 in magnitude. So the series has no finite sum; it diverges.

(c) $\sum\limits_{n=0}^{\infty} (n + 1)\left(\dfrac{1}{2}\right)^n$

The series is *not* geometric. Do not be fooled by $(\frac{1}{2})^n$; there is *also* a variable factor $(n + 1)$, which means the series is not geometric. To see this another way, just consider the first few terms.

$$\sum\limits_{n=0}^{\infty} (n + 1)\left(\dfrac{1}{2}\right)^n = 1 + 1 + \dfrac{3}{4} + \dfrac{1}{2} + \cdots$$

Clearly this is not a geometric series.

(d) $\sum\limits_{n=1}^{\infty} \dfrac{2}{3n}$

This series is not geometric. There is no power of any ratio r. If this is not obvious, rewrite the series as

$$\sum\limits_{n=1}^{\infty} \dfrac{2}{3n} = \sum\limits_{n=1}^{\infty} \dfrac{2}{3} \cdot \dfrac{1}{n} = \dfrac{2}{3} + \dfrac{1}{3} + \dfrac{2}{9} + \cdots$$

Notice that counter n begins at 1. Because $2/(3n)$ is not defined for $n = 0$, the counter cannot begin at 0.

Thus far we have considered only series of *constant* terms. When such series converge, they converge to one finite value. Now we shall consider series of *variable* terms. Such series represent functions, provided that they converge. To begin, let us use a simple geometric series, but let the ratio r be a variable rather than a constant. So we shall call it x instead of r. Here is the series.

$$\sum\limits_{n=0}^{\infty} x^n = 1 + x + x^2 + x^3 + \cdots$$

As long as the ratio x is such that $|x| < 1$, then the series converges to

$$\dfrac{a}{1 - r} = \dfrac{1}{1 - x}$$

This means that

$$\sum\limits_{n=0}^{\infty} x^n = \dfrac{1}{1 - x} \qquad |x| < 1$$

which shows that the series $\sum\limits_{n=0}^{\infty} x^n$ is equal to the function $f(x) = 1/(1 - x)$, provided that $|x| < 1$. The domain of f is $|x| < 1$. We can also conclude that

$$\frac{1}{1 - x} = 1 + x + x^2 + x^3 + \cdots \qquad |x| < 1$$

This last result is used frequently in advanced mathematics.

Example 11 *Represent the following functions as series by using the series for* $\dfrac{1}{1 - x}$.

$$\text{(a)} \quad f(x) = \frac{3}{1 - x} \qquad \text{(b)} \quad g(x) = \frac{1}{1 + x^2}$$

(a)
$$\begin{aligned}
\frac{3}{1 - x} &= 3 \cdot \frac{1}{1 - x} \\
&= 3(1 + x + x^2 + x^3 + \cdots) \\
&= 3 + 3x + 3x^2 + 3x^3 + \cdots \qquad |x| < 1
\end{aligned}$$

(b) $\dfrac{1}{1 + x^2}$

The numerator 1 fits the form. However, the denominator must be changed to the $1 - (\ )$ form. This can be done as

$$\frac{1}{1 + x^2} = \frac{1}{1 - (-x^2)}$$

Now that we have fit the form of the expression $1/(1 - x)$, we can use the series for $1/(1 - x)$. In other words, because

$$\frac{1}{1 - x} = 1 + x + x^2 + x^3 + \cdots \qquad |x| < 1$$

it follows that

$$\frac{1}{1 - (-x^2)} = 1 + (-x^2) + (-x^2)^2 + (-x^2)^3 + \cdots$$

which simplifies to

$$\frac{1}{1 + x^2} = 1 - x^2 + x^4 - x^6 + \cdots$$

The series will converge to $1/(1 + x^2)$ as long as $|-x^2| < 1$. This is the same as $|x^2| < 1$. It is also the same as $|x| < 1$.

The trigonometric functions, exponential functions, and logarithmic functions can also be represented by infinite series. Although calculus is needed to derive these series, we can still examine them. The series were developed early in the eighteenth century by British mathematicians Brook Taylor (1685–1731) and Colin Maclaurin (1698–1746). Accurate tables of sines, cosines, and other functions are obtained from these and other series.

$$\sin x = x - \frac{x^3}{3!} + \frac{x^5}{5!} - \frac{x^7}{7!} + \frac{x^9}{9!} - \cdots$$

$$\cos x = 1 - \frac{x^2}{2!} + \frac{x^4}{4!} - \frac{x^6}{6!} + \frac{x^8}{8!} - \cdots$$

$\left. \right\}$ for all real x in *radians*

$$e^x = 1 + x + \frac{x^2}{2!} + \frac{x^3}{3!} + \frac{x^4}{4!} + \cdots \qquad \text{for all real } x$$

$$\ln(1 + x) = x - \frac{x^2}{2} + \frac{x^3}{3} - \frac{x^4}{4} + \cdots \qquad |x| < 1$$

Example 12 *Use four terms of the series for sine in order to compute an approximate value for* $\sin 1.2$.

A calculator is in order for this kind of exercise, needless to say.

$$\sin x = x - \frac{x^3}{3!} + \frac{x^5}{5!} - \frac{x^7}{7!} + \cdots$$

$$\sin 1.2 \approx (1.2) - \frac{(1.2)^3}{3!} + \frac{(1.2)^5}{5!} - \frac{(1.2)^7}{7!}$$

$$\approx 1.2 - \frac{1.728}{6} + \frac{2.48832}{120} - \frac{3.5831808}{5040}$$

$$\approx 1.2 - .288 + .020736 - .000711$$

$$\approx .932025$$

Table IV shows $\sin 1.2 \approx .9320$. The actual value of $\sin 1.2$, correct to six decimal places, is .932039. Adding another term to our series approximation would improve our result, which is already correct to four decimal places.

Example 13 *Approximate the value of e by summing the first six terms of the series for e^x with $x = 1$.*

Since

$$e^x = 1 + x + \frac{x^2}{2!} + \frac{x^3}{3!} + \frac{x^4}{4!} + \frac{x^5}{5!} + \cdots$$

then

$$e^1 = 1 + 1 + \frac{1}{2!} + \frac{1}{3!} + \frac{1}{4!} + \frac{1}{5!} + \cdots$$

or

$$e \approx 1 + 1 + \frac{1}{2} + \frac{1}{6} + \frac{1}{24} + \frac{1}{120}$$

$$\approx 1 + 1 + .5 + .16666 + .04166 + .00833$$

$$\approx 2.71665$$

The value of e correct to five decimal places is 2.71828. Our estimate can be improved by adding additional terms of the series to our sum. As it stands now, it is off by only .00163.

Example 14 *Write the series using summation notation. Let n go from 0 to ∞.*

$$1 + \frac{x}{2} + \frac{x^2}{3} + \frac{x^3}{4} + \cdots$$

Considering that 1 is the same as x^0, the series can be written

$$\frac{x^0}{1} + \frac{x^1}{2} + \frac{x^2}{3} + \frac{x^3}{4} + \cdots$$

Each numerator is a power of x, with the exponents being consecutive integers beginning at 0. The denominators are consecutive integers beginning at 1. Thus

$$1 + \frac{x}{2} + \frac{x^2}{3} + \frac{x^3}{4} + \cdots = \sum_{n=0}^{\infty} \frac{x^n}{n+1}$$

Note that since $n = 0, 1, 2, 3$, and so on, $n + 1 = 1, 2, 3, 4$, etc. as desired for the denominator.

An interesting relationship between the irrational number e and the trigonometric functions sine and cosine can be obtained when ix is used as the exponent in the series for e^x,

$$e^x = 1 + x + \frac{x^2}{2!} + \frac{x^3}{3!} + \frac{x^4}{4!} + \frac{x^5}{5!} + \cdots$$

Consider

$$e^{ix} = 1 + ix + \frac{(ix)^2}{2!} + \frac{(ix)^3}{3!} + \frac{(ix)^4}{4!} + \frac{(ix)^5}{5!} + \cdots$$

$$= 1 + ix + \frac{i^2 x^2}{2!} + \frac{i^3 x^3}{3!} + \frac{i^4 x^4}{4!} + \frac{i^5 x^5}{5!} + \cdots$$

$$= 1 + ix - 1 \cdot \frac{x^2}{2!} - i \cdot \frac{x^3}{3!} + 1 \cdot \frac{x^4}{4!} + i \cdot \frac{x^5}{5!} - \cdots$$

This series can be separated into real and imaginary parts.

$$e^{ix} = \left(1 - \frac{x^2}{2!} + \frac{x^4}{4!} - \cdots\right) + i\left(x - \frac{x^3}{3!} + \frac{x^5}{5!} - \cdots\right)$$

The real part is the series for $\cos x$. The imaginary part is the series for $\sin x$, which suggests that

$$e^{ix} = \cos x + i \sin x$$

This relationship is called **Euler's formula**. It was introduced by Leonhard Euler, a famous Swiss mathematician (1707–1783). Since it involves sine and cosine, θ is often used instead of x.

$$\boxed{e^{i\theta} = \cos \theta + i \sin \theta}$$

EXERCISES 10.3

1. Determine the number to which each geometric series converges.

*(a) $80 + 40 + 20 + 10 + \cdots$

(b) $1 + \frac{3}{4} + \frac{9}{16} + \frac{27}{64} + \cdots$

*(c) $\sum_{n=0}^{\infty} 4\left(\frac{2}{3}\right)^n$

(d) $\sum_{n=0}^{\infty} 5\left(\frac{1}{2}\right)^n$

*(e) $\sum_{n=0}^{\infty} \frac{3}{6^n}$

(f) $\sum_{n=0}^{\infty} \frac{3^n}{4^n}$

*(g) $\displaystyle\sum_{n=0}^{\infty} 9\left(-\frac{1}{2}\right)^{n+1}$

(h) $\displaystyle\sum_{n=0}^{\infty} 5\left(-\frac{3}{5}\right)^{n}$

*(i) $\displaystyle\sum_{n=0}^{\infty} \frac{2^{n+1}}{3^n}$

(j) $\displaystyle\sum_{n=0}^{\infty} \frac{4^{n+2}}{7^{n+1}}$

2. Determine which series are geometric and which are not. If geometric, determine whether it converges or diverges.

*(a) $\displaystyle\sum_{n=0}^{\infty} 8\left(\frac{3}{2}\right)^{n}$

(b) $\displaystyle\sum_{n=0}^{\infty} \frac{5}{2^n}$

*(c) $\displaystyle\sum_{n=0}^{\infty} \frac{1}{3} \cdot 2^{n+1}$

(d) $\displaystyle\sum_{n=0}^{\infty} n!$

*(e) $\displaystyle\sum_{n=0}^{\infty} \frac{7n}{n+1}$

(f) $\displaystyle\sum_{n=0}^{\infty} \frac{3^{n+2}}{5^{n+1}}$

*(g) $\displaystyle\sum_{n=0}^{\infty} 3^{-n}$

(h) $\displaystyle\sum_{n=0}^{\infty} 7^n 2^{-n}$

*(i) $\displaystyle\sum_{n=0}^{\infty} \left(\frac{2}{3}\right)^{n}\left(\frac{5}{7}\right)^{n}$

(j) $\displaystyle\sum_{n=0}^{\infty} \left(\frac{4}{5}\right)^{n+1}\left(\frac{7}{3}\right)^{n}$

3. Determine the first four terms of each series.

*(a) $\displaystyle\sum_{n=0}^{\infty} x^{n+1}$

(b) $\displaystyle\sum_{n=0}^{\infty} x^{2n}$

*(c) $\displaystyle\sum_{n=0}^{\infty} (-1)^n x^n$

(d) $\displaystyle\sum_{n=0}^{\infty} (-1)^{n+1} x^n$

*(e) $\displaystyle\sum_{n=0}^{\infty} (2x)^n$

(f) $\displaystyle\sum_{n=1}^{\infty} \frac{x^n}{2n}$

*(g) $\displaystyle\sum_{n=0}^{\infty} n! x^n$

(h) $\displaystyle\sum_{n=0}^{\infty} \frac{x^{2n}}{(n+1)!}$

*(i) $\displaystyle\sum_{n=0}^{\infty} (n+1) x^n$

(j) $\displaystyle\sum_{n=0}^{\infty} (-1)^{n+1}(n+1)! x^n$

4. Represent each function as a series by using the series for $\dfrac{1}{1-x}$. Also, determine the values of x for which the series will converge.

*(a) $\dfrac{4}{1-x}$

(b) $\dfrac{1}{1-x^2}$

*(c) $\dfrac{1}{1+x}$

(d) $\dfrac{x}{1-x}$

*(e) $\dfrac{1}{1-2x}$

(f) $\dfrac{5}{1-x}$

*(g) $\dfrac{2}{1 - x^3}$ (h) $\dfrac{5}{x - 1}$

5. Use five terms of the appropriate series to obtain approximations. Then compare your result with a table in the appendix. *Use a calculator.*

*(a) $\sin 1$ (b) $\cos 1$

*(c) $\cos .7$ (d) $\sin .4$

*(e) e^2 (f) $e^{1.5}$

*(g) $\ln 1.5$ (h) $\ln .6$

6. Write each series using summation notation. Let the sum go from $n = 0$ to ∞. (*Note:* The sign can be made to alternate by using a power of -1 that is dependent on the counter n. *Also*, remember that $x^0 = 1$, $0! = 1$, and $1! = 1$.)

*(a) $1 + x + \dfrac{x^2}{2!} + \dfrac{x^3}{3!} + \dfrac{x^4}{4!} + \cdots$ (b) $\dfrac{1}{2!} + \dfrac{x}{3!} + \dfrac{x^2}{4!} + \dfrac{x^3}{5!} + \cdots$

*(c) $\dfrac{x}{2} + \dfrac{x^2}{4} + \dfrac{x^3}{6} + \dfrac{x^4}{8} + \cdots$ (d) $x - \dfrac{x^2}{2!} + \dfrac{x^3}{3!} - \dfrac{x^4}{4!} + \cdots$

*(e) $1 + \dfrac{x^2}{2!} + \dfrac{x^4}{4!} + \dfrac{x^6}{6!} + \cdots$ (f) $x + \dfrac{x^3}{3!} + \dfrac{x^5}{5!} + \dfrac{x^7}{7!} + \cdots$

*(g) $1 - \dfrac{x^2}{2!} + \dfrac{x^4}{4!} - \dfrac{x^6}{6!} + \cdots$ (h) $x - \dfrac{x^3}{3!} + \dfrac{x^5}{5!} - \dfrac{x^7}{7!} + \cdots$

7. Using summation notation, rewrite the series given for

*(a) e^x (b) $\ln(1 + x)$

*(c) $\sin x$ (d) $\cos x$

8. Use Euler's formula to obtain the results:

$$e^{\pi i} = -1 \quad \text{and} \quad e^{2\pi i} = 1$$

10.4 MATHEMATICAL INDUCTION

A student has been examining sums of the form $4 + 8 + 12 + 16 + \cdots + 4n$.

When $n = 1$, $4 = 4$

When $n = 2$, $4 + 8 = 12$

When $n = 3$, $4 + 8 + 12 = 24$

When $n = 4$, $4 + 8 + 12 + 16 = 40$

Several guesses and some insight lead the student to the conclusion that the sum of n terms of that form equals $2n(n + 1)$. In other words,

$$4 + 8 + 12 + 16 + \cdots + 4n = 2n(n + 1)$$

This is verified for $n = 1, 2, 3, 4$ as follows.

When $n = 1$, $4 = 2(1)(1 + 1) = 4$

When $n = 2$, $4 + 8 = 2(2)(2 + 1) = 12$

When $n = 3$, $4 + 8 + 12 = 2(3)(3 + 1) = 24$

When $n = 4$, $4 + 8 + 12 + 16 = 2(4)(4 + 1) = 40$

But how can he *prove* that, for any n, $4 + 8 + 12 + \cdots + 4n = 2n(n + 1)$? Even if it is demonstrated that the equality is also true for $n = 5, 6, 7, 8, 9$ and 10, the student cannot be sure that it will hold true for $n = 25$ or $n = 103$. Proof of the equality for all positive integers n is accomplished by a method called **mathematical induction**.

Proof by mathematical induction proceeds as follows. First, show that the equality is indeed true for the smallest intended value of n. Usually this means verifying the equation for $n = 1$. Then assume that the equality is true for $n = k$ and show that this assumption ensures that the equality is also true for the next n, $n = k + 1$.

The proof suggests that if the equality is true for 1, then it must also work for $1 + 1$ or 2. If it works for 2, then it must work for $2 + 1$, or 3. If it holds true for 3, it must hold true for 4; and so on. Proving that if it works for k, then it must work for $k + 1$, and demonstrating that it does indeed work for 1 proves that it works for $1, 2, 3, 4, 5, \ldots$.

Imagine seven dominoes placed in a row.

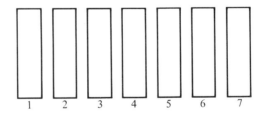

If the first domino falls to the right, then the second domino will also fall. If the second domino falls, then the third will fall. If the third falls, the fourth will fall. And so on. Observation leads to the conclusion that if domino k falls, then domino $k + 1$ must also fall. In other words, if you assume domino k falls, then you know that domino $k + 1$ will fall. So what happens when domino 1 falls? One falls, so two falls. Two falls, so three falls, $\ldots$. All the dominoes fall.

Example 15   *Use mathematical induction to prove the following equality.*

$$4 + 8 + 12 + \cdots + 4n = 2n(n + 1)$$

First let $n = 1$ to see if the statement is true for the first possible value of n. When 1 is substituted for n in the equation, the equation becomes

$$4 \overset{?}{=} 2(2)$$

or

$$4 = 4$$

which is true. Next, assume that the equality is true for $n = k$. In other words, assume that

$$4 + 8 + 12 + \cdots + 4k = 2k(k + 1)$$

Finally, use the equality above to prove that the original equation is indeed true for $n = k + 1$.

$$4 + 8 + 12 + \cdots + 4k + 4(k + 1) \overset{?}{=} 2(k + 1)(k + 2)$$

This can be done here by using the assumption that

$$4 + 8 + 12 + \cdots + 4k \quad \text{equals} \quad 2k(k + 1)$$

Therefore $2k(k + 1)$ can be substituted for $4 + 8 + 12 + \cdots + 4k$ in

$$\underline{4 + 8 + 12 + \cdots + 4k} + 4(k + 1) \overset{?}{=} 2(k + 1)(k + 2)$$

to give

$$2k(k + 1) + 4(k + 1) \overset{?}{=} 2(k + 1)(k + 2)$$

The left side can now be manipulated in steps into the form $2(k + 1)(k + 2)$. First factor out $(k + 1)$ from both terms on the left side.

$$(2k + 4)(k + 1) \overset{?}{=} 2(k + 1)(k + 2)$$

Next, factor 2 out of $2k + 4$.

$$2(k + 2)(k + 1) \overset{?}{=} 2(k + 1)(k + 2)$$

Finally, interchange the order of the factors $(k + 2)$ and $(k + 1)$. The result proves the equality.

$$2(k + 1)(k + 2) = 2(k + 1)(k + 2)$$

Example 16 *Use mathematical induction to prove the following equality.*

$$\frac{1}{1 \cdot 2} + \frac{1}{2 \cdot 3} + \frac{1}{3 \cdot 4} + \cdots + \frac{1}{n(n+1)} = \frac{n}{n+1}$$

First, the equality is true for $n = 1$, since

$$\frac{1}{1 \cdot 2} \overset{?}{=} \frac{1}{1+1}$$

$$\frac{1}{2} = \frac{1}{2}$$

Now, assume that it is true for $n = k$.

$$\frac{1}{1 \cdot 2} + \frac{1}{2 \cdot 3} + \frac{1}{3 \cdot 4} + \cdots + \frac{1}{k(k+1)} = \frac{k}{k+1}$$

Use this result to show that the equality must be true for $n = k + 1$. That is, show that

$$\frac{1}{1 \cdot 2} + \frac{1}{2 \cdot 3} + \frac{1}{3 \cdot 4} + \cdots + \frac{1}{k(k+1)} + \frac{1}{(k+1)(k+2)} = \frac{k+1}{k+2}$$

Use the assumption to substitute

$$\frac{k}{k+1}$$

for

$$\frac{1}{1 \cdot 2} + \frac{1}{2 \cdot 3} + \frac{1}{3 \cdot 4} + \cdots + \frac{1}{k(k+1)}$$

in

$$\underbrace{\frac{1}{1 \cdot 2} + \frac{1}{2 \cdot 3} + \frac{1}{3 \cdot 4} + \cdots + \frac{1}{k(k+1)}} + \frac{1}{(k+1)(k+2)} \overset{?}{=} \frac{k+1}{k+2}$$

to get

$$\frac{k}{k+1} + \frac{1}{(k+1)(k+2)} \overset{?}{=} \frac{k+1}{k+2}$$

Now, find a common denominator for the fractions on the left and add them.

$$\frac{k}{(k+1)} \cdot \frac{(k+2)}{(k+2)} + \frac{1}{(k+1)(k+2)} \stackrel{?}{=} \frac{k+1}{k+2}$$

or

$$\frac{k(k+2)+1}{(k+1)(k+2)} \stackrel{?}{=} \frac{k+1}{k+2}$$

The numerator, $k(k+2)+1$, can be written $k^2 + 2k + 1$ and then factored as $(k+1)(k+1)$. The result is

$$\frac{(k+1)(k+1)}{(k+1)(k+2)} \stackrel{?}{=} \frac{k+1}{k+2}$$

which reduces to

$$\frac{k+1}{k+2} = \frac{k+1}{k+2}$$

Thus the equality has been proved true for all positive integers n.

Example 17 *Use mathematical induction to prove that $2^n > n$.*
First, the inequality is true for $n = 1$, since $2^1 > 1$; that is, $2 > 1$.
Now, assume that it is true for $n = k$; that is, assume that

$$2^k > k$$

Use this result to show that the inequality must be true for $n = k + 1$. That is, show that

$$2^{k+1} > k + 1$$

Note that

$$2^{k+1} = 2^k \cdot 2$$
$$= 2 \cdot 2^k$$

So we need only show that

$$2 \cdot 2^k > k + 1$$

By our assumption that $2^k > k$, it follows that

$$2 \cdot 2^k > 2 \cdot k$$

So now we need only show that

$$2k > k + 1$$

or

$$k + k > k + 1$$

which is true for all $k > 1$.

EXERCISES 10.4

Prove each result by using mathematical induction.

*1. $1 + 2 + 3 + 4 + \cdots + n = \dfrac{n(n + 1)}{2}$

2. $1 + 3 + 5 + \cdots + (2n - 1) = n^2$

*3. $\dfrac{1}{2} + \dfrac{1}{2^2} + \dfrac{1}{2^3} + \cdots + \dfrac{1}{2^n} = 1 - \dfrac{1}{2^n}$

4. $1 + 5 + 9 + \cdots + (4n - 3) = n(2n - 1)$

*5. $1^2 + 2^2 + 3^2 + \cdots + n^2 = \dfrac{n(n + 1)(2n + 1)}{6}$

6. $1 \cdot 2 + 2 \cdot 3 + 3 \cdot 4 + \cdots + n(n + 1) = \dfrac{n(n + 1)(n + 2)}{3}$

*7. $1^3 + 2^3 + 3^3 + \cdots + n^3 = \dfrac{n^2(n + 1)^2}{4}$

8. $2^2 + 4^2 + 6^2 + \cdots + (2n)^2 = \dfrac{2n(n + 1)(2n + 1)}{3}$

*9. $a + (a + d) + (a + 2d) + \cdots + [a + (n - 1)d] = \dfrac{n}{2}[2a + (n - 1)d]$

10. $a + ar + ar^2 + \cdots + ar^{n-1} = \dfrac{a(1 - r^n)}{1 - r}$

*11. $(ab)^n = a^n b^n$

12. $\left(\dfrac{a}{b}\right)^n = \dfrac{a^n}{b^n}$

*13. $a(b_1 + b_2 + b_3 + \cdots + b_n) = ab_1 + ab_2 + ab_3 + \cdots + ab_n$

14. $\ln(a_1 a_2 a_3 \cdots a_n) = \ln a_1 + \ln a_2 + \ln a_3 + \cdots + \ln a_n$

*15. $3^n > 3n$ (Note: the "first" one need not be $n = 1$; it could be 2 or 3 etc.)

16. $e^n > n$

10.5   ITERATION

The concept of iteration will be explained by means of an example. Approximations of the square root of n can be obtained by using the formula

$$x_{i+1} = \frac{1}{2}\left(x_i + \frac{n}{x_i}\right) \qquad n > 0$$

Supply a guess (or initial value) for $\sqrt{n}$. The guess is called x_1. Then substitute x_1 and n into the formula to get x_2, a better approximation to $\sqrt{n}$.

$$x_2 = \frac{1}{2}\left(x_1 + \frac{n}{x_1}\right)$$

Now use x_2 for x_i in the formula to produce a still better approximation, x_3.

$$x_3 = \frac{1}{2}\left(x_2 + \frac{n}{x_2}\right)$$

An approximation x_4 can be obtained by using x_3 and n in the formula. The process can be continued indefinitely. Usually a decision is made to stop once two successive approximations are "close enough" to each other. For example, if two consecutive approximations differ by less than one thousandth—that is,

$$|x_{i+1} - x_i| < .001$$

then that might be good enough.

The repetitious procedure just suggested is an example of an **iterative** process. The number obtained at any step in the process is substituted back into the formula to produce the next successive result. This iterative process for obtaining square roots is not new. It was used by the early Greeks. If you examine the formula, you'll see why it works. The right side is an average of the estimate and the number obtained by dividing the estimate into the number whose square root is sought. If the approximation x_i is too small, then n/x_i will be larger than x_i. Averaging x_i and n/x_i thus increases the size of the approximation that will be x_{i+1}. If the approximation x_i is too large, then n/x_i will be smaller than x_i. The average of x_i and n/x_i will thus produce a smaller approximation x_{i+1}.

Let's use this process to approximate $\sqrt{19}$. Let $x_1 = 4$ be the initial approximation. This means that $n = 19$ and $x_1 = 4$. So

$$x_2 = \frac{1}{2}\left(x_1 + \frac{n}{x_1}\right) = \frac{1}{2}\left(4 + \frac{19}{4}\right)$$

This yields $x_2 = 4.375$. Next, compute x_3 from

$$x_3 = \frac{1}{2}\left(x_2 + \frac{n}{x_2}\right) = \frac{1}{2}\left(4.375 + \frac{19}{4.375}\right) = 4.3589$$

The process can be continued. The square root of 19, to five decimal places, is 4.35889.

Here we show a partial flowchart of the logic of the general iterative process of approximating $\sqrt{n}$ beginning with initial value x_1.

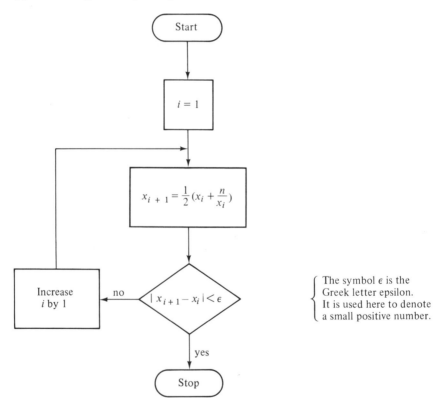

The formula used to obtain the square-root approximations is a special case of a more general application called **Newton's method**. Isaac Newton, a founder of the calculus, developed a technique for approximating zeros of functions by using the calculus. When the method is applied to $f(x) = x^2 - n$, his formula becomes the same as the formula used by the early Greeks. Note that the zeros of $f(x) = x^2 - n$ are the square roots of n (positive and negative). If x_1 is selected positive, then the successive approximations will approach $\sqrt{n}$. However, if the initial guess is negative, then the successive approximations will approach $-\sqrt{n}$.

EXERCISES 10.5

1. Use the iterative procedure demonstrated in this section to approximate each square root. Continue until two successive approximations agree in the third place after the decimal. Use an integer approximation x_1 in each exercise.

   *(a) $\sqrt{2}$ (b) $\sqrt{3}$ *(c) $\sqrt{5}$
   (d) $\sqrt{7}$ *(e) $\sqrt{11}$ (f) $\sqrt{34}$
   *(g) $\sqrt{107}$ (h) $\sqrt{151}$ *(i) $\sqrt{274}$

2. Use the formula shown to approximate each cube root. Use an integer approximation for x_1 and continue until $|x_{i+1} - x_i| < .01$.

$$x_{i+1} = \frac{1}{3}\left(2x_i + \frac{n}{x_i^2}\right)$$

   *(a) $\sqrt[3]{10}$ (b) $\sqrt[3]{23}$ *(c) $\sqrt[3]{55}$
   (d) $\sqrt[3]{73}$ *(e) $\sqrt[3]{100}$ (f) $\sqrt[3]{250}$

REVIEW EXERCISES FOR CHAPTER 10

*1. Generate the first three terms of the sequence

$$a_n = \frac{1 - n^2}{2n}$$

2. Determine a_{10} for an arithmetic sequence in which $a_1 = 3$ and $d = 7$.

*3. Compute the value of $\sum_{i=0}^{6} (i - 3)^2$.

4. Use summation notation to write the expression in a condensed form.

$$b_1 x^n + b_2 x^{n-1} + b_3 x^{n-2} + \cdots + b_n x$$

*5. Simplify

$$\frac{\dfrac{(2e)^{n+1}}{n+1}}{\dfrac{(2e)^n}{n}}$$

6. Determine the value of $\binom{10}{7}$.

*7. Determine the number to which the geometric series converges.

$$\sum_{n=0}^{\infty} \frac{5}{3^n}$$

8. Use the series for $\dfrac{1}{1 - x}$ to represent the following function as a series and determine the values of x for which the series converges.

$$\frac{2}{1 - 3x}$$

*9. Write the series using summation notation. Let the sum go from $n = 0$ to ∞.

$$2 + \frac{4x}{2!} + \frac{8x^2}{3!} + \frac{16x^3}{4!} + \cdots$$

10. Use mathematical induction to prove that

$$1^2 + 3^2 + \cdots + (2n - 1)^2 = \frac{n(2n - 1)(2n + 1)}{3}$$

Appendix

TABLE I.   Powers of e

x	e^x	e^{-x}	x	e^x	e^{-x}
0.00	1.0000	1.0000	2.5	12.182	0.0821
0.05	1.0513	0.9512	2.6	13.464	0.0743
0.10	1.1052	0.9048	2.7	14.880	0.0672
0.15	1.1618	0.8607	2.8	16.445	0.0608
0.20	1.2214	0.8187	2.9	18.174	0.0550
0.25	1.2840	0.7788	3.0	20.086	0.0498
0.30	1.3499	0.7408	3.1	22.198	0.0450
0.35	1.4191	0.7047	3.2	24.533	0.0408
0.40	1.4918	0.6703	3.3	27.113	0.0369
0.45	1.5683	0.6376	3.4	29.964	0.0334
0.50	1.6487	0.6065	3.5	33.115	0.0302
0.55	1.7333	0.5769	3.6	36.598	0.0273
0.60	1.8221	0.5488	3.7	40.447	0.0247
0.65	1.9155	0.5220	3.8	44.701	0.0224
0.70	2.0138	0.4966	3.9	49.402	0.0202
0.75	2.1170	0.4724	4.0	54.598	0.0183
0.80	2.2255	0.4493	4.1	60.340	0.0166
0.85	2.3396	0.4274	4.2	66.686	0.0150
0.90	2.4596	0.4066	4.3	73.700	0.0136
0.95	2.5857	0.3867	4.4	81.451	0.0123
1.0	2.7183	0.3679	4.5	90.017	0.0111
1.1	3.0042	0.3329	4.6	99.484	0.0101
1.2	3.3201	0.3012	4.7	109.95	0.0091
1.3	3.6693	0.2725	4.8	121.51	0.0082
1.4	4.0552	0.2466	4.9	134.29	0.0074
1.5	4.4817	0.2231	5.0	148.41	0.0067
1.6	4.9530	0.2019	5.5	244.69	0.0041
1.7	5.4739	0.1827	6.0	403.43	0.0025
1.8	6.0496	0.1653	6.5	665.14	0.0015
1.9	6.6859	0.1496	7.0	1,096.6	0.0009
2.0	7.3891	0.1353	7.5	1,808.0	0.0006
2.1	8.1662	0.1225	8.0	2,981.0	0.0003
2.2	9.0250	0.1108	8.5	4,914.8	0.0002
2.3	9.9742	0.1003	9.0	8,103.1	0.0001
2.4	11.023	0.0907	10.0	22,026	0.00005

TABLE II.   Natural Logarithms (base e)

$$\ln 10 \approx 2.3026$$

n	0	1	2	3	4	5	6	7	8	9
1.0	0.0000	0.0100	0.0198	0.0296	0.0392	0.0488	0.0583	0.0677	0.0770	0.0862
1.1	0.0953	0.1044	0.1133	0.1222	0.1310	0.1398	0.1484	0.1570	0.1655	0.1740
1.2	0.1823	0.1906	0.1989	0.2070	0.2151	0.2231	0.2311	0.2390	0.2469	0.2546
1.3	0.2624	0.2700	0.2776	0.2852	0.2927	0.3001	0.3075	0.3148	0.3221	0.3293
1.4	0.3365	0.3436	0.3507	0.3577	0.3646	0.3716	0.3784	0.3853	0.3920	0.3988
1.5	0.4055	0.4121	0.4187	0.4253	0.4318	0.4383	0.4447	0.4511	0.4574	0.4637
1.6	0.4700	0.4762	0.4824	0.4886	0.4947	0.5008	0.5068	0.5128	0.5188	0.5247
1.7	0.5306	0.5365	0.5423	0.5481	0.5539	0.5596	0.5653	0.5710	0.5766	0.5822
1.8	0.5878	0.5933	0.5988	0.6043	0.6098	0.6152	0.6206	0.6259	0.6313	0.6366
1.9	0.6419	0.6471	0.6523	0.6575	0.6627	0.6678	0.6729	0.6780	0.6831	0.6881
2.0	0.6931	0.6981	0.7031	0.7080	0.7130	0.7178	0.7227	0.7275	0.7324	0.7372
2.1	0.7419	0.7467	0.7514	0.7561	0.7608	0.7655	0.7701	0.7747	0.7793	0.7839
2.2	0.7885	0.7930	0.7975	0.8020	0.8065	0.8109	0.8154	0.8198	0.8242	0.8286
2.3	0.8329	0.8372	0.8416	0.8459	0.8502	0.8544	0.8587	0.8629	0.8671	0.8713
2.4	0.8755	0.8796	0.8838	0.8879	0.8920	0.8961	0.9002	0.9042	0.9083	0.9123
2.5	0.9163	0.9203	0.9243	0.9282	0.9322	0.9361	0.9400	0.9439	0.9478	0.9517
2.6	0.9555	0.9594	0.9632	0.9670	0.9708	0.9746	0.9783	0.9821	0.9858	0.9895
2.7	0.9933	0.9969	1.0006	1.0043	1.0080	1.0116	1.0152	1.0188	1.0225	1.0260
2.8	1.0296	1.0332	1.0367	1.0403	1.0438	1.0473	1.0508	1.0543	1.0578	1.0613
2.9	1.0647	1.0682	1.0716	1.0750	1.0784	1.0818	1.0852	1.0886	1.0919	1.0953
3.0	1.0986	1.1019	1.1053	1.1086	1.1119	1.1151	1.1184	1.1217	1.1249	1.1282
3.1	1.1314	1.1346	1.1378	1.1410	1.1442	1.1474	1.1506	1.1537	1.1569	1.1600
3.2	1.1632	1.1663	1.1694	1.1725	1.1756	1.1787	1.1817	1.1848	1.1878	1.1909
3.3	1.1939	1.1970	1.2000	1.2030	1.2060	1.2090	1.2119	1.2149	1.2179	1.2208
3.4	1.2238	1.2267	1.2296	1.2326	1.2355	1.2384	1.2413	1.2442	1.2470	1.2499
3.5	1.2528	1.2556	1.2585	1.2613	1.2641	1.2669	1.2698	1.2726	1.2754	1.2782
3.6	1.2809	1.2837	1.2865	1.2892	1.2920	1.2947	1.2975	1.3002	1.3029	1.3056
3.7	1.3083	1.3110	1.3137	1.3164	1.3191	1.3218	1.3244	1.3271	1.3297	1.3324
3.8	1.3350	1.3376	1.3403	1.3429	1.3455	1.3481	1.3507	1.3533	1.3558	1.3584
3.9	1.3610	1.3635	1.3661	1.3686	1.3712	1.3737	1.3762	1.3788	1.3813	1.3838
4.0	1.3863	1.3888	1.3913	1.3938	1.3962	1.3987	1.4012	1.4036	1.4061	1.4085
4.1	1.4110	1.4134	1.4159	1.4183	1.4207	1.4231	1.4255	1.4279	1.4303	1.4327
4.2	1.4351	1.4375	1.4398	1.4422	1.4446	1.4469	1.4493	1.4516	1.4540	1.4563
4.3	1.4586	1.4609	1.4633	1.4656	1.4679	1.4702	1.4725	1.4748	1.4770	1.4793
4.4	1.4816	1.4839	1.4861	1.4884	1.4907	1.4929	1.4952	1.4974	1.4996	1.5019
4.5	1.5041	1.5063	1.5085	1.5107	1.5129	1.5151	1.5173	1.5195	1.5217	1.5239
4.6	1.5261	1.5282	1.5304	1.5326	1.5347	1.5369	1.5390	1.5412	1.5433	1.5454
4.7	1.5476	1.5497	1.5518	1.5539	1.5560	1.5581	1.5602	1.5623	1.5644	1.5665
4.8	1.5686	1.5707	1.5728	1.5748	1.5769	1.5790	1.5810	1.5831	1.5851	1.5872
4.9	1.5892	1.5913	1.5933	1.5953	1.5974	1.5994	1.6014	1.6034	1.6054	1.6074
5.0	1.6094	1.6114	1.6134	1.6154	1.6174	1.6194	1.6214	1.6233	1.6253	1.6273
5.1	1.6292	1.6312	1.6332	1.6351	1.6371	1.6390	1.6409	1.6429	1.6448	1.6467
5.2	1.6487	1.6506	1.6525	1.6544	1.6563	1.6582	1.6601	1.6620	1.6639	1.6658
5.3	1.6677	1.6696	1.6715	1.6734	1.6753	1.6771	1.6790	1.6808	1.6827	1.6845
5.4	1.6864	1.6882	1.6901	1.6919	1.6938	1.6956	1.6974	1.6993	1.7011	1.7029

TABLE II. Natural Logarithms (base e)

$$\ln 10 \approx 2.3026$$

n	0	1	2	3	4	5	6	7	8	9
5.5	1.7047	1.7066	1.7084	1.7102	1.7120	1.7138	1.7156	1.7174	1.7192	1.7210
5.6	1.7228	1.7246	1.7263	1.7281	1.7299	1.7317	1.7334	1.7352	1.7370	1.7387
5.7	1.7405	1.7422	1.7440	1.7457	1.7475	1.7492	1.7509	1.7527	1.7544	1.7561
5.8	1.7579	1.7596	1.7613	1.7630	1.7647	1.7664	1.7682	1.7699	1.7716	1.7733
5.9	1.7750	1.7766	1.7783	1.7800	1.7817	1.7834	1.7851	1.7867	1.7884	1.7901
6.0	1.7918	1.7934	1.7951	1.7967	1.7984	1.8001	1.8017	1.8034	1.8050	1.8066
6.1	1.8083	1.8099	1.8116	1.8132	1.8148	1.8165	1.8181	1.8197	1.8213	1.8229
6.2	1.8245	1.8262	1.8278	1.8294	1.8310	1.8326	1.8342	1.8358	1.8374	1.8390
6.3	1.8406	1.8421	1.8437	1.8453	1.8469	1.8485	1.8500	1.8516	1.8532	1.8547
6.4	1.8563	1.8579	1.8594	1.8610	1.8625	1.8641	1.8656	1.8672	1.8687	1.8703
6.5	1.8718	1.8733	1.8749	1.8764	1.8779	1.8795	1.8810	1.8825	1.8840	1.8856
6.6	1.8871	1.8886	1.8901	1.8916	1.8931	1.8946	1.8961	1.8976	1.8991	1.9006
6.7	1.9021	1.9036	1.9051	1.9066	1.9081	1.9095	1.9110	1.9125	1.9140	1.9155
6.8	1.9169	1.9184	1.9199	1.9213	1.9228	1.9242	1.9257	1.9272	1.9286	1.9301
6.9	1.9315	1.9330	1.9344	1.9359	1.9373	1.9387	1.9402	1.9416	1.9430	1.9445
7.0	1.9459	1.9473	1.9488	1.9502	1.9516	1.9530	1.9544	1.9559	1.9573	1.9587
7.1	1.9601	1.9615	1.9629	1.9643	1.9657	1.9671	1.9685	1.9699	1.9713	1.9727
7.2	1.9741	1.9755	1.9769	1.9782	1.9796	1.9810	1.9824	1.9838	1.9851	1.9865
7.3	1.9879	1.9892	1.9906	1.9920	1.9933	1.9947	1.9961	1.9974	1.9988	2.0001
7.4	2.0015	2.0028	2.0042	2.0055	2.0069	2.0082	2.0096	2.0109	2.0122	2.0136
7.5	2.0149	2.0162	2.0176	2.0189	2.0202	2.0215	2.0229	2.0242	2.0255	2.0268
7.6	2.0282	2.0295	2.0308	2.0321	2.0334	2.0347	2.0360	2.0373	2.0386	2.0399
7.7	2.0412	2.0425	2.0438	2.0451	2.0464	2.0477	2.0490	2.0503	2.0516	2.0528
7.8	2.0541	2.0554	2.0567	2.0580	2.0592	2.0605	2.0618	2.0631	2.0643	2.0656
7.9	2.0669	2.0681	2.0694	2.0707	2.0719	2.0732	2.0744	2.0757	2.0769	2.0782
8.0	2.0794	2.0807	2.0819	2.0832	2.0844	2.0857	2.0869	2.0882	2.0894	2.0906
8.1	2.0919	2.0931	2.0943	2.0956	2.0968	2.0980	2.0992	2.1005	2.1017	2.1029
8.2	2.1041	2.1054	2.1066	2.1078	2.1090	2.1102	2.1114	2.1126	2.1138	2.1150
8.3	2.1163	2.1175	2.1187	2.1199	2.1211	2.1223	2.1235	2.1247	2.1258	2.1270
8.4	2.1282	2.1294	2.1306	2.1318	2.1330	2.1342	2.1353	2.1365	2.1377	2.1389
8.5	2.1401	2.1412	2.1424	2.1436	2.1448	2.1459	2.1471	2.1483	2.1494	2.1506
8.6	2.1518	2.1529	2.1541	2.1552	2.1564	2.1576	2.1587	2.1599	2.1610	2.1622
8.7	2.1633	2.1645	2.1656	2.1668	2.1679	2.1691	2.1702	2.1713	2.1725	2.1736
8.8	2.1748	2.1759	2.1770	2.1782	2.1793	2.1804	2.1815	2.1827	2.1838	2.1849
8.9	2.1861	2.1872	2.1883	2.1894	2.1905	2.1917	2.1928	2.1939	2.1950	2.1961
9.0	2.1972	2.1983	2.1994	2.2006	2.2017	2.2028	2.2039	2.2050	2.2061	2.2072
9.1	2.2083	2.2094	2.2105	2.2116	2.2127	2.2138	2.2148	2.2159	2.2170	2.2181
9.2	2.2192	2.2203	2.2214	2.2225	2.2235	2.2246	2.2257	2.2268	2.2279	2.2289
9.3	2.2300	2.2311	2.2322	2.2332	2.2343	2.2354	2.2364	2.2375	2.2386	2.2396
9.4	2.2407	2.2418	2.2428	2.2439	2.2450	2.2460	2.2471	2.2481	2.2492	2.2502
9.5	2.2513	2.2523	2.2534	2.2544	2.2555	2.2565	2.2576	2.2586	2.2597	2.2607
9.6	2.2618	2.2628	2.2638	2.2649	2.2659	2.2670	2.2680	2.2690	2.2701	2.2711
9.7	2.2721	2.2732	2.2742	2.2752	2.2762	2.2773	2.2783	2.2793	2.2803	2.2814
9.8	2.2824	2.2834	2.2844	2.2854	2.2865	2.2875	2.2885	2.2895	2.2905	2.2915
9.9	2.2925	2.2935	2.2946	2.2956	2.2966	2.2976	2.2986	2.2996	2.3006	2.3016

TABLE III. Common Logarithms (base 10)

n	0	1	2	3	4	5	6	7	8	9
1.0	.0000	.0043	.0086	.0128	.0170	.0212	.0253	.0294	.0334	.0374
1.1	.0414	.0453	.0492	.0531	.0569	.0607	.0645	.0682	.0719	.0755
1.2	.0792	.0828	.0864	.0899	.0934	.0969	.1004	.1038	.1072	.1106
1.3	.1139	.1173	.1206	.1239	.1271	.1303	.1335	.1367	.1399	.1430
1.4	.1461	.1492	.1523	.1553	.1584	.1614	.1644	.1673	.1703	.1732
1.5	.1761	.1790	.1818	.1847	.1875	.1903	.1931	.1959	.1987	.2014
1.6	.2041	.2068	.2095	.2122	.2148	.2175	.2201	.2227	.2253	.2279
1.7	.2304	.2330	.2355	.2380	.2405	.2430	.2455	.2480	.2504	.2529
1.8	.2553	.2577	.2601	.2625	.2648	.2672	.2695	.2718	.2742	.2765
1.9	.2788	.2810	.2833	.2856	.2878	.2900	.2923	.2945	.2967	.2989
2.0	.3010	.3032	.3054	.3075	.3096	.3118	.3139	.3160	.3181	.3201
2.1	.3222	.3243	.3263	.3284	.3304	.3324	.3345	.3365	.3385	.3404
2.2	.3424	.3444	.3464	.3483	.3502	.3522	.3541	.3560	.3579	.3598
2.3	.3617	.3636	.3655	.3674	.3692	.3711	.3729	.3747	.3766	.3784
2.4	.3802	.3820	.3838	.3856	.3874	.3892	.3909	.3927	.3945	.3962
2.5	.3979	.3997	.4014	.4031	.4048	.4065	.4082	.4099	.4116	.4133
2.6	.4150	.4166	.4183	.4200	.4216	.4232	.4249	.4265	.4281	.4298
2.7	.4314	.4330	.4346	.4362	.4378	.4393	.4409	.4425	.4440	.4456
2.8	.4472	.4487	.4502	.4518	.4533	.4548	.4564	.4579	.4594	.4609
2.9	.4624	.4639	.4654	.4669	.4683	.4698	.4713	.4728	.4742	.4757
3.0	.4771	.4786	.4800	.4814	.4829	.4843	.4857	.4871	.4886	.4900
3.1	.4914	.4928	.4942	.4955	.4969	.4983	.4997	.5011	.5024	.5038
3.2	.5051	.5065	.5079	.5092	.5105	.5119	.5132	.5145	.5159	.5172
3.3	.5185	.5198	.5211	.5224	.5237	.5250	.5263	.5276	.5289	.5302
3.4	.5315	.5328	.5340	.5353	.5366	.5378	.5391	.5403	.5416	.5428
3.5	.5441	.5453	.5465	.5478	.5490	.5502	.5514	.5527	.5539	.5551
3.6	.5563	.5575	.5587	.5599	.5611	.5623	.5635	.5647	.5658	.5670
3.7	.5682	.5694	.5705	.5717	.5729	.5740	.5752	.5763	.5775	.5786
3.8	.5798	.5809	.5821	.5832	.5843	.5855	.5866	.5877	.5888	.5899
3.9	.5911	.5922	.5933	.5944	.5955	.5966	.5977	.5988	.5999	.6010
4.0	.6021	.6031	.6042	.6053	.6064	.6075	.6085	.6096	.6107	.6117
4.1	.6128	.6138	.6149	.6160	.6170	.6180	.6191	.6201	.6212	.6222
4.2	.6232	.6243	.6253	.6263	.6274	.6284	.6294	.6304	.6314	.6325
4.3	.6335	.6345	.6355	.6365	.6375	.6385	.6395	.6405	.6415	.6425
4.4	.6435	.6444	.6454	.6464	.6474	.6484	.6493	.6503	.6513	.6522
4.5	.6532	.6542	.6551	.6561	.6571	.6580	.6590	.6599	.6609	.6618
4.6	.6628	.6637	.6646	.6656	.6665	.6675	.6684	.6693	.6702	.6712
4.7	.6721	.6730	.6739	.6749	.6758	.6767	.6776	.6785	.6794	.6803
4.8	.6812	.6821	.6830	.6839	.6848	.6857	.6866	.6875	.6884	.6893
4.9	.6902	.6911	.6920	.6928	.6937	.6946	.6955	.6964	.6972	.6981
5.0	.6990	.6998	.7007	.7016	.7024	.7033	.7042	.7050	.7059	.7067
5.1	.7076	.7084	.7093	.7101	.7110	.7118	.7126	.7135	.7143	.7152
5.2	.7160	.7168	.7177	.7185	.7193	.7202	.7210	.7218	.7226	.7235
5.3	.7243	.7251	.7259	.7267	.7275	.7284	.7292	.7300	.7308	.7316
5.4	.7324	.7332	.7340	.7348	.7356	.7364	.7372	.7380	.7388	.7396

TABLE III. Common Logarithms (base 10)

n	0	1	2	3	4	5	6	7	8	9
5.5	.7404	.7412	.7419	.7427	.7435	.7443	.7451	.7459	.7466	.7474
5.6	.7482	.7490	.7497	.7505	.7513	.7520	.7528	.7536	.7543	.7551
5.7	.7559	.7566	.7574	.7582	.7589	.7597	.7604	.7612	.7619	.7627
5.8	.7634	.7642	.7649	.7657	.7664	.7672	.7679	.7686	.7694	.7701
5.9	.7709	.7716	.7723	.7731	.7738	.7745	.7752	.7760	.7767	.7774
6.0	.7782	.7789	.7796	.7803	.7810	.7818	.7825	.7832	.7839	.7846
6.1	.7853	.7860	.7868	.7875	.7882	.7889	.7896	.7903	.7910	.7917
6.2	.7924	.7931	.7938	.7945	.7952	.7959	.7966	.7973	.7980	.7987
6.3	.7993	.8000	.8007	.8014	.8021	.8028	.8035	.8041	.8048	.8055
6.4	.8062	.8069	.8075	.8082	.8089	.8096	.8102	.8109	.8116	.8122
6.5	.8129	.8136	.8142	.8149	.8156	.8162	.8169	.8176	.8182	.8189
6.6	.8195	.8202	.8209	.8215	.8222	.8228	.8235	.8241	.8248	.8254
6.7	.8261	.8267	.8274	.8280	.8287	.8293	.8299	.8306	.8312	.8319
6.8	.8325	.8331	.8338	.8344	.8351	.8357	.8363	.8370	.8376	.8382
6.9	.8388	.8395	.8401	.8407	.8414	.8420	.8426	.8432	.8439	.8445
7.0	.8451	.8457	.8463	.8470	.8476	.8482	.8488	.8494	.8500	.8506
7.1	.8513	.8519	.8525	.8531	.8537	.8543	.8549	.8555	.8561	.8567
7.2	.8573	.8579	.8585	.8591	.8597	.8603	.8609	.8615	.8621	.8627
7.3	.8633	.8639	.8645	.8651	.8657	.8663	.8669	.8675	.8681	.8686
7.4	.8692	.8698	.8704	.8710	.8716	.8722	.8727	.8733	.8739	.8745
7.5	.8751	.8756	.8762	.8768	.8774	.8779	.8785	.8791	.8797	.8802
7.6	.8808	.8814	.8820	.8825	.8831	.8837	.8842	.8848	.8854	.8859
7.7	.8865	.8871	.8876	.8882	.8887	.8893	.8899	.8904	.8910	.8915
7.8	.8921	.8927	.8932	.8938	.8943	.8949	.8954	.8960	.8965	.8971
7.9	.8976	.8982	.8987	.8993	.8998	.9004	.9009	.9015	.9020	.9025
8.0	.9031	.9036	.9042	.9047	.9053	.9058	.9063	.9069	.9074	.9079
8.1	.9085	.9090	.9096	.9101	.9106	.9112	.9117	.9122	.9128	.9133
8.2	.9138	.9143	.9149	.9154	.9159	.9165	.9170	.9175	.9180	.9186
8.3	.9191	.9196	.9201	.9206	.9212	.9217	.9222	.9227	.9232	.9238
8.4	.9243	.9248	.9253	.9258	.9263	.9269	.9274	.9279	.9284	.9289
8.5	.9294	.9299	.9304	.9309	.9315	.9320	.9325	.9330	.9335	.9340
8.6	.9345	.9350	.9355	.9360	.9365	.9370	.9375	.9380	.9385	.9390
8.7	.9395	.9400	.9405	.9410	.9415	.9420	.9425	.9430	.9435	.9440
8.8	.9445	.9450	.9455	.9460	.9465	.9469	.9474	.9479	.9484	.9489
8.9	.9494	.9499	.9504	.9509	.9513	.9518	.9523	.9528	.9533	.9538
9.0	.9542	.9547	.9552	.9557	.9562	.9566	.9571	.9576	.9581	.9586
9.1	.9590	.9595	.9600	.9605	.9609	.9614	.9619	.9624	.9628	.9633
9.2	.9638	.9643	.9647	.9652	.9657	.9661	.9666	.9671	.9675	.9680
9.3	.9685	.9689	.9694	.9699	.9703	.9708	.9713	.9717	.9722	.9727
9.4	.9731	.9736	.9741	.9745	.9750	.9754	.9759	.9763	.9768	.9773
9.5	.9777	.9782	.9786	.9791	.9795	.9800	.9805	.9809	.9814	.9818
9.6	.9823	.9827	.9832	.9836	.9841	.9845	.9850	.9854	.9859	.9863
9.7	.9868	.9872	.9877	.9881	.9886	.9890	.9894	.9899	.9903	.9908
9.8	.9912	.9917	.9921	.9926	.9930	.9934	.9939	.9943	.9948	.9952
9.9	.9956	.9961	.9965	.9969	.9974	.9978	.9983	.9987	.9991	.9996

TABLE IV. Trigonometric Functions—Radians

t	sin t	cos t	tan t	cot t	sec t	csc t
.00	.0000	1.0000	.0000	. . . . .	1.000	. . . . .
.01	.0100	1.0000	.0100	99.997	1.000	100.00
.02	.0200	.9998	.0200	49.993	1.000	50.00
.03	.0300	.9996	.0300	33.323	1.000	33.34
.04	.0400	.9992	.0400	24.987	1.001	25.01
.05	.0500	.9988	.0500	19.983	1.001	20.01
.06	.0600	.9982	.0601	16.647	1.002	16.68
.07	.0699	.9976	.0701	14.262	1.002	14.30
.08	.0799	.9968	.0802	12.473	1.003	12.51
.09	.0899	.9960	.0902	11.081	1.004	11.13
.10	.0998	.9950	.1003	9.967	1.005	10.02
.11	.1098	.9940	.1104	9.054	1.006	9.109
.12	.1197	.9928	.1206	8.293	1.007	8.353
.13	.1296	.9916	.1307	7.649	1.009	7.714
.14	.1395	.9902	.1409	7.096	1.010	7.166
.15	.1494	.9888	.1511	6.617	1.011	6.692
.16	.1593	.9872	.1614	6.197	1.013	6.277
.17	.1692	.9856	.1717	5.826	1.015	5.911
.18	.1790	.9838	.1820	5.495	1.016	5.586
.19	.1889	.9820	.1923	5.200	1.018	5.295
.20	.1987	.9801	.2027	4.933	1.020	5.033
.21	.2085	.9780	.2131	4.692	1.022	4.797
.22	.2182	.9759	.2236	4.472	1.025	4.582
.23	.2280	.9737	.2341	4.271	1.027	4.386
.24	.2377	.9713	.2447	4.086	1.030	4.207
.25	.2474	.9689	.2553	3.916	1.032	4.042
.26	.2571	.9664	.2660	3.759	1.035	3.890
.27	.2667	.9638	.2768	3.613	1.038	3.749
.28	.2764	.9611	.2876	3.478	1.041	3.619
.29	.2860	.9582	.2984	3.351	1.044	3.497
.30	.2955	.9553	.3093	3.233	1.047	3.384
.31	.3051	.9523	.3203	3.122	1.050	3.278
.32	.3146	.9492	.3314	3.018	1.053	3.179
.33	.3240	.9460	.3425	2.920	1.057	3.086
.34	.3335	.9428	.3537	2.827	1.061	2.999
.35	.3429	.9394	.3650	2.740	1.065	2.916
.36	.3523	.9359	.3764	2.657	1.068	2.839
.37	.3616	.9323	.3879	2.578	1.073	2.765
.38	.3709	.9287	.3994	2.504	1.077	2.696
.39	.3802	.9249	.4111	2.433	1.081	2.630
.40	.3894	.9211	.4228	2.365	1.086	2.568
.41	.3986	.9171	.4346	2.301	1.090	2.509
.42	.4078	.9131	.4466	2.239	1.095	2.452
.43	.4169	.9090	.4586	2.180	1.100	2.399
.44	.4259	.9048	.4708	2.124	1.105	2.348

TABLE IV. Trigonometric Functions—Radians

t	sin t	cos t	tan t	cot t	sec t	csc t
.45	.4350	.9004	.4831	2.070	1.111	2.299
.46	.4439	.8961	.4954	2.018	1.116	2.253
.47	.4529	.8916	.5080	1.969	1.122	2.208
.48	.4618	.8870	.5206	1.921	1.127	2.166
.49	.4706	.8823	.5334	1.875	1.133	2.125
.50	.4794	.8776	.5463	1.830	1.139	2.086
.51	.4882	.8727	.5594	1.788	1.146	2.048
.52	.4969	.8678	.5726	1.747	1.152	2.013
.53	.5055	.8628	.5859	1.707	1.159	1.978
.54	.5141	.8577	.5994	1.668	1.166	1.945
.55	.5227	.8525	.6131	1.631	1.173	1.913
.56	.5312	.8473	.6269	1.595	1.180	1.883
.57	.5396	.8419	˙.6310	1.560	1.188	1.853
.58	.5480	.8365	.6552	1.526	1.196	1.825
.59	.5564	.8309	.6696	1.494	1.203	1.797
.60	.5646	.8253	.6841	1.462	1.212	1.771
.61	.5729	.8196	.6989	1.431	1.220	1.746
.62	.5810	.8139	.7139	1.401	1.229	1.721
.63	.5891	.8080	.7291	1.372	1.238	1.697
.64	.5972	.8021	.7445	1.343	1.247	1.674
.65	.6052	.7961	.7602	1.315	1.256	1.652
.66	.6131	.7900	.7761	1.288	1.266	1.631
.67	.6210	.7838	.7923	1.262	1.276	1.610
.68	.6288	.7776	.8087	1.237	1.286	1.590
.69	.6365	.7712	.8253	1.212	1.297	1.571
.70	.6442	.7648	.8423	1.187	1.307	1.552
.71	.6518	.7584	.8595	1.163	1.319	1.534
.72	.6594	.7518	.8771	1.140	1.330	1.517
.73	.6669	.7452	.8949	1.117	1.342	1.500
.74	.6743	.7358	.9131	1.095	1.354	1.483
.75	.6816	.7317	.9316	1.073	1.367	1.467
.76	.6889	.7248	.9505	1.052	1.380	1.452
.77	.6961	.7179	.9697	1.031	1.393	1.437
.78	.7033	.7109	.9893	1.011	1.407	1.422
.79	.7104	.7038	1.009	.9908	1.421	1.408
.80	.7174	.6967	1.030	.9712	1.435	1.394
.81	.7243	.6895	1.050	.9520	1.450	1.381
.82	.7311	.6822	1.072	.9331	1.466	1.368
.83	.7379	.6749	1.093	.9146	1.482	1.355
.84	.7446	.6675	1.116	.8964	1.498	1.343
.85	.7513	.6600	1.138	.8785	1.515	1.331
.86	.7578	.6524	1.162	.8609	1.533	1.320
.87	.7643	.6448	1.185	.8437	1.551	1.308
.88	.7707	.6372	1.210	.8267	1.569	1.297
.89	.7771	.6294	1.235	.8100	1.589	1.287

TABLE IV. Trigonometric Functions—Radians

t	$\sin t$	$\cos t$	$\tan t$	$\cot t$	$\sec t$	$\csc t$
.90	.7833	.6216	1.260	.7936	1.609	1.277
.91	.7895	.6137	1.286	.7774	1.629	1.267
.92	.7956	.6058	1.313	.7615	1.651	1.257
.93	.8016	.5978	1.341	.7458	1.673	1.247
.94	.8076	.5898	1.369	.7303	1.696	1.238
.95	.8134	.5817	1.398	.7151	1.719	1.229
.96	.8192	.5735	1.428	.7001	1.744	1.221
.97	.8249	.5653	1.459	.6853	1.769	1.212
.98	.8305	.5570	1.491	.6707	1.795	1.204
.99	.8360	.5487	1.524	.6563	1.823	1.196
1.00	.8415	.5403	1.557	.6421	1.851	1.188
1.01	.8468	.5319	1.592	.6281	1.880	1.181
1.02	.8521	.5234	1.628	.6142	1.911	1.174
1.03	.8573	.5148	1.665	.6005	1.942	1.166
1.04	.8624	.5062	1.704	.5870	1.975	1.160
1.05	.8674	.4976	1.743	.5736	2.010	1.153
1.06	.8724	.4889	1.784	.5604	2.046	1.146
1.07	.8772	.4801	1.827	.5473	2.083	1.140
1.08	.8820	.4713	1.871	.5344	2.122	1.134
1.09	.8866	.4625	1.917	.5216	2.162	1.128
1.10	.8912	.4536	1.965	.5090	2.205	1.122
1.11	.8957	.4447	2.014	.4964	2.249	1.116
1.12	.9001	.4357	2.066	.4840	2.295	1.111
1.13	.9044	.4267	2.120	.4718	2.344	1.106
1.14	.9086	.4176	2.176	.4596	2.395	1.101
1.15	.9128	.4085	2.234	.4475	2.448	1.096
1.16	.9168	.3993	2.296	.4356	2.504	1.091
1.17	.9208	.3902	2.360	.4237	2.563	1.086
1.18	.9246	.3809	2.427	.4120	2.625	1.082
1.19	.9284	.3717	2.498	.4003	2.691	1.077
1.20	.9320	.3624	2.572	.3888	2.760	1.073
1.21	.9356	.3530	2.650	.3773	2.833	1.069
1.22	.9391	.3436	2.733	.3659	2.910	1.065
1.23	.9425	.3342	2.820	.3546	2.992	1.061
1.24	.9458	.3248	2.912	.3434	3.079	1.057
1.25	.9490	.3153	3.010	.3323	3.171	1.054
1.26	.9521	.3058	3.113	.3212	3.270	1.050
1.27	.9551	.2963	3.224	.3102	3.375	1.047
1.28	.9580	.2867	3.341	.2993	3.488	1.044
1.29	.9608	.2771	3.467	.2884	3.609	1.041
1.30	.9636	.2675	3.602	.2776	3.738	1.038
1.31	.9662	.2579	3.747	.2669	3.878	1.035
1.32	.9687	.2482	3.903	.2562	4.029	1.032
1.33	.9711	.2385	4.072	.2456	4.193	1.030
1.34	.9735	.2288	4.256	.2350	4.372	1.027

TABLE IV. Trigonometric Functions—Radians

t	$\sin t$	$\cos t$	$\tan t$	$\cot t$	$\sec t$	$\csc t$
1.35	.9757	.2190	4.455	.2245	4.566	1.025
1.36	.9779	.2092	4.673	.2140	4.779	1.023
1.37	.9799	.1994	4.913	.2035	5.014	1.021
1.38	.9819	.1896	5.177	.1931	5.273	1.018
1.39	.9837	.1798	5.471	.1828	5.561	1.017
1.40	.9854	.1700	5.798	.1725	5.883	1.015
1.41	.9871	.1601	6.165	.1622	6.246	1.013
1.42	.9887	.1502	6.581	.1519	6.657	1.011
1.43	.9901	.1403	7.055	.1417	7.126	1.010
1.44	.9915	.1304	7.602	.1315	7.667	1.009
1.45	.9927	.1205	8.238	.1214	8.299	1.007
1.46	.9939	.1106	8.989	.1113	9.044	1.006
1.47	.9949	.1006	9.887	.1011	9.938	1.005
1.48	.9959	.0907	10.938	.0910	11.029	1.004
1.49	.9967	.0807	12.350	.0810	12.390	1.003
1.50	.9975	.0707	14.101	.0709	14.137	1.003
1.51	.9982	.0608	16.428	.0609	16.458	1.002
1.52	.9987	.0508	19.670	.0508	19.965	1.001
1.53	.9992	.0408	24.498	.0408	24.519	1.001
1.54	.9995	.0308	32.461	.0308	32.476	1.000
1.55	.9998	.0208	48.078	.0208	48.089	1.000
1.56	.9999	.0108	92.620	.0108	92.626	1.000
1.57	1.0000	.0008	1255.8	.0008	1255.8	1.000
1.58	1.0000	−.0092	−108.65	−.0092	−108.65	1.000
1.59	.9998	−.0192	−52.067	−.0192	−52.08	1.000
1.60	.9996	−.0292	−34.233	−.0292	−34.25	1.000

TABLE V.   Trigonometric Functions—Degrees

θ	$\sin \theta$	$\cos \theta$	$\tan \theta$	$\cot \theta$	$\sec \theta$	$\csc \theta$
0°	.0000	1.0000	.0000	—	1.0000	—
1°	.0175	.9998	.0175	57.2900	1.0001	57.2987
2°	.0349	.9994	.0349	28.6363	1.0006	28.6537
3°	.0523	.9986	.0524	19.0811	1.0014	19.1073
4°	.0698	.9976	.0699	14.3007	1.0024	14.3356
5°	.0872	.9962	.0875	11.4301	1.0038	11.4737
6°	.1045	.9945	.1051	9.5144	1.0055	9.5668
7°	.1219	.9925	.1228	8.1443	1.0075	8.2055
8°	.1392	.9903	.1405	7.1154	1.0098	7.1853
9°	.1564	.9877	.1584	6.3138	1.0125	6.3925
10°	.1736	.9848	.1763	5.6713	1.0154	5.7588
11°	.1908	.9816	.1944	5.1446	1.0187	5.2408
12°	.2079	.9781	.2126	4.7046	1.0223	4.8097
13°	.2250	.9744	.2309	4.3315	1.0263	4.4454
14°	.2419	.9703	.2493	4.0108	1.0306	4.1336
15°	.2588	.9659	.2679	3.7321	1.0353	3.8637
16°	.2756	.9613	.2867	3.4874	1.0403	3.6280
17°	.2924	.9563	.3057	3.2709	1.0457	3.4203
18°	.3090	.9511	.3249	3.0777	1.0515	3.2361
19°	.3256	.9455	.3443	2.9042	1.0576	3.0716
20°	.3420	.9397	.3640	2.7475	1.0642	2.9238
21°	.3584	.9336	.3839	2.6051	1.0711	2.7904
22°	.3746	.9272	.4040	2.4751	1.0785	2.6695
23°	.3907	.9205	.4245	2.3559	1.0864	2.5593
24°	.4067	.9135	.4452	2.2460	1.0946	2.4586
25°	.4226	.9063	.4663	2.1445	1.1034	2.3662
26°	.4384	.8988	.4877	2.0503	1.1126	2.2812
27°	.4540	.8910	.5095	1.9626	1.1223	2.2027
28°	.4695	.8829	.5317	1.8807	1.1326	2.1301
29°	.4848	.8746	.5543	1.8040	1.1434	2.0627
30°	.5000	.8660	.5774	1.7321	1.1547	2.0000
31°	.5150	.8572	.6009	1.6643	1.1666	1.9416
32°	.5299	.8480	.6249	1.6003	1.1792	1.8870
33°	.5446	.8387	.6494	1.5399	1.1924	1.8361
34°	.5592	.8290	.6745	1.4826	1.2062	1.7883
35°	.5736	.8192	.7002	1.4281	1.2208	1.7434
36°	.5878	.8090	.7265	1.3764	1.2361	1.7013
37°	.6018	.7986	.7536	1.3270	1.2521	1.6616
38°	.6157	.7880	.7813	1.2799	1.2690	1.6243
39°	.6293	.7771	.8098	1.2349	1.2868	1.5890
40°	.6428	.7660	.8391	1.1918	1.3054	1.5557
41°	.6561	.7547	.8693	1.1504	1.3250	1.5243
42°	.6691	.7431	.9004	1.1106	1.3456	1.4945
43°	.6820	.7314	.9325	1.0724	1.3673	1.4663
44°	.6947	.7193	.9657	1.0355	1.3902	1.4396
45°	.7071	.7071	1.0000	1.0000	1.4142	1.4142

TABLE V.   Trigonometric Functions—Degrees

θ	$\sin \theta$	$\cos \theta$	$\tan \theta$	$\cot \theta$	$\sec \theta$	$\csc \theta$
46°	.7193	.6947	1.0355	.9657	1.4396	1.3902
47°	.7314	.6820	1.0724	.9325	1.4663	1.3673
48°	.7431	.6691	1.1106	.9004	1.4945	1.3456
49°	.7547	.6561	1.1504	.8693	1.5243	1.3250
50°	.7660	.6428	1.1918	.8391	1.5557	1.3054
51°	.7771	.6293	1.2349	.8098	1.5890	1.2868
52°	.7880	.6157	1.2799	.7813	1.6243	1.2690
53°	.7986	.6018	1.3270	.7536	1.6616	1.2521
54°	.8090	.5878	1.3764	.7265	1.7013	1.2361
55°	.8192	.5736	1.4281	.7002	1.7434	1.2208
56°	.8290	.5592	1.4826	.6745	1.7883	1.2062
57°	.8387	.5446	1.5399	.6494	1.8361	1.1924
58°	.8480	.5299	1.6003	.6249	1.8870	1.1792
59°	.8572	.5150	1.6643	.6009	1.9416	1.1666
60°	.8660	.5000	1.7321	.5774	2.0000	1.1547
61°	.8746	.4848	1.8040	.5543	2.0627	1.1434
62°	.8829	.4695	1.8807	.5317	2.1301	1.1326
63°	.8910	.4540	1.9626	.5095	2.2027	1.1223
64°	.8988	.4384	2.0503	.4877	2.2812	1.1126
65°	.9063	.4226	2.1445	.4663	2.3662	1.1034
66°	.9135	.4067	2.2460	.4452	2.4586	1.0946
67°	.9205	.3907	2.3559	.4245	2.5593	1.0864
68°	.9272	.3746	2.4751	.4040	2.6695	1.0785
69°	.9336	.3584	2.6051	.3839	2.7904	1.0711
70°	.9397	.3420	2.7475	.3640	2.9238	1.0642
71°	.9455	.3256	2.9042	.3443	3.0716	1.0576
72°	.9511	.3090	3.0777	.3249	3.2361	1.0515
73°	.9563	.2924	3.2709	.3057	3.4203	1.0457
74°	.9613	.2756	3.4874	.2867	3.6280	1.0403
75°	.9659	.2588	3.7321	.2679	3.8637	1.0353
76°	.9703	.2419	4.0108	.2493	4.1336	1.0306
77°	.9744	.2250	4.3315	.2309	4.4454	1.0263
78°	.9781	.2079	4.7046	.2126	4.8097	1.0223
79°	.9816	.1908	5.1446	.1944	5.2408	1.0187
80°	.9848	.1736	5.6713	.1763	5.7588	1.0154
81°	.9877	.1564	6.3138	.1584	6.3925	1.0125
82°	.9903	.1392	7.1154	.1405	7.1853	1.0098
83°	.9925	.1219	8.1443	.1228	8.2055	1.0075
84°	.9945	.1045	9.5144	.1051	9.5668	1.0055
85°	.9962	.0872	11.4301	.0875	11.4737	1.0038
86°	.9976	.0698	14.3007	.0699	14.3356	1.0024
87°	.9986	.0523	19.0811	.0524	19.1073	1.0014
88°	.9994	.0349	28.6363	.0349	28.6537	1.0006
89°	.9998	.0175	57.2900	.0175	57.2987	1.0001
90°	1.0000	.0000	—	.0000	—	1.0000

TABLE VI.　Powers and Roots

n	n^2	$\sqrt{n}$	n^3	$\sqrt[3]{n}$	n	n^2	$\sqrt{n}$	n^3	$\sqrt[3]{n}$
1	1	1.000	1	1.000	51	2601	7.141	132,651	3.708
2	4	1.414	8	1.260	52	2704	7.211	140,608	3.732
3	9	1.732	27	1.442	53	2809	7.280	148,877	3.756
4	16	2.000	64	1.587	54	2916	7.348	157,464	3.780
5	25	2.236	125	1.710	55	3025	7.416	166,376	3.803
6	36	2.449	216	1.817	56	3136	7.483	175,616	3.826
7	49	2.646	343	1.913	57	3249	7.550	185,193	3.848
8	64	2.828	512	2.000	58	3364	7.616	195,112	3.871
9	81	3.000	729	2.080	59	3481	7.681	205,379	3.893
10	100	3.162	1000	2.154	60	3600	7.746	216,000	3.915
11	121	3.317	1331	2.224	61	3721	7.810	226,981	3.936
12	144	3.464	1728	2.289	62	3844	7.874	238,328	3.958
13	169	3.606	2197	2.351	63	3969	7.937	250,047	3.979
14	196	3.742	2744	2.410	64	4096	8.000	262,144	4.000
15	225	3.873	3375	2.466	65	4225	8.062	274,625	4.021
16	256	4.000	4096	2.520	66	4356	8.124	287,496	4.041
17	289	4.123	4913	2.571	67	4489	8.185	300,763	4.062
18	324	4.243	5832	2.621	68	4624	8.246	314,432	4.082
19	361	4.359	6859	2.668	69	4761	8.307	328,509	4.102
20	400	4.472	8000	2.714	70	4900	8.367	343,000	4.121
21	441	4.583	9261	2.759	71	5041	8.426	357,911	4.141
22	484	4.690	10,648	2.802	72	5184	8.485	373,248	4.160
23	529	4.796	12,167	2.844	73	5329	8.544	389,017	4.179
24	576	4.899	13,824	2.884	74	5476	8.602	405,224	4.198
25	625	5.000	15,625	2.924	75	5625	8.660	421,875	4.217
26	676	5.099	17,576	2.962	76	5776	8.718	438,976	4.236
27	729	5.196	19,683	3.000	77	5929	8.775	456,533	4.254
28	784	5.291	21,952	3.037	78	6084	8.832	474,552	4.273
29	841	5.385	24,389	3.072	79	6241	8.888	493.039	4.291
30	900	5.477	27,000	3.107	80	6400	8.944	512,000	4.309
31	961	5.568	29,791	3.141	81	6561	9.000	531,441	4.327
32	1024	5.657	32,768	3.175	82	6724	9.055	551,368	4.344
33	1089	5.745	35,937	3.208	83	6889	9.110	571,787	4.362
34	1156	5.831	39,304	3.240	84	7056	9.165	592,704	4.380
35	1225	5.916	42,875	3.271	85	7225	9.220	614,126	4.397
36	1296	6.000	46,656	3.302	86	7396	9.274	636,056	4.414
37	1369	6.083	50,653	3.332	87	7569	9.327	658,503	4.431
38	1444	6.164	54,872	3.362	88	7744	9.381	681,472	4.448
39	1521	6.245	59,319	3.391	89	7921	9.434	704,969	4.465
40	1600	6.325	64,000	3.420	90	8100	9.487	729,000	4.481
41	1681	6.403	68,921	3.448	91	8281	9.539	753,571	4.498
42	1764	6.481	74,088	3.476	92	8464	9.592	778,688	4.514
43	1849	6.557	79,507	3.503	93	8649	9.643	804,357	4.531
44	1936	6.633	85,184	3.530	94	8836	9.695	830,584	4.547
45	2025	6.708	91,125	3.557	95	9025	9.747	857,375	4.563
46	2116	6.782	97,336	3.583	96	9216	9.798	884,736	4.579
47	2209	6.856	103,823	3.609	97	9409	9.849	912,673	4.595
48	2304	6.928	110,592	3.634	98	9604	9.899	941,192	4.610
49	2401	7.000	117,649	3.659	99	9801	9.950	970,299	4.626
50	2500	7.071	125,000	3.684	100	10,000	10.000	1,000,000	4.642

Answers to Selected Exercises

Exercises 1.1 (page 4)

1. (a) rational, integer, whole, natural (c) rational (e) irrational (g) rational, integer
(i) rational, integer, whole, natural (k) rational (m) rational (o) irrational (q) rational, integer
(s) irrational **2.** (a) 4 (c) $\frac{7}{8}$ (e) 0 (g) $\frac{33}{2}$ (i) -30 (k) 64 **3.** (a) $\frac{19}{20}$ (c) $-\frac{3}{4}$ (e) 7 (g) $\frac{8}{3}$
4. (a) $(x + 6)5 - 7 = 16$; $x = -\frac{7}{5}$ (c) $x + x + x = 180°$; $x = 60°$ **5.** Number: $10m + n$;
incorrect: $10n + m$; difference $(10m + n) - (10n + m)$, which is $9(m - n)$, or $9 \cdot$ (some integer).
7. (a) $\frac{73}{99}$ (c) $\frac{691}{999}$ (e) $\frac{120}{99}$ or $\frac{40}{33}$

Exercises 1.2 (page 14)

1. (a) $(2 + a)x$ (c) $3x(x + 2)$ (e) $(2 + m)(x + y)$ (g) $(w + x + y)\sqrt{5}$ (i) $mn(m - n - 1)$
(k) $4(y + 1)$ (m) cannot be factored (o) $x(wy + wz + yz)$ **2.** (a) $(y + 7)(y - 2)$
(c) $(m - 5)(m - 4)$ (e) $2(x + 2)(x - 1)$ (g) $4(x + 6)(x - 6)$ (i) $(5y - 2)(y - 3)$
(k) cannot be factored (m) $a^3(a + 3)(a - 3)$ (o) $n(n - 6)(n + 2)$ (q) $(3x + 2)(2x - 3)$
(s) $(x^m + y^m)^2$ **3.** (a) $(x + 2)(x^2 - 2x + 4)$ (c) $(a - x)(a^2 + ax + x^2)$
(e) $(1 + x^2)(1 - x^2 + x^4)$ (g) $(3x - 4y)(9x^2 + 12xy + 16y^2)$ **4.** (a) $-4, -1$
(c) $-2, 5$ (e) $-7, 2$ (g) $-2, -\frac{3}{2}$ (i) $-2, -\frac{4}{5}$ (k) $-5, \frac{3}{2}$ (m) $-\frac{2}{3}, \frac{3}{2}$ **5.** (a) $2\sqrt{2}$ (c) $2\sqrt{15}$
(e) $5\sqrt{10}$ (g) $2\sqrt{17}$ **6.** (a) $-5, -1$ (c) $2 \pm \sqrt{3}$ (e) $6 \pm 3\sqrt{3}$ (g) $\dfrac{3 \pm \sqrt{41}}{2}$ (i) $\dfrac{-3 \pm \sqrt{41}}{4}$
(k) $\dfrac{3 \pm \sqrt{5}}{4}$ **7.** (a) $1 \pm \sqrt{2}$ (c) $\dfrac{-3 \pm \sqrt{37}}{2}$ (e) $-3, -1$ (g) $1 \pm \sqrt{6}$ (i) $\dfrac{9 \pm \sqrt{57}}{6}$ (k) $\dfrac{3 \pm \sqrt{29}}{10}$
8. (a) $\pm\sqrt{3}, \pm 2$ (c) $\pm 1, \pm\frac{3}{2}$

Exercises 1.3 (page 18)

1. (a) $c^5 + 5c^4d + 10c^3d^2 + 10c^2d^3 + 5cd^4 + d^5$
(c) $x^6 + 6x^5y + 15x^4y^2 + 20x^3y^3 + 15x^2y^4 + 6xy^5 + y^6$
(e) $p^7 - 7p^6q + 21p^5q^2 - 35p^4q^3 + 35p^3q^4 - 21p^2q^5 + 7pq^6 - q^7$

(g) $x^8 + 8x^7a + 28x^6a^2 + 56x^5a^3 + 70x^4a^4 + 56x^3a^5 + 28x^2a^6 + 8xa^7 + a^8$

(i) $32x^5 + 80x^4y + 80x^3y^2 + 40x^2y^3 + 10xy^4 + y^5$

(k) $32x^5 - 240x^4y + 720x^3y^2 - 1080x^2y^3 + 810xy^4 - 243y^5$

(m) $x^9 - 9x^8y + 36x^7y^2 - 84x^6y^3 + 126x^5y^4 - 126x^4y^5 + 84x^3y^6 - 36x^2y^7 + 9xy^8 - y^9$

(o) $x^9 + 3x^6y^2 + 3x^3y^4 + y^6$ (q) $32 - 80x^3 + 80x^6 - 40x^9 + 10x^{12} - x^{15}$

(s) $\dfrac{x^4}{16} + \dfrac{x^3}{2} + \dfrac{3x^2}{2} + 2x + 1$ (u) $\dfrac{x^6}{64} + \dfrac{3x^5y}{16} + \dfrac{15x^4y^2}{16} + \dfrac{5x^3y^3}{2} + \dfrac{15x^2y^4}{4} + 3xy^5 + y^6$

(w) $x^8 - 4x^5 + 6x^2 - \dfrac{4}{x} + \dfrac{1}{x^4}$ **2.** (a) $x^2 + 5x + 4$ (c) $a^2 + 8a + 12$ (e) $y^2 - 10y + 16$

(g) $14 + 5x - x^2$ (i) $2x^2 + 11x + 15$ (k) $9y^2 - 18y + 5$ (m) $14x^2 - 41x + 15$

(o) $2x^2 + 3xy + y^2$

Exercises 1.4 (page 22)

1. (a) $\dfrac{bx + ay}{ab}$ (c) $\dfrac{15 + 7x^2}{3xy}$ (e) $\dfrac{4x^2 - 4x - 5}{(x)(x-5)(x+5)}$ (g) $\dfrac{-4x + 60}{(x-5)(x+3)^2}$ (i) $\dfrac{11x^2 + 14x}{3(x-8)(x+2)(x+1)}$

2. (a) $\dfrac{2x}{x+1}$ (c) $\dfrac{x-4}{x^2}$ (e) $\dfrac{3x(10y+1)}{2(x+1)}$ (g) $\dfrac{2}{x-2}$ (i) $3t$ (k) $-\dfrac{a+b}{a}$ **3.** (a) $\dfrac{2x+1}{3x-1}$ (c) $\dfrac{2y+x}{x+4y}$

(e) $\dfrac{1+t}{1-t}$ (g) $\dfrac{-1}{(x+h-1)(x-1)}$ (i) $\dfrac{ace - be}{cd - cef}$ **4.** (a) $\frac{9}{10}$ (c) 21 (e) 8 (g) $\frac{11}{2}$ (i) $-\frac{5}{3}$ **5.** $\frac{1}{14}$

Exercises 1.5 (page 27)

1. (a) x^{25} (c) a^{33} (e) $12m^{17}$ (g) $4x^{12}y^7$ (i) $x^{12}y^{30}$ (k) x^8y^{12} (m) a^{20}/b^{15} (o) $x^{30}y^{48}$ **2.** (a) $\frac{3}{2}$

(c) 81 (e) 0 (g) $\frac{8}{9}$ (i) $\frac{11}{16}$ (k) $x^8y^6/2$ (m) $1/(64x^{33})$ (o) $16/(9n^{14})$ (q) $1/y^3$ (s) x^{3n-3}

(u) x^{8n-5} **3.** (a) $\dfrac{a^3 + b^3}{ab}$ (c) $\dfrac{a+b}{ab}$ (e) $\dfrac{1}{x+y}$ (g) $\dfrac{x+1}{x^3}$ (i) $\dfrac{y^2}{xy^2 + 1}$ (k) $2x^2y$ (m) $\dfrac{b^{2y} - a^{2x}}{a^xb^y}$

4. (a) $x^n(x+1)$ (c) $x^n(x^n+1)$ (e) $y^{n-1}(y^2+1)$ (g) $(x^n+9)(x^n-9)$ (i) $x^{n-1}(x+1)(x-1)$

Exercises 1.6 (page 35)

1. (a) 12 (c) 5 (e) 4 (g) 149 (i) $\frac{1}{4}$ (k) $\frac{1}{2}$ (m) $4x^6$ (o) $-3xy^2$ (q) $4m^{14}n^8$ (s) $625x^{24}$ (u) $\dfrac{4}{x^2}$

(w) $\dfrac{27x^6}{y^3}$ (y) $\dfrac{x^4y^8}{81}$ **2.** (a) $2\sqrt{5}$ (c) $7\sqrt{2}$ (e) $4\sqrt{3}$ (g) $7\sqrt{3}$ (i) $3\sqrt{14}$ (k) $6\sqrt{5}$ (m) $9\sqrt{2}$

(o) $12\sqrt{7}$ (q) $2\sqrt[3]{3}$ (s) $3\sqrt[3]{2}$ (u) $2\sqrt[3]{5}$ (w) $\frac{3}{2}$ (y) $1/\sqrt{3}$, or $\sqrt{3}/3$ **3.** (a) $\sqrt[6]{2}$ (c) $\sqrt[12]{432}$

4. (a) $3\sqrt{7}/7$ (c) $\sqrt{30}/3$ (e) $5(2-\sqrt{3})$ (g) $w(\sqrt{x}-\sqrt{y})/(x-y)$ (i) $9+4\sqrt{5}$ (k) $\sqrt{7}$

5. (a) $2\sqrt[3]{49}/7$ (c) $5\sqrt[3]{2}/4$ (e) $\sqrt[3]{50}/5$ (g) $-5(1 + \sqrt[3]{2} + \sqrt[3]{4})$

6. (a) $7/(3\sqrt{7})$ (c) $1/(3\sqrt{2})$ (e) $2/(\sqrt{5}-1)$ (g) $2/(3\sqrt[3]{2})$ (i) $1/\sqrt{11}$ (k) $1/(\sqrt{a+2}+\sqrt{a})$

7. (a) $4(x^2+4)^3(2x+1)^5(7x^2+2x+12)$

(c) $2(3x+2)^3(x^2-3)^4(21x^2+10x-18)$ (e) $45(5x-4)^8(3x+1)^4(18x-11)$

8. (a) $3(x+3)^{1/2}(5x+6)$ (c) $\dfrac{3x+2}{\sqrt{x+1}}$ (e) $\dfrac{x^2(9-11x^2)}{(1-x^2)^{2/3}}$ (g) $\dfrac{2(11x^2-15)}{(x^2-3)^{2/5}}$ (i) $\dfrac{3(5x^2-4x+10)}{(x^2+2)^{7/5}}$

9. (a) $\dfrac{2(1-x^{1/3})}{x^{1/3}}$ (c) $\dfrac{3+x^{3/2}}{x^{1/2}}$ (e) $\dfrac{x^{4/3}+1}{x^{2/3}}$ (g) $\dfrac{1+x^{1/3}}{x^{2/3}}$ (i) $\dfrac{x+1}{\sqrt{x}}$ **10.** (a) $\frac{63}{2}$ (c) $\frac{11}{9}$ (e) $\frac{47}{9}$ (g) 7

(i) 621 (k) $\frac{59}{3}$ (m) $\frac{30}{17}$

Exercises 1.7 (page 40)

1. (a) $-\frac{17}{3}, 5$ (c) $1, \frac{7}{5}$ (e) no solution (g) 0 (i) $-6, 6$ **2.** (a) $|u|$ (c) $3|m|$
(e) 8 (g) $|y|$ (i) $6x^2|y|$ (k) $|x|$ (m) 1 (o) $9 - x$ (q) $x^2 + 1$ (s) $3 - x$
(u) $|7 - x|$ **3.** (a) 1 (c) 1 (e) -1 (g) $\dfrac{|x+1|}{x+1}$

Exercises 1.8 (page 43)

1. $h = \dfrac{V}{lw}$ **3.** $r = \dfrac{C}{2\pi}$ **5.** $a = \dfrac{2s}{t^2}$ **7.** $w = \dfrac{P - 2l}{2}$ **9.** $E = IR$ **11.** $t = \dfrac{s}{v}$

13. $p = \dfrac{A}{1 + rt}$ **15.** $l = \dfrac{2S - na}{n}$ **17.** $b_2 = \dfrac{2A - b_1 h}{h}$ **19.** $R_1 = \dfrac{RR_2}{R_2 - R}$ **21.** $I = \sqrt{\dfrac{P}{R}}$

23. $C = \dfrac{5F - 160}{9}$ **25.** $d = \dfrac{bc}{a}$ **27.** $l = \dfrac{g}{4\pi^2 f^2}$ **29.** $C = \dfrac{ny}{n - x}$ **31.** $h = \dfrac{S - 2\pi r^2}{2\pi r}$

33. $r = \dfrac{S - a}{S}$

Exercises 1.9 (page 50)

1. (a) $3i$ (c) $i\sqrt{3}$ (e) $10i$ (g) $3i\sqrt{5}$ (i) $9i\sqrt{3}$ **2.** (a) $\dfrac{-1 \pm i\sqrt{3}}{2}$ (c) $\dfrac{3 \pm i\sqrt{19}}{2}$
(e) $\dfrac{-3 \pm 3i\sqrt{3}}{2}$ (g) $\dfrac{1 \pm i\sqrt{29}}{3}$ (i) $\pm 2i\sqrt{2}$ (k) $1 \pm 2i\sqrt{2}$ **3.** (a) real and unequal
(c) imaginary and unequal (e) real and equal (g) real and unequal
(i) real and unequal (k) imaginary and unequal (m) real and unequal
(o) real and equal **4.** (a) $7 + 4i$ (c) $13 - 3i$ (e) $14 - 3i$ (g) $-9 + 19i$
(i) $63 + 16i$ (k) $-2i$ (m) $1 - i$ (o) $-\frac{1}{2} + \frac{1}{2}i$ (q) $\frac{1}{5} + \frac{3}{5}i$
5. $\dfrac{a + bi}{c + di} = \dfrac{a + bi}{c + di} \cdot \dfrac{c - di}{c - di} = \dfrac{ac - adi + bci + bd}{c^2 + d^2} = \dfrac{ac + bd}{c^2 + d^2} + \dfrac{bc - ad}{c^2 + d^2}i$ **6.** (a) $-i$
(c) 1 (e) $-3i$

Review Exercises for Chapter 1 (page 51)

1. (a) $\frac{8}{5}$ (c) 16 (e) $\pm\sqrt{3}$ (g) 0, 2 (i) -40 (k) $\frac{21}{8}$ (m) $(1 \pm 3i\sqrt{3})/2$ (o) $(1 \pm \sqrt{13})/2$
(q) $\pm i\sqrt{5}$ **2.** (a) $(x - 13)(x - 1)$ (c) cannot be factored using real numbers
(e) $(x + 2)(x^2 - 2x + 4)$ (g) $x(x + 1)(x - 1)$ (i) $7(2x - 1)$ (k) $6(x - 2)(x + 1)$
(m) $(x^2 + 4)(x + 2)(x - 2)$ (o) $x^{2n}(x + 1)$ (q) $\dfrac{2(4x + 11)}{(x + 3)^{1/2}}$
3. (a) $m^4 + 4m^3 n + 6m^2 n^2 + 4mn^3 + n^4$ (c) $x^5 - 10x^4 + 40x^3 - 80x^2 + 80x - 32$
4. (a) $\dfrac{cm + abn}{a^2 bc^2}$ (c) $\dfrac{x - 9}{2x(x + y)}$ (e) $\dfrac{x + 1}{2x}$ (g) $\dfrac{9xy - 3y}{5x + xy}$ (i) $\dfrac{1}{xy^2 + x^2 y}$ **5.** (a) $\dfrac{1}{243a^{45}}$
(c) $-12x^6 y^{12}$ (e) $2\sqrt{30}$ (g) $2\sqrt{5}$ (i) $5|n|$ **6.** (a) $x = \dfrac{1 - y}{y}$ (c) $x = \dfrac{2m - 1}{5}$
(e) $x = \dfrac{a - t}{3 + 2a}$

Exercises 2.2 (page 57)

1. (a) 5   (c) $\sqrt{29}$ (e) $3\sqrt{5}$ (g) $\sqrt{17}$ (i) $\sqrt{137}$ (k) $6\sqrt{5}$ **2.** (a) $(2, 7)$ (c) $(2, 4)$
(e) $(1, 3)$ (g) $\left(-4, \frac{7}{2}\right)$ (i) $\left(-\frac{13}{2}, \frac{7}{2}\right)$ **3.** $2\sqrt{13}$

Exercises 2.3 (page 70)

1. (a) $4x + 3y + 5 = 0$ (c) $x - 7y - 2 = 0$ (e) $x + 9y - 4 = 0$
(g) $3x - 1 = 0$ (i) $6x - y - 4 = 0$ **2.** (a) $\frac{1}{2}$ (c) 3   (e) 5   (g) -3 (i) $-\frac{5}{13}$
(k) undefined   **3.** (a) $y = 2x + 1$ (c) $y = 5x - 8$ (e) $y = -3x + 7$
(g) $y = -6x - 5$ (i) $y = \frac{1}{2}x - 1$ (k) $y = -\frac{1}{3}x - 4$ **4.** (a) $y = 3x + 3$
(c) $y = -2x + 6$ (e) $y = x + 6$ (g) $y = \frac{2}{3}x$ (i) $y = -\frac{1}{2}x - \frac{5}{2}$
6. $y = 0$; the slope is 0.   **8.** (a) $y = 2x - 7$ (c) $y = -x - 1$
(e) $y = -4x + 16$ (g) $y = \frac{1}{2}x + 4$ (i) $3x + 2y = 26$ **9.** (a) 2, $(0, -1)$
(c) 1, $(0, 2)$ (e) 3, $(0, 3)$ (g) 2, $(0, -6)$ (i) $\frac{1}{3}, (0, \frac{4}{3})$ (k) 2, $(0, -3)$ (m) $\frac{2}{3}, (0, -6)$
(o) $-\frac{2}{3}, (0, \frac{1}{3})$

10.   (a)    (c)    (e)

(g) 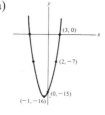   (i) 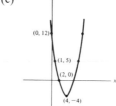   (k)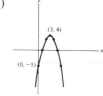

13. $y = \frac{1}{2}x - \frac{5}{2}$ **14.** (a) $y = -\frac{1}{2}x + \frac{15}{2}$ (c) $y = -x + 6$ (e) $y = 3x + 13$
15. The x intercept is obtained by letting $y = 0$. When 0 is used for y in the given equation, the result is $x/a = 1$, or $x = a$. This yields the point $(a, 0)$ as the x intercept. The y intercept is obtained in a similar manner.

Exercises 2.4 (page 79)

1.   (a)    (c)    (e)

(g)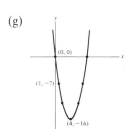

(i)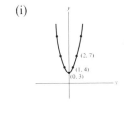

(k)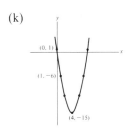

(m)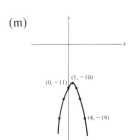

(o)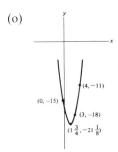

(q)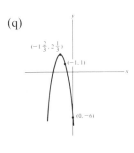

(s)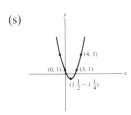

2. (a) $(-4, 0), (5, 0)$ (c) $(-\frac{7}{2}, 0), (2, 0)$ (e) none   (g) $((-3+\sqrt{29})/2, 0)$, $((-3 - \sqrt{29})/2, 0)$ (i) $(-\frac{1}{4}, 0), (6, 0)$ **3.** \$5135, from 50 units   **5.** 20 seconds; 6550 feet   **7.** 40,000 square meters

Exercises 2.5 (page 82)

1. (a) true   (c) false   (e) false   (g) true   (i) false   **2.** (a) $\{x \mid x \text{ real}, x > 13\}$
(c) $\{x \mid x \text{ real}, x \geq 0\}$ (e) $\{x \mid x \text{ real}, -50 < x < 400, x \neq 0\}$ (g) $\{x \mid x \text{ real}, -7 \leq x < 2\}$
(i) $\{x \mid x \text{ real}, x > 0\}$ (k) $\{x \mid x \text{ real}, |x| > 17\}$ (m) $\{x \mid x \text{ real}, 7 \leq |x| \leq 100\}$
3. (a) $\{x \mid x \text{ odd}, x > 10\}$; $\{11, 13, 15, 17, 19, \ldots\}$
(c) $\{x \mid x \text{ even}, 4 \leq x \leq 300\}$; $\{4, 6, 8, 10, \ldots, 300\}$
(e) $\{x \mid x \text{ integer}, x > 0\}$; $\{1, 2, 3, 4, 5, 6, 7, 8, \ldots\}$
(g) $\{x \mid x \text{ integer}, x < 0\}$; $\{\ldots, -8, -7, -6, -5, -4, -3, -2, -1\}$
(i) $\{x \mid x \text{ even}, x > 0\}$; $\{2, 4, 6, 8, \ldots\}$
4. (a) $[-2, 6)$
(c) $(-\infty, -7]$
(e) $[-2, \infty)$
(g) $[-9, -4]$
(i) $(5, 6)$

5. (a) $\{x \mid 4 \le x \le 10\}$

(c) $\{x \mid -2 < x < 6\}$

(e) $\{x \mid 5 < x \le 8\}$

(g) $\{x \mid x > 2\}$

(i) $\{x \mid x < 5\}$

(k) $\{x \mid x \le 10\}$

6. (a) closed (b) open (c) open (d) closed (e) half open (f) half open

Exercises 2.6 (page 91)

1. (a) $x < 5$ (c) $x < \frac{3}{2}$ (e) $x \le -\frac{4}{3}$ (g) $x \ge 6$ (i) $x \ge -\frac{13}{7}$ (k) $x < -1$ (m) $x < \frac{2}{3}$
(o) $x < \frac{1}{4}$ **2.** (a) $x \ge 5$ or $x \le -2$ (c) $1 < x < 3$ (e) $x > -3$ or $x < -4$ (g) $0 \le x \le 3$
(i) $x > 1$ or $x < -1$ (k) $-\sqrt{7} < x < \sqrt{7}$ (m) $-5 < x < 3$ (o) $x < 4$ or $x > 9$
(q) $-\frac{1}{2} < x < 3$ (s) $x < -1$ or $x > \frac{2}{3}$ **3.** (a) $x < 6$ or $x > \frac{55}{8}$ (c) $\frac{13}{2} < x < 7$
(e) $x < -3$ or $2 < x < 4$ (g) $-3 < x \le 4$ or $x \ge 5$ (i) $-4 < x < 3$ (k) $4 < x < 6$
4. (a) $-6 < x < 6$ (c) $-4 < n < 4$ (e) $-\frac{13}{7} < x < \frac{13}{7}$ (g) $-8 < m < 4$ (i) $-8 \le x \le 16$
(k) $-5 < x < \frac{5}{3}$ (m) $-\frac{8}{7} \le z \le \frac{16}{7}$ (o) $-\frac{16}{9} < x < \frac{32}{9}$ (q) $6 - a < x < 6 + a$
5. (a) $x > 7$ or $x < -7$ (c) $w > 7, w < -7$ (e) $x > 54, x < -36$ (g) $x > \frac{23}{2}, x < -\frac{9}{2}$
(i) $x > \frac{11}{5}, x < -\frac{29}{5}$ **6.** (a) no solution (c) true for all real numbers x (e) $x = -5$ only
(g) $x > 2$ (i) $x < 7, x \ne 0$ (k) true for all real numbers x (m) $x > 9$

Review Exercises for Chapter 2 (page 93)

1. $5\sqrt{5}$ **3.** (a) $-\frac{1}{2}$ (c) $\frac{7}{3}$ **4.** (a) $y = -\frac{1}{6}x + \frac{23}{6}$ (c) $y = -2x + 17$ (e) $y = \frac{1}{3}x - \frac{11}{3}$

5.

6. (a)

(c)

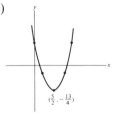

$(\frac{5}{2}, -\frac{13}{4})$

7. (a) $x \le \frac{15}{17}$ (c) $x < -5, x > 2$ (e) $x > \frac{19}{5}, x < \frac{13}{5}$ **8.** (a) -16 **9.** (a) -24

Exercises 3.2 (page 107)

1. (a) function (c) function (e) function (g) not a function (i) not a function
2. (a) all the reals (c) all the reals (e) $x \ge 0$ (g) $x \ge -\frac{2}{3}$ (i) all the reals (k) $x \ne 0$
(m) $x \ne 5$ (o) $x \ne \pm 3$ (q) $x \ge 8$ (s) $x \ge 0, x \ne 1$ (u) $x \ne 3, 4$ **3.** (a) $0 \le x \le 50$
(c) $x \ge -10$ (e) $0 \le x < 9$ (g) $0 \le x < 8$ (i) $1 \le x \le 8, 11 \le x \le 15$ **4.** (a) $x > 0$
(c) $x \ge 0$ (e) $n = 3, 4, 5, 6, \ldots$ **5.** (a) $D: x \ge 3; R: y \ge 0$ (c) $D:$ all the reals; $R: y \ge 2$
(e) $D: x \le 0; R:$ all the reals (g) $D: -3 \le x \le 3; R: -3 \le y \le 3$
(i) $D: -2 \le x \le 2; R: -6 \le y \le 6$ **6.** (a) $x < -2, x \ge 5$ (c) $x \le -7, x \ge 2$ (e) $x > -1$
7. (a) $D:$ all the reals; $R:$ all the reals (c) $D: x \ne 0; R: y \ne 0$ (e) $D: x \ge 0; R: y \le 0$
(g) $D:$ all the reals; $R:$ all the reals (i) $D: x \ge 0; R:$ all the reals (k) $D: x \ne 4; R: y \ne -1$
(m) $D: x \ne -1; R: y \ne 1$ (o) $D: x \le 0; R: y \ge 0$ (q) $D:$ all the reals; $R:$ all the reals
(s) $D: x \ge 0; R: y \ge 0$ (u) $D: x \ge 0; R: y \ge 1$ (w) $D: x \ge 0; R: y \le 5$

8. (a) $D: -4 \leq x \leq 4; R: -4 \leq y \leq 4$ (c) $D: x \leq -4, x \geq 4; R$: all the reals
(e) $D: x \geq 1, x \leq -1$ $R: y \leq 0$ (g) D: all the reals; $R: 0 < y \leq \frac{2}{3}$
(i) $D: x \leq -8, x > 0; R: y \neq \pm\sqrt{2}$ (k) $D: x \neq -1, 0; R: y \leq -16, y > 0$
(m) $D: x < -2, x = 0, x > 2; R: y < -3, y = 0, y > 3$
(o) $D: -7\sqrt{3}/6 \leq x \leq 7\sqrt{3}/6; R$: all the reals (q) $D: x \neq 0; R: y \neq 0$
(s) D: all the reals; $R: y \geq -9/4$

Exercises 3.3 (page 114)

1. (a) -2 (b) 1 (c) -5 (d) -20 (e) $3a - 5$ (f) $-\frac{7}{2}$ (g) $-\frac{13}{2}$ (h) $9m - 5$ (i) $3x - 2$
(j) $3x - 20$ **2.** (a) 19 (c) 179 (e) -8 (g) $t^2 + 8t - 1$ (i) $-47/16$ **3.** (a) $2 - \sqrt{2}$
(c) $-6 + 8\sqrt{7}$ (e) 528 **4.** (a) $7x + 7h + 1$ (c) $x^2 + 2xh + h^2 + 3x + 3h - 4$
(e) $x^3 + 3x^2h + 3xh^2 + h^3$ (g) $x^5 + 5x^4h + 10x^3h^2 + 10x^2h^3 + 5xh^4 + h^5$ **5.** (a) 1
(c) $2x + 3 + h$ (e) $6x + 5 + 3h$ (g) $3x^2 + 3xh + h^2$ (i) $\dfrac{-1}{x(x + h)}$ (k) $\dfrac{-1}{2x(x + h)}$ (m) 0
6. (a) 1 (c) $x + 5$ (e) $x^2 + 4x + 16$ **7.** (a) $x \neq -2$ (c) $x \geq 0$ (e) all the reals
(g) $x \neq \pm 3$ (i) $x \leq 0$ **8.** (a) $(f + g)(x) = x + 3$, D: all the reals; $(f - g)(x) = x - 3$,
D: all the reals; $(f \cdot g)(x) = 3x$, D: all the reals; $(f \div g)(x) = x/3$, D: all the reals
(c) $(f + g)(x) = x^2 + x + 11$, D: all the reals; $(f - g)(x) = -x^2 + x - 7$, D: all the reals;
$(f \cdot g)(x) = x^3 + 2x^2 + 9x + 18$, D: all the reals; $(f \div g)(x) = \dfrac{x + 2}{x^2 + 9}$, D: all the reals
(e) $(f + g)(x) = \sqrt{x} + \sqrt[3]{x}$, $D: x \geq 0$; $(f - g)(x) = \sqrt{x} - \sqrt[3]{x}$, $D: x \geq 0$; $(f \cdot g)(x) = x^{5/6}$,
$D: x \geq 0$; $(f \div g)(x) = x^{1/6}$, $D: x > 0$ (g) $(f + g)(x) = \dfrac{x^2 - 9x + 21}{(x - 3)\sqrt{x}}$, $D: x > 0, x \neq 3$;
$(f - g)(x) = \dfrac{-x^2 + 11x - 21}{(x - 3)\sqrt{x}}$, $D: x > 0, x \neq 3$; $(f \cdot g)(x) = \dfrac{x - 7}{x - 3}$, $D: x > 0, x \neq 3$;
$(f \div g)(x) = \dfrac{x}{x^2 - 10x + 21}$, $D: x > 0, x \neq 3, 7$ **9.** (a) 3 (b) $F(x) = 3x$ (c) 12 lb
(d) 21 lb (e) 27 in.

Exercises 3.4 (page 124)

1. (a)

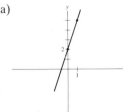

(c)

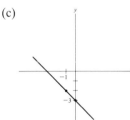

(e)

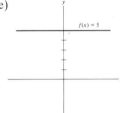

(g)

2. (a)

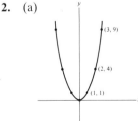

(c)

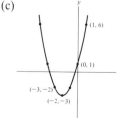

(e)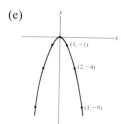

(g)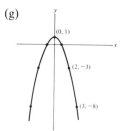

(i)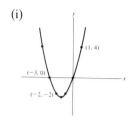

(k)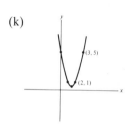

3. (a) $-\frac{17}{3}$ (c) $\frac{1}{3}$ (e) none   (g) $-4, 4$ (i) none   (k) $0, 5$ (m) $0, 1, -5$ (o) 6
(q) $-2, 2$ (s) 7   (u) $-1/7$ (w) $0, \frac{1}{2}$ (y) $0, 1/3$

4 (a)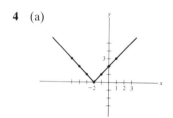

D: all the reals; *R:* $y \geq 0$

(c)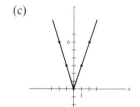

D: all the reals; *R:* $y \geq 0$

(e)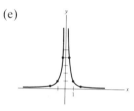

D: $x \neq 0$; *R:* $y > 0$
asymptotes: $x = 0, y = 0$

(g)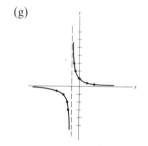

D: $x \neq -1$; *R:* $y \neq 0$;
asymptotes: $x = -1, y = 0$

(i)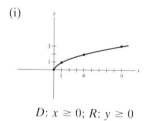

D: $x \geq 0$; *R:* $y \geq 0$

(k)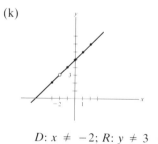

D: $x \neq -2$; *R:* $y \neq 3$

(m)

(o)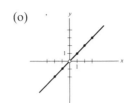

(q)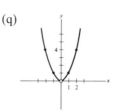

(s)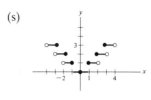

D: $x \ne 1$; R: $y \ne -3$ D: $x \ne 0$; R: $y \ne 0$ D: $x \ne 0$; R: $y > 0$

D: all the reals;
R: all the whole numbers
—that is, all the
nonnegative integers

5. (a)

(c)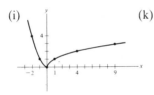

(e)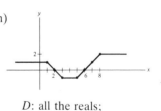

D: all the reals;
R: all the whole numbers

D: $x \ge -3$; R: $-1 \le y \le 2$ D: all the reals; R: $y \le 0$

(g)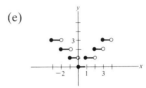

(i)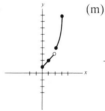

(k)

(m)

D: $x \le 4$
R: $0 \le y \le 3$, $y = 4$

D: all the reals;
R: $y \ge 0$

D: $0 \le x \le 3$;
R: $1 \le y < 3$, $4 \le y \le 9$

D: all the reals;
R: $-1 \le x \le 2$

Exercises 3.5 (page 128)

1. (a) $(f \circ g)(x) = x^2 + 6x + 9$; $(g \circ f)(x) = x^2 + 3$ (c) $(f \circ g)(x) = 1/x^2$; $(g \circ f)(x) = 1/x^2$
(e) $(f \circ g)(x) = \dfrac{2 - x}{3 - x}$; $(g \circ f)(x) = \dfrac{x + 2}{x + 1}$ (g) $(f \circ g)(x) = [\![x^2 + 1]\!]$; $(g \circ f)(x) = [\![x + 1]\!]^2$
(i) $(f \circ g)(x) = \dfrac{x^2 - 3}{x^2 + 2}$; $(g \circ f)(x) = \dfrac{-5(x + 1)^2}{3x^2 + 6x + 2}$ **2.** (a) 48   (c) 10   (e) 3   (g) -1
(i) $7^{2/3} + 1$ (k) $\sqrt[3]{6}$
3. (a) $9x^2 - 12x + 11$ (c) $3x^2 + 6x + 22$ (e) $9x^2 - 30x + 32$ (g) $9x^4 - 12x^2 + 11$
4. (a) $f \circ g$, where $f(x) = x^5$ and $g(x) = 9x + 1$
(c) $f \circ g$ where $f(x) = x^{2/3}$ and $g(x) = x^2 + 3$ (e) $f \circ g$, where $f(x) = \sqrt{x}$ and $g(x) = 5x^2 + 9$
5. (a) $g(x) = \sqrt[3]{x} - 1$ (b) $g(x) = \sqrt[3]{x - 1}$ **6.** (a) $256x^2 + 16x - 2$ (b) $16x^2 + 48x - 8$

Exercises 3.6 (page 135)

1. (a) $\{(3, 0), (4, 1), (8, 2), (6, -3)\}$; function   (c) $\{(2, 3), (-8, 4), (-2, 6), (2, 10)\}$; not a function
(e) $y = \dfrac{x - 2}{9}$; function   (g) $y = \pm\sqrt{x}$; not a function   (i) $y = \sqrt[3]{x}$; function

(k) $y = \dfrac{5}{3x - 1}$; function

(m) $y = \pm\sqrt{25 - x^2}$; not a function   (o) $y = \dfrac{-1 \pm \sqrt{1 + 16x}}{8}$; not a function

(q) $y = \dfrac{-3 \pm \sqrt{4x - 11}}{2}$; not a function   (s) $y = \dfrac{7 \pm \sqrt{5 + 4x}}{2}$; not a function

2. (a) $f^{-1}(x) = \dfrac{x + 4}{7}$ (c) $f^{-1}(x) = \sqrt[3]{x - 1}$ (e) $f^{-1}(x) = \dfrac{9 - 2x}{x}$

(g) $f^{-1}(x) = \dfrac{6x + 3}{x - 1}$ (i) $f^{-1}(x) = \dfrac{5}{3x - 1}$ (j) $f^{-1}(x) = \dfrac{2x}{x - 7}$

4. (a)
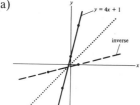

(c)
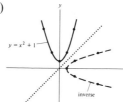

(e)
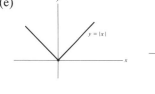

(g)
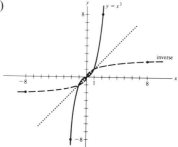

(i)
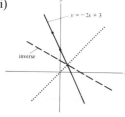

(k)
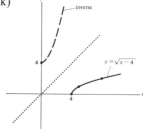

(m)

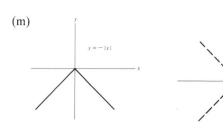

5. (a) no (b) no (c) yes (d) no (e) yes (f) no (g) yes

Exercises 3.7 (page 140)

1. (a)

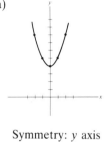

Symmetry: *y* axis

(c)

Symmetry: origin

(e)

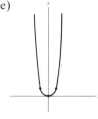

Symmetry: *y* axis

(g)

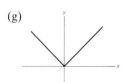

Symmetry: *y* axis

(i)

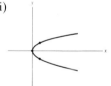

Symmetry: *x* axis

(k)

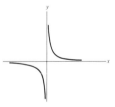

Symmetry: origin

(m)

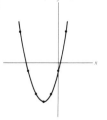

(o)

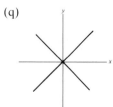

(q)

Symmetry:
x axis, *y* axis,
and origin

2. (a) symmetric with respect to x axis, y axis, and origin   (c) symmetric with respect to x axis, y axis, and origin   (e) symmetric with respect to x axis, y axis, and origin   (g) symmetric with respect to the origin   (i) no symmetry   (k) symmetric with respect to the y axis   (m) symmetric with respect to the origin   **3.** (a) odd   (c) odd   (e) neither   (g) neither   (i) even   (k) odd   **5.** (a) yes (b) no

Exercises 3.8 (page 143)

1. (a)

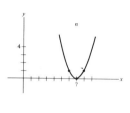
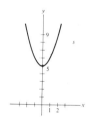

(c)

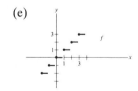
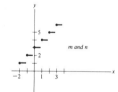
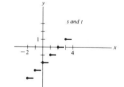

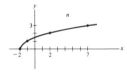
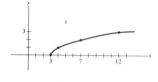
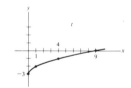

(e)

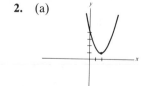
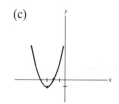

2. (a)   (c)   (e)   (g)

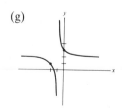

Exercises 3.9 (page 148)

1. (a)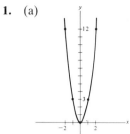

(c)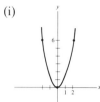

(e)

(g)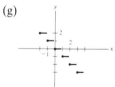

(i)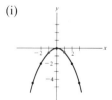

(k)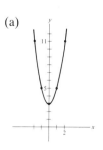

2. (a)

(c)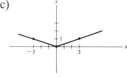

(e)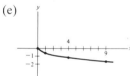

(g)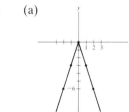

(i)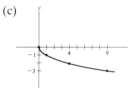

3. (a)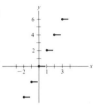

(c)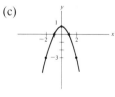

(e)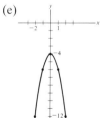

(g)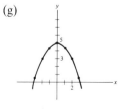

(i)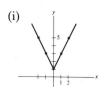

(k)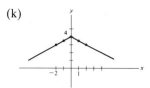

(m)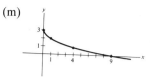

(o)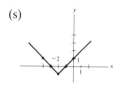

(q)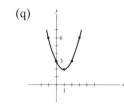

(s)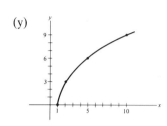

(u)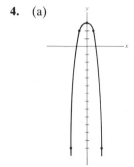

(w)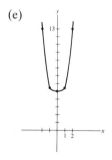

(y)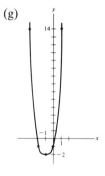

4. (a)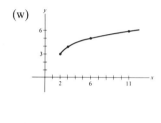

(c)

(e)

(g)

(i)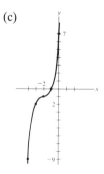

Review Exercises for Chapter 3 (page 149)

1. (a) $x \neq -5$ (c) $x > 0$ (e) $x \geq -\frac{1}{2}, x \neq 9$ **2.** (a) D: all the reals; R: all the reals (c) D: $-3 \leq x \leq 3$; R: $-3 \leq y \leq 3$ (e) D: $0 < x \leq \frac{5}{7}$; R: all the reals **3.** (a) $f(1) = 3, f(-2) = 15,$ $f\left(\frac{2}{3}\right) = \frac{31}{9}, f(x + h) = x^2 + 2xh + h^2 - 3x - 3h + 5$

5. (a)

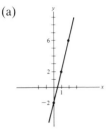

D: all the reals; R: all the reals

(c)

D: all the reals; R: all the reals

(e)

D: $x \geq -1$; R: $y \geq 0$

(g)

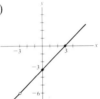

D: $x \neq -3$; R: $y \neq -6$

6. (a) -2 and 5 **7.** (a) $(f \circ g)(x) = 25x^2 + 45x + 3; (g \circ f)(x) = 5x^2 + 45x + 15$

8. (a) $y = \dfrac{x + 2}{3}$ (c) $y = \dfrac{x \pm \sqrt{x^2 + 4x}}{2}$

9. (a)

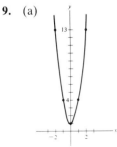

(c)

(e)

(g) 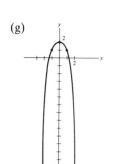　　(i)

Exercises 4.2 (page 166)

1. (a) $r = \dfrac{C}{2\pi}$ (b) $d = \dfrac{C}{\pi}$ (c) $V = 2\pi r^3$ (d) $V = \dfrac{\pi h^3}{108}$ (e) $V = \dfrac{\pi d^3}{6}$ (f) $V = \dfrac{4\pi h^3}{3}$ (g) $V = \dfrac{\pi r^3}{2}$

(h) $V = \dfrac{\pi d^3}{8}$ **2.** (a) $\sqrt{13}$ (c) $\frac{21}{2}$ (e) $\frac{75}{7}$ (g) $\frac{15}{2}$ **3.** (a) $100 - x$ (b) $(x)(100 - x)$

5. $S = 4xy + 2x^2$ **7.** 105 cm **9.** $w = 100 - x$ **11.** (a) $S = \pi l \sqrt{l^2 - 49}$
(b) $V = \frac{1}{3}\pi r^2 \sqrt{100 - r^2}$ **12.** (a) $A = 5x - x^2$ **13.** $\frac{7}{2}\sqrt{x^2 - 49}$

14. $A(t) = \frac{1}{2}t\sqrt{100 - t^2}$ **15.** $\frac{486}{17}$ **17.** (a) $l = 2y$ (b) $w = 4 - x$ (c) $A = 8y - \dfrac{y^3}{2}$

19. $\sqrt{29}$ **21.** $P(x) = 2x + \dfrac{50}{x}$ **23.** $\sqrt{x^2 + 4} + 8 - x$ **25.** $\dfrac{C^2}{4\pi}$

26. (a) x^2 (b) $x^2 + 2xh + h^2$ (c) $2xh + h^2$ **27.** $A = 2y\sqrt{49 - y^2}$ **29.** $S = 2x^2 + \dfrac{4000}{x}$

30. $S = 2\pi r^2 + \dfrac{100}{r}$ **31.** $A = (14 - x)\sqrt{14x - x^2}$ **33.** $\frac{20}{3}$ ft **35.** (a) $h^2/4 + r^2 = 49$

(b) $V = \pi h(196 - h^2)/4$ (c) $V = 2\pi r^2\sqrt{49 - r^2}$ **37.** $V(x) = 1200x - 140x^2 + 4x^3$

39. $A(x) = 158 - 4x - \dfrac{300}{x}$ **40.** (a) $\frac{25}{3}$ (b) $\frac{20}{3}$ **41.** (a) $y = \dfrac{x^2}{7}$ (b) $y = \dfrac{x^2 + 49}{7}$

(c) $y = \dfrac{x^2}{7}$ (d) $y = \dfrac{7 \pm \sqrt{49 - 4x^2}}{2}$ **43.** (a) $r = \dfrac{h}{3}$ (b) $\dfrac{27\pi}{8}$ (c) $\dfrac{9}{\sqrt[3]{2}}$ (d) $\dfrac{3}{\sqrt[3]{2}}$

45. $A = \dfrac{280x - 7x^2}{4}$

Exercises 4.3 (page 181)

1. (a) \$52 (c) \$444 (e) \$68 **2.** (a) $C(x) = 200x + x^2$; $R(x) = 300x$; $P(x) = 100x - x^2$
(c) $C(x) = x - x^3$; $R(x) = 7x^2$; $P(x) = x^3 + 7x^2 - x$ (e) $C(x) = 7x^2 - 20x$; $R(x) = 3x + 50$;
$P(x) = 50 + 23x - 7x^2$ **3.** $P(3) = 8$, a *profit* of \$8, $P(10) = -160$, a *loss* of \$160
4. (a) 3 (c) 25 **5.** (a) 200 (b) demanded: 150 (approx.); supplied: 300 (approx.); surplus
(c) demanded: 300 (approx.); supplied: 100 (approx.); shortage **7.** (a) \$130 (b) \$128
(c) \$2 (d) \$2 **9.** (a) \$350 (c) \$5.50

Exercises 4.4 (page 186)

1. (a) 768 feet (b) after 24 seconds (c) -416 ft/sec (d) 352 ft/sec (e) after 11 seconds
(f) 2704 feet (g) $v(7) = +128$ ft/sec and $v(15) = -128$ ft/sec. Both speeds are the same, but the
directions are different. The $+$ indicates that the rocket is on its way up; the $-$ indicates that the

rocket is on its way down. (h) 22   **3.** (a) -8 ft/sec (b) 224 feet (c) after $3\frac{1}{2}$ seconds
(d) 120 ft/sec   **5.** (a) 106 ft/sec (b) moon: 1060 feet; earth: 175.6 feet (c) moon: 40 seconds;
earth: 6.6 seconds

Exercises 5.1 (page 190)

1. (a) polynomial (b) polynomial (c) polynomial (d) not a polynomial (e) not a polynomial
(f) not a polynomial (g) polynomial (h) polynomial   **2.** (a) degree 4, leading coefficient 3
(b) degree 2, leading coefficient 1 (c) degree 3, leading coefficient -2
(d) degree 3, leading coefficient -1 (e) degree 3, leading coefficient 10   **3.** (a) $\frac{2}{3}$ (c) 0
(e) $-9, 2$ (g) $(7 \pm \sqrt{41})/2$ (i) $0, 3, 4$ (k) $0, (-7 \pm \sqrt{37})/2$ (m) $0, (-5 \pm \sqrt{33})/4$

Exercises 5.2 (page 197)

1. (a) $x^2 + 5x + 2$ (c) $x^2 + 5x + 8, R = 13$ (e) $x^2 - 5, R = -24$ (g) $2x^3 + 4x^2 + 5x + 3,$
$R = 9$ (i) $x^3 - 1$ (k) $x^2 + x + 1$ (m) $x^4 + 2x^3 + 4x^2 + 8x + 16$
2. (a) $(x - 2)(x - 3)(x + 1)$ (c) $(x - 1)(x + 3)(x + 2)$ (e) $(x + 3)(x + 3)(x + 5)$
(g) $(x + 4)(2x + 1)(x + 5)$ (i) $(x + 4)(3x + 5)(x - 2)$ **3.** (a) $1, \pm 3$ (c) $7, \pm 1$
(e) $-2, 1 \pm i\sqrt{3}$ (g) $-5, -1 \pm 2i$ (i) $1, 4, \pm i\sqrt{3}$ (k) $-\frac{1}{4}, (3 \pm \sqrt{5})/2$ (m) $\pm 2, \pm 2i$
(o) $\pm\frac{1}{2}, (-1 \pm i\sqrt{3})/2$ (q) $-2, -1, 1, 3$ **4.** (a) $2, 3, -1$ (c) $-2, (-5 \pm \sqrt{13})/2$
(e) $\frac{3}{2}, 2, 2$ **5.** (a) The only possible rational zeros are $-2, -1, 1,$ and $2; f(-2) = -6 \neq 0;$
$f(-1) = 1 \neq 0; f(1) = 3 \neq 0; f(2) = 10 \neq 0.$ None of the four numbers is a zero of f;
so we conclude that f has no rational zeros.   **6.** (a) $-2, 0, 1, 3$ (c) $0, 0, -2, \pm i$
7. (a) $-3, (3 \pm 3i\sqrt{3})/2$

Exercises 5.3 (page 203)

1. (a) $3x^2 + 3x + 10, R = 22$ (c) $-x^2 + 6x - 2, R = 0$ (e) $2x^3 - x^2 + x - 2, R = -2$
(g) $-x^2 + 7x - 5, R = 0$ (i) $-x^2 - 9x + 4, R = 0$ **2.** (a) $-3, -1, 2$ (c) $2, (3 \pm \sqrt{5})/2$
(e) $-\frac{3}{2}, -1, 2$ (g) $\pm 3, \pm\sqrt{7}$ (i) $\frac{5}{2}, -1, 2, -3$ **3.** (a) -1 (c) 1294 (e) $-\frac{3}{2}$ (g) -12

Exercises 5.4 (page 209)

1. (a)

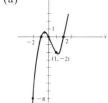

(c)

(e)

(g)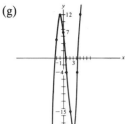

(i)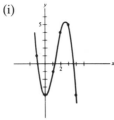

(k)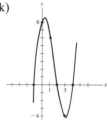

(m)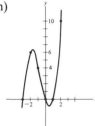

(o)

(q)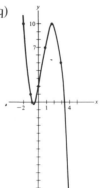

(s)

2. (a) yes (c) yes (e) cannot tell

Exercises 5.5 (page 219)

1. (a) $x \neq \frac{2}{3}$ (c) all the reals (e) $x \neq 1, \frac{5}{2}$ (g) $x \neq 2$ (i) $x \neq -1, 2, 4$ **2.** (a) -5
(c) no real zeros (e) 3 (g) $\pm 3/\sqrt{5}$ (i) 1 **3.** (a) $x + 1 - \dfrac{2x - 7}{x^2 + 3x + 2}$ (c) $1 + \dfrac{5x - 10}{x^2 + x + 1}$
(e) $x + 5 + \dfrac{2x - 9}{x^2 + 1}$ (g) $x^3 - x^2 + x - 1 - \dfrac{7}{x + 1}$ (i) $x^3 + 4x + \dfrac{13x}{x^2 - 3}$ **4.** (a) $x = 5$
(c) $x = 4$ (e) $x = -2, 4$ (g) $x = \frac{3}{2}$ (i) $x = -3 + \sqrt{11}, x = -3 - \sqrt{11}$ **5.** (a) $y = \frac{5}{6}$
(c) none (e) $y = 10$ (g) $y = 0$ (i) none

6. (a)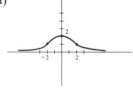

(c)

(e)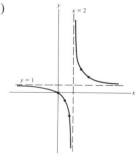

(g)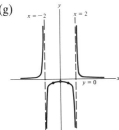

(i)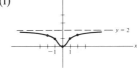

(k)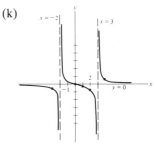

(m)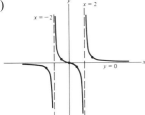

Review Exercises for Chapter 5 (page 221)

1. (a) $-1, 3, 4$ (c) $\pm 3, (-1 \pm i\sqrt{7})/4$ (e) $-2, (3 \pm \sqrt{5})/2$

2. (a)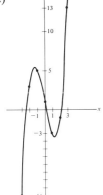

(c)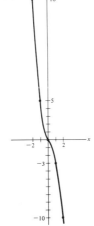

3. (a) zeros: 1; domain: $x \neq -4, 3$; vertical asymptotes: $x = -4, x = 3$; horizontal asymptote: $y = 0$ (c) zeros: -2; domain: $x \neq -3, 0, 2$; vertical asymptotes: $x = 0, x = -3$; no horizontal asymptotes

4. (a)

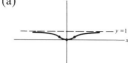

Exercises 6.2 (page 228)

1. (a)

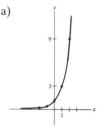

(c)

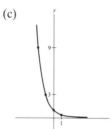

(e)

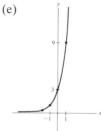

(g)

(i)

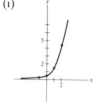

(k)

(m)

(o)

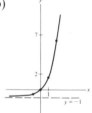

(q)

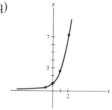

2. (a) 1   (b) e (c) 9   (d) e^3 (e) e (f) 9/2   (g) e^3 (h) $e/16$ (i) e^{n-4} (j) $2e^{2n+1}$
3. (a) 4   (c) -3 (e) 1   (g) $\frac{4}{7}$ (i) $\frac{1}{3}$ (k) $\frac{1}{2}$ (m) 1   (o) -2 (q) $\frac{5}{2}$ (s) -2 (u) 0, 2   (w) ± 1
5. Any function with negative base and variable exponent would not be defined for $x = \frac{1}{2}, \frac{1}{4}$, and so on, where even roots of negative numbers would be suggested. Furthermore, for some x the functional values would be positive and for others they would be negative—in a somewhat alternating manner.

Exercises 6.3 (page 235)

1. (a) $\log_3 81 = 4$ (c) $\log_{10} 1000 = 3$ (e) $\log_9 3 = \frac{1}{2}$ (g) $\log_4 \frac{1}{4} = -1$ (i) $\log_2 b = a$
(k) $\log_3(x + 1) = y$ **2.** (a) $10^2 = 100$ (c) $25^{1/2} = 5$ (e) $3^{-2} = \frac{1}{9}$ **3.** (a) 4   (c) 10
(e) $\frac{1}{3}$ (g) $\frac{3}{4}$ (i) -3 (k) 0   **4.** (a) $x = \log_3 7$ (c) $x = \log e$ (e) $x = \frac{1}{3}\log_2 17$

(g) $x = 1 + \log_5 16$ **5.** (a) 16 (c) $\frac{243}{4}$ (e) 49 (g) 64 (i) 4   **6.** (a) m (c) x^2 (e) $\frac{1}{2}$ (g) e

(i) $4e$ **7.** (a) $e^2/3$ (c) $e^4/2$ (e) $\pm e^4$ **8.** (a) $\ln 5$ (c) $\dfrac{1}{a} \ln \dfrac{1}{c}$ (e) $\dfrac{13 - e}{7}$ (g) $\dfrac{1}{t} \ln \left(\dfrac{a - b}{a_0} \right)$

(i) $\dfrac{1}{c} - \dfrac{1}{c} \ln \left(\dfrac{a - df - g}{b} \right)$

9. (a)

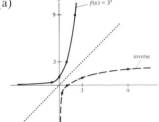

(c)

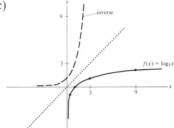

(e)

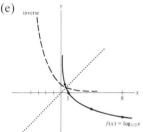

(g)

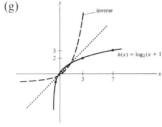

10. (a)

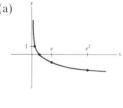

(c)

(e)

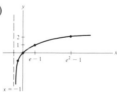

11. (a)

(c)

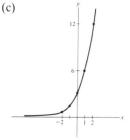

12. (a) 8 (b) 10 (c) 1 (d) 1 (e) 0 (f) 0 (g) $x + y$ (h) x^2
13. (a) 9 (b) 16 (c) 2 (d) 3 (e) 1 (f) 0   **14.** (a) $x < 0$
(c) $x > 1$ (e) $x > 2, x < -2$ (g) $x > 1$ **15.** (a) 4 (c) $\frac{1}{2}$ (e) $\frac{1}{3}$

Exercises 6.4 (page 242)

1. (a) 13 (c) 19.5 (e) 24 (g) 24.5 (i) -3.5 (k) 4 (m) 3 **2.** (a) $\log_t 35$ (b) $\log_b 750$
(c) $\log_b 576$ (d) $\log_a 3.5$ (e) $\log_t 120$ (f) $\log_b 30$ **3.** (a) $\log_b 7x$ (b) $\log_b x^3$ (c) $\log_b x^2$
(d) $\log_b(x - 1)$ **4.** (a) 2 (c) $(1 + \sqrt{5})/2$ (e) $\frac{11}{4}$
5. (a) $x = \log \frac{8}{3}$ (c) $x = \dfrac{\log c}{\log(ab)}$, or $x = \log_{ab} c$ (e) $x = \dfrac{1}{c}\log_b \dfrac{d}{a}$
6. (a) From $10^2 = \dfrac{I}{I_0}$ it follows that $I = 100I_0$. (b) 1000 times the intensity (c) 10 times
(d) The earthquake of magnitude 8 is 1000 times greater.
8. $\log_{10}(-1)$ is not defined; that is, $\log(-1)^2 \neq 2\log(-1)$. **10.** (a) $e^{t \ln 7}$ (c) $e^{2 \ln x}$

Exercises 6.5 (page 248)

1. (a) 1.5866 (c) 0.7324 (e) 4.1139 (g) 0.1761 (i) -2.1871 **2.** (a) 258 (c) 1420 (e) 50.3
(g) .0065 (i) .0186 **3.** (a) 3.7945 (c) 62.4 **4.** (a) 2.6895 (c) 1.4718 (e) 3.3647
(g) -1.7847 (i) -3.8265 **5.** (a) 75.33 (c) 11,620 (e) 276.0 (g) .1442 (i) 4.362

Exercises 6.6 (page 250)

1. (a) 1.5239 (c) 6.3026 (e) 9.2104 (g) 8.3826 (i) -0.6162 (k) -4.6357 **2.** (a) 1.0513
(c) 14.880 (e) 90.017

Exercises 6.7 (page 254)

1. $7459 **3.** 8.66 years **5.** $4445 **6.** .086 **7.** 12,214 **8.** about 5 hours
9. 2.22 grams **11.** 9.9% **13.** $1221 **14.** (a) $-.00012$ (b) 7636–7638 years
15. (a) 63.76 units/volume (b) 53.65 minutes **17.** (a) $50°$ (b) $-.04$ (c) $32°$ (d) $11°$

Exercises 6.8 (page 258)

1. (a) 2.67 (c) 2.27 (e) 3.26 (g) 3.07 (i) 1.20 **2.** (a) 2.58 (c) 1.89 (e) 4.42 (g) 4.96
3. $\log_b N = \dfrac{\log_B N}{\log_B b}$

Exercises 6.9 (page 260)

1. (a) 1.732 (c) 4.918 (e) 398.2 (g) 6.156 (i) 697.7 (k) 4.704 (m) 294.1 (o) 57.70 (q) 1079

Review Exercises for Chapter 6 (page 260)

1. (a)   (c)   (e)

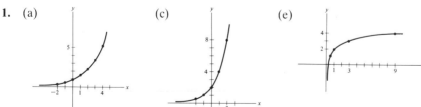

(g)

2. (a) 150 (c) -2 (e) e (g) 18   **3.** (a) 4520 (c) .2833
(e) 4.2326

4. (a) $\log_4 17$ (c) $\dfrac{1}{u} \ln\left(\dfrac{y-v}{w}\right)$ (e) $-1 + \sqrt{11}$ **5.** 1.8982   **7.** (a) $k \approx .03$
(b) 23.1 years

Exercises 7.2 (page 269)

1. (a) $(-1, 0)$ (b) $(0, -1)$ (c) $(-1, 0)$ (d) $\left(-\dfrac{1}{2}, \sqrt{3}/2\right)$ (e) $(-1, 0)$ (f) $(1, 0)$ (g) $(0, 1)$

(k) $(\sqrt{2}/2, -\sqrt{2}/2)$ (m) $(-\sqrt{3}/2, 1/2)$ **3.** $\dfrac{z}{2}\sqrt{3}$ **5.** (a) $2x + 5 + 5\sqrt{3}$ (b) $(2x - 5)\dfrac{5\sqrt{3}}{2}$

Exercises 7.3 (page 273)

1.

t	0	$\dfrac{\pi}{6}$	$\dfrac{\pi}{4}$	$\dfrac{\pi}{3}$	$\dfrac{\pi}{2}$	π	$\dfrac{3\pi}{2}$
$\cos t$	1	$\dfrac{\sqrt{3}}{2}$	$\dfrac{\sqrt{2}}{2}$	$\dfrac{1}{2}$	0	-1	0
$\sin t$	0	$\dfrac{1}{2}$	$\dfrac{\sqrt{2}}{2}$	$\dfrac{\sqrt{3}}{2}$	1	0	-1
$\tan t$	0	$\dfrac{1}{\sqrt{3}}$	1	$\sqrt{3}$	$-$*	0	$-$
$\cot t$	$-$	$\sqrt{3}$	1	$\dfrac{1}{\sqrt{3}}$	0	$-$	0
$\sec t$	1	$\dfrac{2}{\sqrt{3}}$	$\sqrt{2}$	2	$-$	-1	$-$
$\csc t$	$-$	2	$\sqrt{2}$	$\dfrac{2}{\sqrt{3}}$	1	$-$	-1

*Dash indicates undefined.

2.

	I	II	III	IV
$\cos t$	$+$	$-$	$-$	$+$
$\sin t$	$+$	$+$	$-$	$-$
$\tan t$	$+$	$-$	$+$	$-$
$\cot t$	$+$	$-$	$+$	$-$
$\sec t$	$+$	$-$	$-$	$+$
$\csc t$	$+$	$+$	$-$	$-$

3. (a) $\cos t = 0$; $\sin t = -1$; $\tan t$ is undefined; $\cot t = 0$; $\sec t$ is undefined; $\csc t = -1$
(c) $\cos t = -\frac{3}{4}$; $\sin t = \frac{\sqrt{7}}{4}$, $\tan t = -\frac{\sqrt{7}}{3}$; $\cot t = -\frac{3}{\sqrt{7}}$; $\sec t = -\frac{4}{3}$; $\csc t = \frac{4}{\sqrt{7}}$
(e) $\cos t = -\frac{1}{\sqrt{5}}$, $\sin t = \frac{2}{\sqrt{5}}$; $\tan t = -2$; $\cot t = -\frac{1}{2}$; $\sec t = -\sqrt{5}$; $\csc t = \frac{\sqrt{5}}{2}$

Exercises 7.4 (page 280)

3. (a) 0 (b) 4 (c) $\cos^2 t$ (d) $\cos^2 t$ (e) $\tan^2 t$ (g) 2 (i) $\csc x$

Exercises 7.5 (page 284)

1. (a) $\pi/5$ (c) $5\pi/12$ (e) $3\pi/4$ (g) $7\pi/6$ (i) $5\pi/3$ (k) $25\pi/9$ **2.** (a) 30° (c) 36° (e) 135°
(g) 540° (i) 480° (k) 405° **3.** (a) 229.2° (c) .12215 (e) 292.23° (g) .40135 (i) 5730°
(k) 1.425665 **5.** 45°

Exercises 7.6 (page 295)

1. (a) $\theta = 5$ (c) $\theta = 1$ (e) $s = 8\pi/5$ in. (g) $r = 20/\pi$ ft (i) $r = 1$ mm (k) $r = 54/\pi$ ft
2. (a) 9π cm² (c) $49\pi/6$ in.² (e) $27\pi/2$ ft² (g) $5\pi/4$ mm² **3.** $3\pi/2$ in.² **4.** $4\pi/27$
5. (a) .8290 (c) 19.0811 (e) .2924 (g) .1219 (i) 1.0457 (k) 2.5593 (m) .1763 (o) .0175
6. (a) 21° (c) 2° (e) 76°
7. $\sin x = 2/\sqrt{13}$; $\cos x = 3/\sqrt{13}$; $\tan x = \frac{2}{3}$; $\sin y = 3/\sqrt{13}$; $\cos y = 2/\sqrt{13}$; $\tan y = \frac{3}{2}$
9. (a) 1.4 (c) 9.8 (e) 4.5 **10.** (a) 37° (c) 55°
11. $\cot \theta = \text{adj./opp.}$; $\sec \theta = \text{hyp/adj.}$; $\csc \theta = \text{hyp/opp.}$ **13.** 59 ft **15.** 180 feet
17. (a) 10.4 feet (b) 12.6 feet (c) 13.1 feet **18.** (a) 595.9 feet (b) 777.8 feet

19. 5230 feet **20.** (a) $\cos t = \frac{2\sqrt{2}}{3}$; $\tan t = \frac{1}{2\sqrt{2}}$; $\cot t = 2\sqrt{2}$, $\sec t = \frac{3}{2\sqrt{2}}$; $\csc t = 3$
(c) $\sin u = \frac{1}{4}$; $\cos u = \frac{\sqrt{15}}{4}$; $\sec u = \frac{4}{\sqrt{15}}$; $\cot u = \sqrt{15}$; $\tan u = \frac{1}{\sqrt{15}}$
(e) $\cos t = \frac{\sqrt{5}}{3}$; $\tan t = \frac{2}{\sqrt{5}}$; $\cot t = \frac{\sqrt{5}}{2}$; $\sec t = \frac{3}{\sqrt{5}}$; $\csc t = \frac{3}{2}$ (g) $\cos \theta = \frac{1}{\sqrt{3}}$;
$\sin \theta = \frac{\sqrt{6}}{3}$; $\tan \theta = \sqrt{2}$, $\cot \theta = \frac{1}{\sqrt{2}}$; $\csc \theta = \frac{\sqrt{6}}{2}$ (i) $\cos t = \frac{\sqrt{47}}{7}$; $\sec t = \frac{7}{\sqrt{47}}$;
$\tan t = \frac{\sqrt{94}}{47}$; $\cot t = \frac{\sqrt{94}}{2}$; $\csc t = \frac{7}{\sqrt{2}}$

21. (a) $\cos t = \frac{\sqrt{9 - m^2}}{3}$; $\tan t = \frac{m}{\sqrt{9 - m^2}}$; $\csc t = \frac{3}{m}$; $\sec t = \frac{3}{\sqrt{9 - m^2}}$;
$\cot t = \frac{\sqrt{9 - m^2}}{m}$ (c) $\cot u = \frac{7}{2m}$; $\sin u = \frac{2m}{\sqrt{4m^2 + 49}}$; $\csc u = \frac{\sqrt{4m^2 + 49}}{2m}$;
$\cos u = \frac{7}{\sqrt{4m^2 + 49}}$; $\sec u = \frac{\sqrt{4m^2 + 49}}{7}$ (e) $\cos \theta = \frac{\sqrt{m^2 - 16}}{m}$; $\sin \theta = \frac{4}{m}$; $\csc \theta = \frac{m}{4}$;
$\cot \theta = \frac{\sqrt{m^2 - 16}}{4}$; $\tan \theta = \frac{4}{\sqrt{m^2 - 16}}$

Exercises 7.7 (page 307)

1. (a) .9320 (b) .8776 (c) .3429 (d) .0108 (e) .2341 (f) 1.500 (g) 1.673 (h) .1113
(i) 1.0000 (j) .0100 (k) .6216 (l) 3.619 (m) .5080 (n) 3.738 (o) 2.205   **2.** (a) .3051
(b) .3429 (c) .9004 (d) .7291 (e) 2.433 (f) 3.270 (g) 4.566 (h) .7648 (i) .9246
3. (a) .59 (b) 1.47 (c) .15 (d) 1.16 (e) 1.29 (f) .06   **4.** (a) $-\frac{1}{2}$ (c) $-\sqrt{3}/2$ (e) $-\frac{1}{2}$
(g) $-\frac{1}{2}$ (i) $\sqrt{2}/2$ **5.** (a) $\sqrt{2}/2$ (c) $-\frac{1}{2}$ (e) $-\sqrt{2}/2$ (g) $-\sqrt{2}/2$ (i) $-\sqrt{2}/2$ (k) $\sqrt{2}/2$
6. (a) 1 (c) $\sqrt{3}$ (e) $2/\sqrt{3}$ (g) $-\sqrt{2}$ (i) $-1/\sqrt{3}$ (k) 2   **7.** (a) 1 (c) $1/\sqrt{3}$ (d) -2
(f) $-1/\sqrt{3}$ (g) $-2\sqrt{3}$ (i) -2 **8.** (a) $\frac{1}{2}$ (c) $-\sqrt{3}/2$ (e) $\frac{1}{2}$ (g) $-\sqrt{2}/2$ (i) 0
9. (a) $\sqrt{2}/2$ (c) $-\frac{1}{2}$ (e) $\sqrt{2}/2$ (g) $\sqrt{2}/2$ (i) $-\sqrt{2}/2$ **10.** (a) .6820 (c) .9703 (e) $-$.5592
(g) .0523 (i) $-$.9816 (k) .5150 (m) -1.1504 (o) 5.6713 (q) -1.0154 **11.** (a) .9208
(c) $-$.4176 (e) $-$.2571 (g) $-$.1409 (i) -1.247 (k) 92.62 (m) .8573 (o) $-$.5480

Exercises 7.8 (page 324)

1. (a)

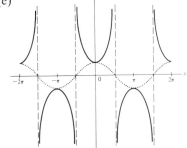

(c)

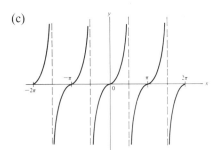

(e)

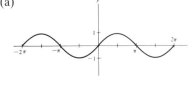

2. (a)

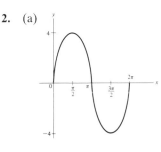

amplitude: 4;
period: 2π

(c)

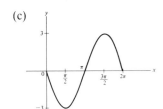

amplitude: 3;
period: 2π

(e)

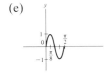

amplitude: 1;
period: $\pi/2$

(g) 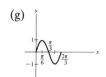 amplitude: 1;
period: $2\pi/3$

(i) 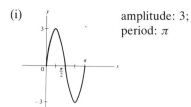 amplitude: 3;
period: π

(k) 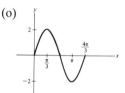 amplitude: 2;
period: $\pi/2$

(m) 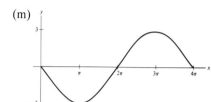 amplitude: 3;
period: 4π

(o) amplitude: 2;
period: $4\pi/3$

3. (a) period: 3π; amplitude: $\frac{5}{7}$ (c) period: $2\pi/7$; amplitude: $\frac{5}{3}$ (e) period: $2\pi^2$; amplitude: π

4. (a)  amplitude: 1;
period: 2π;
phase shift: π

(c) 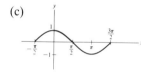 amplitude: 1;
period: 2π;
phase shift: $-\pi/2$

(e) 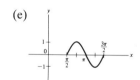 amplitude: 1;
period: π;
phase shift: $\pi/2$

(g) 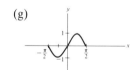 amplitude: 1;
period: π;
phase shift: $-\pi/2$

(i) 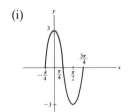 amplitude: 3;
period: π;
phase shift: $-\pi/4$

(k) 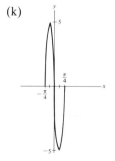 amplitude: 5;
period: $\pi/2$;
phase shift: $-\pi/4$

(m)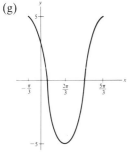
amplitude: 2;
period: $2\pi/3$;
phase shift: $\pi/3$

(o)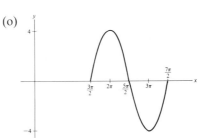
amplitude: 4;
period: 2π;
phase shift: $3\pi/2$

(q)
amplitude: 2;
period: π;
phase shift: $\frac{1}{2}$

(s)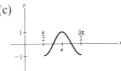
amplitude: 1;
period: 2π;
phase shift: -3

5. Both graphs are the same—namely, that of $y = \cos x$. The graph of $y = \cos x$ is illustrated in the section.

6. (a) 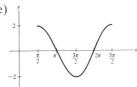   (c) 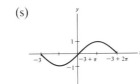   (e)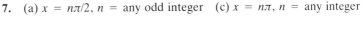

(g)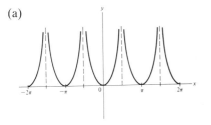

7. (a) $x = n\pi/2$, $n =$ any odd integer   (c) $x = n\pi$, $n =$ any integer

8. (a)   (c)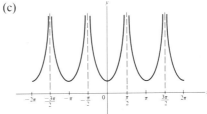

9. (a) 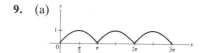 (c) 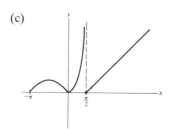 (e)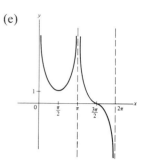

Exercises 7.9 (page 341)

1. (a) $(\sqrt{6} - \sqrt{2})/4$ (b) $(\sqrt{6} - \sqrt{2})/4$ (d) $(\sqrt{2} - \sqrt{6})/4$ **2.** (a) $-\sqrt{3}/2$ (c) $\sqrt{3}$ (e) $-\sqrt{3}/2$
(g) $-\frac{1}{2}$ (i) $2/\sqrt{3}$ (k) 1 (m) $-\sqrt{3}/2$ (o) $-\sqrt{3}/2$ **3.** (a) $-\sqrt{2}/2$ (c) $-\sqrt{3}/2$ (e) $-\frac{1}{2}$
(g) $\sqrt{3}$ (i) 1 (k) $\sqrt{2}$ (m) $-\frac{1}{2}$ (o) $-\sqrt{2}/2$ **4.** (a) .2250 (b) $-.1392$ (c) .8006 or .8016
(e) $-.7923$ (g) .7660 (i) $-.8071$ or $-.8080$ **5.** (a) 3/5 (b) 12/13 (c) 63/65. (d) 16/65
(e) 33/65 (f) 56/65 **8.** Its period is π. **9.** (a) $\cos 4\theta$ (b) $\cos 14\theta$ (c) $\cos 6\theta$ (d) $\cos 10\theta$
(e) $\sin 6u$ (f) $\sin \theta$ (g) $\frac{1}{2}\sin 10x$ (h) $2 \sin 6w$ (i) $4 \sin 14x$ (j) $\frac{1}{4}\sin 10\theta$ (k) $2 \cos 2x$
(l) $3 \cos 18t$ (m) $-\cos 6\theta$ (n) $-\cos 16x$

10. (a) $\frac{1}{2}\sqrt{2 + \sqrt{2}}$ (c) $\frac{1}{2}\sqrt{2 - \sqrt{3}}$ (e) $2 - \sqrt{3}$ **11.** (a) $\sqrt{6}/3$ (c) $\sqrt{6}/2$ (e) $\sqrt{2}/2$
12. (a) $\sqrt{30}/10$ (b) $\sqrt{70}/10$ (c) $\sqrt{30}/3$ (d) $\sqrt{70}/7$ (e) $\sqrt{21}/3$ (f) $\sqrt{21}/7$ **13.** (a) $\sqrt{10}/10$
(b) $-3\sqrt{10}/10$ (c) $-1/3$ **14.** (a) $\cos \theta = 2/\sqrt{5}$, $\sin \theta = 1/\sqrt{5}$ (c) $\cos \theta = 3/\sqrt{13}$,
$\sin \theta = 2/\sqrt{13}$ (e) $\cos \theta = 4/5$, $\sin \theta = 3/5$ **15.** (a) $\frac{1}{2}(1 - \cos 2x)$
(c) $\frac{1}{8}(3 + 4 \cos 2x + \cos 4x)$ (d) $\frac{1}{8}(1 - \cos 4x)$ **16.** (a) $-120/169$ (c) $-120/119$
17. (a) $-\frac{1}{2}$ (b) $-\sqrt{3}/2$ (c) $\sqrt{3}$ **19.** (a) $\sin 3t = 3 \sin t - 4 \sin^3 t$
(b) $\cos 3t = 4 \cos^3 t - 3 \cos t$ **22.** (a) 1 (b) $\sqrt{3}$ (c) $-1/\sqrt{3}$ (d) -1 (e) 0 (f) undefined
22. (a) 1 (b) $\sqrt{3}$ (c) $-1/\sqrt{3}$ (d) -1 (e) 0 (f) undefined

24. $\cot (u + v) = \dfrac{\cot u \cot v - 1}{\cot u + \cot v}$, $\cot 2t = \dfrac{\cot^2 t - 1}{2 \cot t}$ **27.** (d) $\frac{1}{2}(\cos 7x + \cos 3x)$
(f) $\frac{1}{2}(\sin 8x + \sin 2x)$ **29.** (a) symmetric with respect to the origin (c) symmetric with respect
to the origin (e) symmetric with respect to the y axis (g) symmetric with respect to the y axis

Exercises 7.10 (page 349)

1. (a) $\pi/3$, $2\pi/3$ (c) $\pi/4$, $7\pi/4$ (e) $\pi/6$, $11\pi/6$ (g) $4\pi/3$, $5\pi/3$ (i) $3\pi/4$, $5\pi/4$ **2.** In all answers
here, n represents any integer. (a) $x = \pi/2 + 2n\pi$ (c) $y = n\pi$ (e) $x = 3\pi/2 + 2n\pi$ (g) $x = \pi/3$
$+ n\pi$; $x = 2\pi/3 + n\pi$ (i) $x = \pi/6 + 2n\pi$; $x = 5\pi/6 + 2n\pi$ (k) no solution (m) $x = n\pi$;
$x = 3\pi/2 + 2n\pi$ (o) $v = \pi/4 + n\pi$; $v = 3\pi/4 + n\pi$ (q) $\theta = \pi/12 + n\pi$; $\theta = 5\pi/12 + n\pi$
(s) $\theta = \pi/6 + n\pi$, $2\pi/3 + n\pi$ (u) $x = \pi/12 + n\pi$, $7\pi/12 + n\pi$

Exercises 7.11 (page 358)

1. (a) $\pi/6$ (c) $\pi/2$ (e) 0 (g) $-\pi/3$ (i) $5\pi/6$ (k) $-\pi/3$ (m) .39 (o) .74 (q) .60 (s) 2.94
2. (a) $\sqrt{3}/2$ (c) $\sqrt{3}$ (e) 1 (g) $\sqrt{3}/2$ (i) $\sqrt{2}/2$ (k) $\sqrt{3}$ (m) $-1/\sqrt{3}$ **3.** (a) .9987
(c) 1.260 (e) $-.8087$ (g) .9128 (i) .4466 **4.** (a) 3/5 (c) $\sqrt{21}/2$ (e) $10\sqrt{101}$ (g) $-3/5$
(i) $\sqrt{21}/5$ **5.** (a) $\cos^{-1}\left(\dfrac{ab}{c}\right)$ (b) $\sin^{-1}\left(\dfrac{c - a}{b}\right)$ (c) $\tan^{-1}(y - 16)$ (e) $\dfrac{1}{3}\cos^{-1}\left(\dfrac{bc}{5}\right)$

(g) $\dfrac{1}{a}\left(\tan^{-1}\dfrac{a}{b}-b\right)$ **6.** (a) $\dfrac{x}{\sqrt{1-x^2}}$ (c) $\sqrt{1+9x^2}$ (e) $\sqrt{x^2+4}/2$

(g) $(x+1)/\sqrt{x^2+2x+26}$ **7.** (a) $\pi/6$ (c) π (e) $\pi/4$ (g) $3\pi/4$

8. (a)

inverse is dashed

(c)

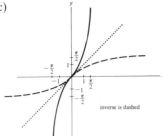

inverse is dashed

9. (a) x (b) t (c) $3u$ (d) $(m+2)/5$ **10.** $4/5$

Exercises 7.12 (page 371)

1. (a) $(\sqrt{3}/2,\ \frac{1}{2})$ (c) $(3,0)$ (e) $(0,2)$ (g) $(-1,0)$ (i) $(0,0)$ (k) $(-3\sqrt{2}/4,\ -3\sqrt{2}/4)$
(m) $(-\sqrt{3}/4,\ -\frac{1}{4})$ (o) $(-5\sqrt{2}/2,\ 5\sqrt{2}/2)$ (q) $(\sqrt{3},-1)$ (s) $(-.5403,\ -.8415)$ (u) $(\sqrt{3},-1)$
(w) $(-2\sqrt{2},\ 2\sqrt{2})$ **2.** (a) $(2\sqrt{2},\ \pi/4)$ (c) $(2,\ \pi/6)$ (e) $(-5,0)$ (g) $(-\sqrt{2},\ -\pi/4)$

(i) $(-2,\ -\pi/6)$ (k) $(6,\ \pi/2)$ **3.** (a) circle (c) cardioid   **4.** (a) $r=\dfrac{-3}{\sin\theta-2\cos\theta}$

(c) $r(\cos\theta-\sin\theta)=0$ (e) $r^2=25$ (g) $r^2=\dfrac{16}{\cos2\theta}$ (i) $r^2=\dfrac{9}{1+6\sin^2\theta}$

(k) $r(\sin\theta-5r\cos^2\theta)=0$ **5.** (a) $x^2+y^2-6y=0$ (c) $x^2+y^2-2x=0$
(e) $x^2+y^2=25$ (g) $x=3$ (i) $y=x/\sqrt{3}$ (k) $y=1$
6. (a) $(-2,\ 7\pi/6)$ (c) $(-3,\ 5\pi/3)$ (e) $(4,\ 3\pi/2)$

7. (a)

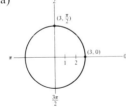

(c)

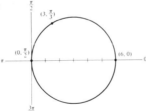

(e)

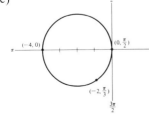

(g)

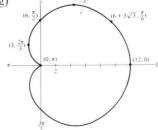

(i)

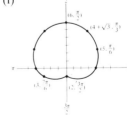

(k)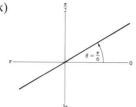

8. (a)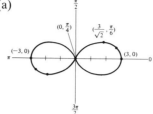

(c)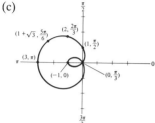

(e)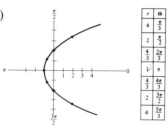

r	Θ
4	$\frac{\pi}{3}$
2	$\frac{\pi}{2}$
4	$\frac{2\pi}{3}$
ν	π
4	$\frac{4\pi}{3}$
2	$\frac{3\pi}{2}$
4	$\frac{5\pi}{3}$

(g)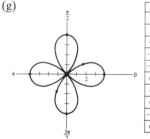

r	Θ
4	0
2	$\frac{\pi}{6}$
0	$\frac{\pi}{4}$
-2	$\frac{\pi}{3}$
-4	$\frac{\pi}{2}$
0	$\frac{3\pi}{4}$
4	π
0	$\frac{5\pi}{4}$
-4	$\frac{3\pi}{2}$
0	$\frac{7\pi}{4}$

(i)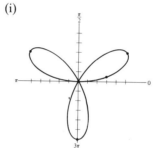

r	Θ
0	0
3	$\frac{\pi}{18}$
6	$\frac{\pi}{6}$
0	$\frac{\pi}{3}$
-6	$\frac{\pi}{2}$
0	$\frac{2\pi}{3}$
6	$\frac{5\pi}{6}$
0	π

9. $\pi/2$

Exercises 7.13 (page 379)

1. (a) $2(\cos 30° + i \sin 30°)$ (c) $1(\cos 90° + i \sin 90°)$ (e) $1(\cos 270° + i \sin 270°)$

(g) $2(\cos 60° + i \sin 60°)$ (i) $5(\cos 53° + i \sin 53°)$ 2. (a) $3i$ (c) $\sqrt{2} + i\sqrt{2}$ (e) $\dfrac{\sqrt{2}}{2} - i\dfrac{\sqrt{2}}{2}$

(g) $0 - 7i$ (i) $-2\sqrt{3} + 2i$ 3. (a) $3(\cos 60° + i \sin 60°)$ (c) $35\left(\cos \dfrac{3\pi}{4} + i \sin \dfrac{3\pi}{4}\right)$

(e) $2\left(\cos \dfrac{17\pi}{12} + i \sin \dfrac{17\pi}{12}\right)$ 4. (a) $3(\cos 30° + i \sin 30°)$ (c) $\dfrac{5}{7}\left(\cos \dfrac{\pi}{4} + i \sin \dfrac{\pi}{4}\right)$

(e) $\dfrac{1}{2}\left(\cos \dfrac{\pi}{12} - i \sin \dfrac{\pi}{12}\right)$ 5. (a) $81(\cos 120° + i \sin 120°)$ (c) $2401(\cos 180° + i \sin 180°)$

(e) $16(\cos 120° + i \sin 120°)$ (g) $1024(\cos 900° + i \sin 900°)$ 6. (a) $1, \ -\dfrac{1}{2} \pm \dfrac{i\sqrt{3}}{2}$

(c) $2, \ -1 \pm i\sqrt{3}$ (e) $\dfrac{\sqrt{2}}{2} + \dfrac{\sqrt{2}}{2}i, \ -\dfrac{\sqrt{2}}{2} + \dfrac{\sqrt{2}}{2}i, \ -\dfrac{\sqrt{2}}{2} - \dfrac{\sqrt{2}}{2}i, \ \dfrac{\sqrt{2}}{2} - \dfrac{\sqrt{2}}{2}i$

(g) $2^{1/8}(\cos 11.25° + i \sin 11.25°)$; $2^{1/8}(\cos 101.25° + i \sin 101.25°)$; $2^{1/8}(\cos 191.25° + i \sin 191.25°)$; $2^{1/8}(\cos 281.25° + i \sin 281.25°)$

Exercises 7.14 (page 385)

1. (a) 5.7 (b) 30° (c) 8.1 (d) 10.3 **2.** (a) 8.2 (c) 15.2 (e) triangle cannot be constructed
(g) 114° or 14° **3.** (a) 10.2 (b) 13.7 (c) 94° (e) 90° (f) 118° (g) 91° **4.** (a) 5 (c) 21
(e) 18 (g) 46° **5.** (a) $y = \dfrac{15 \sin x}{\sin (x + 3)}$ (c) $y = \sin^{-1}\left(\dfrac{x \sin 26°}{x - 2}\right)$ **7.** (a) 27° (b) 113 ft
(c) 106 ft **9.** 129 ft **11.** 367 ft

Exercises 7.15 (page 395)

1. (a) 17 kg (c) 10 kg (e) 12 kg **2.** (a) 5 (c) 3 (e) $9\sqrt{2}$ (g) 1 (i) 1 **3.** (a) g, h, i, j
(b) Two are: $\langle \sqrt{3}/2, \frac{1}{2}\rangle$ and $\langle -\sqrt{2}/2, -\sqrt{2}/2\rangle$ **4.** (a) $\langle 4\sqrt{3}, 4\rangle$ (c) $\langle 0, 3\rangle$ (e) $\langle -\sqrt{3}/4, -\frac{1}{4}\rangle$
(g) $\langle -\sqrt{2}/2, \sqrt{2}/2\rangle$ **5.** (a) 45° (c) 315° (e) 0° (g) 120° (i) 210° **6.** (a) $\langle 8, 4\rangle$
(c) $\langle 42, -12\rangle$ (e) $\langle 23, 6\rangle$ (g) $\langle -53, 34\rangle$ (i) $\langle 0, 0\rangle$

Review Exercises for Chapter 7 (page 396)

1. (a) $\sqrt{2}/2$ (c) $-\sqrt{3}/2$ (e) $-2/\sqrt{3}$ (g) $-\sqrt{2}$ (i) $-\sqrt{3}$ **2.** (a) $\sqrt{5}/3$ (c) $(2 - 2\sqrt{30})/15$
(e) $4\sqrt{5}/9$ (g) $-2\sqrt{6}/5$ (i) $\sqrt{15}/5$ **3.** (a) $x = \pi/6 + 2n\pi; x = 5\pi/6 + 2n\pi$
(c) $\theta = 7\pi/12 + n\pi; \theta = 11\pi/12 + n\pi$

4. (a) 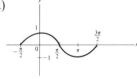 (c)

5. (a) 330° **6.** (a) $5\pi/6$ **7.** (a) $2\sqrt{6}/5$ **8.** 3 **9.** (a) $\frac{1}{2}$ (c) $3\sqrt{5}/7$ (e) $5\pi/6$
10. $\cos \theta = \sqrt{6}/3; \sin \theta = \sqrt{3}/3$ **12.** $x^4 + y^4 - 10y^3 + 2x^2y^2 - 10x^2y - 25x^2 = 0$

14. (a) 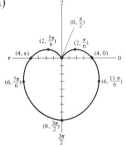   **15.** (a) 4.8 (c) 35° **16.** $\sqrt{65}$ **18.** $\langle 6\sqrt{2}, 6\sqrt{2}\rangle$

Exercises 8.2 (page 403)

1. (a) $x^2 + y^2 = 36$ (c) $x^2 + y^2 = 7$ (e) $(x - 3)^2 + (y - 12)^2 = 16$
(g) $(x + 2)^2 + (y + 7)^2 = 100$ (i) $(x - 5)^2 + (y + 4)^2 = 14$

2. (a)

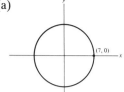

center: (0, 0);
radius: 7

(c)

center: (0, 0);
radius: $\sqrt{15}$

(e)

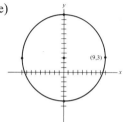

center: (0, 3);
radius: 9

(g)

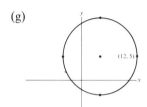

center: (4, 5);
radius: 8

(i)

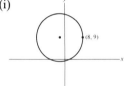

center: (−2, 9);
radius: 10

(k)

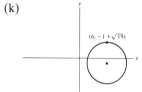

center: (6, −1);
radius: $\sqrt{19}$

3. (a)

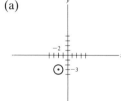

center: (−2, −3);
radius: 1

(c)

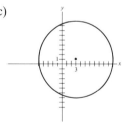

center: (3, 1);
radius: 8

(e)

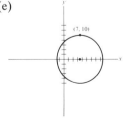

center: (7, 0);
radius: 10

(g)

center: $(0, \frac{3}{2})$;
radius: $\sqrt{13}/2$

(i) 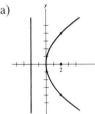   center: $(\frac{3}{2}, -\frac{1}{2})$; radius: $\sqrt{14}/2$

5. (a) $x^2 + y^2 = 25$ (c) $(x - 1)^2 + (y + 4)^2 = 169$ (e) $(x - 4)^2 + (y + 3)^2 = 13$
(g) $(x + 5)^2 + (y - 3)^2 = 25$

Exercises 8.3 (page 409)

1. (a) 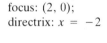   vertex: $(0, 0)$;
focus: $(2, 0)$;
directrix: $x = -2$

(c)   vertex: $(0, 0)$;
focus: $(0, 3)$;
directrix: $y = -3$

(e) 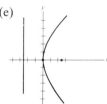   vertex $(0, 0)$;
focus: $(\frac{5}{2}, 0)$;
directrix: $x = -\frac{5}{2}$

(g)    vertex: $(0, 0)$;
focus: $(-\frac{1}{4}, 0)$;
directrix: $x = \frac{1}{4}$

(i) 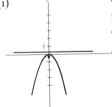   vertex: $(0, 0)$;
focus: $(0, -\frac{1}{4})$;
directrix: $y = \frac{1}{4}$

(k)   vertex: $(0, 0)$;
focus: $(1, 0)$;
directrix: $x = -1$

(m) 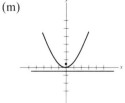   vertex: $(0, 0)$;
focus: $(0, \frac{1}{2})$;
directrix: $y = -\frac{1}{2}$

(o) 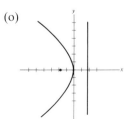   vertex: $(0, 0)$;
focus: $(-\frac{11}{6}, 0)$;
directrix: $x = \frac{11}{6}$

(q) 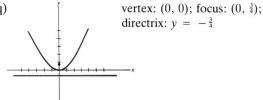 vertex: $(0, 0)$; focus: $(0, \frac{3}{4})$;
directrix: $y = -\frac{3}{4}$

2. (a) $y^2 = 20x$ (c) $x^2 = 2y$ (e) $y^2 = 4x$ **3.** (a) $x^2 = 16y$ (c) $y^2 = -16x$ (e) $y^2 = -24x$
(g) $y^2 = 40x$ (i) $x^2 = -8y$

Exercises 8.4 (page 415)

1. (a) 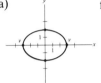 foci: $(\pm\sqrt{5}, 0)$ (c) 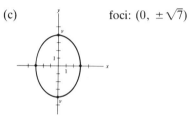 foci: $(0, \pm\sqrt{7})$

(e) 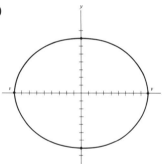 foci: $(\pm 4\sqrt{2}, 0)$ (g) 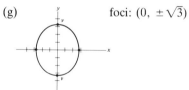 foci: $(0, \pm\sqrt{3})$

(i) foci: $\left(0, \pm\dfrac{\sqrt{11}}{2}\right)$

2. (a) 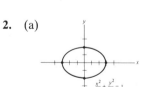   (c) 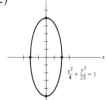   (e)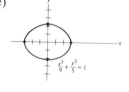

(g)

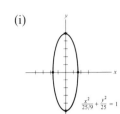

$$\frac{x^2}{4} + \frac{y^2}{1/4} = 1$$

(i)

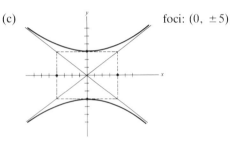

$$\frac{x^2}{25/9} + \frac{y^2}{25} = 1$$

3. (a) major axis: 14; minor axis: 12 (c) major axis: $2\sqrt{3}$; minor axis: 2 **4.** (a) $\dfrac{x^2}{7} + \dfrac{y^2}{16} = 1$

(c) $\dfrac{x^2}{9} + \dfrac{y^2}{4} = 1$ (e) $\dfrac{x^2}{34} + \dfrac{y^2}{9} = 1$

Exercises 8.5 (page 420)

1. (a) 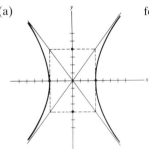 foci: $(\pm 5, 0)$ (c) foci: $(0, \pm 5)$

(e) 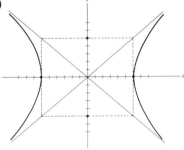 foci: $(\pm 2\sqrt{61}, 0)$

(g) 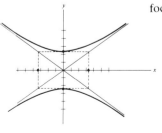 foci: $(0, \pm 4)$ (i) 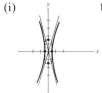 foci: $(\pm \sqrt{19}/3, 0)$

2. (a)

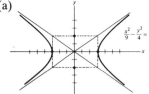

$\frac{x^2}{9} - \frac{y^2}{4} = 1$

(c)

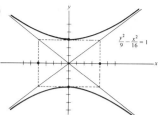

$\frac{y^2}{9} - \frac{x^2}{16} = 1$

(e)

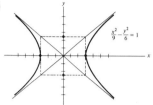

$\frac{x^2}{9} - \frac{y^2}{6} = 1$

(g)

$\frac{y^2}{64} - \frac{x^2}{1} = 1$

(i)

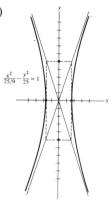

$\frac{x^2}{25/9} - \frac{y^2}{25} = 1$

3. (a) $\dfrac{x^2}{16} - \dfrac{y^2}{9} = 1$ (c) $\dfrac{x^2}{9} - \dfrac{y^2}{49} = 1$ (e) $\dfrac{y^2}{16} - \dfrac{x^2}{\frac{25}{9}} = 1$

Exercises 8.6 (page 426)

1. (a)

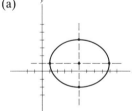

(c)

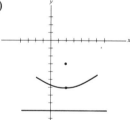

(e)

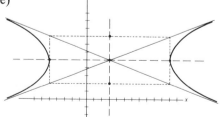

2. (a)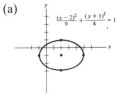
$$\frac{(x-2)^2}{9} + \frac{(y+1)^2}{4} = 1$$

(c)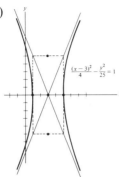
$$\frac{(x-3)^2}{4} - \frac{y^2}{25} = 1$$

(e)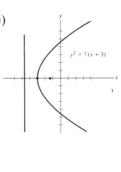
$$y^2 = 7(x+3)$$

(g)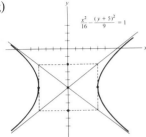
$$\frac{x^2}{16} - \frac{(y+5)^2}{9} = 1$$

(i)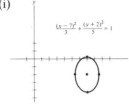
$$\frac{(x-7)^2}{3} + \frac{(y+2)^2}{5} = 1$$

(k)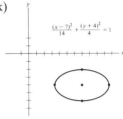
$$\frac{(x-7)^2}{14} + \frac{(y+4)^2}{4} = 1$$

(m)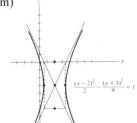
$$\frac{(x-2)^2}{2} - \frac{(y+3)^2}{9} = 1$$

(o)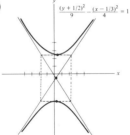
$$\frac{(y+1/2)^2}{9} - \frac{(x-1/3)^2}{4} = 1$$

(q)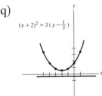
$$(x+2)^2 = 3\left(y - \frac{1}{2}\right)$$

(s)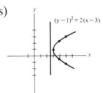
$$(y-1)^2 = 2(x-3)$$

Exercises 8.7 (page 432)

1. (a) $\cos \theta = \dfrac{7}{5\sqrt{2}}$; $\sin \theta = \dfrac{1}{5\sqrt{2}}$ (c) $\cos \theta = \dfrac{1}{\sqrt{5}}$; $\sin \theta = \dfrac{2}{\sqrt{5}}$

(e) $\cos \theta = \dfrac{\sqrt{26}}{6}$; $\sin \theta = \dfrac{\sqrt{10}}{6}$ **2.** (a) $x = \dfrac{3}{5}\bar{x} - \dfrac{4}{5}\bar{y}$; $y = \dfrac{4}{5}\bar{x} + \dfrac{3}{5}\bar{y}$

(c) $x = \dfrac{1}{2}\bar{x} - \dfrac{\sqrt{3}}{2}\bar{y}$; $y = \dfrac{\sqrt{3}}{2}\bar{x} + \dfrac{1}{2}\bar{y}$ (e) $x = \dfrac{1}{\sqrt{5}}\bar{x} - \dfrac{2}{\sqrt{5}}\bar{y}$; $y = \dfrac{2}{\sqrt{5}}\bar{x} + \dfrac{1}{\sqrt{5}}\bar{y}$

3. (a) $\dfrac{\bar{x}^2}{7} - \dfrac{\bar{y}^2}{3} = 1$ (c) $\dfrac{\bar{y}^2}{2} - \dfrac{\bar{x}^2}{10} = 1$ (e) $\dfrac{\bar{y}^2}{10} - \dfrac{\bar{x}^2}{15} = 1$ **4.** (a) $(\bar{y} - 4)^2 = 4(\bar{x} + 3)$

(c) $\dfrac{(\bar{x} - 1)^2}{\frac{9}{8}} + \dfrac{(\bar{y} + \frac{3}{4})^2}{\frac{9}{16}} = 1$ (e) $(\bar{y} + 1)^2 = -1(\bar{x} - \frac{4}{3})$ **5.** (a) $\left(1 - \dfrac{7\sqrt{3}}{2}, \frac{7}{2} + \sqrt{3}\right)$

(c) $(-2\sqrt{3}, -2)$ (e) $(0, 7\sqrt{2})$ **6.** (a) $\left(1 + \dfrac{7\sqrt{3}}{2}, \frac{7}{2} - \sqrt{3}\right)$ (c) $(-2\sqrt{3}, 2)$ (e) $(7\sqrt{2}, 0)$

Review Exercises for Chapter 8 (page 433)

1. (a) 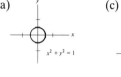 (c) 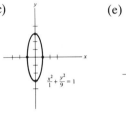 (e)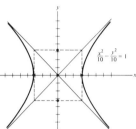

(g) 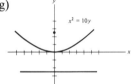 (i)

2. (a) 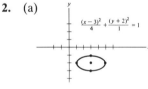 (c) 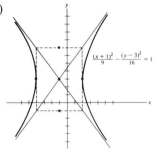 (e)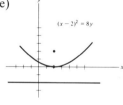

(g) 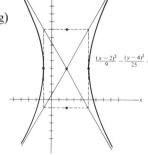 (i)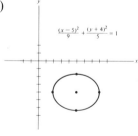

Exercises 9.1 (page 440)

1. (a)

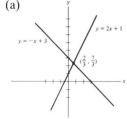

(c)

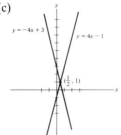

(e)

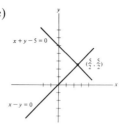

(g)

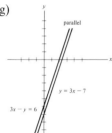

(i)

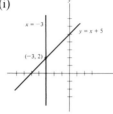

(k)

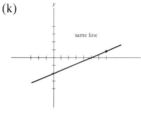

2. (a) $x = 3, y = 5$ (c) $x = 3, y = 3$ (e) $x = 6, y = 2$ (g) $x = \frac{7}{19}, y = \frac{54}{19}$
(i) no solution (inconsistent) (k) $x = -5, y = -4$ **3.** (a) $x = 5, y = 1$ (c) $x = 4, y = -1$
(e) infinite number of solutions (dependent) (g) $x = 2, y = -1$ (i) $x = 3, y = -4$
(k) $x = -\frac{1}{2}, y = \frac{3}{2}$ **4.** (a) $x = 1, y = 2, z = 3$ (c) $x = 2, y = 0, z = -3$
(e) $x = 1, y = -2, z = 4$ (g) $r = 2, s = -3, t = 4$ (i) $x = 2, y = -3, z = -1$
(k) $w = -2, x = 1, y = -1, z = 3$ **5.** $\frac{16}{3}$

Exercises 9.2 (page 451)

1. (a) $x = 1, y = 3$ (c) $m = -2, n = -5$ (e) $x = -5, y = 4$ (g) $x = 1, y = -\frac{1}{2}$
(i) $a = -12, b = -14$ **2.** (a) $x = -3, y = 4, z = -1$ (c) $x = 5, y = 1, z = 2$
(e) $x = -5, y = 3, z = 2$ (g) $t = -7, u = -6, v = 2$ (i) $p = -4, q = 2, r = 1$
3. (a) no solution (c) infinite number of solutions

Exercises 9.3 (page 458)

1. (a) 10 (c) 12 (e) -19 (g) 0 (i) 0 **2.** (a) $x = 3, y = 4$ (c) $x = -2, y = -5$
(e) $p = \frac{2}{3}, q = -\frac{5}{3}$ (g) $u = \frac{23}{17}, v = -\frac{4}{17}$ **3.** (a) 123 (c) 0 (e) 234 (g) -227
4. (a) $x = \frac{4}{5}, y = \frac{7}{5}, z = \frac{16}{5}$ (c) $x = \frac{32}{9}, y = -\frac{7}{6}, z = \frac{65}{18}$ (e) $x = \frac{583}{248}, y = \frac{33}{248}, z = \frac{167}{248}$
(g) $x = \frac{31}{175}, y = \frac{201}{175}, z = \frac{16}{25}$

Exercises 9.4 (page 463)

1. (a) 4 (c) 33 (e) -3262 (g) 2304 (i) -1470 **2.** (a) $w = 6, x = -1, y = 0, z = 4$
(c) $A = 1, B = 0, D = -1, F = 1$ (e) $r = 6, s = 2, t = 3, u = -3$

Exercises 9.5 (page 467)

1. (a) $\dfrac{2}{x} + \dfrac{7}{x+5}$ (c) $\dfrac{9}{x+5} - \dfrac{3}{x-3} + \dfrac{1}{x-7}$ (e) $\dfrac{4}{x} - \dfrac{2}{x-1} + \dfrac{1}{x+4}$

(g) $\dfrac{\frac{3}{5}}{x-3} + \dfrac{6}{x-6} - \dfrac{\frac{3}{5}}{x+2}$ (i) $\dfrac{10}{(x+5)^2} + \dfrac{1}{x+5} + \dfrac{6}{x}$ (k) $\dfrac{4}{(x^2+1)^2} + \dfrac{5x+1}{x^2+1}$

2. (a) $1 - \dfrac{4}{x+3} + \dfrac{4}{x-3}$ (c) $x + 3 + \dfrac{5}{x+1} + \dfrac{1}{x+2}$

Exercises 9.6 (page 469)

1. $x^2 + y^2 - 6x + 4y - 12 = 0$ 3. $(x+2)^2 + (y+2)^2 = 25$

Exercises 9.7 (page 472)

1. (a) $(3, 4), (-4, -3)$ (c) $\left(\dfrac{2+\sqrt{59}}{5}, \dfrac{-1+2\sqrt{59}}{5}\right), \left(\dfrac{2-\sqrt{59}}{5}, \dfrac{-1-2\sqrt{59}}{5}\right)$

(e) $(0, 2), \left(\dfrac{4\sqrt{2}}{3}, -\dfrac{14}{9}\right), \left(-\dfrac{4\sqrt{2}}{3}, -\dfrac{14}{9}\right)$ (g) $\left(\sqrt{\dfrac{17}{2}}, \pm\sqrt{\dfrac{15}{2}}\right), \left(-\sqrt{\dfrac{17}{2}}, \pm\sqrt{\dfrac{15}{2}}\right)$

(i) $\left(\dfrac{1+\sqrt{73}}{4}, \dfrac{9-3\sqrt{73}}{8}\right), \left(\dfrac{1-\sqrt{73}}{4}, \dfrac{9+3\sqrt{73}}{8}\right)$ (k) no solution

(m) $(0, 0), (\sqrt{7}, 7\sqrt{7}), (-\sqrt{7}, -7\sqrt{7})$ (o) $(\pm\sqrt{5}, -2), (\pm\sqrt{2}, -5)$

2. (a) 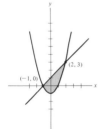 (c) 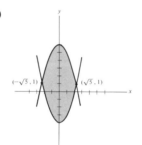 (e)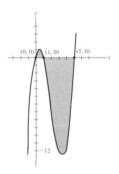

3. $\left(\dfrac{5+\sqrt{13}}{2}, \dfrac{-1+\sqrt{13}}{2}\right), \left(\dfrac{5-\sqrt{13}}{2}, \dfrac{-1-\sqrt{13}}{2}\right)$ 4. (a) 6 and 4 or -4 and -6

(c) length $20\sqrt{2}$ cm; width $5\sqrt{2}$ cm   5. (a) base $= \sqrt{3}$; height $= 2\sqrt{3}$

(c) $\frac{37}{8}$ inches and $\frac{77}{8}$ inches

Review Exercises for Chapter 9 (page 474)

1. (a) $x = 6, y = -4$ (c) $x = 7, y = 5$ 2. (a) $x = \frac{1}{2}, y = 7$ 3. (a) $x = 9, y = 5$

4. (a) $\dfrac{3x-2}{x^2+1} + \dfrac{4}{x-5}$ 5. (a) $(1, 5), (6, 0)$

Exercises 10.1 (page 481)

1. (a) 4, 7, 10, 13 (c) $-3, 0, 3, 6$ (e) 1, 2, $\frac{11}{3}$, 6 (g) 0, $\frac{4}{3}$, 4, 8 (i) $-\frac{1}{2}, 0, \frac{3}{2}, 4$
2. (a) $a_n = n + 1$ (c) $a_n = 1/n$ (e) $a_n = n/(n + 1)$ (g) $a_n = (n + 2)^2$ (i) $a_n = 5/n^2$
3. (a) 47 (c) 217 (e) 7200 (g) 400 (i) 158   **4.** (a) 640 (c) $\frac{3}{256}$ (e) $\frac{1093}{729}$ (g) 729 (i) $\frac{1275}{2}$
(k) 160 (m) $4(3)^{n-1}$ or $-4(-3)^{n-1}$ **5.** (a) arithmetic (c) neither (e) arithmetic
(g) geometric   **7.** (a) 1024 vibrations/second (b) 64 vibrations/second
9. $2^{18} - 1$, or 262,143   **11.** $2^{64} - 1$, or approximately 1.8×10^{19}

Exercises 10.2 (page 488)

1. (a) 285 (c) 63 (e) 127 (g) -5 (i) 0 (k) 0 (m) 10 (o) 11   **2.** (a) $\sum_{i=1}^{7} x_i$ (c) $\sum_{i=0}^{n} a_i x^i$

(e) $\sum_{n=0}^{10} \frac{1}{2^n}$ (g) $\sum_{i=0}^{43} x_i f(x_i)$ **3.** (a) 7 (c) 10 (e) $(n + 3)(n + 2)(n + 1)$ (g) $\frac{1}{(n - 1)!}$

(i) $\frac{1}{(x + 2)(x)(x - 1)}$ (k) $\frac{n + 1}{2}$ (m) $\frac{e}{n + 1}$ (o) $\frac{x^2}{(2n + 2)(2n + 1)}$

5. $p(x) = \sum_{i=0}^{n} a_i x^i$, where n is a nonnegative integer and the a_i are real numbers.

6. (a) 10 (c) 190 (e) 1   **7.** (a) $\binom{n}{n} = \frac{n!}{n!0!} = \frac{n!}{n!1} = \frac{n!}{n!} = 1$

(c) $\binom{n}{1} = \frac{n!}{1!(n - 1)!} = \frac{n(n - 1)!}{1(n - 1)!} = \frac{n}{1} = n$ **8.** (a) $a^5 + 5a^4b + 10a^3b^2 + 10a^2b^3 + 5ab^4 + b^5$
(c) $x^4 - 4x^3y + 6x^2y^2 - 4xy^3 + y^4$ (e) $x^5 - 10x^4y + 40x^3y^2 - 80x^2y^3 + 80xy^4 - 32y^5$
(g) $a^7 - 7a^6b + 21a^5b^2 - 35a^4b^3 + 35a^3b^4 - 21a^2b^5 + 7ab^6 - b^7$
(i) $256x^8 - 1024x^7y + 1792x^6y^2 - 1792x^5y^3 + 1120x^4y^4 - 448x^3y^5 + 112x^2y^6 - 16xy^7 + y^8$

Exercises 10.3 (page 497)

1. (a) 160 (c) 12 (e) $\frac{18}{5}$ (g) -3 (i) 6   **2.** (a) geometric, diverges (c) geometric, diverges
(e) not geometric (g) geometric, converges (i) geometric, converges   **3.** (a) x, x^2, x^3, x^4
(c) $1, -x, x^2, -x^3$ (e) $1, 2x, 4x^2, 8x^3$ (g) $1, x, 2x^2, 6x^3$ (i) $1, 2x, 3x^2, 4x^3$
4. (a) $4 + 4x + 4x^2 + 4x^3 + \cdots$; $|x| < 1$ (c) $1 - x + x^2 - x^3 + \cdots$; $|x| < 1$
(e) $1 + 2x + 4x^2 + 8x^3 + \cdots$; $|x| < \frac{1}{2}$ (g) $2 + 2x^3 + 2x^6 + 2x^9 + \cdots$; $|x| < 1$
5. (a) .8415 (c) .7648 (e) 7.0000 (g) .4073   **6.** (a) $\sum_{n=0}^{\infty} \frac{x^n}{n!}$ (c) $\sum_{n=0}^{\infty} \frac{x^{n+1}}{2(n + 1)}$ (e) $\sum_{n=0}^{\infty} \frac{x^{2n}}{(2n)!}$

(g) $\sum_{n=0}^{\infty} (-1)^n \frac{x^{2n}}{(2n)!}$ **7.** (a) $\sum_{n=0}^{\infty} \frac{x^n}{n!}$ (c) $\sum_{n=0}^{\infty} (-1)^n \frac{x^{2n+1}}{(2n + 1)!}$

Exercises 10.4 (page 504)

1. For $n = 1, 1 = 1$. Use assumption of true for $n = k$ to substitute into

$$1 + 2 + 3 + 4 + \cdots + k + k + 1 \stackrel{?}{=} \frac{(k + 1)(k + 2)}{2}$$

The result is

$$\frac{k(k + 1)}{2} + k + 1 \stackrel{?}{=} \frac{(k + 1)(k + 2)}{2}$$

or

$$\frac{k(k + 1) + 2(k + 1)}{2} \overset{?}{=} \frac{(k + 1)(k + 2)}{2}$$

or

$$\frac{(k + 2)(k + 1)}{2} = \frac{(k + 1)(k + 2)}{2}$$

3. For $n = 1$, $\frac{1}{2} = \frac{1}{2}$. Use assumption of true for $n = k$ to substitute into

$$\frac{1}{2} + \frac{1}{2^2} + \frac{1}{2^3} + \cdots + \frac{1}{2^k} + \frac{1}{2^{k+1}} \overset{?}{=} 1 - \frac{1}{2^{k+1}}$$

The result is

$$1 - \frac{1}{2^k} + \frac{1}{2^{k+1}} \overset{?}{=} 1 - \frac{1}{2^{k+1}}$$

or

$$1 - \frac{2}{2^{k+1}} + \frac{1}{2^{k+1}} \overset{?}{=} 1 - \frac{1}{2^{k+1}}$$

or

$$1 - \frac{1}{2^{k+1}} = 1 - \frac{1}{2^{k+1}}$$

5. For $n = 1$, $1 = 1$. Use assumption of true for $n = k$ to substitute into

$$1^2 + 2^2 + 3^2 + \cdots + k^2 + (k + 1)^2 \overset{?}{=} \frac{(k + 1)(k + 2)(2k + 3)}{6}$$

The result is

$$\frac{k(k + 1)(2k + 1)}{6} + (k + 1)^2 \overset{?}{=} \frac{(k + 1)(k + 2)(2k + 3)}{6}$$

or

$$\frac{k(k + 1)(2k + 1) + 6(k + 1)^2}{6} \overset{?}{=} \frac{(k + 1)(k + 2)(2k + 3)}{6}$$

$$\frac{(k + 1)[k(2k + 1) + 6(k + 1)]}{6} \overset{?}{=} \frac{(k + 1)(k + 2)(2k + 3)}{6}$$

$$\frac{(k + 1)(2k^2 + 7k + 6)}{6} \overset{?}{=} \frac{(k + 1)(k + 2)(2k + 3)}{6}$$

$$\frac{(k + 1)(k + 2)(2k + 3)}{6} = \frac{(k + 1)(k + 2)(2k + 3)}{6}$$

7. For $n = 1$, $1 = 1$. Use assumption of true for $n = k$ to substitute into

$$1^3 + 2^3 + 3^3 + \cdots + k^3 + (k + 1)^3 \overset{?}{=} \frac{(k + 1)^2(k + 2)^2}{4}$$

The result is

$$\frac{k^2(k + 1)^2}{4} + (k + 1)^3 \overset{?}{=} \frac{(k + 1)^2(k + 2)^2}{4}$$

$$\frac{k^2(k + 1)^2 + 4(k + 1)^3}{4} \overset{?}{=} \frac{(k + 1)^2(k + 2)^2}{4}$$

$$\frac{(k + 1)^2[k^2 + 4(k + 1)]}{4} \overset{?}{=} \frac{(k + 1)^2(k + 2)^2}{4}$$

$$\frac{(k + 1)^2(k + 2)^2}{4} = \frac{(k + 1)^2(k + 2)^2}{4}$$

9. For $n = 1$, $a = a$. Use assumption of true for $n = k$ to substitute into

$$a + (a + d) + (a + 2d) + \cdots + [a + (k - 1)d] + (a + kd) \overset{?}{=} \frac{k + 1}{2}[2a + kd]$$

The result is

$$\frac{k}{2}[2a + (k - 1)d] + (a + kd) \overset{?}{=} \frac{k + 1}{2}[2a + kd]$$

$$\frac{k[2a + (k - 1)d] + 2(a + kd)}{2} \overset{?}{=} \frac{k + 1}{2}[2a + kd]$$

$$\frac{2ak + k^2d - kd + 2a + 2kd}{2} \overset{?}{=} \frac{k + 1}{2}[2a + kd]$$

$$\frac{2ak + k^2d + 2a + kd}{2} \overset{?}{=} \frac{k + 1}{2}[2a + kd]$$

$$\frac{(k + 1)(2a + kd)}{2} = \frac{k + 1}{2}[2a + kd]$$

11. For $n = 1$, $ab = ab$. Now show that $(ab)^{k+1} = a^{k+1}b^{k+1}$. The assumption that $(ab)^k = a^k b^k$ can be used once the equation above is transformed.

$$(ab)^k(ab) \overset{?}{=} a^k a b^k b$$

or

$$(ab)^k ab \overset{?}{=} a^k b^k ab$$

Now substitute $a^k b^k$ for $(ab)^k$.

$$a^k b^k ab = a^k b^k ab$$

13. For $n = 2$, $a(b_1 + b_2) = ab_1 + ab_2$, which is true as the ordinary distributive property. Now assume true for $n = k$:

$$a(b_1 + b_2 + b_3 + \cdots + b_k) = ab_1 + ab_2 + ab_3 + \cdots + ab_k$$

Then

$$a(b_1 + b_2 + b_3 + \cdots + b_k + b_{k+1}) = a(b_1 + b_2 + b_3 + \cdots + b_k) + a(b_{k+1})$$
$$= ab_1 + ab_2 + ab_3 + \cdots + ab_k + ab_{k+1}$$

15. For $n = 2$, $3^n > 3n$ is true since it becomes $9 > 6$. Assume true for $n = k$, namely, $3^k > 3k$ and show that $3^{k+1} > 3(k + 1)$. Since $3^{k+1} = 3^k \cdot 3^1 = 3 \cdot 3^k$, we can show that $3 \cdot 3^k > 3(k + 1)$, or simply that $3^k > k + 1$. And since our assumption is that $3^k > 3k$, we need only show that $3k > k + 1$. Since $3k = 2k + k$, we can show that $k + 2k > k + 1$, which is the same as $2k > 1$. And clearly this is true for any natural number k.

Exercises 10.5 (page 507)

1. (a) 1.414   (c) 2.236   (e) 3.316   (g) 10.344   (i) 16.552 (actually, 16.55294)   **2.** (a) 2.15
(c) 3.80   (e) 4.64

Review Exercises for Chapter 10 (page 507)

1. $0, -\frac{3}{4}, -\frac{4}{3}$ **3.** 28   **5.** $\dfrac{2ne}{n + 1}$ **7.** $\frac{15}{2}$ **9.** $\displaystyle\sum_{n=0}^{\infty} \dfrac{2^{n+1}x^n}{(n + 1)!}$

Index